Currents

Stories, Essays, Poems, and Plays

Edited by

Kevin McNeilly
The University of British Columbia

Noel Elizabeth Currie
Simon Fraser University

William H. New
The University of British Columbia

William E. Messenger
The University of British Columbia

Prentice Hall Canada Inc., Scarborough, Ontario

Canadian Cataloguing in Publication Data

Main entry under title:

Currents: stories, essays, poems and plays

2nd ed.
Previously published under title: A 20th century anthology: essays, stories, and poems.
Includes index.
ISBN 0-13-085276-7

1. English literature. 2. American literature. Canadian literature (English).°
I. Messenger, William E., 1931-. II. Title: *A 20th century anthology: essays, stories, and poems.*

© 2000 Prentice-Hall Canada Inc., Scarborough, Ontario
Pearson Education

Previous editions were published as A 20th Century Anthology: essays, stories, and poems. Copyright © 1984 Prentice Hall Canada Inc.

Prentice-Hall, Inc., Upper Saddle River, New Jersey
Prentice-Hall International (UK) Limited, London
Prentice-Hall of Australia, Pty. Limited, Sydney
Prentice-Hall Hispanoamericana, S.A., Mexico City
Prentice-Hall of India Private Limited, New Delhi
Prentice-Hall of Japan, Inc., Tokyo
Simon & Schuster Southeast Asia Private Limited, Singapore
Editora Prentice-Hall do Brasil, Ltda., Rio de Janeiro

ISBN 0-13-085276-7

Vice-President,
 Editorial Director: Laura Pearson
Signing Representative:
 Katherine McWhirter
Acquisitions Editor: David Stover
Developmental Editor: Carina Blafield
Copy Editor: Cy Strom
Proofreader: Pat Thorvaldson
Production Editor: Sarah Dann

Production Coordinator: Wendy Moran
Permissions/
 Photo Research: Michaele Sinko
Art Director: Mary Opper
Cover Design: Sarah Battersby
Cover Image: Photonica/Edgar Lissel
Page Layout: April Haisell

1 2 3 4 5   04 03 02 01 00
Printed and bound in Canada.

Visit the Prentice Hall Canada Web site! Send us your comments, browse our catalogues, and more. **www.phcanada.com** Or reach us through e-mail at **phabinfo_pubcanada@prenhall.com**

The following pages constitute an extension of the copyright page. Every reasonable effort has been made to find copyright holders. The publishers would be pleased to have any errors or omissions brought to their attention.

Elbow: From *Landmark Essays on Voice & Writing*, Hermagoras Press, by Elbow. With permission of Lawrence Erlbaum Associates, Inc.

T.S. Eliot: Reprinted by permission of Faber and Faber Ltd from *Collected Poems 1909–1962* by T.S. Eliot.

Nissim Ezekiel: From *The Exact Name*, 1965. Reprinted by permission of the author.

Kenneth Fearing: From *Dead Reckoning*, published by Random House Inc.

E.M. Forster: "Me, Them and You" from E.M. Forster, *Abinger Harvest*, published by Edward Arnold (Publishers) Ltd. Reprinted by permission of the publisher. "The Other Side of the Hedge" from *The Collected Tales of E.M. Forster* published by Sidgwick & Jackson, London. Reprinted by permission of the publisher.

Janet Frame: *The Reservoir*, George Braziller Publishers, New York. 1963.

Robert Frost: "After Apple-Picking", "Nothing Gold Can Stay" and "Stopping by Woods on a Snowy Evening from *The Poetry of Robert Frost*, edited by Edward Connery Lathem, Copyright 1951, © 1958 by Robert Frost, © 1967 by Lesley Frost Ballantine, Copyright 1923, 1930, 1939, © 1969 by Henry Holt and Company, Inc. Reprinted by permission of Henry Holt and Company, Inc. "Acquainted with the Night" from "Acquainted with the Night" and "Design" "Design" from *The Poetry of Robert Frost* edited by Edward Connery Lathem, Copyright 1936, 1956 by Robert Frost. Copyright 1964 by Lesley Frost Ballantine. Copyright 1928, © 1969 by Henry Holt and Company. Reprinted by permission of Henry Holt and Company, Inc.

Northrop Frye: From *Architects of Modern Thought*, Toronto: Canadian Broadcasting Corp. Reprinted by permission of the author.

Mavis Gallant: "From the Fifteenth District" by Mavis Gallant. (New York: Random House, 1979). Copyright © 1979 by Mavis Gallant. Reprinted by permission of Georges Borchard, Inc. for the author.

Shirley Geok-Lin Lim: Copyright, Shirley Geok-Lin Lim from *Monsoon History*, Skoob: London, 1994.

Zulfikar Ghose: From *The Violent West*, 1972. Copyright © 1972 by Zulfikar Ghose. Reprinted by permission of Wallace & Sheil Agency, Inc.

Allen Ginsberg: 12 lines from "A Supermarket in California" from *Collected Poems 1947–1980* by Allen Ginsberg. Copyright © 1955 by Allen Ginsberg. Copyright renewed. Reprinted by permission of HarperCollins Publishers, Inc.

Nikki Giovanni: "Kidnap Poem" from *The Women and the Men* by Nikki Giovanni. Copyright © 1970, 1974, 1975 by Nikki Giovanni. By permission of William Morrow & Co., Inc.

Lorna Goodison: "The Nanny" from *I Am Becoming My Mother* by Lorna Goodison, New Beacon Books Ltd, 1986. "Road of the Dread" from *Selected Poems*, by Lorna Goodison. The University of Michigan Press, 1993.

Nadine Gordimer: From *The Essential Gesture: Writing, Politics and Places* by Nadine Gordimer and Stephen Clingman Copyright © 1988 by Felix B.V.I.O. Reprinted by permission of Alfred A. Knopf Inc.

Stephen Jay Gould: "Evolution as Fact and Theory", from *Hen's Teeth and Horse's Toes: Further Reflections in Natural History* by Stephen Jay Gould. Copyright © 1983 by Stephen Jay Gould. Reprinted by permission of W.W. Norton & Company, Inc.

Ralph Gustafson: "Of Green Steps and Laundry" from *The Moment is All* by Ralph Gustafson. Used by permission, McClelland and Stewart, Inc. *The Canadian Publishers*. "Partial Argument" from *Corners in the Glass* by Ralph Gustafson. Used by permission, McClelland and Stewart, Inc. *The Canadian Publishers*.

Marilyn Hacker: From *Assumptions* by Marilyn Hacker. Published by Alfred A. Knopf, 1985. Reprinted by permission of Frances Collin Literary Agent. Copyright © 1985 by Marilyn Hacker.

Thomas Hardy: From *Collected Poems*, Macmillan London Ltd, 1919.

Tony Harrison: "On Not Being Milton" © copyright Tony Harrison.

Gwen Harwood: "Father and Child" from *Selected Poems* (ETT Imprint, Watsons Bay 1997).

Seamus Heaney: "The Forge" and "The Wife's Tale" reprinted by permission of Faber and Faber Ltd from *Door into the Dark* by Seamus Heaney. "Personal Helicon" reprinted by permission of Faber and Faber Ltd from *Death of a Naturalist* by Seamus Heaney.

Ernest Hemingway: Reprinted with permission of Scribner, a Division of Simon & Schuster from *Men Without Women* by Ernest Hemingway. Copyright 1927 Charles Scribner's Sons. Copyright renewed 1955 by Ernest Hemingway.

Gwendolyn MacEwan: Permission granted by the author's family.

Hugh MacLennan: Published with permission of the Hugh MacLennan Estate.

Joan MacLeod: Reprinted with permission from Joan MacLeod and Playwrights Canada Press.

Louise MacNeice: Reprinted by permission of Faber and Faber Ltd from *Collected Poems of Louise MacNeice*.

Jay Macpherson: "The Boatman" and "The Fisherman" from *Poems Twice Told* by Jay Macpherson. Copyright © Oxford University Press Canada 1981. Reprinted by permission of Oxford University Press Canada.

Derek Mahon: © Derek Mahon 1979. Reprinted from *Poems 1962–1978* by Derek Mahon (1979) by permission of Oxford University Press.

David Malouf: Reprinted with permission of the author.

Eli Mandel: Reprinted by permission of The Estate of Eli Mandel.

Bill Manhire: Reprinted with permission of the author.

Daphne Marlatt: From *Touch to my Tongue* by Daphne Marlatt, Longspoon Press, 1984 and *Readings from the Labyrinth* by Daphne Marlatt, NeWest Press, 1998.

Medbh McGuckian: By kind permission of the author and The Gallery Press. From *The Flower Master and Other Poems* (1993).

W.S. Merwin: "In the Winter of My Thirty-Eighth Year" and "When the War is Over" from *The Lice*. Rupert Hart-Davis.

Rohinton Mistry: *Tales from Firozsha Baag* by Rohinton Mistry. Used by permission, McClelland & Stewart, Inc. *The Canadian Publishers*.

Edwin Morgan: From *The Second Life*. Reprinted by permission of Edinburgh University Press.

Daniel David Moses: Used by permission of the author.

Alice Munro: From *Dance of the Happy Shades* by Alice Munro. Reprinted with permission of McGraw-Hill Ryerson Limited.

Les Murray: Reproduced by permission of Les Murray c/o Margaret Connolly and Associates.

Howard Nemerov: From *The Collected Poems of Howard Nemerov*, The University of Chicago Press, 1977. Reprinted by permission of the author.

Lucy Ng: from Reprinted by the permission of the author.

Arthur Nortje: Reproduced from *Dead Roots* by Arthur Nortje by permission of Heinemann Educational Books Ltd.

Alden Nowlan: from *The Things Which Are*, 1962. Reprinted by permission of the author.

Michael Ondaatje: "Prometheus, with Wings" from *The Dainty Monsters*, Coach House Press, Toronto, 1967. "King Kong Meets Wallace Stevens" and "Bearhug" from *There's a Trick with a Knife*, McClelland & Stewart, 1979. Reprinted by permission of the author.

Wilfred Owen: From *Wilfred Owen The Complete Poems and Fragments*, edited by Jon Stallworthy. Hogarth Press. Reprinted with permission of the Estate of Wilfred Owen.

George Orwell: Reprinted with permission of Mark Hamilton as the Literary Executor of the Estate of the Late Sonia Brownell Orwell, Martin Secker & Warburg Ltd. and A M Heath & Co. Ltd. Copyright © George Orwell, 1946.

P.K. Page: "Poor Bird" Hologram published by Brick Books, 1994. "The Stenographers" from *As Ten As Twenty*, "Cook's Mountains" from *Cry Ararat*. Reprinted by permission of the author.

Sylvia Plath: "The Colossus" from *The Colossus* by Sylvia Plath published by Faber & Faber, London © Ted Hughes, 1967. "You're" from *Ariel* by Sylvia Plath published by Faber & Faber, London © Ted Hughes, 1965.

William Plomer: "The Boer War" from *The Fivefold Screen* reprinted by permission of Sir Rupert Hart-Davis. "The Devil Dancers" from *Collected Poems* by William Plomer, published by Jonathan Cape Ltd. Reprinted by permission of the Estate of William Plomer and the publisher.

Ezra Pound: "Ancient Wisdom, Rather Comic", "In a Station of the Metro" and "A Pact" by Ezra Pound, from *Personae*. Copyright 1926 by Ezra Pound. Reprinted by permission of New Directions Publishing Corp.

E.J. Pratt: From *Complete Poems* by E.J. Pratt © University of Toronto Press Incorporated. Reprinted by permission of University of Toronto Press Incorporated.

Al Purdy: From *Rooms For Rent In the Outer Planets* by Al Purdy, Harbour Publishing, Madeira Park, 1996.

Contents

Traditions

Topics and Questions for Study, Discussion, and Writing

Preface to the Second Edition

Currents: by renaming this revised edition of *A 20th-Century Anthology*, we want to assert the currency and immediacy of the literature gathered in this volume, as well as emphasize a multiplicity of modes, directions, and approaches—that literature cannot be reduced to a single thematic. We have been guided by a few motivations and principles. We have tried especially to maintain the balance established by the first edition between breadth and depth. Since this is a textbook used exclusively in Canada, we have tried to emphasize Canadian writers in the new material. The two one-act plays might serve to illustrate the kinds of editorial choices we have made: one by a crucial figure for twentieth-century drama, Samuel Beckett, and the other by the innovative Canadian playwright Joan MacLeod. Although no two plays could possibly represent the theatre of the twentieth century, we hope that these can supplement class discussion of drama. In deleting selections from the first edition, and replacing them with new ones, we have been guided by comments from the editors of the first edition and other users of this anthology. Finally, however, our choices have been determined by our own senses of which authors and texts reflect important trends in the century, and by our experience of what works well in the classroom.

A significant change occurs in the critical apparatus following the "Traditions" section. While we have kept the "Elements of Literature" portion, essentially adapting and updating it, the "Ideas, Themes" portion has been revised much more substantially, and renamed accordingly. The focus has shifted from thematic to critical approaches to literature; we provide brief discussions of some of the century's major theoretical and critical developments, always with reference to texts. We aim to provide readers with a sense of the variety of possible approaches to the works included in this anthology.

As the twentieth century ends and the twenty-first begins, it is clear that there are many literatures in English, encompassing a wide variety of possible forms and stances. *Currents* reflects this essential plurality.

Preface to the First Edition

A 20th-Century Anthology provides an introduction to modern literature in English. Though there is something implicitly paradoxical about an "overview" of an era that is not yet complete, the century is near enough to its end to afford us at least a qualified sense of its unique character. And it is this character—observable in history and expressed in art—that this book attempts to convey to you. By offering you glimpses of people and ideas and words and events, the book will help you read modern writing with greater sensitivity to the forces that so far have animated it and animated the century as well.

Our aim in bringing together these twentieth-century works is fourfold: we have collected stories, poems, and essays which explore ideas that have preoccupied twentieth-century minds; we have done so in part to exemplify many of the literary forms and techniques that twentieth-century writers have used; we want to draw attention to the links between art and the society in which it takes place; and we want most of all to present a selection of works which are a pleasure to read—sometimes because they amuse, sometimes because they teach us something, sometimes because they echo with association, sometimes because they appeal to our sense of beauty or justice, sometimes because they challenge fondly held beliefs and stir us to rethink them, sometimes because they confirm our commitment to life and moral values, and always because they use language creatively and effectively.

In *A 20th-Century Anthology*, then, we have collected essays, stories, and poems which we hope will do at least these four things:

1. encourage you to read for pleasure,
2. increase your understanding and appreciation of literary forms and the uses of language,
3. help you confront the major ideas and themes dealt with by twentieth-century writers,
4. help you see how art and society interrelate, especially how they do so in our own age.

1. Reading for Pleasure

This first aim is the most important. If you don't read for pleasure, you are unlikely to do much reading at all, and you would then be missing something. "To read literature" should be synonymous with "to enjoy." But the pleasures of reading aren't just the simple pleasures of being entertained, though these are important. The greatest pleasure, as Aristotle noted long ago, is that of learning something—which is one reason this first aim is the most important; it includes all the others.

2. Appreciating Form and Language

You should enjoy learning about literary forms and techniques. Why is one work a sonnet, another a short story, another an essay? Why is one work written in formal language, another in colloquial language, another in seeming nonsense? Why is one work simple and direct, another complicated and difficult, another couched in a dense thicket of metaphors? Coming to know and understand the different ways in which different ideas can or need to be expressed will help you to understand and appreciate what the more verbally expressive people among us have to say about the society and the world we find ourselves living in.

3. Understanding the Age

What twentieth-century writers have been telling and are trying to tell us are some truths about ourselves and about the way we live and the reasons for which we live, about the ideas that underlie our behaviour and the standards and values that help shape it. "The unexamined life," as Socrates said long ago, "is not worth living." But of course not even philosophers and writers have all the answers: much of what we stand to learn from literature, as from life, consists of questions—questions about ourselves as individuals and as members of society, questions about order and change, about our values in the present and about our connections with the values of the past. Examining some of the major questions through the eyes and minds of our writers helps us understand ourselves and our century.

4. Acknowledging the Importance of Art and Society to Each Other

Art—especially literary art—is a record of people in particular places at particular times. As T.S. Eliot once said, "the great poet, in writing himself, writes his time." But literature also reaches beyond immediate issues; it reaches toward an expression of what it means to be human, of the truth of being human in any age. Literature is one of the main ways in which a society records its ideas and its values, values that one generation hands on as heritage to the next. In the eighteenth century Samuel Johnson wrote that the poet is "the interpreter of nature, and the legislator of mankind." In the nineteenth century Percy Bysshe Shelley wrote that "poets are the unacknowledged legislators of the world." In our own century Ezra Pound put it this way: "Artists are the antennae of the race."

Although lodged in its own place and time, literature charts its own territory and speaks to ages other than its own. But it first of all speaks to its own age. Our literature speaks to us of political turmoil and of war; of old generations giving way to new; of new technologies and new frameworks of ideas for dealing with them; of new kinds of behaviour and new ways of seeing ourselves in relation to our society; and of the nature and continuing power and importance of art, even—or especially—in a society as marked by technology and violence and depersonalization as our own. It speaks to us of the human condition in the twentieth century.

✧   ✧   ✧   ✧   ✧

As with any anthology, we have had to balance our choices against the size of the book. Many good writers are represented only briefly, some not at all. Since this is an introductory anthology rather than a definitive one, we have sought a broader and more varied representation than would have been possible had we tried to do fuller justice to the acknowledged major writers of the century. Though there is a loss of depth in the representation of, for example, T.S. Eliot, there is a corresponding gain in the inclusion of less-known writers from Canada and the South Pacific and the English-speaking third world—a gain both in linguistic variety and in the breadth of perspective toward the cultural and political experience of our age.

We have also had to exclude some genres. We have included no plays: George Bernard Shaw, Eugene O'Neill, Harold Pinter, and Tom Stoppard, for example, are unrepresented. The enquiring reader must seek among the works of such writers for supplements to our selections. The same goes for novels: the longest piece of fiction we have included, Joseph Conrad's "The Secret Sharer," is a long story, not a short novel. Some poems, too, are absent simply because of their length: like the drama and the novel, the long poem has been an important literary form in the twentieth century; enquiring students will want to look into such poems as Hart Crane's

The Bridge, T.S. Eliot's *The Waste Land* and *Four Quartets*, David Jones's *In Parenthesis*, William Carlos Williams's *Paterson*, Basil Bunting's *Briggflatts*, Ezra Pound's *Cantos*, W.H. Auden's *The Age of Anxiety*, Michael Ondaatje's *The Collected Works of Billy the Kid*.

So much for omissions. There remains here a wealth of literary enjoyment: stories, lyrics, satires, fables, ballads, entertainments, allegories, arguments, and more. Each work, we think, is enjoyable in and for itself. But the variety of forms and subjects should also be enjoyable. As well as works using traditional forms, for example, there are some that are unconventional, experimental in one way or another. There are essays and poems about the reading of poetry and the writing of fiction, and there are poems and stories to be read in connection with them. There are scientific enquiries, attacks on social and technological desecrations, autobiographical reminiscences, stories about growing up, and flights of fancy and imagination. And many works—drawn from the English literatures of Canada, the United States, the United Kingdom, the South Pacific, the Caribbean, Africa, and South Asia—detail the political history of the century: the changes in allegiance; the decline of old empires and the growth of new nations with new vocabularies, both political and metaphoric; the impact of economics and race on political attitudes; and the increasing power, as the century unfolds, of the politics of feminism. Other works focus on such topics of our time as war, education, religion, freedom, guilt and responsibility, individuality, love, and the relations between generations. Others treat thought processes, truth, imagination, myth, time and change, history, the past. Still others discuss art and the artist, literature, language, and the function of art in our society and in our individual lives.

❖   ❖   ❖   ❖   ❖

Appreciating the literature and understanding the century are intertwined pursuits. How to begin? How to proceed? Many approaches are possible. One is chronological—the approach that governs the organization of this book. If you want, you can study the authors in historical sequence from 1900 to the present day. Or you can focus on recurrent ideas and the language and style that convey them, and approach the literature thematically, formally, or analytically. The extensive study and discussion questions (grouped, for convenience, at the end of the book) suggest how you might take some of these approaches.

Yet another possibility this book affords lies in the section we have called "Traditions." In it we include many works from earlier centuries—not to try to provide a rough history of English literature (though it at least suggests one) but to call attention to one of the contexts in which twentieth-century writing occurs, namely the literary one. However unique the twentieth century is, its literature is not isolated from the past, nor are modern writers unfamiliar with their cultural heritage. Many modern works are written in modes and forms (satires, allegories, sonnets, villanelles, elegies, tales) that have a long history; others allude to earlier works and writers (Webb draws directly on Marvell; Bishop refers to Bunyan); motifs recur from century to century (Classical and Biblical allusions, journeys and quests, gardens, birds and animals, cycles and seasons).

The "Traditions" section not only offers you the chance to read some substantial early works for themselves; it also gives you the chance to trace some of the connections between present literature and the past. How twentieth-century writers have adapted old stories (for example those of Bluebeard or Ulysses) to their own time and condition tells us much about the pressures and aspirations of the age as well as about the individual vision of each artist. Further, in a century so marked as ours by violent and accelerating change, such echoes and allusions and adaptations remind us of our debt to the past, of the essential continuity—despite the forces of change—that history, faith, and the human imagination not only permit but insist upon.

The
Twentieth
Century

Thomas Hardy

(ENGLAND, 1840–1928)

The Darkling Thrush

I leant upon a coppice gate
    When Frost was spectre-gray,
And Winter's dregs made desolate
    The weakening eye of day.
5 The tangled bine-stems scored the sky
    Like strings of broken lyres,
And all mankind that haunted nigh
    Had sought their household fires.

The land's sharp features seemed to be
10   The Century's corpse outleant,
His crypt the cloudy canopy,
    The wind his death-lament.
The ancient pulse of germ and birth
    Was shrunken hard and dry,
15 And every spirit upon earth
    Seemed fervourless as I.

At once a voice arose among
    The bleak twigs overhead
In a full-hearted evensong
20   Of joy illimited;
An aged thrush, frail, gaunt, and small,
    In blast-beruffled plume,
Had chosen thus to fling his soul
    Upon the growing gloom.

25 So little cause for carolings
    Of such ecstatic sound
Was written on terrestrial things
    Afar or nigh around,
That I could think there trembled through
30   His happy good-night air
Some blessed Hope, whereof he knew
    And I was unaware.

                (December 1900)

The Convergence of the Twain

(Lines on the loss of the "Titanic")

I

In a solitude of the sea
Deep from human vanity,
And the Pride of Life that planned her, stilly couches she.

II

Steel chambers, late the pyres
Of her salamandrine fires,
Cold currents thrid, and turn to rhythmic tidal lyres.

III

Over the mirrors meant
To glass the opulent
The sea-worm crawls—grotesque, slimed, dumb, indifferent.

IV

Jewels in joy designed
To ravish the sensuous mind
Lie lightless, all their sparkles bleared and black and blind.

V

Dim moon-eyed fishes near
Gaze at the gilded gear
And query: "What does this vaingloriousness down here?" . . .

VI

Well: while was fashioning
This creature of cleaving wing,
The Immanent Will that stirs and urges everything

VII

Prepared a sinister mate
For her—so gaily great—
A Shape of Ice, for the time far and dissociate.

VIII

And as the smart ship grew
In stature, grace, and hue,
In shadowy silent distance grew the Iceberg too.

IX

Alien they seemed to be:
No mortal eye could see
The intimate welding of their later history.

Or sign that they were bent
By paths coincident
30 On being anon twin halves of one august event.

Till the Spinner of the Years
Said "Now!" And each one hears,
And consummation comes, and jars two hemispheres.

(1912)

Channel Firing

That night your great guns, unawares,
Shook all our coffins as we lay,
And broke the chancel window-squares,
We thought it was the Judgment-day

5   And sat upright. While drearisome
Arose the howl of wakened hounds:
The mouse let fall the altar-crumb,
The worms drew back into the mounds,

The glebe cow drooled. Till God called, "No;
10 It's gunnery practice out at sea
Just as before you went below;
The world is as it used to be:

"All nations striving strong to make
Red war yet redder. Mad as hatters
15 They do no more for Christés sake
Than you who are helpless in such matters.

"That this is not the judgment-hour
For some of them's a blessed thing,
For if it were they'd have to scour
20 Hell's floor for so much threatening. . . .

"Ha, ha. It will be warmer when
I blow the trumpet (if indeed
I ever do; for you are men,
And rest eternal sorely need)."

25 So down we lay again. "I wonder,
Will the world ever saner be,"
Said one, "than when He sent us under
In our indifferent century!"

And many a skeleton shook his head.

30 "Instead of preaching forty year,"
My neighbour Parson Thirdly said,
"I wish I had stuck to pipes and beer."

Again the guns disturbed the hour,
Roaring their readiness to avenge,
35 As far inland as Stourton Tower,
And Camelot, and starlit Stonehenge.

(April 1914)

Joseph Conrad

(POLAND/ENGLAND, 1857–1924)

The Secret Sharer

I

On my right hand there were lines of fishing-stakes resembling a mysterious system of half-submerged bamboo fences, incomprehensible in its division of the domain of tropical fishes, and crazy of aspect as if abandoned for ever by some nomad tribe of fishermen now gone to the other end of the ocean; for there was no sign of human habitation as far as the eye could reach. To the left a group of barren islets, suggesting ruins of stone walls, towers, and block-houses, had its foundations set in a blue sea that itself looked solid, so still and stable did it lie below my feet; even the track of light from the westering sun shone smoothly, without that animated glitter which tells of an imperceptible tipple. And when I turned my head to take a parting glance at the tug which had just left us anchored outside the bar, I saw the straight line of the flat shore joined to the stable sea, edge to edge, with a perfect and unmarked closeness, in one levelled floor half brown, half blue under the enormous dome of the sky. Corresponding in their insignificance to the islets of the sea, two small clumps of trees, one on each side of the only fault in the impeccable joint, marked the mouth of the river Meinam we had just left on the first preparatory stage of our homeward journey; and, far back on the inland level, a larger and loftier mass, the grove surrounding the great Paknam pagoda, was the only thing on which the eye could rest from the vain task of exploring the monotonous sweep of the horizon. Here and there gleams as of a few scattered pieces of silver marked the windings of the great river; and on the nearest of them, just within the bar, the tug steaming right into the land became lost to my sight, hull and funnel and masts, as though the impassive earth had swallowed her up without an effort, without a tremor. My eye followed the light cloud of her smoke, now here, now there, above the plain, according to the devious curves of the stream, but always fainter and farther away, till I lost it at last behind the mitre-shaped hill of the great pagoda. And then I was left alone with my ship, anchored at the head of the Gulf of Siam.

She floated at the starting-point of a long journey, very still in an immense stillness, the shadows of her spars flung far to the eastward by the setting sun. At that moment I was alone on her decks. There was not a sound in her—and around us nothing moved, nothing lived, not a canoe on the water, not a bird in the air, not a cloud in the sky. In this breathless pause at the threshold of a long passage we seemed to be measuring our fitness for a long and arduous enterprise, the appointed task of both our existences to be carried out, far from all human eyes, with only sky and sea for spectators and for judges.

There must have been some glare in the air to interfere with one's sight, because it was only just before the sun left us that my roaming eyes made out beyond the highest ridge of the principal islet of the group something which did away with the solemnity of perfect solitude. The tide of darkness flowed on swiftly; and with tropical suddenness a swarm of stars came out above the shadowy earth, while I lingered yet, my hand resting lightly on my ship's rail as if on the shoulder of a trusted friend. But, with all that multitude of celestial bodies staring down at one, the comfort of quiet communion with her was gone for good. And there were also disturbing sounds by this time—voices, footsteps forward; the steward flitted along the main-deck, a busily ministering spirit; a hand-bell tinkled urgently under the poop-deck. . . .

I found my two officers waiting for me near the supper table, in the lighted cuddy. We sat down at once, and as I helped the chief mate, I said:

"Are you aware that there is a ship anchored inside the islands? I saw her mastheads above the ridge as the sun went down."

He raised sharply his simple face, overcharged by a terrible growth of whisker, and emitted his usual ejaculations: "Bless my soul, sir! You don't say so!"

My second mate was a round-cheeked, silent young man, grave beyond his years, I thought; but as our eyes happened to meet I detected a slight quiver on his lips. I looked down at once. It was not my part to encourage sneering on board my ship. It must be said, too, that I knew very little of my officers. In consequence of certain events of no particular significance, except to myself, I had been appointed to the command only a fortnight before. Neither did I know much of the hands forward. All these people had been together for eighteen months or so, and my position was that of the only stranger on board. I mention this because it has some bearing on what is to follow. But what I felt most was my being a stranger to the ship; and if all the truth must be told, I was somewhat of a stranger to myself. The youngest man on board (barring the second mate), and untried as yet by a position of the fullest responsibility, I was willing to take the adequacy of the others for granted. They had simply to be equal to their tasks; but I wondered how far I should turn out faithful to that ideal conception of one's own personality every man sets up for himself secretly.

Meantime the chief mate, with an almost visible effect of collaboration on the part of his round eyes and frightful whiskers, was trying to evolve a theory of the anchored ship. His dominant trait was to take all things into earnest consideration. He was of a painstaking turn of mind. As he used to say, he "liked to account to himself" for practically everything that came in his way, down to a miserable scorpion he had found in his cabin a week before. The why and the wherefore of that scorpion—how it got on board and came to select his room rather than the pantry (which was a dark place and more what a scorpion would be partial to), and how on earth it managed to drown itself in the inkwell of his writing-desk—had exercised him infinitely. The ship within the islands was much more easily accounted for; and just as we were about to rise from table he made his pronouncement. She was, he doubted not, a ship from home lately arrived. Probably she drew too much water to cross the bar except at the top of spring tides. Therefore she went into that natural harbour to wait for a few days in preference to remaining in an open roadstead.

"That's so," confirmed the second mate, suddenly, in his slightly hoarse voice. "She draws over twenty feet. She's the Liverpool ship *Sephora* with a cargo of coal. Hundred and twenty-three days from Cardiff."

We looked at him in surprise.

"The tugboat skipper told me when he came on board for your letters, sir," explained the young man. "He expects to take her up the river the day after to-morrow."

After thus overwhelming us with the extent of his information he slipped out of the cabin. The mate observed regretfully that he "could not account for that young fellow's whims." What prevented him telling us all about it at once, he wanted to know.

I detained him as he was making a move. For the last two days the crew had had plenty of hard work, and the night before they had very little sleep. I felt painfully that I—a stranger— was doing something unusual when I directed him to let all hands turn in without setting an anchor-watch. I proposed to keep on deck myself till one o'clock or thereabouts. I would get the second mate to relieve me at that hour.

"He will turn out the cook and the steward at four," I concluded, "and then give you a call. Of course at the slightest sign of any sort of wind we'll have the hands up and make a start at once."

He concealed his astonishment. "Very well, sir." Outside the cuddy he put his head in the second mate's door to inform him of my unheard-of caprice to take a five hours' anchor-watch on myself. I heard the other raise his voice incredulously—"What? The Captain himself?" Then a few more murmurs, a door closed, then another. A few moments later I went on deck.

My strangeness, which had made me sleepless, had prompted that unconventional arrangement, as if I had expected in those solitary hours of the night to get on terms with the ship of which I knew nothing, manned by men of whom I knew very little more. Fast alongside a wharf, littered like any ship in port with a tangle of unrelated things, invaded by unrelated shore people, I had hardly seen her yet properly. Now, as she lay cleared for sea, the stretch of her main-deck seemed to me very fine under the stars. Very fine, very roomy for her size, and very inviting. I descended the poop and paced the waist, my mind picturing to myself the coming passage through the Malay Archipelago, down the Indian Ocean, and up the Atlantic. All its phases were familiar enough to me, every characteristic, all the alternatives which were likely to face me on the high sea—everything! . . . except the novel responsibility of command. But I took heart from the reasonable thought that the ship was like other ships, the men like other men, and that the sea was not likely to keep any special surprises expressly for my discomfiture.

Arrived at that comforting conclusion, I bethought myself of a cigar and went below to get it. All was still down there. Everybody at the after end of the ship was sleeping profoundly. I came out again on the quarter-deck, agreeably at ease in my sleeping-suit on that warm breathless night, barefooted, a glowing cigar in my teeth, and, going forward, I was met by the profound silence of the fore end of the ship. Only as I passed the door of the forecastle I heard a deep, quiet, trustful sigh of some sleeper inside. And suddenly I rejoiced in the great security of the sea as compared with the unrest of the land, in my choice of that untempted life presenting no disquieting problems, invested with an elementary moral beauty by the absolute straightforwardness of its appeal and by the singleness of its purpose.

The riding-light in the fore-rigging burned with a clear, untroubled, as if symbolic, flame, confident and bright in the mysterious shades of the night. Passing on my way aft along the other side of the ship, I observed that the rope side-ladder, put over, no doubt, for the master of the tug when he came to fetch away our letters, had not been hauled in as it should have been. I became annoyed at this, for exactitude in small matters is the very soul of discipline. Then I reflected that I had myself peremptorily dismissed my officers from duty, and by my own act had prevented the anchor-watch being formally set and things properly attended to. I asked myself whether it was wise ever to interfere with the established routine of duties even from the kindest of motives. My action might have made me appear eccentric. Goodness only knew how that absurdly whiskered mate would "account" for my conduct, and what the whole ship thought of that informality of their new captain. I was vexed with myself.

Not from compunction certainly, but, as it were mechanically, I proceeded to get the ladder in myself. Now a side-ladder of that sort is a light affair and comes in easily, yet my vigorous tug, which should have brought it flying on board, merely recoiled upon my body in a totally unexpected jerk. What the devil! . . . I was so astounded by the immovableness of that ladder that I remained stock-still, trying to account for it to myself like that imbecile mate of mine. In the end, of course, I put my head over the rail.

The side of the ship made an opaque belt of shadow on the darkling glassy shimmer of the sea. But I saw at once something elongated and pale floating very close to the ladder. Before I could form a guess a faint flash of phosphorescent light, which seemed to issue suddenly from the naked body of a man, flickered in the sleeping water with the elusive, silent play of summer lightning in a night sky. With a gasp I saw revealed to my stare a pair of feet, the long legs, a broad livid back immersed right up to the neck in a greenish cadaverous glow. One hand, awash, clutched the bottom rung of the ladder. He was complete but for the head. A headless corpse! The cigar dropped out of my gaping mouth with a tiny plop and a short hiss quite audible in the absolute stillness of all things under heaven. At that I suppose he raised up his face, a dimly pale oval in the shadow of the ship's side. But even then I could only barely make out down there the shape of his black-haired head. However, it was enough for the horrid, frost-bound sensation which had gripped me about the chest to pass off. The moment of vain exclamations was past, too. I only climbed on the spare spar and leaned over the rail as far as I could, to bring my eyes nearer to that mystery floating alongside.

As he hung by the ladder, like a resting swimmer, the sea-lightning played about his limbs at every stir; and he appeared in it ghastly, silvery, fish-like. He remained as mute as a fish, too. He made no motion to get out of the water, either. It was inconceivable that he should not attempt to come on board, and strangely troubling to suspect that perhaps he did not want to. And my first words were prompted by just that troubled incertitude.

"What's the matter?" I asked in my ordinary tone, speaking down to the face upturned exactly under mine.

"Cramp," it answered, no louder. Then slightly anxious, "I say, no need to call any one."

"I was not going to," I said.

"Are you alone on deck?"

"Yes."

I had somehow the impression that he was on the point of letting go the ladder to swim away beyond my ken—mysterious as he came. But, for the moment, this being appearing as if he had risen from the bottom of the sea (it was certainly the nearest land to the ship) wanted only to know the time. I told him. And he, down there, tentatively:

"I suppose your captain's turned in?"

"I am sure he isn't," I said.

He seemed to struggle with himself, for I heard something like the low, bitter murmur of doubt. "What's the good?" His next words came out with a hesitating effort.

"Look here, my man. Could you call him out quietly?"

I thought the time had come to declare myself.

"*I* am the captain."

I heard a "By Jove!" whispered at the level of the water. The phosphorescence flashed in the swirl of the water all about his limbs, his other hand seized the ladder.

"My name's Leggatt."

The voice was calm and resolute. A good voice. The self-possession of that man had somehow induced a corresponding state in myself. It was very quietly that I remarked:

"You must be a good swimmer."

"Yes. I've been in the water practically since nine o'clock. The question for me now is whether I am to let go this ladder and go on swimming till I sink from exhaustion, or—to come on board here."

I felt this was no mere formula of desperate speech, but a real alternative in the view of a strong soul. I should have gathered from this that he was young; indeed, it is only the young who are ever confronted by such clear issues. But at the time it was pure intuition on my part. A mysterious communication was established already between us two—in the face of that silent, darkened tropical sea. I was young, too; young enough to make no comment. The man in the water began suddenly to climb up the ladder, and I hastened away from the rail to fetch some clothes.

Before entering the cabin I stood still, listening in the lobby at the foot of the stairs. A faint snore came through the closed door of the chief mate's room. The second mate's door was on the hook, but the darkness in there was absolutely soundless. He, too, was young and could sleep like a stone. Remained the steward, but he was not likely to wake up before he was called. I got a sleeping-suit out of my room and, coming back on deck, saw the naked man from the sea sitting on the main-hatch, glimmering white in the darkness, his elbows on his knees and his head in his hands. In a moment he had concealed his damp body in a sleeping-suit of the same grey-stripe pattern as the one I was wearing and followed me like my double on the poop. Together we moved right aft, barefooted, silent.

"What is it?" I asked in a deadened voice, taking the lighted lamp out of the binnacle, and raising it to his face.

"An ugly business."

He had rather regular features; a good mouth; light eyes under somewhat heavy, dark eyebrows; a smooth, square forehead; no growth on his cheeks; a small, brown moustache, and a well-shaped, round chin. His expression was concentrated, meditative, under the inspecting light of the lamp I held up to his face; such as a man thinking hard in solitude might wear. My sleeping-suit was just right for his size. A well-knit young fellow of twenty-five at most. He caught his lower lip with the edge of white, even teeth.

"Yes," I said, replacing the lamp in the binnacle. The warm, heavy tropical night closed upon his head again.

"There's a ship over there," he murmured.

"Yes, I know. The *Sephora*. Did you know of us?"

"Hadn't the slightest idea. I am the mate of her——" He paused and corrected himself. "I should say I *was*."

"Aha! Something wrong?"

"Yes. Very wrong indeed. I've killed a man."

"What do you mean? Just now?"

"No, on the passage. Weeks ago. Thirty-nine south. When I say a man——"

"Fit of temper," I suggested, confidently.

The shadowy, dark head, like mine, seemed to nod imperceptibly above the ghostly grey of my sleeping-suit. It was, in the night, as though I had been faced by my own reflection in the depths of a sombre and immense mirror.

"A pretty thing to have to own up to for a Conway boy," murmured my double, distinctly.

"You're a Conway boy?"

"I am," he said, as if startled. Then, slowly . . . "Perhaps you too——"

It was so; but being a couple of years older I had left before he joined. After a quick interchange of dates a silence fell; and I thought suddenly of my absurd mate with his terrific whiskers and the "Bless my soul—you don't say so" type of intellect. My double gave me an inkling of his thoughts by saying: "My father's a parson in Norfolk. Do you see me before a judge and jury on that charge? For myself I can't see the necessity. There are fellows that an angel from heaven—And I am not that. He was one of those creatures that are just simmering all the time with a silly sort of wickedness. Miserable devils that have no business to live at all. He wouldn't do his duty and wouldn't let anybody else do theirs. But what's the good of talking! You know well enough the sort of ill-conditioned snarling cur——"

He appealed to me as if our experiences had been as identical as our clothes. And I knew well enough the pestiferous danger of such a character where there are no means of legal repression. And I knew well enough also that my double there was no homicidal ruffian. I did not think of asking him for details, and he told me the story roughly in brusque, disconnected sentences. I needed no more. I saw it all going on as though I were myself inside that other sleeping-suit.

"It happened while we were setting a reefed foresail, at dusk. Reefed foresail! You understand the sort of weather. The only sail we had left to keep the ship running; so you may guess what it had been like for days. Anxious sort of job, that. He gave me some of his cursed insolence at the sheet. I tell you I was overdone with this terrific weather that seemed to have no end to it. Terrific, I tell you—and a deep ship. I believe the fellow himself was half crazed with funk. It was no time for gentlemanly reproof, so I turned round and felled him like an ox. He up and at me. We closed just as an awful sea made for the ship. All hands saw it coming and took to the rigging, but I had him by the throat, and went on shaking him like a rat, the men above us yelling, 'Look out! look out!' Then a crash as if the sky had fallen on my head. They say that for over ten minutes hardly anything was to be seen of the ship—just the three masts and a bit of the forecastle head and of the poop all awash driving along in a smother of foam. It was a miracle that they found us, jammed together behind the forebits. It's clear that I meant business, because I was holding him by the throat still when they picked us up. He was black in the face. It was too much for them. It seems they rushed us aft together, gripped as we were, screaming 'Murder!' like a lot of lunatics, and broke into the cuddy. And the ship running for her life, touch and go all the time, any minute her last in a sea fit to turn your hair grey only a-looking at it. I understand that the skipper, too, started raving like the rest of them. The man had been deprived of sleep for more than a week, and to have this sprung on him at the height of a furious gale nearly drove him out of his mind. I wonder they didn't fling me overboard after getting the carcass of their precious ship-mate out of my fingers. They had rather a job to separate us, I've been told. A sufficiently fierce story to make an old judge and a respectable jury sit up a bit. The first thing I heard when I came to myself was the maddening howling of that endless gale, and on that the voice of the old man. He was hanging on to my bunk, staring into my face out of his sou'wester.

" 'Mr. Leggatt, you have killed a man. You can act no longer as chief mate of this ship.' "

His care to subdue his voice made it sound monotonous. He rested a hand on the end of the skylight to steady himself with, and all that time did not stir a limb, so far as I could see. "Nice little tale for a quiet tea-party," he concluded in the same tone.

One of my hands, too, rested on the end of the skylight; neither did I stir a limb, so far as I knew. We stood less than a foot from each other. It occurred to me that if old "Bless my soul—you don't say so" were to put his head up the companion and catch sight of us, he would think he was seeing double, or imagine himself come upon a scene of weird witchcraft; the strange captain having a quiet confabulation by the wheel with his own grey ghost. I became very much concerned to prevent anything of the sort. I heard the other's soothing undertone.

"My father's a parson in Norfolk," it said. Evidently he had forgotten he had told me this important fact before. Truly a nice little tale.

"You had better slip down into my stateroom now," I said, moving off stealthily. My double followed my movements; our bare feet made no sound; I let him in, closed the door with care, and, after giving a call to the second mate, returned on deck for my relief.

"Not much sign of any wind yet," I remarked when he approached.

"No, sir. Not much," he assented, sleepily, in his hoarse voice, with just enough deference, no more, and barely suppressing a yawn.

"Well, that's all you have to look out for. You have got your orders."

"Yes, sir."

I paced a turn or two on the poop and saw him take up his position face forward with his elbow in the ratlines of the mizzen-rigging before I went below. The mate's faint snoring was still going on peacefully. The cuddy lamp was burning over the table on which stood a vase with flowers, a polite attention from the ship's provision merchant—the last flowers we should see for the next three months at the very least. Two bunches of bananas hung from the beam symmetrically, one on each side of the rudder-casing. Everything was as before in the ship—except that two of her captain's sleeping-suits were simultaneously in use, one motionless in the cuddy, the other keeping very still in the captain's stateroom.

It must be explained here that my cabin had the form of the capital letter L, the door being within the angle and opening into the short part of the letter. A couch was to the left, the bed-place to the right; my writing-desk and the chronometers' table faced the door. But any one opening it, unless he stepped right inside, had no view of what I call the long (or vertical) part of the letter. It contained some lockers surmounted by a bookcase; and a few clothes, a thick jacket or two, caps, oilskin coat, and such like, hung on hooks. There was at the bottom of that part a door opening into my bath-room, which could be entered also directly from the saloon. But that way was never used.

The mysterious arrival had discovered the advantage of this particular shape. Entering my room, lighted strongly by a big bulkhead lamp swung on gimbals above my writing-desk, I did not see him anywhere till he stepped out quietly from behind the coats hung in the recessed part.

"I heard somebody moving about, and went in there at once," he whispered.

I, too, spoke under my breath.

"Nobody is likely to come in here without knocking and getting permission."

He nodded. His face was thin and the sunburn faded, as though he had been ill. And no wonder. He had been, I heard presently, kept under arrest in his cabin for nearly seven weeks. But there was nothing sickly in his eyes or in his expression. He was not a bit like me, really; yet, as we stood leaning over my bed-place, whispering side by side, with our dark heads together and our backs to the door, anybody bold enough to open it stealthily would have been treated to the uncanny sight of a double captain busy talking in whispers with his other self.

"But all this doesn't tell me how you came to hang on to our side-ladder," I inquired, in the hardly audible murmurs we used, after he had told me something more of the proceedings on board the *Sephora* once the bad weather was over.

"When we sighted Java Head I had had time to think all those matters out several times over. I had six weeks of doing nothing else, and with only an hour or so every evening for a tramp on the quarter-deck."

He whispered, his arms folded on the side of my bed-place, staring through the open port. And I could imagine perfectly the manner of this thinking out—a stubborn if not a steadfast operation; something of which I should have been perfectly incapable.

"I reckoned it would be dark before we closed with the land," he continued, so low that I had to strain my hearing, near as we were to each other, shoulder touching shoulder almost. "So I asked to speak to the old man. He always seemed very sick when he came to see me—as if he could not look me in the face. You know, that foresail saved the ship. She was too deep to have run long under bare poles. And it was I that managed to set it for him. Anyway, he came. When I had him in my cabin—he stood by the door looking at me as if I had the halter round my neck already—I asked him right away to leave my cabin door unlocked at night while the ship was going through Sunda Straits. There would be the Java coast within two or three miles, off Angier Point. I wanted nothing more. I've had a prize for swimming my second year in the Conway."

"I can believe it," I breathed out.

"God only knows why they locked me in every night. To see some of their faces you'd have thought they were afraid I'd go about at night strangling people. Am I a murdering brute? Do I look it? By Jove! if I had been he wouldn't have trusted himself like that into my room. You'll say I might have chucked him aside and bolted out, there and then—it was dark already. Well, no. And for the same reason I wouldn't think of trying to smash the door. There would have been a rush to stop me at the noise, and I did not mean to get into a confounded scrimmage. Somebody else might have got killed—for I would not have broken out only to get chucked back, and I did not want any more of that work. He refused, looking more sick than ever. He was afraid of the men, and also of that old second mate of his who had been sailing with him for years—a grey-headed old humbug; and his steward, too, had been with him devil knows how long—seventeen years or more—a dogmatic sort of loafer who hated me like poison, just because I was the chief mate. No chief mate ever made more than one voyage in the *Sephora*, you know. Those two old chaps ran the ship. Devil only knows what the skipper wasn't afraid of (all his nerve went to pieces altogether in that hellish spell of bad weather we had)—of what the law would do to him—of his wife, perhaps. Oh, yes! she's on board. Though I don't think she would have meddled. She would have been only too glad to have me out of the ship in any way. The 'brand of Cain' business, don't you see. That's all right. I was ready enough to go off wandering on the face of the earth—and that was price enough to pay for an Abel of that sort. Anyhow, he wouldn't listen to me. 'This thing must take its course. I represent the law here.' He was shaking like a leaf. 'So you won't?' 'No!' 'Then I hope you will be able to sleep on that,' I said, and turned my back on him. 'I wonder that *you* can,' cries he, and locks the door.

"Well, after that, I couldn't. Not very well. That was three weeks ago. We have had a slow passage through the Java Sea; drifted about Carimata for ten days. When we anchored here they thought, I suppose, it was all right. The nearest land (and that's five miles) is the ship's destination; the consul would soon set about catching me; and there would have been no object in bolting to these islets there. I don't suppose there's a drop of water on them. I don't know how it was, but to-night that steward, after bringing me my supper, went out to let me eat it, and left the door unlocked. And I ate it—all there was, too. After I had finished I strolled out on the quarter-deck. I don't know that I meant to do anything. A breath of fresh air was all I wanted, I believe. Then a sudden temptation came over me. I kicked off my slippers and was in the water before I had made up my mind fairly. Somebody heard the splash and they raised an awful hullabaloo. 'He's gone! Lower the boats! He's committed suicide! No, he's swimming.' Certainly I was swimming. It's not so easy for a swimmer like me to commit suicide by drowning. I landed on the nearest islet before the boat left the ship's side. I heard them pulling about in the dark, hailing, and so on, but after a bit they gave up. Everything quieted down and the anchorage became as still as death. I sat down on a stone and began to think. I felt certain they would start searching for me at daylight. There was no place to hide on those stony things—and if there had been, what would have been the good? But now I was clear of that ship, I was not going back. So after a while I took off all my clothes, tied them up in a bundle with a stone inside, and dropped them in the deep water on the outer side of that islet. That was suicide enough for me. Let them think what they liked, but I didn't mean to drown myself. I meant to swim till I sank—but that's not the same thing. I struck out for another of these little islands, and it was from that one that I first saw your riding-light. Something to swim for. I went on easily, and on the way I came upon a flat rock a foot or two above water. In the daytime, I dare say, you might make it out with a glass from your poop. I scrambled up on it and rested myself for a bit. Then I made another start. That last spell must have been over a mile."

His whisper was getting fainter and fainter, and all the time he stared straight out through the port-hole, in which there was not even a star to be seen. I had not interrupted him. There was something that made comment impossible in his narrative, or perhaps in himself; a sort of feeling, a quality, which I can't find a name for. And when he ceased, all I found was a futile whisper: "So you swam for our light?"

"Yes—straight for it. It was something to swim for. I couldn't see any stars low down because the coast was in the way, and I couldn't see the land, either. The water was like glass. One might have been swimming in a confounded thousand-feet deep cistern with no place for scrambling out anywhere; but what I didn't like was the notion of swimming round and round like a crazed bullock before I gave out; and as I didn't mean to go back . . . No. Do you see me being hauled back, stark naked, off one of these little islands by the scruff of the neck and fighting like a wild beast? Somebody would have got killed for certain, and I did not want any of that. So I went on. Then your ladder——"

"Why didn't you hail the ship?" I asked, a little louder.

He touched my shoulder lightly. Lazy footsteps came right over our heads and stopped. The second mate had crossed from the other side of the poop and might have been hanging over the rail, for all we knew.

"He couldn't hear us talking—could he?" My double breathed into my very ear, anxiously.

His anxiety was an answer, a sufficient answer, to the question I had put to him. An answer containing all the difficulty of that situation. I closed the port-hole quietly, to make sure. A louder word might have been overheard.

"Who's that?" he whispered then.

"My second mate. But I don't know much more of the fellow than you do."

And I told him a little about myself. I had been appointed to take charge while I least expected anything of the sort, not quite a fortnight ago. I didn't know either the ship or the people. Hadn't had the time in port to look about me or size anybody up. And as to the crew, all they knew was that I was appointed to take the ship home. For the rest, I was almost as much of a stranger on board as himself, I said. And at the moment I felt it most acutely. I felt that it would take very little to make me a suspect person in the eyes of the ship's company.

He had turned about meantime; and we, the two strangers in the ship, faced each other in identical attitudes.

"Your ladder——" he murmured, after a silence. "Who'd have thought of finding a ladder hanging over at night in a ship anchored out here! I felt just then a very unpleasant faintness. After the life I've been leading for nine weeks, anybody would have got out of condition. I wasn't capable of swimming round as far as your rudder-chains. And, lo and behold! there was a ladder to get hold of. After I gripped it I said to myself, 'What's the good?' When I saw a man's head looking over I thought I would swim away presently and leave him shouting—in whatever language it was. I didn't mind being looked at. I—I liked it. And then you speaking to me so quietly—as if you had expected me—made me hold on a little longer. It had been a confounded lonely time—I don't mean while swimming. I was glad to talk a little to some-body that didn't belong to the *Sephora*. As to asking for the captain, that was a mere impulse. It could have been no use, with all the ship knowing about me and the other people pretty certain to be round here in the morning. I don't know—I wanted to be seen, to talk with somebody, before I went on. I don't know what I would have said. . . . 'Fine night, isn't it?' or something of the sort."

"Do you think they will be round here presently?" I asked with some incredulity.

"Quite likely," he said, faintly.

He looked extremely haggard all of a sudden. His head rolled on his shoulders.

"H'm. We shall see then. Meantime get into that bed," I whispered. "Want help? There."

It was a rather high bed-place with a set of drawers underneath. This amazing swimmer really needed the lift I gave him by seizing his leg. He tumbled in, rolled over on his back, and flung one arm across his eyes. And then, with his face nearly hidden, he must have looked exactly as I used to look in that bed. I gazed upon my other self for a while before drawing across carefully the two green serge curtains which ran on a brass rod. I thought for a moment of pinning them together for greater safety, but I sat down on the couch, and once there I felt unwilling to rise and hunt for a pin. I would do it in a moment. I was extremely tired, in a peculiarly intimate way, by the strain of stealthiness, by the effort of whispering and the gen-eral secrecy of this excitement. It was three o'clock by now and I had been on my feet since nine, but I was not sleepy; I could not have gone to sleep. I sat there, fagged out, looking at the curtains, trying to clear my mind of the confused sensation of being in two places at once, and greatly bothered by an exasperating knocking in my head. It was a relief to discover sud-denly that it was not in my head at all, but on the outside of the door. Before I could collect myself the words "Come in" were out of my mouth, and the steward entered with a tray, bringing in my morning coffee. I had slept, after all, and I was so frightened that I shouted, "This way! I am here, steward," as though he had been miles away. He put down the tray on the table next the couch and only then said, very quietly, "I can see you are here, sir." I felt him give me a keen look, but I dared not meet his eyes just then. He must have wondered why I had drawn the curtains of my bed before going to sleep on the couch. He went out, hooking the door open as usual.

I heard the crew washing decks above me. I knew I would have been told at once if there had been any wind. Calm, I thought, and I was doubly vexed. Indeed, I felt dual more than ever. The steward reappeared suddenly in the doorway. I jumped up from the couch so quickly that he gave a start.

"What do you want here?"

"Close your port, sir—they are washing decks."

"It is closed," I said, reddening.

"Very well, sir." But he did not move from the doorway and returned my stare in an extraordinary, equivocal manner for a time. Then his eyes wavered, all his expression changed, and in a voice unusually gentle, almost coaxingly:

"May I come in to take the empty cup away, sir?"

"Of course!" I turned my back on him while he popped in and out. Then I unhooked and closed the door and even pushed the bolt. This sort of thing could not go on very long. The cabin was as hot as an oven, too. I took a peep at my double, and discovered that he had not moved, his arm was still over his eyes; but his chest heaved; his hair was wet; his chin glistened with perspiration. I reached over him and opened the port.

"I must show myself on deck," I reflected.

Of course, theoretically, I could do what I liked, with no one to say nay to me within the whole circle of the horizon; but to lock my cabin door and take the key away I did not dare. Directly I put my head out of the companion I saw the group of my two officers, the second mate barefooted, the chief mate in long india-rubber boots, near the break of the poop, and the steward half-way down the poop-ladder talking to them eagerly. He happened to catch sight of me and dived, the second ran down on the main-deck shouting some order or other, and the chief mate came to meet me, touching his cap.

There was a sort of curiosity in his eye that I did not like. I don't know whether the steward had told them that I was "queer" only, or downright drunk, but I know the man meant to have a good look at me. I watched him coming with a smile which, as he got into point-blank range, took effect and froze his very whiskers. I did not give him time to open his lips.

"Square the yards by lifts and braces before the hands go to breakfast."

It was the first particular order I had given on board that ship; and I stayed on deck to see it executed, too. I had felt the need of asserting myself without loss of time. That sneering young cub got taken down a peg or two on that occasion, and I also seized the opportunity of having a good look at the face of every foremast man as they filed past me to go to the after braces. At breakfast time, eating nothing myself, I presided with such frigid dignity that the two mates were only too glad to escape from the cabin as soon as decency permitted; and all the time the dual working of my mind distracted me almost to the point of insanity. I was constantly watching myself, my secret self, as dependent on my actions as my own personality, sleeping in that bed, behind that door which faced me as I sat at the head of the table. It was very much like being mad, only it was worse because one was aware of it.

I had to shake him for a solid minute, but when at last he opened his eyes it was in the full possession of his senses, with an inquiring look.

"All's well so far," I whispered. "Now you must vanish into the bath-room."

He did so, as noiseless as a ghost, and then I rang for the steward, and facing him boldly, directed him to tidy up my stateroom while I was having my bath—"and be quick about it." As my tone admitted of no excuses, he said, "Yes, sir," and ran off to fetch his dust-pan and brushes. I took a bath and did most of my dressing, splashing, and whistling softly for the steward's edification, while the secret sharer of my life stood drawn up bolt upright in that little space, his face looking very sunken in daylight, his eyelids lowered under the stern, dark line of his eyebrows drawn together by a slight frown.

When I left him there to go back to my room the steward was finishing dusting. I sent for the mate and engaged him in some insignificant conversation. It was, as it were, trifling with the terrific character of his whiskers; but my object was to give him an opportunity for a good look at my cabin. And then I could at last shut, with a clear conscience, the door of my state-room and get my double back into the recessed part. There was nothing else for it. He had to sit still on a small folding stool, half smothered by the heavy coats hanging there. We listened to the steward going into the bath-room out of the saloon, filling the water-bottles there, scrubbing the bath, setting things to rights, whisk, bang, clatter—out again into the saloon— turn the key—click. Such was my scheme for keeping my second self invisible. Nothing better could be contrived under the circumstances. And there we sat; I at my writing-desk ready to appear busy with some papers, he behind me out of sight of the door. It would not have been prudent to talk in daytime; and I could not have stood the excitement of that queer sense of whispering to myself. Now and then, glancing over my shoulder, I saw him far back there, sitting rigidly on the low stool, his bare feet close together, his arms folded, his head hanging on his breast—and perfectly still. Anybody would have taken him for me.

I was fascinated by it myself. Every moment I had to glance over my shoulder.

I was looking at him when a voice outside the door said:

"Beg pardon, sir."

"Well!" . . . I kept my eyes on him, and so when the voice outside the door announced, "There's a ship's boat coming our way, sir," I saw him give a start—the first movement he had made for hours. But he did not raise his bowed head.

"All right. Get the ladder over."

I hesitated. Should I whisper something to him? But what? His immobility seemed to have been never disturbed. What could I tell him he did not know already? . . . Finally I went on deck.

II

The skipper of the *Sephora* had a thin red whisker all round his face, and the sort of complexion that goes with hair of that colour; also the particular, rather smeary shade of blue in the eyes. He was not exactly a showy figure; his shoulders were high, his stature but middling—one leg slightly more bandy than the other. He shook hands, looking vaguely around. A spiritless tenacity was his main characteristic, I judged. I behaved with a politeness which seemed to disconcert him. Perhaps he was shy. He mumbled to me as if he were ashamed of what he was saying; gave his name (it was something like Archbold—but at this distance of years I hardly am sure), his ship's name, and a few other particulars of that sort, in the manner of a criminal making a reluctant and doleful confession. He had had terrible weather on the passage out—terrible—terrible—wife aboard, too.

By this time we were seated in the cabin and the steward brought in a tray with a bottle and glasses. "Thanks! No." Never took liquor. Would have some water, though. He drank two tumblerfuls. Terrible thirsty work. Ever since daylight had been exploring the islands round his ship.

"What was that for—fun?" I asked, with an appearance of polite interest.

"No!" He sighed. "Painful duty."

As he persisted in his mumbling and I wanted my double to hear every word, I hit upon the notion of informing him that I regretted to say I was hard of hearing.

"Such a young man, too!" he nodded, keeping his smeary blue, unintelligent eyes fastened upon me. "What was the cause of it—some disease?" he inquired, without the least sympathy and as if he thought that, if so, I'd got no more than I deserved.

"Yes; disease," I admitted in a cheerful tone which seemed to shock him. But my point was gained, because he had to raise his voice to give me his tale. It is not worth while to record that version. It was just over two months since all this had happened, and he had thought so much about it that he seemed completely muddled as to its bearings, but still immensely impressed.

"What would you think of such a thing happening on board your own ship? I've had the *Sephora* for these fifteen years. I am a well-known shipmaster."

He was densely distressed—and perhaps I should have sympathised with him if I had been able to detach my mental vision from the unsuspected sharer of my cabin as though he were my second self. There he was on the other side of the bulkhead, four or five feet from us, no more, as we sat in the saloon. I looked politely at Captain Archbold (if that was his name), but it was the other I saw, in a grey sleeping-suit, seated on a low stool, his bare feet close together, his arms folded, and every word said between us falling into the ears of his dark head bowed on his chest.

"I have been at sea now, man and boy, for seven-and-thirty years, and I've never heard of such a thing happening in an English ship. And that it should be my ship. Wife on board, too."

I was hardly listening to him.

"Don't you think," I said, "that the heavy sea which, you told me, came aboard just then might have killed the man? I have seen the sheer weight of a sea kill a man very neatly, by simply breaking his neck."

"Good God!" he uttered, impressively, fixing his smeary blue eyes on me. "The sea! No man killed by the sea ever looked like that." He seemed positively scandalised at my suggestion. And as I gazed at him, certainly not prepared for anything original on his part, he advanced his head close to mine and thrust his tongue out at me so suddenly that I couldn't help starting back.

After scoring over my calmness in this graphic way he nodded wisely. If I had seen the sight, he assured me, I would never forget it as long as I lived. The weather was too bad to give the corpse a proper sea burial. So next day at dawn they took it up on the poop, covering its face with a bit of bunting; he read a short prayer, and then, just as it was, in its oilskins and long boots, they launched it amongst those mountainous seas that seemed ready every moment to swallow up the ship herself and the terrified lives on board of her.

"That reefed foresail saved you," I threw in.

"Under God—it did," he exclaimed fervently. "It was by a special mercy, I firmly believe, that it stood some of those hurricane squalls."

"It was the setting of that sail which——" I began.

"God's own hand in it," he interrupted me. "Nothing less could have done it. I don't mind telling you that I hardly dared give the order. It seemed impossible that we could touch anything without losing it, and then our last hope would have been gone."

The terror of that gale was on him yet. I let him go on for a bit, then said, casually—as if returning to a minor subject:

"You were very anxious to give up your mate to the shore people, I believe?"

He was. To the law. His obscure tenacity on that point had in it something incomprehensible and a little awful; something, as it were, mystical, quite apart from his anxiety that he should not be suspected of "countenancing any doings of that sort." Seven-and-thirty virtuous years at sea, of which over twenty of immaculate command, and the last fifteen in the *Sephora*, seemed to have laid him under some pitiless obligation.

"And you know," he went on, groping shamefacedly amongst his feelings, "I did not engage that young fellow. His people had some interest with my owners. I was in a way forced to take him on. He looked very smart, very gentlemanly, and all that. But do you know—I never liked him, somehow. I am a plain man. You see, he wasn't exactly the sort for the chief mate of a ship like the *Sephora*."

I had become so connected in thoughts and impressions with the secret sharer of my cabin that I felt as if I, personally, were being given to understand that I, too, was not the sort that would have done for the chief mate of a ship like the *Sephora*. I had no doubt of it in my mind.

"Not at all the style of man. You understand," he insisted, superfluously, looking hard at me.

I smiled urbanely. He seemed at a loss for a while.

"I suppose I must report a suicide."

"Beg pardon?"

"Sui-cide! That's what I'll have to write to my owners directly I get in."

"Unless you manage to recover him before to-morrow," I assented, dispassionately. . . . "I mean, alive."

He mumbled something which I really did not catch, and I turned my ear to him in a puzzled manner. He fairly bawled:

"The land—I say, the mainland is at least seven miles off my anchorage."

"About that."

My lack of excitement, of curiosity, of surprise, of any sort of pronounced interest, began to arouse his distrust. But except for the felicitous pretence of deafness I had not tried to pretend anything. I had felt utterly incapable of playing the part of ignorance properly, and therefore was afraid to try. It is also certain that he had brought some ready-made suspicions with him, and that he viewed my politeness as a strange and unnatural phenomenon. And yet how else could I have received him? Not heartily! That was impossible for psychological reasons, which I need not state here. My only object was to keep off his inquiries. Surlily? Yes, but surliness might have provoked a point-blank question. From its novelty to him and from its nature, punctilious courtesy was the manner best calculated to restrain the man. But there was the danger of his breaking through my defence bluntly. I could not, I think, have met him by a direct lie, also for psychological (not moral) reasons. If he had only known how afraid I was of his putting my feeling of identity with the other to the test! But, strangely enough—(I thought of it only afterwards)—I believe that he was not a little disconcerted by the reverse side of that weird situation, by something in me that reminded him of the man he was seeking—suggested a mysterious similitude to the young fellow he had distrusted and disliked from the first.

However that might have been, the silence was not very prolonged. He took another oblique step.

"I reckon I had no more than a two-mile pull to your ship. Not a bit more."

"And quite enough, too, in this awful heat," I said.

Another pause full of mistrust followed. Necessity, they say, is mother of invention, but fear, too, is not barren of ingenious suggestions. And I was afraid he would ask me point-blank for news of my other self.

"Nice little saloon, isn't it?" I remarked, as if noticing for the first time the way his eyes roamed from one closed door to the other. "And very well fitted out too. Here, for instance," I continued, reaching over the back of my seat negligently and flinging the door open, "is my bath-room."

He made an eager movement, but hardly gave it a glance. I got up, shut the door of the bath-room, and invited him to have a look round, as if I were very proud of my accommodation. He had to rise and be shown round, but he went through the business without any raptures whatever.

"And now we'll have a look at my stateroom," I declared, in a voice as loud as I dared to make it, crossing the cabin to the starboard side with purposely heavy steps.

He followed me in and gazed around. My intelligent double had vanished. I played my part.

"Very convenient—isn't it?"

"Very nice. Very comf . . ." He didn't finish and went out brusquely as if to escape from some unrighteous wiles of mine. But it was not to be. I had been too frightened not to feel vengeful; I felt I had him on the run, and I meant to keep him on the run. My polite insistence must have had something menacing in it, because he gave in suddenly. And I did not let him off a single item; mate's room, pantry, storerooms, the very sail-locker which was also under the poop—he had to look into them all. When at last I showed him out on the quarterdeck he drew a long, spiritless sigh, and mumbled dismally that he must really be going back to his ship now. I desired my mate, who had joined us, to see to the captain's boat.

The man of whiskers gave a blast on the whistle which he used to wear hanging round his neck, and yelled, "*Sephora*'s away!" My double down there in my cabin must have heard, and certainly could not feel more relieved than I. Four fellows came running out from somewhere forward and went over the side, while my own men, appearing on deck too, lined the rail. I escorted my visitor to the gangway ceremoniously, and nearly overdid it. He was a tenacious beast. On the very ladder he lingered, and in that unique, guiltily conscientious manner of sticking to the point:

"I say . . . you . . . you don't think that——"

I covered his voice loudly:

"Certainly not. . . . I am delighted. Good-bye."

I had an idea of what he meant to say, and just saved myself by the privilege of defective hearing. He was too shaken generally to insist, but my mate, close witness of that parting, looked mystified and his face took on a thoughtful cast. As I did not want to appear as if I wished to avoid all communication with my officers, he had the opportunity to address me.

"Seems a very nice man. His boat's crew told our chaps a very extraordinary story, if what I am told by the steward is true. I suppose you had it from the captain, sir?"

"Yes. I had a story from the captain."

"A very horrible affair—isn't it, sir?"

"It is."

"Beats all these tales we hear about murders in Yankee ships."

"I don't think it beats them. I don't think it resembles them in the least."

"Bless my soul—you don't say so! But of course I've no acquaintance whatever with American ships, not I, so I couldn't go against your knowledge. It's horrible enough for me. . . . But the queerest part is that those fellows seemed to have some idea the man was hidden aboard here. They had really. Did you ever hear of such a thing?"

"Preposterous—isn't it?"

We were walking to and fro athwart the quarter-deck. No one of the crew forward could be seen (the day was Sunday), and the mate pursued:

"There was some little dispute about it. Our chaps took offence. 'As if we would harbour a thing like that,' they said. 'Wouldn't you like to look for him in our coal-hole?' Quite a tiff. But they made it up in the end. I suppose he did drown himself. Don't you, sir?"

"I don't suppose anything."

"You have no doubt in the matter, sir?"

"None whatever."

I left him suddenly. I felt I was producing a bad impression, but with my double down there it was most trying to be on deck. And it was almost as trying to be below. Altogether a nerve-trying situation. But on the whole I felt less torn in two when I was with him. There was no one in the whole ship whom I dared take into my confidence. Since the hands had got to know his story, it would have been impossible to pass him off for any one else, and an accidental discovery was to be dreaded now more than ever. . . .

The steward being engaged in laying the table for dinner, we could talk only with our eyes when I first went down. Later in the afternoon we had a cautious try at whispering. The Sunday quietness of the ship was against us; the stillness of air and water around her was against us; the elements, the men were against us—everything was against us in our secret partnership; time itself—for this could not go on forever. The very trust in Providence was, I suppose, denied to his guilt. Shall I confess that this thought cast me down very much? And as to the chapter of accidents which counts for so much in the book of success, I could only hope that it was closed. For what favourable accident could be expected?

"Did you hear everything?" were my first words as soon as we took up our position side by side, leaning over my bed-place.

He had. And the proof of it was his earnest whisper, "The man told you he hardly dared to give the order."

I understood the reference to be to that saving foresail.

"Yes. He was afraid of it being lost in the setting."

"I assure you he never gave the order. He may think he did, but he never gave it. He stood there with me on the break of the poop after the maintopsail blew away, and whimpered about our last hope—positively whimpered about it and nothing else—and the night coming on! To hear one's skipper go on like that in such weather was enough to drive any fellow out of his mind. It worked me up into a sort of desperation. I just took it into my own hands and went away from him, boiling, and——But what's the use telling you? *You* know! . . . Do you think that if I had not been pretty fierce with them I should have got the men to do anything? Not it! The bo's'n perhaps? Perhaps! It wasn't a heavy sea—it was a sea gone mad! I suppose the end of the world will be something like that; and a man may have the heart to see it coming once and be done with it—but to have to face it day after day——I don't blame anybody. I was precious little better than the rest. Only—I was an officer of that old coal-wagon, anyhow——"

"I quite understand," I conveyed that sincere assurance into his ear. He was out of breath with whispering; I could hear him pant slightly. It was all very simple. The same strung-up force which had given twenty-four men a chance, at least, for their lives, had, in a sort of recoil, crushed an unworthy mutinous existence.

But I had no leisure to weigh the merits of the matter—footsteps in the saloon, a heavy knock. "There's enough wind to get under way with, sir." Here was the call of a new claim upon my thoughts and even upon my feelings.

"Turn the hands up," I cried through the door. "I'll be on deck directly."

I was going out to make the acquaintance of my ship. Before I left the cabin our eyes met—the eyes of the only two strangers on board. I pointed to the recessed part where the little camp-stool awaited him and laid my finger on my lips. He made a gesture—somewhat vague—a little mysterious, accompanied by a faint smile, as if of regret.

This is not the place to enlarge upon the sensations of a man who feels for the first time a ship move under his feet to his own independent word. In my case they were not unalloyed. I was not wholly alone with my command; for there was that stranger in my cabin. Or rather, I was not completely and wholly with her. Part of me was absent. That mental feeling of being in two places at once affected me physically as if the mood of secrecy had penetrated my very soul. Before an hour had elapsed since the ship had begun to move, having occasion to ask the mate (he stood by my side) to take a compass bearing of the Pagoda, I caught myself reaching up to his ear in whispers. I say I caught myself, but enough had escaped to startle the man. I can't describe it otherwise than by saying that he shied. A grave, preoccupied manner, as though he were in possession of some perplexing intelligence, did not leave him henceforth. A little later I moved away from the rail to look at the compass with such a stealthy gait that the helmsman noticed it—and I could not help noticing the unusual roundness of his eyes. These are trifling instances, though it's to no commander's advantage to be suspected of ludicrous eccentricities. But I was also more seriously affected. There are to a seaman certain words, gestures, that should in given conditions come as naturally, as instinctively as the winking of a menaced eye. A certain order should spring on to his lips without thinking; a certain sign should get itself made, so to speak, without reflection. But all unconscious alertness had abandoned me. I had to make an effort of will to recall myself back (from the cabin) to the conditions of the moment. I felt that I was appearing an irresolute commander to those people who were watching me more or less critically.

And, besides, there were the scares. On the second day out, for instance, coming off the deck in the afternoon (I had straw slippers on my bare feet) I stopped at the open pantry door and spoke to the steward. He was doing something there with his back to me. At the sound of my voice he nearly jumped out of his skin, as the saying is, and incidentally broke a cup.

"What on earth's the matter with you?" I asked, astonished.

He was extremely confused. "Beg your pardon, sir. I made sure you were in your cabin."

"You see I wasn't."

"No, sir. I could have sworn I had heard you moving in there not a moment ago. It's most extraordinary . . . very sorry, sir."

I passed on with an inward shudder. I was so identified with my secret double that I did not even mention the fact in those scanty, fearful whispers we exchanged. I suppose he had made some slight noise of some kind or other. It would have been miraculous if he hadn't at one time or another. And yet, haggard as he appeared, he looked always perfectly self-controlled, more than calm—almost invulnerable. On my suggestion he remained almost entirely in the bath-room, which, upon the whole, was the safest place. There could be really no shadow of an excuse for any one ever wanting to go in there, once the steward had done with it. It was a very tiny place. Sometimes he reclined on the floor, his legs bent, his head sustained on one elbow. At others I would find him on the camp-stool, sitting in his grey sleeping-suit and with his cropped dark hair like a patient, unmoved convict. At night I would smuggle him into my bed-place, and we would whisper together, with the regular footfalls of the officer of the watch passing and repassing over our heads. It was an infinitely miserable time. It was lucky that some tins of fine preserves were stowed in a locker in my stateroom; hard bread I could always get hold of; and so he lived on stewed chicken, paté de foie gras, asparagus, cooked oysters, sardines—on all sorts of abominable sham delicacies out of tins. My early morning coffee he always drank; and it was all I dared do for him in that respect.

Every day there was the horrible manoeuvring to go through so that my room and then the bath-room should be done in the usual way. I came to hate the sight of the steward, to abhor the voice of that harmless man. I felt that it was he who would bring on the disaster of discovery. It hung like a sword over our heads.

The fourth day out, I think (we were then working down the east side of the Gulf of Siam, tack for tack, in light winds and smooth water)—the fourth day, I say, of this miserable juggling with the unavoidable, as we sat at our evening meal, that man, whose slightest movement I dreaded, after putting down the dishes ran up on deck busily. This could not be dangerous. Presently he came down again; and then it appeared that he had remembered a coat of mine which I had thrown over a rail to dry after having been wetted in a shower which had passed over the ship in the afternoon. Sitting stolidly at the head of the table I became terrified at the sight of the garment on his arm. Of course he made for my door. There was no time to lose.

"Steward," I thundered. My nerves were so shaken that I could not govern my voice and conceal my agitation. This was the sort of thing that made my terrifically whiskered mate tap his forehead with his forefinger. I had detected him using that gesture while talking on deck with a confidential air to the carpenter. It was too far to hear a word, but I had no doubt that this pantomime could only refer to the strange new captain.

"Yes, sir," the pale-faced steward turned resignedly to me. It was this maddening course of being shouted at, checked without rhyme or reason, arbitrarily chased out of my cabin, suddenly called into it, sent flying out of his pantry on incomprehensible errands, that accounted for the growing wretchedness of his expression.

"Where are you going with that coat?"

"To your room, sir."

"Is there another shower coming?"

"I'm sure I don't know, sir. Shall I go up again and see, sir?"

"No! never mind."

My object was attained, as of course my other self in there would have heard everything that passed. During this interlude my two officers never raised their eyes off their respective plates; but the lip of that confounded cub, the second mate, quivered visibly.

I expected the steward to hook my coat on and come out at once. He was very slow about it; but I dominated my nervousness sufficiently not to shout after him. Suddenly I became aware (it could be heard plainly enough) that the fellow for some reason or other was opening the door of the bath-room. It was the end. The place was literally not big enough to swing a cat in. My voice died in my throat and I went stony all over. I expected to hear a yell of surprise and terror, and made a movement, but had not the strength to get on my legs. Everything remained still. Had my second self taken the poor wretch by the throat? I don't know what I could have done next moment if I had not seen the steward come out of my room, close the door, and then stand quietly by the sideboard.

"Saved," I thought. "But, no! Lost! Gone! He was gone!"

I laid my knife and fork down and leaned back in my chair. My head swam. After a while, when sufficiently recovered to speak in a steady voice, I instructed my mate to put the ship round at eight o'clock himself.

"I won't come on deck," I went on. "I think I'll turn in, and unless the wind shifts I don't want to be disturbed before midnight. I feel a bit seedy."

"You did look middling bad a little while ago," the chief mate remarked without showing any great concern.

They both went out, and I stared at the steward clearing the table. There was nothing to be read on that wretched man's face. But why did he avoid my eyes I asked myself. Then I thought I should like to hear the sound of his voice.

"Steward!"

"Sir!" Startled as usual.

"Where did you hang up that coat?"

"In the bath-room, sir." The usual anxious tone. "It's not quite dry yet, sir."

For some time longer I sat in the cuddy. Had my double vanished as he had come? But of his coming there was an explanation, whereas his disappearance would be inexplicable. . . . I went slowly into my dark room, shut the door, lighted the lamp, and for a time dared not turn round. When at last I did I saw him standing bolt-upright in the narrow recessed part. It would not be true to say I had a shock, but an irresistible doubt of his bodily existence flitted through my mind. Can it be, I asked myself, that he is not visible to other eyes than mine? It was like being haunted. Motionless, with a grave face, he raised his hands slightly at me in a gesture which meant clearly, "Heavens! what a narrow escape!" Narrow indeed. I think I had come creeping quietly as near insanity as any man who has not actually gone over the border. That gesture restrained me, so to speak.

The mate with the terrific whiskers was now putting the ship on the other tack. In the moment of profound silence which follows upon the hands going to their stations I heard on the poop his raised voice: "Hard alee!" and the distant shout of the order repeated on the main-deck. The sails, in that light breeze, made but a faint fluttering noise. It ceased. The ship was coming round slowly; I held my breath in the renewed stillness of expectation; one wouldn't have thought that there was a single living soul on her decks. A sudden brisk shout, "Mainsail haul!" broke the spell, and in the noisy cries and rush overhead of the men running away with the main-brace we two, down in my cabin, came together in our usual position by the bed-place.

He did not wait for my question. "I heard him fumbling here and just managed to squat myself down in the bath," he whispered to me. "The fellow only opened the door and put his arm in to hang the coat up. All the same——"

"I never thought of that," I whispered back, even more appalled than before at the close-ness of the shave, and marvelling at that something unyielding in his character which was carrying him through so finely. There was no agitation in his whisper. Whoever was being driven distracted, it was not he. He was sane. And the proof of his sanity was continued when he took up the whispering again.

"It would never do for me to come to life again."

It was something that a ghost might have said. But what he was alluding to was his old captain's reluctant admission of the theory of suicide. It would obviously serve his turn—if I had understood at all the view which seemed to govern the unalterable purpose of his action.

"You must maroon me as soon as ever you can get amongst these islands off the Cambodge shore," he went on.

"Maroon you! We are not living in a boy's adventure tale," I protested. His scornful whis-pering took me up.

"We aren't indeed! There's nothing of a boy's tale in this. But there's nothing else for it. I want no more. You don't suppose I am afraid of what can be done to me? Prison or gallows or whatever they may please. But you don't see me coming back to explain such things to an old fellow in a wig and twelve respectable tradesmen, do you? What can they know whether I am guilty or not—or of *what* I am guilty, either? That's my affair. What does the Bible say? 'Driven off the face of the earth.' Very well. I am off the face of the earth now. As I came at night so I shall go."

"Impossible!" I murmured. "You can't."

"Can't? . . . Not naked like a soul on the Day of Judgment. I shall freeze on to this sleeping-suit. The Last Day is not yet—and . . . you have understood thoroughly. Didn't you?"

I felt suddenly ashamed of myself. I may say truly that I understood—and my hesitation in letting that man swim away from my ship's side had been a mere sham sentiment, a sort of cowardice.

"It can't be done now till next night," I breathed out. "The ship is on the off-shore tack and the wind may fail us."

"As long as I know that you understand," he whispered. "But of course you do. It's a great satisfaction to have got somebody to understand. You seem to have been there on purpose." And in the same whisper, as if we two whenever we talked had to say things to each other which were not fit for the world to hear, he added, "It's very wonderful."

We remained side by side talking in our secret way—but sometimes silent or just exchanging a whispered word or two at long intervals. And as usual he stared through the port. A breath of wind came now and again into our faces. The ship might have been moored in dock, so gently and on an even keel she slipped through the water, that did not murmur even at our passage, shadowy and silent like a phantom sea.

At midnight I went on deck, and to my mate's great surprise put the ship round on the other tack. His terrible whiskers flitted round me in silent criticism. I certainly should not have done it if it had been only a question of getting out of that sleepy gulf as quickly as possible. I believe he told the second mate, who relieved him, that it was a great want of judgment. The other only yawned. That intolerable cub shuffled about so sleepily and lolled against the rails in such a slack, improper fashion that I came down on him sharply.

"Aren't you properly awake yet?"

"Yes, sir! I am awake."

"Well, then, be good enough to hold yourself as if you were. And keep a look-out. If there's any current we'll be closing with some islands before daylight."

The east side of the gulf is fringed with islands, some solitary, others in groups. On the blue background of the high coast they seem to float on silvery patches of calm water, arid and grey, or dark green and rounded like dumps of evergreen bushes, with the larger ones, a mile or two long, showing the outlines of ridges, ribs of grey rock under the dank mantle of matted leafage. Unknown to trade, to travel, almost to geography, the manner of life they harbour is an unsolved secret. There must be villages—settlements of fishermen at least—on the largest of them, and some communication with the world is probably kept up by native craft. But all that forenoon, as we headed for them, fanned along by the faintest of breezes, I saw no sign of man or canoe in the field of the telescope I kept on pointing at the scattered group.

At noon I gave no orders for a change of course, and the mate's whiskers became much concerned and seemed to be offering themselves unduly to my notice. At last I said:

"I am going to stand right in. Quite in—as far as I can take her."

The stare of extreme surprise imparted an air of ferocity also to his eyes, and he looked truly terrific for a moment.

"We're not doing well in the middle of the gulf," I continued, casually. "I am going to look for the land breezes to-night."

"Bless my soul! Do you mean, sir, in the dark amongst the lot of all them islands and reefs and shoals?"

"Well—if there are any regular land breezes at all on this coast one must get close inshore to find them, mustn't one?"

"Bless my soul!" he exclaimed again under his breath. All that afternoon he wore a dreamy, contemplative appearance which in him was a mark of perplexity. After dinner I went into my stateroom as if I meant to take some rest. There we two bent our dark heads over a half-unrolled chart lying on my bed.

"There," I said. "It's got to be Koh-ring. I've been looking at it ever since sunrise. It has got two hills and a low point. It must be inhabited. And on the coast opposite there is what looks like the mouth of a biggish river—with some town, no doubt, not far up. It's the best chance for you that I can see."

"Anything. Koh-ring let it be."

He looked thoughtfully at the chart as if surveying chances and distances from a lofty height—and following with his eyes his own figure wandering on the blank land of Cochin-China, and then passing off that piece of paper clean out of sight into uncharted regions. And it was as if the ship had two captains to plan her course for her. I had been so worried and restless running up and down that I had not had the patience to dress that day. I had remained in my sleeping-suit, with straw slippers and a soft floppy hat. The closeness of the heat in the gulf had been most oppressive, and the crew were used to see me wandering in that airy attire.

"She will clear the south point as she heads now," I whispered into his ear. "Goodness only knows when, though, but certainly after dark. I'll edge her in to half a mile, as far as I may be able to judge in the dark——"

"Be careful," he murmured, warningly—and I realised suddenly that all my future, the only future for which I was fit, would perhaps go irretrievably to pieces in any mishap to my first command.

I could not stop a moment longer in the room. I motioned him to get out of sight and made my way on the poop. That unplayful cub had the watch. I walked up and down for a while thinking things out, then beckoned him over.

"Send a couple of hands to open the two quarter-deck ports," I said, mildly.

He actually had the impudence, or else so forgot himself in his wonder at such an incomprehensible order, as to repeat:

"Open the quarter-deck ports! What for, sir?"

"The only reason you need concern yourself about is because I tell you to do so. Have them opened wide and fastened properly."

He reddened and went off, but I believe made some jeering remark to the carpenter as to the sensible practice of ventilating a ship's quarter-deck. I know he popped into the mate's cabin to impart the fact to him because the whiskers came on deck, as it were by chance, and stole glances at me from below—for signs of lunacy or drunkenness, I suppose.

A little before supper, feeling more restless than ever, I rejoined, for a moment, my second self. And to find him sitting so quietly was surprising, like something against nature, inhuman.

I developed my plan in a hurried whisper.

"I shall stand in as close as I dare and then put her round. I will presently find means to smuggle you out of here into the sail-locker, which communicates with the lobby. But there is an opening, a sort of square for hauling the sails out, which gives straight on the quarter-deck and which is never closed in fine weather, so as to give air to the sails. When the ship's way is deadened in stays and all the hands are aft at the main-braces you will have a clear road to slip out and get overboard through the open quarter-deck port. I've had them both fastened up. Use a rope's end to lower yourself into the water so as to avoid a splash—you know. It could be heard and cause some beastly complication."

He kept silent for a while, then whispered, "I understand."

"I won't be there to see you go," I began with an effort. "The rest . . . I only hope I have understood, too."

"You have. From first to last"—and for the first time there seemed to be a faltering, something strained in his whisper. He caught hold of my arm, but the ringing of the supper bell made me start. He didn't, though; he only released his grip.

After supper I didn't come below again till well past eight o'clock. The faint, steady breeze was loaded with dew; and the wet, darkened sails held all there was of propelling power in it. The night, clear and starry, sparkled darkly, and the opaque, lightless patches shifting slowly against the low stars were the drifting islets. On the port bow there was a big one more distant and shadowily imposing by the great space of sky it eclipsed.

On opening the door I had a back view of my very own self looking at a chart. He had come out of the recess and was standing near the table.

"Quite dark enough," I whispered.

He stepped back and leaned against my bed with a level, quiet glance. I sat on the couch. We had nothing to say to each other. Over our heads the officer of the watch moved here and there. Then I heard him move quickly. I knew what that meant. He was making for the companion; and presently his voice was outside my door.

"We are drawing in pretty fast, sir. Land looks rather close."

"Very well," I answered. "I am coming on deck directly."

I waited till he was gone out of the cuddy, then rose. My double moved too. The time had come to exchange our last whispers, for neither of us was ever to hear each other's natural voice.

"Look here!" I opened a drawer and took out three sovereigns. "Take this anyhow. I've got six and I'd give you the lot, only I must keep a little money to buy some fruit and vegetables for the crew from native boats as we go through Sunda Straits."

He shook his head.

"Take it," I urged him, whispering desperately. "No one can tell what——" He smiled and slapped meaningly the only pocket of the sleeping-jacket. It was not safe, certainly. But I produced a large old silk handkerchief of mine, and tying the three pieces of gold in a corner, pressed it on him. He was touched, I suppose, because he took it at last and tied it quickly round his waist under the jacket, on his bare skin.

Our eyes met; several seconds elapsed, till, our glances still mingled, I extended my hand and turned the lamp out. Then I passed through the cuddy, leaving the door of my room wide open. . . . "Steward!"

He was still lingering in the pantry in the greatness of his zeal, giving a rub-up to a plated cruet stand the last thing before going to bed. Being careful not to wake up the mate, whose room was opposite, I spoke in an undertone.

He looked round anxiously. "Sir!"

"Can you get me a little hot water from the galley?"

"I am afraid, sir, the galley fire's been out for some time now."

"Go and see."

He flew up the stairs.

"Now," I whispered, loudly, into the saloon—too loudly, perhaps, but I was afraid I couldn't make a sound. He was by my side in an instant—the double captain slipped past the stairs—through a tiny dark passage . . . a sliding door. We were in the sail-locker, scrambling on our knees over the sails. A sudden thought struck me. I saw myself wandering barefooted, bareheaded, the sun beating on my dark poll. I snatched off my floppy hat and tried hurriedly in the dark to ram it on my other self. He dodged and fended off silently. I wonder what he thought had come to me before he understood and suddenly desisted. Our hands met gropingly, lingered united in a steady, motionless clasp for a second. . . . No word was breathed by either of us when they separated.

I was standing quietly by the pantry door when the steward returned.

"Sorry, sir. Kettle barely warm. Shall I light the spirit-lamp?"

"Never mind."

I came out on deck slowly. It was now a matter of conscience to shave the land as close as possible—for now he must go overboard whenever the ship was put in stays. Must! There could be no going back for him. After a moment I walked over to leeward and my heart flew into my mouth at the nearness of the land on the bow. Under any other circumstances I would not have held on a minute longer. The second mate had followed me anxiously.

I looked on till I felt I could command my voice.

"She will weather," I said then in a quiet tone.

"Are you going to try that, sir?" he stammered out incredulously.

I took no notice of him and raised my tone just enough to be heard by the helmsman.

"Keep her good full."

"Good full, sir."

The wind fanned my cheek, the sails slept, the world was silent. The strain of watching the dark loom of the land grow bigger and denser was too much for me. I had shut my eyes—because the ship must go closer. She must! The stillness was intolerable. Were we standing still?

When I opened my eyes the second view started my heart with a thump. The black southern hill of Koh-ring seemed to hang right over the ship like a towering fragment of the everlasting night. On that enormous mass of blackness there was not a gleam to be seen, not a sound to be heard. It was gliding irresistibly towards us and yet seemed already within reach of the hand. I saw the vague figures of the watch grouped in the waist, gazing in awed silence.

"Are you going on, sir?" inquired an unsteady voice at my elbow.

I ignored it. I had to go on.

"Keep her full. Don't check her way. That won't do now," I said, warningly.

"I can't see the sails very well," the helmsman answered me, in strange, quavering tones.

Was she close enough? Already she was, I won't say in the shadow of the land, but in the very blackness of it, already swallowed up as it were, gone too close to be recalled, gone from me altogether.

"Give the mate a call," I said to the young man who stood at my elbow as still as death. "And turn all hands up."

My tone had a borrowed loudness reverberated from the height of the land. Several voices cried out together: "We are all on deck, sir."

Then stillness again, with the great shadow gliding closer, towering higher, without a light, without a sound. Such a hush had fallen on the ship that she might have been a bark of the dead floating in slowly under the very gate of Erebus.

"My God! Where are we?"

It was the mate moaning at my elbow. He was thunderstruck, and as it were deprived of the moral support of his whiskers. He clapped his hands and absolutely cried out, "Lost!"

"Be quiet," I said, sternly.

He lowered his tone, but I saw the shadowy gesture of his despair.

"What are we doing here?"

"Looking for the land wind."

He made as if to tear his hair, and addressed me recklessly.

"She will never get out. You have done it, sir. I knew it'd end in something like this. She will never weather, and you are too close now to stay. She'll drift ashore before she's round. O my God!"

I caught his arm as he was raising it to batter his poor devoted head, and shook it violently.

"She's ashore already," he wailed, trying to tear himself away.

"Is she? . . . Keep good full there!"

"Good full, sir," cried the helmsman in a frightened, thin, child-like voice.

I hadn't let go the mate's arm and went on shaking it.

"Ready about, do you hear? You go forward"—shake—"and stop there"—shake—"and hold your noise"—shake—"and see these head-sheets properly overhauled"—shake, shake—shake.

And all the time I dared not look towards the land lest my heart should fail me. I released my grip at last and he ran forward as if fleeing for dear life.

I wondered what my double there in the sail-locker thought of this commotion. He was able to hear everything—and perhaps he was able to understand why, on my conscience, it had to be thus close—no less. My first order "Hard alee!" re-echoed ominously under the towering shadow of Koh-ring as if I had shouted in a mountain gorge. And then I watched the land intently. In that smooth water and light wind it was impossible to feel the ship coming-to. No! I could not feel her. And my second self was making now ready to slip out and lower himself overboard. Perhaps he was gone already . . . ?

The great black mass brooding over our very mastheads began to pivot away from the ship's side silently. And now I forgot the secret stranger ready to depart, and remembered only that I was a total stranger to the ship. I did not know her. Would she do it? How was she to be handled?

I swung the mainyard and waited helplessly. She was perhaps stopped, and her very fate hung in the balance, with the black mass of Koh-ring like the gate of the everlasting night towering over her taffrail. What would she do now? Had she way on her yet? I stepped to the side swiftly, and on the shadowy water I could see nothing except a faint phosphorescent flash revealing the glassy smoothness of the sleeping surface. It was impossible to tell—and I had not learned yet the feel of my ship. Was she moving? What I needed was something easily seen, a piece of paper, which I could throw overboard and watch. I had nothing on me. To run down for it I didn't dare. There was no time. All at once my strained, yearning stare distinguished a white object floating within a yard of the ship's side. White on the black water. A phosphorescent flash passed under it. What was that thing? . . . I recognised my own floppy hat. It must have fallen off his head . . . and he didn't bother. Now I had what I wanted—the saving mark for my eyes. But I hardly thought of my other self, now gone from the ship, to be hidden for ever from all friendly faces, to be a fugitive and a vagabond on the earth, with no brand of the curse on his sane forehead to stay a slaying hand . . . too proud to explain.

And I watched the hat—the expression of my sudden pity for his mere flesh. It had been meant to save his homeless head from the dangers of the sun. And now—behold—it was saving the ship, by serving me for a mark to help out the ignorance of my strangeness. Ha! It was drifting forward, warning me just in time that the ship had gathered sternway.

"Shift the helm," I said in a low voice to the seaman standing still like a statue.

The man's eyes glistened wildly in the binnacle light as he jumped round to the other side and spun round the wheel.

I walked to the break of the poop. On the overshadowed deck all hands stood by the forebraces waiting for my order. The stars ahead seemed to be gliding from right to left. And all was so still in the world that I heard the quiet remark, "She's round," passed in a tone of intense relief between two seamen.

"Let go and haul."

The foreyards ran round with a great noise, amidst cheery cries. And now the frightful whiskers made themselves heard giving various orders. Already the ship was drawing ahead.

And I was alone with her. Nothing! no one in the world should stand now between us, throwing a shadow on the way of silent knowledge and mute affection, the perfect communion of a seaman with his first command.

Walking to the taffrail, I was in time to make out, on the very edge of a darkness thrown by a towering black mass like the very gateway of Erebus—yes, I was in time to catch an evanescent glimpse of my white hat left behind to mark the spot where the secret sharer of my cabin and of my thoughts, as though he were my second self, had lowered himself into the water to take his punishment: a free man, a proud swimmer striking out for a new destiny.

(1910)

William Butler Yeats

(IRELAND, 1865–1939)

A Coat

I made my song a coat
Covered with embroideries
Out of old mythologies
From heel to throat;
5   But the fools caught it,
Wore it in the world's eyes
As though they'd wrought it.
Song, let them take it,
For there's more enterprise
10 In walking naked.

(1914)

The Hawk

'Call down the hawk from the air;
Let him be hooded or caged
Till the yellow eye has grown mild,
For larder and spit are bare,
5   The old cook enraged,
The scullion gone wild.'

'I will not be clapped in a hood,
Nor a cage, nor alight upon wrist,
Now I have learnt to be proud
10 Hovering over the wood
In the broken mist
Or tumbling cloud.'

'What tumbling cloud did you cleave,
Yellow-eyed hawk of the mind,
15 Last evening? that I, who had sat
Dumbfounded before a knave,
Should give to my friend
A pretence of wit.'

(1919)

On Being Asked for a War Poem

I think it better that in times like these
A poet's mouth be silent, for in truth
We have no gift to set a statesman right;
He has had enough of meddling who can please
5 A young girl in the indolence of her youth,
Or an old man upon a winter's night.

(1919)

The Second Coming

Turning and turning in the widening gyre
The falcon cannot hear the falconer;
Things fall apart; the centre cannot hold;
Mere anarchy is loosed upon the world,
5 The blood-dimmed tide is loosed, and everywhere
The ceremony of innocence is drowned;
The best lack all conviction, while the worst
Are full of passionate intensity.
Surely some revelation is at hand;
10 Surely the Second Coming is at hand.
The Second Coming! Hardly are those words out
When a vast image out of *Spiritus Mundi*
Troubles my sight: somewhere in sands of the desert
A shape with lion body and the head of a man,
15 A gaze blank and pitiless as the sun,
Is moving its slow thighs, while all about it
Reel shadows of the indignant desert birds.
The darkness drops again; but now I know
That twenty centuries of stony sleep
20 Were vexed to nightmare by a rocking cradle,
And what rough beast, its hour come round at last,
Slouches towards Bethlehem to be born?

(1921)

Sailing to Byzantium

I

That is no country for old men. The young
In one another's arms, birds in the trees,
—Those dying generations—at their song,
The salmon-falls, the mackerel-crowded seas,
5   Fish, flesh, or fowl, commend all summer long
Whatever is begotten, born, and dies.
Caught in that sensual music all neglect
Monuments of unaging intellect.

II

An aged man is but a paltry thing,
10   A tattered coat upon a stick, unless
Soul clap its hands and sing, and louder sing
For every tatter in its mortal dress,
Nor is there singing school but studying
Monuments of its own magnificence;
15   And therefore I have sailed the seas and come
To the holy city of Byzantium.

III

O sages standing in God's holy fire
As in the gold mosaic of a wall,
Come from the holy fire, perne in a gyre,
20   And be the singing-masters of my soul.
Consume my heart away; sick with desire
And fastened to a dying animal
It knows not what it is; and gather me
Into the artifice of eternity.

IV

25   Once out of nature I shall never take
My bodily form from any natural thing,
But such a form as Grecian goldsmiths make
Of hammered gold and gold enameling
To keep a drowsy Emperor awake;
30   Or set upon a golden bough to sing
To lords and ladies of Byzantium
Of what is past, or passing, or to come.

(1927)

Lapis Lazuli

(For Harry Clifton)

I have heard that hysterical women say
They are sick of the palette and fiddle-bow,
Of poets that are always gay,
For everybody knows or else should know
5   That if nothing drastic is done
Aeroplane and Zeppelin will come out,
Pitch like King Billy bomb-balls in
Until the town lie beaten flat.

All perform their tragic play,
10   There struts Hamlet, there is Lear,
That's Ophelia, that Cordelia;
Yet they, should the last scene be there,
The great stage curtain about to drop,
If worthy their prominent part in the play,
15   Do not break up their lines to weep.
They know that Hamlet and Lear are gay;
Gaiety transfiguring all that dread.
All men have aimed at, found and lost;
Black out; Heaven blazing into the head:
20   Tragedy wrought to its uttermost.
Though Hamlet rambles and Lear rages,
And all the drop-scenes drop at once
Upon a hundred thousand stages,
It cannot grow by an inch or an ounce.

25   On their own feet they came, or on shipboard,
Camel-back, horse-back, ass-back, mule-back,
Old civilisations put to the sword.
Then they and their wisdom went to rack:
No handiwork of Callimachus,
30   Who handled marble as if it were bronze,
Made draperies that seemed to rise
When sea-wind swept the corner, stands;
His long lamp-chimney shaped like the stem
Of a slender palm, stood but a day;
35   All things fall and are built again,
And those that build them again are gay.

Two Chinamen, behind them a third,
Are carved in lapis lazuli,
Over them flies a long-legged bird,
40   A symbol of longevity;
The third, doubtless a serving-man,
Carries a musical instrument.

Every discoloration of the stone,
Every accidental crack or dent,
45 Seems a water-course or an avalanche,
Or lofty slope where it still snows
Though doubtless plum or cherry-branch
Sweetens the little half-way house
Those Chinamen climb towards, and I
50 Delight to imagine them seated there;
There, on the mountain and the sky,
On all the tragic scene they stare.
One asks for mournful melodies;
Accomplished fingers begin to play.
55 Their eyes mid many wrinkles, their eyes,
Their ancient, glittering eyes, are gay.

(1938)

Robert Frost
(U.S.A., 1874–1963)

After Apple-picking

My long two-pointed ladder's sticking through a tree
Toward heaven still,
And there's a barrel that I didn't fill
Beside it, and there may be two or three
5 Apples I didn't pick upon some bough.
But I am done with apple-picking now.
Essence of winter sleep is on the night,
The scent of apples: I am drowsing off.
I cannot rub the strangeness from my sight
10 I got from looking through a pane of glass
I skimmed this morning from the drinking trough
And held against the world of hoary grass.
It melted, and I let it fall and break.
But I was well
15 Upon my way to sleep before it fell,
And I could tell
What form my dreaming was about to take.
Magnified apples appear and disappear,
Stem end and blossom end,
20 And every fleck of russet showing clear.
My instep arch not only keeps the ache,
It keeps the pressure of a ladder-round.

I feel the ladder sway as the boughs bend.
And I keep hearing from the cellar bin
25 The rumbling sound
Of load on load of apples coming in.
For I have had too much
Of apple-picking: I am overtired
Of the great harvest I myself desired.
30 There were ten thousand thousand fruit to touch,
Cherish in hand, lift down, and not let fall.
For all
That struck the earth,
No matter if not bruised or spiked with stubble,
35 Went surely to the cider-apple heap
As of no worth.
One can see what will trouble
This sleep of mine, whatever sleep it is.
Were he not gone,
40 The woodchuck could say whether it's like his
Long sleep, as I describe its coming on,
Or just some human sleep.

                                             (1914)

Nothing Gold Can Stay

Nature's first green is gold,
Her hardest hue to hold.
Her early leaf's a flower;
But only so an hour.
5 Then leaf subsides to leaf.
So Eden sank to grief,
So dawn goes down to day.
Nothing gold can stay.

                        (1923)

Stopping by Woods on a Snowy Evening

Whose woods these are I think I know.
His house is in the village though;
He will not see me stopping here
To watch his woods fill up with snow.

5 My little horse must think it queer
To stop without a farmhouse near
Between the woods and frozen lake
The darkest evening of the year.

He gives his harness bells a shake
10 To ask if there is some mistake.
The only other sound's the sweep
Of easy wind and downy flake.

The woods are lovely, dark and deep,
But I have promises to keep,
15 And miles to go before I sleep,
And miles to go before I sleep.

(1923)

Acquainted with the Night

I have been one acquainted with the night.
I have walked out in rain—and back in rain.
I have outwalked the furthest city light.

I have looked down the saddest city lane.
5 I have passed by the watchman on his beat
And dropped my eyes, unwilling to explain.

I have stood still and stopped the sound of feet
When far away an interrupted cry
Came over houses from another street,

10 But not to call me back or say good-by;
And further still at an unearthly height,
One luminary clock against the sky

Proclaimed the time was neither wrong nor right.
I have been one acquainted with the night.

(1928)

Design

I found a dimpled spider, fat and white,
On a white heal-all, holding up a moth
Like a white piece of rigid satin cloth—
Assorted characters of death and blight
5 Mixed ready to begin the morning right,
Like the ingredients of a witches' broth—
A snow-drop spider, a flower like a froth,
And dead wings carried like a paper kite.

What had that flower to do with being white,
10 The wayside blue and innocent heal-all?
What brought the kindred spider to that height,
Then steered the white moth thither in the night?
What but design of darkness to appall?—
If design govern in a thing so small.

(1936)

E.M. Forster
(ENGLAND, 1879–1970)

Me, Them and You

I have a suit of clothes. It does not fit, but is of stylish cut. I can go anywhere in it and I have been to see the Sargent pictures at the Royal Academy. Underneath the suit was a shirt, beneath the shirt was a vest, and beneath the vest was Me. Me was not exposed much to the public gaze; two hands and a face showed that here was a human being; the rest was swathed in cotton or wool.

Yet Me was what mattered, for it was Me that was going to see Them. Them what? Them persons what governs us, them dukes and duchesses and archbishops and generals and captains of industry. They have had their likenesses done by this famous painter (artists are useful sometimes), and, for the sum of one and six, they were willing to be inspected. I had one and six, otherwise I should have remained in the snow outside. The coins changed hands. I entered the exhibition, and found myself almost immediately in the presence of a respectable family servant.

"Wretched weather," I remarked civilly. There was no reply, the forehead swelled, the lips contracted haughtily. I had begun my tour with a very serious mistake, and had addressed a portrait of Lord Curzon. His face had misled me into thinking him a family servant. I ought to have looked only at the clothes, which were blue and blazing, and which he clutched with a blue-veined hand. They cost a hundred pounds perhaps. How cheap did my own costume seem now, and how impossible it was to imagine that Lord Curzon continues beneath his clothes, that he, too (if I may venture on the parallel), was a Me.

Murmuring in confusion, I left the radiant effigy and went into the next room. Here my attention was drawn by a young Oriental, subtle and charming and not quite sure of his ground. I complimented him in flowery words. He winced, he disclaimed all knowledge of the East. I had been speaking to Sir Philip Sassoon. Here again I ought to have looked first at the clothes. They were slightly horsey and wholly English, and they put mine to shame. Why had he come from Tabriz, or wherever it was, and put them on? Why take the long journey from Samarcand for the purpose of denouncing our Socialists? Why not remain where he felt himself Me? But he resented analysis and I left him.

The third figure—to do her justice—felt that she was Me and no one else could be, and looked exactly what she was: namely, the wife of our Ambassador at Berlin. Erect she stood, with a small balustrade and a diplomatic landscape behind her. She was superbly beautiful and incredibly arrogant, and her pearls would have clothed not mere hundreds of human beings but many of her fellow-portraits on the walls. What beat in the heart—if there was a heart—I could not know, but I heard pretty distinctly the voice that proceeded from the bright red lips. It is not a voice that would promote calm in high places, not a voice to promote amity between two nations at a difficult moment in their intercourse. Her theme was precedence, and perhaps it is wiser to allow her to develop it in solitude.

And I drifted from Them to Them, fascinated by the hands and faces which peeped out of the costumes. Lord Roberts upheld with difficulty the rows of trinkets pinned on his uniform; Sir Thomas Sutherland was fat above a fat black tie; a riding costume supported the chinless cranium of a Duke; a Mr. John Fife "who showed conspicuous ability in the development of the granite industry" came from Aberdeen in black; and a Marquess actually did something: he was carrying the Sword of State on the occasion of King Edward's Coronation; while a page carried his train. Sometimes the painter saw through his sitters and was pleasantly mischievous at their expense; sometimes he seemed taken in by them—which happens naturally enough to a man who spends much time dangling after the rich. In spite of the charm of his work, and the lovely colours, and the gracious pictures of Venice, a pall of upholstery hung over the exhibition. The portraits dominated. Gazing at each other over our heads, they said, "What would the country do without us? We have got the decorations and the pearls, we make fashions and wars, we have the largest houses and eat the best food, and control the most important industries, and breed the most valuable children, and ours is the Kingdom and the Power and the Glory." And, listening to their chorus, I felt this was so, and my clothes fitted worse and worse, and there seemed in all the universe no gulf wider than the gulf between Them and Me—no wider gulf, until I encountered You.

You had been plentiful enough in the snow outside (your proper place), but I had not expected to find You here in the place of honour, too. Yours was by far the largest picture in the show. You were hung between Lady Cowdray and the Hon. Mrs. Langman, and You were entitled "Gassed." You were of godlike beauty—for the upper classes only allow the lower classes to appear in art on condition that they wash themselves and have classical features. These conditions you fulfilled. A line of golden-haired Apollos moved along a duckboard from left to right with bandages over their eyes. They had been blinded by mustard gas. Others sat peacefully in the foreground, others approached through the middle distance. The battlefield was sad but tidy. No one complained, no one looked lousy or overtired, and the aeroplanes overhead struck the necessary note of the majesty of England. It was all that a great war picture should be, and it was modern because it managed to tell a new sort of lie. Many ladies and gentlemen fear that Romance is passing out of war with the sabres and the chargers. Sargent's masterpiece reassures them. He shows that it is possible to suffer with a quiet grace under the new conditions, and Lady Cowdray and the Hon. Mrs. Langman, as they looked over the twenty feet of canvas that divided them, were still able to say, "How touching," instead of "How obscene."

Still, there You were, though in modified form, and in mockery of your real misery, and though the gulf between Them and Me was wide, still wider yawned the gulf between us and You. For what could we do without you? What would become of our incomes and activities if you declined to exist? You are the slush and dirt on which our civilization rests, which it treads under foot daily, which it sentimentalizes over now and then, in hours of danger. But you are not only a few selected youths in khaki, you are old men and women and dirty babies also, and dimly and obscurely you used to move through the mind of Carlyle. "Thou wert our conscript, on Thee the lot fell. . . ." That is as true for the twentieth century as for the nineteenth, though the twentieth century—more cynical—feels that it is merely a true remark, not a useful one, and that economic conditions cannot be bettered by booming on about the brotherhood of man. "For in Thee also a godlike frame lay hidden, but it was not to be unfolded," not while the hard self-satisfied faces stare at each other from the walls and say, "But at all events we founded the Charity Organization Society—and look what we pay in wages, and look what our clothes cost, and clothes mean work."

The misery goes on, the feeble impulses of good return to the sender, and far away, in some other category, far away from the snobbery and glitter in which our souls and bodies have been entangled, is forged the instrument of the new dawn.

(1925)

The Other Side of the Hedge

My pedometer told me that I was twenty-five; and, though it is a shocking thing to stop walking, I was so tired that I sat down on a milestone to rest. People outstripped me, jeering as they did so, but I was too apathetic to feel resentful, and even when Miss Eliza Dimbleby, the great educationist, swept past, exhorting me to persevere, I only smiled and raised my hat.

At first I thought I was going to be like my brother, whom I had had to leave by the roadside a year or two round the corner. He had wasted his breath on singing, and his strength on helping others. But I had travelled more wisely, and now it was only the monotony of the highway that oppressed me—dust under foot and brown crackling hedges on either side, ever since I could remember.

And I had already dropped several things—indeed, the road behind was strewn with the things we all had dropped; and the white dust was settling down on them, so that already they looked no better than stones. My muscles were so weary that I could not even bear the weight of those things I still carried. I slid off the milestone into the road, and lay there prostrate, with my face to the great parched hedge, praying that I might give up.

A little puff of air revived me. It seemed to come from the hedge; and, when I opened my eyes, there was a glint of light through the tangle of boughs and dead leaves. The hedge could not be as thick as usual. In my weak, morbid state, I longed to force my way in, and see what was on the other side. No one was in sight, or I should not have dared to try. For we of the road do not admit in conversation that there is another side at all.

I yielded to the temptation, saying to myself that I would come back in a minute. The thorns scratched my face, and I had to use my arms as a shield, depending on my feet alone to push me forward. Halfway through I would have gone back, for in the passage all the things I was carrying were scraped off me, and my clothes were torn. But I was so wedged that return was impossible, and I had to wriggle blindly forward, expecting every moment that my strength would fail me, and that I should perish in the undergrowth.

Suddenly cold water closed round my head, and I seemed sinking down for ever. I had fallen out of the hedge into a deep pool. I rose to the surface at last, crying for help, and I heard someone on the opposite bank laugh and say: "Another!" And then I was twitched out and laid panting on the dry ground.

Even when the water was out of my eyes, I was still dazed, for I had never been in so large a space, nor seen such grass and sunshine. The blue sky was no longer a strip, and beneath it the earth had risen grandly into hills—clean, bare buttresses, with beech trees in their folds, and meadows and clear pools at their feet. But the hills were not high, and there was in the landscape a sense of human occupation—so that one might have called it a park, or garden, if the words did not imply a certain triviality and constraint.

As soon as I got my breath, I turned to my rescuer and said:

"Where does this place lead to?"

"Nowhere, thank the Lord!" said he, and laughed. He was a man of fifty or sixty—just the kind of age we mistrust on the road—but there was no anxiety in his manner, and his voice was that of a boy of eighteen.

"But it must lead somewhere!" I cried, too much surprised at his answer to thank him for saving my life.

"He wants to know where it leads!" he shouted to some men on the hill side, and they laughed back, and waved their caps.

I noticed then that the pool into which I had fallen was really a moat which bent round to the left and to the right, and that the hedge followed it continually. The hedge was green on this side—its roots showed through the clear water, and fish swam about in them—and it was wreathed over with dog-roses and Traveller's Joy. But it was a barrier, and in a moment I lost all pleasure in the grass, the sky, the trees, the happy men and women, and realized that the place was but a prison, for all its beauty and extent.

We moved away from the boundary, and then followed a path almost parallel to it, across the meadows. I found it difficult walking, for I was always trying to out-distance my companion, and there was no advantage in doing this if the place led nowhere. I had never kept step with anyone since I left my brother.

I amused him by stopping suddenly and saying disconsolately, "This is perfectly terrible. One cannot advance: one cannot progress. Now we of the road—"

"Yes. I know."

"I was going to say, we advance continually."

"I know."

"We are always learning, expanding, developing. Why, even in my short life I have seen a great deal of advance—the Transvaal War, the Fiscal Question, Christian Science, Radium. Here for example—"

I took out my pedometer, but it still marked twenty-five, not a degree more.

"Oh, it's stopped! I meant to show you. It should have registered all the time I was walking with you. But it makes me only twenty-five."

"Many things don't work in here," he said. "One day a man brought in a Lee-Metford, and that wouldn't work."

"The laws of science are universal in their application. It must be the water in the moat that has injured the machinery. In normal conditions everything works. Science and the spirit of emulation—those are the forces that have made us what we are."

I had to break off and acknowledge the pleasant greetings of people whom we passed. Some of them were singing, some talking, some engaged in gardening, hay-making, or other rudimentary industries. They all seemed happy; and I might have been happy too, if I could have forgotten that the place led nowhere.

I was startled by a young man who came sprinting across our path, took a little fence in fine style, and went tearing over a ploughed field till he plunged into a lake, across which he began to swim. Here was true energy, and I exclaimed: "A cross-country race! Where are the others?"

"There are no others," my companion replied; and, later on, when we passed some long grass from which came the voice of a girl singing exquisitely to herself, he said again: "There are no others." I was bewildered at the waste in production, and murmured to myself, "What does it all mean?"

He said: "It means nothing but itself"—and he repeated the words slowly, as if I were a child.

"I understand," I said quietly, "but I do not agree. Every achievement is worthless unless it is a link in the chain of development. And I must not trespass on your kindness any longer. I must get back somehow to the road, and have my pedometer mended."

"First, you must see the gates," he replied, "for we have gates, though we never use them."

I yielded politely, and before long we reached the moat again, at a point where it was spanned by a bridge. Over the bridge was a big gate, as white as ivory, which was fitted into a gap in the boundary hedge. The gate opened outwards, and I exclaimed in amazement, for from it ran a road—just such a road as I had left—dusty under foot, with brown crackling hedges on either side as far as the eye could reach.

"That's my road!" I cried.

He shut the gate and said: "But not your part of the road. It is through this gate that humanity went out countless ages ago, when it was first seized with the desire to walk."

I denied this, observing that the part of the road I myself had left was not more than two miles off. But with the obstinacy of his years he repeated: "It is the same road. This is the beginning, and though it seems to run straight away from us, it doubles so often, that it is never far from our boundary and sometimes touches it." He stooped down by the moat, and traced on its moist margin an absurd figure like a maze. As we walked back through the meadows, I tried to convince him of his mistake.

"The road sometimes doubles, to be sure, but that is part of our discipline. Who can doubt that its general tendency is onward? To what goal we know not—it may be to some mountain where we shall touch the sky, it may be over precipices into the sea. But that it goes forward—who can doubt that? It is the thought of that that makes us strive to excel, each in his own way, and gives us an impetus which is lacking with you. Now that man who passed us—it's true that he ran well, and jumped well, and swam well; but we have men who can run better, and men who can jump better, and who can swim better. Specialization has produced results which would surprise you. Similarly, that girl—".

Here I interrupted myself to exclaim: "Good gracious me! I could have sworn it was Miss Eliza Dimbleby over there, with her feet in the fountain?"

He believed that it was.

"Impossible! I left her on the road, and she is due to lecture this evening at Tunbridge Wells. Why, her train leaves Cannon Street in—of course my watch has stopped like everything else. She is the last person to be here."

"People always are astonished at meeting each other. All kinds come through the hedge, and come at all times—when they are drawing ahead in the race, when they are lagging behind, when they are left for dead. I often stand near the boundary listening to the sounds of the road—you know what they are—and wonder if anyone will turn aside. It is my great happiness to help someone out of the moat, as I helped you. For our country fills up slowly, though it was meant for all mankind."

"Mankind have other aims," I said gently, for I thought him well-meaning; "and I must join them." I bade him good evening, for the sun was declining, and I wished to be on the road by nightfall. To my alarm, he caught hold of me, crying: "You are not to go yet!" I tried to shake him off, for we had no interests in common, and his civility was becoming irksome to me. But for all my struggles the tiresome old man would not let go; and, as wrestling is not my specialty, I was obliged to follow him.

It was true that I could have never found alone the place where I came in, and I hoped that, when I had seen the other sights about which he was worrying, he would take me back to it. But I was determined not to sleep in the country, for I mistrusted it, and the people too, for all their friendliness. Hungry though I was, I would not join them in their evening meals of milk and fruit, and, when they gave me flowers, I flung them away as soon as I could do so unobserved. Already they were lying down for the night like cattle—some out on the bare hillside, others in groups under the beeches. In the light of an orange sunset I hurried on with my unwelcome guide, dead tired, faint for want of food, but murmuring indomitably: "Give me life, with its struggles and victories, with its failures and hatreds, with its deep moral meaning and its unknown goal!"

At last we came to a place where the encircling moat was spanned by another bridge, and where another gate interrupted the line of the boundary hedge. It was different from the first gate; for it was half transparent like horn, and opened inwards. But through it, in the waning light, I saw again just such a road as I had left—monotonous, dusty, with brown crackling hedges on either side, as far as the eye could reach.

I was strangely disquieted at the sight, which seemed to deprive me of all self-control. A man was passing us, returning for the night to the hills, with a scythe over his shoulder and a can of some liquid in his hand. I forgot the destiny of our race. I forgot the road that lay before my eyes, and I sprang at him, wrenched the can out of his hand, and began to drink.

It was nothing stronger than beer, but in my exhausted state it overcame me in a moment. As in a dream, I saw the old man shut the gate, and heard him say: "This is where your road ends, and through this gate humanity—all that is left of it—will come in to us."

Though my senses were sinking into oblivion, they seemed to expand ere they reached it. They perceived the magic song of nightingales, and the odour of invisible hay, and stars piercing the fading sky. The man whose beer I had stolen lowered me down gently to sleep off its effects, and, as he did so, I saw that he was my brother.

(1947)

Wallace Stevens
(U.S.A., 1879-1955)

Anecdote of the Jar

    I placed a jar in Tennessee,
    And round it was, upon a hill.
    It made the slovenly wilderness
    Surround that hill.

5   The wilderness rose up to it,
    And sprawled around, no longer wild.
    The jar was round upon the ground
    And tall and of a port in air.

    It took dominion everywhere.
10   The jar was gray and bare.
    It did not give of bird or bush,
    Like nothing else in Tennessee.

          (1923)

James Joyce
(IRELAND, 1882–1941)

Araby

North Richmond Street, being blind, was a quiet street except at the hour when the Christian Brothers' School set the boys free. An uninhabited house of two storeys stood at the blind end, detached from its neighbours in a square ground. The other houses of the street, conscious of decent lives within them, gazed at one another with brown imperturbable faces.

The former tenant of our house, a priest, had died in the back drawing-room. Air, musty from having been long enclosed, hung in all the rooms, and the waste room behind the kitchen was littered with old useless papers. Among these I found a few paper-covered books, the pages of which were curled and damp: *The Abbot*, by Walter Scott, *The Devout Communicant* and *The Memoirs of Vidocq*. I liked the last best because its leaves were yellow. The wild garden behind the house contained a central apple-tree and a few straggling bushes under one of which I found the late tenant's rusty bicycle-pump. He had been a very charitable priest; in his will he had left all his money to institutions and the furniture of his house to his sister.

When the short days of winter came dusk fell before we had well eaten our dinners. When we met in the street the houses had grown sombre. The space of sky above us was the colour of ever-changing violet and towards it the lamps of the street lifted their feeble lanterns. The cold air stung us and we played till our bodies glowed. Our shouts echoed in the silent streets. The career of our play brought us through the dark muddy lanes behind the houses where we ran the gantlet of the rough tribes from the cottages, to the back doors of the dark dripping gardens where odours arose from the ashpits, to the dark odorous stables where a coachman smoothed and combed the horse or shook music from the buckled harness. When we returned to the street light from the kitchen windows had filled the areas. If my uncle was seen turning the corner we hid in the shadow until we had seen him safely housed. Or if Mangan's sister came out on the doorstep to call her brother in to his tea we watched her from our shadow peer up and down the street. We waited to see whether she would remain or go in and, if she remained, we left our shadow and walked up to Mangan's steps resignedly. She was waiting for us, her figure defined by the light from the half-opened door. Her brother always teased her before he obeyed and I stood by the railings looking at her. Her dress swung as she moved her body and the soft rope of her hair tossed from side to side.

Every morning I lay on the floor in the front parlour watching her door. The blind was pulled down to within an inch of the sash so that I could not be seen. When she came out on the doorstep my heart leaped. I ran to the hall, seized my books and followed her. I kept her brown figure always in my eye and, when we came near the point at which our ways diverged, I quickened my pace and passed her. This happened morning after morning. I had never spoken to her, except for a few casual words, and yet her name was like a summons to all my foolish blood.

Her image accompanied me even in places the most hostile to romance. On Saturday evenings when my aunt went marketing I had to go to carry some of the parcels. We walked through the flaring streets, jostled by drunken men and bargaining women, amid the curses of labourers, the shrill litanies of shop-boys who stood on guard by the barrels of pigs' cheeks, the nasal chanting of street-singers, who sang a *come-all-you* about O'Donovan Rossa, or a ballad about the troubles in our native land. These noises converged in a single sensation of life for me: I imagined that I bore my chalice safely through a throng of foes. Her name sprang to my lips at moments in strange prayers and praises which I myself did not understand. My eyes were often full of tears (I could not tell why) and at times a flood from my heart seemed to pour itself out into my bosom. I thought little of the future. I did not know whether I would ever speak to her or not or, if I spoke to her, how I could tell her of my confused adoration. But my body was like a harp and her words and gestures were like fingers running upon the wires.

One evening I went into the back drawing-room in which the priest had died. It was a dark rainy evening and there was no sound in the house. Through one of the broken panes I heard the rain impinge upon the earth, the fine incessant needles of water playing in the sodden beds. Some distant lamp or lighted window gleamed below me. I was thankful that I could see so little. All my senses seemed to desire to veil themselves and, feeling that I was about to slip from them, I pressed the palms of my hands together until they trembled, murmuring: *O love! O love!* many times.

At last she spoke to me. When she addressed the first words to me I was so confused that I did not know what to answer. She asked me was I going to *Araby*. I forget whether I answered yes or no. It would be a splendid bazaar, she said; she would love to go.

—And why can't you? I asked.

While she spoke she turned a silver bracelet round and round her wrist. She could not go, she said, because there would be a retreat that week in her convent. Her brother and two other boys were fighting for their caps and I was alone at the railings. She held one of the spikes, bowing her head towards me. The light from the lamp opposite our door caught the white curve of her neck, lit up her hair that rested there and, falling, lit up the hand upon the railing. It fell over one side of her dress and caught the white border of a petticoat, just visible as she stood at ease.

—It's well for you, she said.

—If I go, I said, I will bring you something.

What innumerable follies laid waste my waking and sleeping thoughts after that evening! I wished to annihilate the tedious intervening days. I chafed against the work of school. At night in my bedroom and by day in the classroom her image came between me and the page I strove to read. The syllables of the word *Araby* were called to me through the silence in which my soul luxuriated and cast an Eastern enchantment over me. I asked for leave to go to the bazaar on Saturday night. My aunt was surprised and hoped it was not some Freemason affair. I answered few questions in class. I watched my master's face pass from amiability to sternness; he hoped I was not beginning to idle. I could not call my wandering thoughts together. I had hardly any patience with the serious work of life which, now that it stood between me and my desire, seemed to me child's play, ugly monotonous child's play.

On Saturday morning I reminded my uncle that I wished to go to the bazaar in the evening. He was fussing at the hallstand, looking for the hat-brush, and answered me curtly:

—Yes, boy, I know.

As he was in the hall I could not go into the front parlour and lie at the window. I left the house in bad humour and walked slowly towards the school. The air was pitilessly raw and already my heart misgave me.

When I came home to dinner my uncle had not yet been home. Still it was early. I sat staring at the clock for some time and, when its ticking began to irritate me, I left the room. I mounted the staircase and gained the upper part of the house. The high cold empty gloomy rooms liberated me and I went from room to room singing. From the front window I saw my companions playing below in the street. Their cries reached me weakened and indistinct and, leaning my forehead against the cool glass, I looked over at the dark house where she lived. I may have stood there for an hour, seeing nothing but the brown-clad figure cast by my imagination, touched discreetly by the lamplight at the curved neck, at the hand upon the railings and at the border below the dress.

When I came downstairs again I found Mrs Mercer sitting at the fire. She was an old garrulous woman, a pawnbroker's widow, who collected used stamps for some pious purpose. I had to endure the gossip of the tea-table. The meal was prolonged beyond an hour and still my uncle did not come. Mrs Mercer stood up to go: she was sorry she couldn't wait any longer, but it was after eight o'clock and she did not like to be out late, as the night air was bad for her. When she had gone I began to walk up and down the room, clenching my fists. My aunt said:

—I'm afraid you may put off your bazaar for this night of Our Lord.

At nine o'clock I heard my uncle's latchkey in the halldoor. I heard him talking to himself and heard the hallstand rocking when it had received the weight of his overcoat. I could interpret these signs. When he was midway through his dinner I asked him to give me the money to go to the bazaar. He had forgotten.

—The people are in bed and after their first sleep now, he said.

I did not smile. My aunt said to him energetically:

—Can't you give him the money and let him go? You've kept him late enough as it is.

My uncle said he was very sorry he had forgotten. He said he believed in the old saying: *All work and no play makes Jack a dull boy.* He asked me where I was going and, when I had told him a second time he asked me did I know *The Arab's Farewell to his Steed.* When I left the kitchen he was about to recite the opening lines of the piece to my aunt.

I held a florin tightly in my hand as I strode down Buckingham Street towards the station. The sight of the streets thronged with buyers and glaring with gas recalled to me the purpose of my journey. I took my seat in a third-class carriage of a deserted train. After an intolerable delay the train moved out of the station slowly. It crept onward among ruinous houses and over the twinkling river. At Westland Row Station a crowd of people pressed to the carriage doors; but the porters moved them back, saying that it was a special train for the bazaar. I remained alone in the bare carriage. In a few minutes the train drew up beside an improvised wooden platform. I passed out on to the road and saw by the lighted dial of a clock that it was ten minutes to ten. In front of me was a large building which displayed the magical name.

I could not find any sixpenny entrance and, fearing that the bazaar would be closed, I passed in quickly through a turnstile, handing a shilling to a weary-looking man. I found myself in a big hall girdled at half its height by a gallery. Nearly all the stalls were closed and the greater part of the hall was in darkness. I recognised a silence like that which pervades a church after a service. I walked into the centre of the bazaar timidly. A few people were gathered about the stalls which were still open. Before a curtain, over which the words *Café Chantant* were written in coloured lamps, two men were counting money on a salver. I listened to the fall of the coins.

Remembering with difficulty why I had come I went over to one of the stalls and examined porcelain vases and flowered tea-sets. At the door of the stall a young lady was talking and laughing with two young gentlemen. I remarked their English accents and listened vaguely to their conversation.

—O, I never said such a thing!

—O, but you did!

—O, but I didn't!

—Didn't she say that?

—Yes. I heard her.

—O, there's a . . . fib!

Observing me the young lady came over and asked me did I wish to buy anything. The tone of her voice was not encouraging; she seemed to have spoken to me out of a sense of duty. I looked humbly at the great jars that stood like eastern guards at either side of the dark entrance to the stall and murmured:

—No, thank you.

The young lady changed the position of one of the vases and went back to the two young men. They began to talk of the same subject. Once or twice the young lady glanced at me over her shoulder.

I lingered before her stall, though I knew my stay was useless, to make my interest in her wares seem the more real. Then I turned away slowly and walked down the middle of the bazaar. I allowed the two pennies to fall against the sixpence in my pocket. I heard a voice call from one end of the gallery that the light was out. The upper part of the hall was now completely dark.

Gazing up into the darkness I saw myself as a creature driven and derided by vanity; and my eyes burned with anguish and anger.

(1916)

Virginia Woolf
(ENGLAND, 1882-1941)

Monday or Tuesday

Lazy and indifferent, shaking space easily from his wings, knowing his way, the heron passes over the church beneath the sky. White and distant, absorbed in itself, endlessly the sky covers and uncovers, moves and remains. A lake? Blot the shores of it out! A mountain? Oh, perfect— the sun gold on its slopes. Down that falls. Ferns then, or white feathers, for ever and ever—

Desiring truth, awaiting it, laboriously distilling a few words, for ever desiring—(a cry starts to the left, another to the right. Wheels strike divergently. Omnibuses conglomerate in conflict)—for ever desiring—(the clock asseverates with twelve distinct strokes that it is midday; light sheds gold scales; children swarm)—for ever desiring truth. Red is the dome; coins hang on the trees; smoke trails from the chimneys; bark, shout, cry "Iron for sale"— and truth?

Radiating to a point men's feet and women's feet, black or gold-encrusted—(This foggy weather—Sugar? No, thank you—The commonwealth of the future)—the firelight darting and making the room red, save for the black figures and their bright eyes, while outside a van discharges, Miss Thingummy drinks tea at her desk, and plate-glass preserves fur coats—

Flaunted, leaf-light, drifting at corners, blown across the wheels, silver-splashed, home or not home, gathered, scattered, squandered in separate scales, swept up, down, torn, sunk, assembled—and truth?

Now to recollect by the fireside on the white square of marble. From ivory depths words rising shed their blackness, blossom and penetrate. Fallen the book; in the flame, in the smoke, in the momentary sparks—or now voyaging, the marble square pendant, minarets beneath and the Indian seas, while space rushes blue and stars glint—truth? or now, content with closeness?

Lazy and indifferent the heron returns; the sky veils her stars; then bares them.

(1921)

Evening over Sussex: Reflections in a Motor Car

Evening is kind to Sussex, for Sussex is no longer young, and she is grateful for the veil of evening as an elderly woman is glad when a shade is drawn over a lamp, and only the outline of her face remains. The outline of Sussex is still very fine. The cliffs stand out to sea, one behind another. All Eastbourne, all Bexhill, all St. Leonards, their parades and their lodging houses, their beadshops and their sweet shops and their placards and their invalids and chars-à-bancs, are all obliterated. What remains is what there was when William came over from France ten centuries ago: a line of cliffs running out to sea. Also the fields are redeemed. The freckle of red villas on the coast is washed over by a thin lucid lake of brown air, in which they and their redness are drowned. It was still too early for lamps and too early for stars.

But, I thought, there is always some sediment of irritation when the moment is as beautiful as it is now. The psychologists must explain; one looks up, one is overcome by beauty extravagantly greater than one would expect—there are now pink clouds over Battle; the fields are mottled, marbled—one's perceptions blow out rapidly like air balls expanded by some rush of air, and then, when all seems blown to its fullest and tautest, with beauty and beauty and beauty, a pin pricks; it collapses. But what is the pin? So far as I could tell, the pin had something to do with one's own impotency. I cannot hold this—I cannot express this—I am overcome by it—I am mastered. Somewhere in that region one's discontent lay; and it was allied with the idea that one's nature demands mastery over all that it receives; and mastery here meant the power to convey what one saw now over Sussex so that another person could share it. And further, there was another prick of the pin: one was wasting one's chance; for beauty spread at one's right hand, at one's left; at one's back too; it was escaping all the time; one could only offer a thimble to a torrent that could fill baths, lakes.

But relinquish, I said (it is well known how in circumstances like these the self splits up and one self is eager and dissatisfied and the other stern and philosophical), relinquish these impossible aspirations; be content with the view in front of us, and believe me when I tell you that it is best to sit and soak; to be passive; to accept; and do not bother because nature has given you six little pocket knives with which to cut up the body of a whale.

While these two selves then held a colloquy about the wise course to adopt in the presence of beauty, I (a third party now declared itself) said to myself, how happy they were to enjoy so simple an occupation. There they sat as the car sped along, noticing everything: a hay stack; a rust red roof; a pond; an old man coming home with his sack on his back; there they sat, matching every colour in the sky and earth from their colour box, rigging up little models of Sussex barns and farmhouses in the red light that would serve in the January gloom. But I, being somewhat different, sat aloof and melancholy. While they are thus busied, I said to myself: Gone, gone; over, over; past and done with, past and done with. I feel life left behind even as the road is left behind. We have been over that stretch, and are already forgotten. There, windows were lit by our lamps for a second; the light is out now. Others come behind us.

Then suddenly a fourth self (a self which lies in ambush, apparently dormant, and jumps upon one unawares. Its remarks are often entirely disconnected with what has been happening, but must be attended to because of their very abruptness) said: "Look at that." It was a light; brilliant, freakish; inexplicable. For a second I was unable to name it. "A star"; and for that second it held its odd flicker of unexpectedness and danced and beamed. "I take your meaning," I said. "You, erratic and impulsive self that you are, feel that the light over the downs there emerging, dangles from the future. Let us try to understand this. Let us reason it out. I feel suddenly attached not to the past but to the future. I think of Sussex in five hundred years to come. I think much grossness will have evaporated. Things will have been scorched up, eliminated. There will be magic gates. Draughts fan-blown by electric power will cleanse houses. Lights intense and firmly directed will go over the earth, doing the work. Look at the moving light in that hill; it is the headlight of a car. By day and by night Sussex in five centuries will be full of charming thoughts, quick, effective beams."

The sun was now low beneath the horizon. Darkness spread rapidly. None of my selves could see anything beyond the tapering light of our headlamps on the hedge. I summoned them together. "Now," I said, "comes the season of making up our accounts. Now we have got to collect ourselves; we have got to be one self. Nothing is to be seen any more, except one wedge of road and bank which our lights repeat incessantly. We are perfectly provided for. We are warmly wrapped in a rug; we are protected from wind and rain. We are alone. Now is the time of reckoning. Now I, who preside over the company, am going to arrange in order the trophies which we have all brought in. Let me see; there was a great deal of beauty brought in today: farmhouses; cliffs standing out to sea; marbled fields; mottled fields; red feathered skies; all that. Also there was disappearance and the death of the individual. The vanishing road and the window lit for a second and then dark. And then there was the sudden dancing light, that was hung in the future. What we have made then today," I said, "is this: that beauty; death of the individual; and the future. Look, I will make a little figure for your satisfaction; here he comes. Does this little figure advancing through beauty, through death, to the economical, powerful and efficient future when houses will be cleansed by a puff of hot wind satisfy you? Look at him; there on my knee." We sat and looked at the figure we had made that day. Great sheer slabs of rock, tree tufted, surrounded him. He was for a second very, very solemn. Indeed it seemed as if the reality of things were displayed there on the rug. A violent thrill ran through us; as if a charge of electricity had entered in to us. We cried out together: "Yes, yes," as if affirming something, in a moment of recognition.

And then the body who had been silent up to now began its song, almost at first as low as the rush of the wheels: "Eggs and bacon; toast and tea; fire and a bath; fire and a bath; jugged hare," it went on, and "red currant jelly; a glass of wine; with coffee to follow, with coffee to follow—and then to bed; and then to bed."

"Off with you," I said to my assembled selves. "Your work is done. I dismiss you. Goodnight."

And the rest of the journey was performed in the delicious society of my own body.

(1942)

E.J. Pratt
(CANADA, 1883–1964)

Newfoundland Seamen

This is their culture, this—their master passion
Of giving shelter and of sharing bread,
Of answering rocket signals in the fashion
Of losing life to save it. In the spread
5   Of time—the Gilbert-Grenfell-Bartlett span—
The headlines cannot dim their daily story,
Nor calls like London! Gander! Teheran!
Outplay the drama of the sled and dory.

The wonders fade. There overhead a mile,
10 Planes bank like gulls: like curlews scream the jets.
The caravans move on in radar file
Scarce noticed by the sailors at their nets,
Bracing their bodies to their tasks, as when,
Centuries before Argentia's smoking funnels,
15 That small ancestral band of Devon men
Red-boned their knuckles on the *Squirrel* gunwales.

As old as it is new, as new as old,
Enduring as a cape, as fresh as dulse,
This is the Terra Nova record told
20 Of uncontractual blood behind the pulse
On sea or land. Was it but yesterday
That without terms and without drill commands,
A rescue squad found Banting where he lay
With the torn tissues of his healing hands?
                    (31 March 1949)

William Carlos Williams

(U.S.A., 1883–1963)

The Red Wheelbarrow

so much depends
upon

a red wheel
barrow

5   glazed with rain
water

beside the white
chickens

(1923)

The Use of Force

They were new patients to me, all I had was the name, Olson. Please come down as soon as you can, my daughter is very sick.

When I arrived I was met by the mother, a big startled looking woman, very clean and apologetic who merely said, Is this the doctor? and let me in. In the back, she added, You must excuse us, doctor, we have her in the kitchen where it is warm. It is very damp here sometimes.

The child was fully dressed and sitting on her father's lap near the kitchen table. He tried to get up, but I motioned for him not to bother, took off my overcoat and started to look things over. I could see that they were all very nervous, eyeing me up and down distrustfully. As often, in such cases, they weren't telling me more than they had to, it was up to me to tell them; that's why they were spending three dollars on me.

The child was fairly eating me up with her cold, steady eyes, and no expression to her face whatever. She did not move and seemed, inwardly, quiet; an unusually attractive little thing, and as strong as a heifer in appearance. But her face was flushed, she was breathing rapidly, and I realized that she had a high fever. She had magnificent blonde hair, in profusion. One of those picture children often reproduced in advertising leaflets and the photogravure sections of the Sunday papers.

She's had a fever for three days, began the father, and we don't know what it comes from. My wife has given her things, you know, like people do, but it don't do no good. And there's been a lot of sickness around. So we tho't you'd better look her over and tell us what is the matter.

As doctors often do I took a trial shot at it as a point of departure. Had she had a sore throat?

Both parents answered me together, No. . . No, she says her throat don't hurt her.

Does your throat hurt you? added the mother to the child. But the little girl's expression didn't change nor did she move her eyes from my face.

Have you looked?

I tried to, said the mother, but I couldn't see.

As it happens we had been having a number of cases of diphtheria in the school to which this child went during that month and we were all, quite apparently, thinking of that, though no one had as yet spoken of the thing.

Well, I said, suppose we take a look at the throat first. I smiled in my best professional manner and asking for the child's first name I said, come on, Mathilda, open your mouth and let's take a look at your throat.

Nothing doing.

Aw, come on, I coaxed, just open your mouth wide and let me take a look. Look, I said opening both hands wide, I haven't anything in my hands. Just open up and let me see.

Such a nice man, put in the mother. Look how kind he is to you. Come on, do what he tells you to. He won't hurt you.

At that I ground my teeth in disgust. If only they wouldn't use the word "hurt" I might be able to get somewhere. But I did not allow myself to be hurried or disturbed but speaking quietly and slowly I approached the child again.

As I moved my chair a little nearer suddenly with one catlike movement both her hands clawed instinctively for my eyes and she almost reached them too. In fact she knocked my glasses flying and they fell, though unbroken, several feet away from me on the kitchen floor.

Both the mother and father almost turned themselves inside out in embarrassment and apology. You bad girl, said the mother, taking her and shaking her by one arm. Look what you've done. The nice man . . .

For heaven's sake, I broke in. Don't call me a nice man to her. I'm here to look at her throat on the chance that she might have diphtheria and possibly die of it. But that's nothing to her. Look here, I said to the child, we're going to look at your throat. You're old enough to understand what I'm saying. Will you open it now by yourself or shall we have to open it for you?

Not a move. Even her expression hadn't changed. Her breaths however were coming faster and faster. Then the battle began. I had to do it. I had to have a throat culture for her own protection. But first I told the parents that it was entirely up to them. I explained the danger but said that I would not insist on a throat examination so long as they would take the responsibility.

If you don't do what the doctor says you'll have to go to the hospital, the mother admonished her severely.

Oh yeah? I had to smile to myself. After all, I had already fallen in love with the savage brat; the parents were contemptible to me. In the ensuing struggle they grew more and more abject, crushed, exhausted while she surely rose to magnificent heights of insane fury of effort bred of her terror of me.

The father tried his best, and he was a big man but the fact that she was his daughter, his shame at her behavior and his dread of hurting her made him release her just at the critical moment several times when I had almost achieved success, till I wanted to kill him. But his dread also that she might have diphtheria made him tell me to go on, go on though he himself was almost fainting, while the mother moved back and forth behind us raising and lowering her hands in an agony of apprehension.

Put her in front of you on your lap, I ordered, and hold both her wrists.

But as soon as he did the child let out a scream. Don't, you're hurting me. Let go of my hands. Let them go I tell you. Then she shrieked terrifyingly, hysterically. Stop it! Stop it! You're killing me!

Do you think she can stand it, doctor! said the mother.

You get out, said the husband to his wife. Do you want her to die of diphtheria?

Come on now, hold her, I said.

Then I grasped the child's head with my left hand and tried to get the wooden tongue depressor between her teeth. She fought, with clenched teeth, desperately! But now I also had grown furious—at a child. I tried to hold myself down but I couldn't. I know how to expose a throat for inspection. And I did my best. When finally I got the wooden spatula behind the last teeth and just the point of it into the mouth cavity, she opened up for an instant but before I could see anything she came down again and gripping the wooden blade between her molars she reduced it to splinters before I could get it out again.

Aren't you ashamed, the mother yelled at her. Aren't you ashamed to act like that in front of the doctor?

Get me a smooth-handled spoon of some sort, I told the mother. We're going through with this. The child's mouth was already bleeding. Her tongue was cut and she was screaming in wild hysterical shrieks. Perhaps I should have desisted and come back in an hour or more. No doubt it would have been better. But I have seen at least two children lying dead in bed of neglect in such cases, and feeling that I must get a diagnosis now or never I went at it again. But the worst of it was that I too had got beyond reason. I could have torn the child apart in my own fury and enjoyed it. It was a pleasure to attack her. My face was burning with it.

The damned little brat must be protected against her own idiocy, one says to one's self at such times. Others must be protected against her. It is a social necessity. And all these things are true. But a blind fury, a feeling of adult shame, bred of a longing for muscular release are the operatives. One goes on to the end.

In a final unreasoning assault I overpowered the child's neck and jaws. I forced the heavy silver spoon back of her teeth and down her throat till she gagged. And there it was—both tonsils covered with membrane. She had fought valiantly to keep me from knowing her secret. She had been hiding that sore throat for three days at least and lying to her parents in order to escape just such an outcome as this.

Now truly she *was* furious. She had been on the defensive before but now she attacked. Tried to get off her father's lap and fly at me while tears of defeat blinded her eyes

1950)

This Is Just To Say

    I have eaten
    the plums
    that were in
    the icebox

5   and which
    you were probably
    saving
    for breakfast

    Forgive me
10   they were delicious
    so sweet
    and so cold

      (1934)

D.H. Lawrence

(ENGLAND, 1885–1930)

Snake

A snake came to my water-trough
On a hot, hot day, and I in pyjamas for the heat,
To drink there.

In the deep, strange-scented shade of the great dark carob-tree
5 I came down the steps with my pitcher
And must wait, must stand and wait, for there he was at the trough before me.
He reached down from a fissure in the earth-wall in the gloom
And trailed his yellow-brown slackness soft-bellied down, over the edge of the stone trough
And rested his throat upon the stone bottom,
10 And where the water had dripped from the tap, in a small clearness,
He sipped with his straight mouth,
Softy drank through his straight gums, into his slack long body,
Silently.

Someone was before me at my water-trough,
15 And I, like a second comer, waiting.

He lifted his head from his drinking, as cattle do,
And looked at me vaguely, as drinking cattle do,
And flickered his two-forked tongue from his lips, and mused a moment,
And stooped and drank a little more,
20 Being earth-brown, earth-golden from the burning bowels of the earth
On the day of Sicilian July, with Etna smoking.

The voice of my education said to me
He must be killed,
For in Sicily the black, black snakes are innocent, the gold are venomous.

25 And voices in me said, If you were a man
You would take a stick and break him now, and finish him off.

But must I confess how I liked him,
How glad I was he had come like a guest in quiet, to drink at my water-trough
And depart peaceful, pacified, and thankless,
30 Into the burning bowels of this earth?

Was it cowardice, that I dared not kill him?
Was is perversity, that I longed to talk to him?
Was it humility, to feel so honoured?
I felt so honoured.

35 And yet those voices:
    If you were not afraid, you would kill him!

    And truly I was afraid, I was most afraid,
    But even so, honoured still more
    That he should seek my hospitality
40 From out the dark door of the secret earth.

    He drank enough
    And lifted his head, dreamily, as one who has drunken,
    And flickered his tongue like a forked night on the air, so black,
    Seeming to lick his lips,
45 And looked around like a god, unseeing, into the air,
    And slowly turned his head,
    And slowly, very slowly, as if thrice adream,
    Proceeded to draw his slow length curving round
    And climb again the broken bank of my wall-face.

50 And as he put his head into that dreadful hole,
    And as he slowly drew up, snake-easing his shoulders, and entered farther,
    A sort of horror, a sort of protest against his withdrawing into that horrid black hole,
    Deliberately going into the blackness, and slowly drawing himself after,
    Overcame me now his back was turned.

55 I looked round, I put down my pitcher,
    I picked up a clumsy log
    And threw it at the water-trough with a clatter.

    I think it did not hit him,
    But suddenly that part of him that was left behind convulsed in undignified haste,
60 Writhed like lightning, and was gone
    Into the black hole, the earth-lipped fissure in the wall-front,
    At which, in the intense still noon, I stared with fascination.

    And immediately, I regretted it.
    I thought how paltry, how vulgar, what a mean act!
65 I despised myself and the voices of my accursed human education.

    And I thought of the albatross,
    And I wished he would come back, my snake.

    For he seemed to me again like a king,
    Like a king in exile, uncrowned in the underworld,
70 Now due to be crowned again.

    And so, I missed my chance with one of the lords
    Of life.
    And I have something to expiate;
    A pettiness.

                                        Taormina (1923)

The Horse Dealer's Daughter

"Well, Mabel, and what are you going to do with yourself?" asked Joe, with foolish flippancy. He felt quite safe himself. Without listening for an answer, he turned aside, worked a grain of tobacco to the tip of his tongue, and spat it out. He did not care about anything, since he felt safe himself.

The three brothers and the sister sat round the desolate breakfast table, attempting some sort of desultory consultation. The morning's post had given the final tap to the family fortune, and all was over. The dreary dining-room itself, with its heavy mahogany furniture, looked as if it were waiting to be done away with.

But the consultation amounted to nothing. There was a strange air of ineffectuality about the three men, as they sprawled at table, smoking and reflecting vaguely on their own condition. The girl was alone, a rather short, sullen-looking young woman of twenty-seven. She did not share the same life as her brothers. She would have been good-looking, save for the impressive fixity of her face, "bulldog," as her brothers called it.

There was a confused tramping of horses' feet outside. The three men all sprawled round in their chairs to watch. Beyond the dark holly bushes that separated the strip of lawn from the high-road, they could see a cavalcade of shire horses swinging out of their own yard, being taken for exercise. This was the last time. These were the last horses that would go through their hands. The young men watched with critical, callous look. They were all frightened at the collapse of their lives, and the sense of disaster in which they were involved left them no inner freedom.

Yet they were three fine, well-set fellows enough. Joe, the eldest, was a man of thirty-three, broad and handsome in a hot, flushed way. His face was red, he twisted his black moustache over a thick finger, his eyes were shallow and restless. He had a sensual way of uncovering his teeth when he laughed, and his bearing was stupid. Now he watched the horses with a glazed look of helplessness in his eyes, a certain stupor of downfall.

The great draught-horses swung past. They were tied head to tail, four of them, and they heaved along to where a lane branched off from the high-road, planting their great hoofs floutingly in the fine black mud, swinging their great rounded haunches sumptuously, and trotting a few sudden steps as they were led into the lane, round the corner. Every movement showed a massive, slumbrous strength, and a stupidity which held them in subjection. The groom at the head looked back, jerking the leading rope. And the cavalcade moved out of sight up the lane, the tail of the last horse, bobbed up tight and stiff, held out taut from the swinging great haunches as they rocked behind the hedges in a motion-like sleep.

Joe watched with glazed hopeless eyes. The horses were almost like his own body to him. He felt he was done for now. Luckily he was engaged to a woman as old as himself, and therefore her father, who was steward of a neighbouring estate, would provide him with a job. He would marry and go into harness. His life was over, he would be a subject animal now.

He turned uneasily aside, the retreating steps of the horses echoing in his ears. Then, with foolish restlessness, he reached for the scraps of bacon-rind from the plates, and making a faint whistling sound, flung them to the terrier that lay against the fender. He watched the dog swallow them, and waited till the creature looked into his eyes. Then a faint grin came on his face, and in a high, foolish voice he said:

"You won't get much more bacon, shall you, you little b——?"

The dog faintly and dismally wagged its tail, then lowered its haunches, circled round, and lay down again.

There was another helpless silence at the table, Joe sprawled uneasily in his seat, not willing to go till the family conclave was dissolved. Fred Henry, the second brother, was erect, clean-limbed, alert. He had watched the passing of the horses with more *sang-froid*. If he was an animal, like Joe, he was an animal which controls, not one which is controlled. He was master of any horse, and he carried himself with a well-tempered air of mastery. But he was not master of the situations of life. He pushed his coarse brown moustache upwards, off his lip, and glanced irritably at his sister, who sat impassive and inscrutable.

"You'll go and stop with Lucy for a bit, shan't you?" he asked. The girl did not answer.

"I don't see what else you can do," persisted Fred Henry.

"Go as a skivvy," Joe interpolated laconically.

The girl did not move a muscle.

"If I was her, I should go in for training for a nurse," said Malcolm, the youngest of them all. He was the baby of the family, a young man of twenty-two, with a fresh, jaunty *museau*.

But Mabel did not take any notice of him. They had talked at her and round her for so many years, that she hardly heard them at all.

The marble clock on the mantelpiece softly chimed the half-hour, the dog rose uneasily from the hearthrug and looked at the party at the breakfast table. But still they sat on in ineffectual conclave.

"Oh, all right," said Joe suddenly, apropos of nothing. "I'll get a move on."

He pushed back his chair, straddled his knees with a downward jerk, to get them free, in horsey fashion, and went to the fire. Still he did not go out of the room; he was curious to know what the others would do or say. He began to charge his pipe, looking down at the dog and saying in a high, affected voice:

"Going wi' me? Going wi' me are ter? Tha'rt goin' further than tha counts on just now, dost hear?"

The dog faintly wagged its tail, the man stuck out his jaw and covered his pipe with his hands, and puffed intently, losing himself in the tobacco, looking down all the while at the dog with an absent brown eye. The dog looked up at him in mournful distrust. Joe stood with his knees stuck out, in real horsey fashion.

"Have you had a letter from Lucy?" Fred Henry asked of his sister.

"Last week," came the neutral reply.

"And what does she say?"

There was no answer.

"Does she *ask* you to go and stop there?" persisted Fred Henry.

"She says I can if I like."

"Well, then, you'd better. Tell her you'll come on Monday."

This was received in silence.

"That's what you'll do then, is it?" said Fred Henry, in some exasperation.

But she made no answer. There was a silence of futility and irritation in the room. Malcolm grinned fatuously.

"You'll have to make up your mind between now and next Wednesday," said Joe loudly, "or else find yourself lodgings on the kerbstone."

The face of the young woman darkened, but she sat on immutable.

"Here's Jack Fergusson!" exclaimed Malcolm, who was looking aimlessly out of the window.

"Where?" exclaimed Joe, loudly.

"Just gone past."

"Coming in?"

Malcolm craned his neck to see the gate.

"Yes," he said.

There was a silence. Mabel sat on like one condemned, at the head of the table. Then a whistle was heard from the kitchen. The dog got up and barked sharply. Joe opened the door and shouted:

"Come on."

After a moment a young man entered. He was muffled up in overcoat and a purple woollen scarf, and his tweed cap, which he did not remove, was pulled down on his head. He was of medium height, his face was rather long and pale, his eyes looked tired.

"Hello, Jack! Well, Jack!" exclaimed Malcolm and Joe. Fred Henry merely said, "Jack."

"What's doing?" asked the newcomer, evidently addressing Fred Henry.

"Same. We've got to be out by Wednesday. Got a cold?"

"I have—got it bad, too."

"Why don't you stop in?"

"*Me* stop in? When I can't stand on my legs, perhaps I shall have a chance." The young man spoke huskily. He had a slight Scotch accent.

"It's a knock-out, isn't it," said Joe, boisterously, "if a doctor goes round croaking with a cold. Looks bad for the patients, doesn't it?"

The young doctor looked at him slowly.

"Anything the matter with *you*, then?" he asked sarcastically.

"Not as I know of. Damn your eyes, I hope not. Why?"

"I thought you were very concerned about the patients, wondered if you might be one yourself."

"Damn it, no, I've never been patient to no flaming doctor, and hope I never shall be," returned Joe.

At this point Mabel rose from the table, and they all seemed to become aware of her existence. She began putting the dishes together. The young doctor looked at her, but did not address her. He had not greeted her. She went out of the room with the tray, her face impassive and unchanged.

"When are you off then, all of you?" asked the doctor.

"I'm catching the eleven-forty," replied Malcolm. "Are you goin' down wi' th' trap, Joe?"

"Yes, I've told you I'm goin' down wi' th' trap, haven't I?"

"We'd better be getting her in then. So long, Jack, if I don't see you before I go," said Malcolm, shaking hands.

He went out, followed by Joe, who seemed to have his tail between his legs.

"Well, this is the devil's own," exclaimed the doctor, when he was left alone with Fred Henry. "Going before Wednesday, are you?"

"That's the orders," replied the other.

"Where, to Northampton?"

"That's it."

"The devil!" exclaimed Fergusson, with quiet chagrin.

And there was silence between the two.

"All settled up, are you?" asked Fergusson.

"About."

There was another pause.

"Well, I shall miss yer, Freddy, boy," said the young doctor.

"And I shall miss thee, Jack," returned the other.

"Miss you like hell," mused the doctor.

Fred Henry turned aside. There was nothing to say. Mabel came in again, to finish clearing the table.

"What are *you* going to do, then, Miss Pervin?" asked Fergusson. "Going to your sister's, are you?"

Mabel looked at him with her steady, dangerous eyes, that always made him uncomfortable, unsettling his superficial ease.

"No," she said.

"Well, what in the name of fortune *are* you going to do? Say what you mean to do," cried Fred Henry, with futile intensity.

But she only averted her head, and continued her work. She folded the white table-cloth, and put on the chenille cloth.

"The sulkiest bitch that ever trod!" muttered her brother.

But she finished her task with perfectly impassive face, the young doctor watching her interestedly all the while. Then she went out.

Fred Henry stared after her, clenching his lips, his blue eyes fixing in sharp antagonism, as he made a grimace of sour exasperation.

"You could bray her into bits, and that's all you'd get out of her," he said, in a small, narrowed tone.

The doctor smiled faintly.

"What's she *going* to do, then?" he asked.

"Strike me if *I* know!" returned the other.

There was a pause. Then the doctor stirred.

"I'll be seeing you to-night, shall I?" he said to his friend.

"Ay—where's it to be? Are we going over to Jessdale?"

"I don't know. I've got such a cold on me. I'll come round to the 'Moon and Stars', anyway."

"Let Lizzie and May miss their night for once, eh?"

"That's it—if I feel as I do now."

"All's one—"

The two young men went through the passage and down to the back door together. The house was large, but it was servantless now, and desolate. At the back was a small bricked house-yard, and beyond that a big square, gravelled fine and red, and having stables on two sides. Sloping, dank, winter-dark fields stretched away on the open sides.

But the stables were empty. Joseph Pervin, the father of the family, had been a man of no education, who had become a fairly large horse dealer. The stables had been full of horses, there was a great turmoil and come-and-go of horses and of dealers and grooms. Then the kitchen was full of servants. But of late things had declined. The old man had married a second time, to retrieve his fortunes. Now he was dead and everything was gone to the dogs, there was nothing but debt and threatening.

For months, Mabel had been servantless in the big house, keeping the home together in penury for her ineffectual brothers. She had kept house for ten years. But previously it was with unstinted means. Then, however brutal and coarse everything was, the sense of money had kept her proud, confident. The men might be foul-mouthed, the women in the kitchen might have bad reputations, her brothers might have illegitimate children. But so long as there was money, the girl felt herself established, and brutally proud, reserved.

No company came to the house, save dealers and coarse men. Mabel had no associates of her own sex, after her sister went away. But she did not mind. She went regularly to church, she attended to her father. And she lived in the memory of her mother, who had died when she was fourteen, and whom she had loved. She had loved her father, too, in a different way, depending upon him, and feeling secure in him, until at the age of fifty-four he married again. And then she had set hard against him. Now he had died and left them all hopelessly in debt.

She had suffered badly during the period of poverty. Nothing, however, could shake the curious sullen, animal pride that dominated each member of the family. Now, for Mabel, the end had come. Still she would not cast about her. She would follow her own way just the same. She would always hold the keys of her own situation. Mindless and persistent, she endured from day to day. Why should she think? Why should she answer anybody? It was enough that this was the end, and there was no way out. She need not pass any more darkly along the main street of the small town, avoiding every eye. She need not demean herself any more, going into the shops and buying the cheapest food. This was at an end. She thought of nobody, not even of herself. Mindless and persistent, she seemed in a sort of ecstasy to be coming nearer to her fulfilment, her own glorification, approaching her dead mother, who was glorified.

In the afternoon she took a little bag, with shears and sponge and a small scrubbing brush, and went out. It was a grey, wintry day, with saddened, dark green fields and an atmosphere blackened by the smoke of foundries not far off. She went quickly, darkly along the causeway, heeding nobody, through the town to the churchyard.

There she always felt secure, as if no one could see her, although as a matter of fact she was exposed to the stare of every one who passed along under the churchyard wall. Nevertheless, once under the shadow of the great looming church, among the graves, she felt immune from the world, reserved within the thick churchyard wall as in another country.

Carefully she clipped the grass from the grave, and arranged the pinky white, small chrysanthemums in the tin cross. When this was done, she took an empty jar from a neighbouring grave, brought water, and carefully, most scrupulously sponged the marble headstone and the coping-stone.

It gave her sincere satisfaction to do this. She felt in immediate contact with the world of her mother. She took minute pains, went through the park in a state bordering on pure happiness, as if in performing this task she came into a subtle, intimate connection with her mother. For the life she followed here in the world was far less real than the world of death she inherited from her mother.

The doctor's house was just by the church. Fergusson, being a mere hired assistant, was slave to the country-side. As he hurried now to attend to the outpatients in the surgery, glancing across the graveyard with his quick eye, he saw the girl at her task at the grave. She seemed so intent and remote, it was like looking into another world. Some mystical element was touched in him. He slowed down as he walked, watching her as if spell-bound.

She lifted her eyes, feeling him looking. Their eyes met. And each looked away again at once, each feeling, in some way, found out by the other. He lifted his cap and passed on down the road. There remained distinct in his consciousness, like a vision, the memory of her face, lifted from the tombstone in the churchyard, and looking at him with slow, large, portentous eyes. It *was* portentous, her face. It seemed to mesmerize him. There was a heavy power in her eyes which laid hold of his whole being, as if he had drunk some powerful drug. He had been feeling weak and done before. Now the life came back into him, he felt delivered from his own fretted, daily self.

He finished his duties at the surgery as quickly as might be, hastily filling up the bottles of the waiting people with cheap drugs. Then, in perpetual haste, he set off again to visit several cases in another part of his round, before teatime. At all times he preferred to walk if he could, but particularly when he was not well. He fancied the motion restored him.

The afternoon was falling. It was grey, deadened, and wintry, with a slow, moist, heavy coldness sinking in and deadening all the faculties. But why should he think or notice? He hastily climbed the hill and turned across the dark green fields, following the black cinder-track. In the distance, across a shallow dip in the country, the small town was clustered like smouldering ash, a tower, a spire, a heap of low, raw, extinct houses. And on the nearest fringe of the town, sloping into the dip, was Oldmeadow, the Pervins' house. He could see the stables and the outbuildings distinctly, as they lay towards him on the slope. Well, he would not go there many more times! Another resource would be lost to him, another place gone: the only company he cared for in the alien, ugly little town he was losing. Nothing but work, drudgery, constant hastening from dwelling to dwelling among the colliers and the iron-workers. It wore him out, but at the same time he had a craving for it. It was a stimulant to him to be in the homes of the working people, moving, as it were, through the innermost body of their life. His nerves were excited and gratified. He could come so near, into the very lives of the rough, inarticulate, powerfully emotional men and women. He grumbled, he said he hated the hellish hole. But as a matter of fact it excited him, the contact with the rough, strongly-feeling people was a stimulant applied direct to his nerves.

Below Oldmeadow, in the green, shallow, soddened hollow of fields, lay a square, deep pond. Roving across the landscape, the doctor's quick eye detected a figure in black passing through the gate of the field, down towards the pond. He looked again. It would be Mabel Pervin. His mind suddenly became alive and attentive.

Why was she going down there? He pulled up on the path on the slope above, and stood staring. He could just make sure of the small black figure moving in the hollow of the failing day. He seemed to see her in the midst of such obscurity, that he was like a clairvoyant, seeing rather with the mind's eye than with ordinary sight. Yet he could see her positively enough, whilst he kept his eye attentive. He felt, if he looked away from her, in the thick, ugly failing dusk, he would lose her altogether.

He followed her minutely as she moved, direct and intent, like something transmitted rather than stirring in voluntary activity, straight down the field towards the pond. There she stood on the bank for a moment. She never raised her head. Then she waded slowly into the water.

He stood motionless as the small black figure walked slowly and deliberately towards the centre of the pond, very slowly, gradually moving deeper into the motionless water, and still moving forward as the water got up to her breast. Then he could see her no more in the dusk of the dead afternoon.

"There!" he exclaimed. "Would you believe it?"

And he hastened straight down, running over the wet, soddened fields, pushing through the hedges, down into the depression of callous wintry obscurity. It took him several minutes to come to the pond. He stood on the bank, breathing heavily. He could see nothing. His eyes seemed to penetrate the dead water. Yes, perhaps that was the dark shadow of her black clothing beneath the surface of the water.

He slowly ventured into the pond. The bottom was deep, soft clay, he sank in, and the water clasped dead cold round his legs. As he stirred he could smell the cold, rotten clay that fouled up into the water. It was objectionable in his lungs. Still, repelled and yet not heeding, he moved deeper into the pond. The cold water rose over his thighs, over his loins, upon his abdomen. The lower part of his body was all sunk in the hideous cold element. And the bottom was so deeply soft and uncertain, he was afraid of pitching with his mouth underneath. He could not swim, and was afraid.

He crouched a little, spreading his hands under the water and moving them round, trying to feel for her. The dead cold pond swayed upon his chest. He moved again, a little deeper, and again, with his hands underneath, he felt all around under the water. And he touched her clothing. But it evaded his fingers. He made a desperate effort to grasp it.

And so doing he lost his balance and went under, horribly, suffocating in the foul earthy water, struggling madly for a few moments. At last, after what seemed an eternity, he got his footing, rose again into the air and looked around. He gasped, and knew he was in the world. Then he looked at the water. She had risen near him. He grasped her clothing, and drawing her nearer, turned to take his way to land again.

He went very slowly, carefully, absorbed in the slow progress. He rose higher, climbing out of the pond. The water was now only about his legs; he was thankful, full of relief to be out of the clutches of the pond. He lifted her and staggered on to the bank, out of the horror of wet, grey clay.

He laid her down on the bank. She was quite unconscious and running with water. He made the water come from her mouth, he worked to restore her. He did not have to work very long before he could feel the breathing begin again in her; she was breathing naturally. He worked a little longer. He could feel her live beneath his hands; she was coming back. He wiped her face, wrapped her in his overcoat, looked round into the dim, dark grey world, then lifted her and staggered down the bank and across the fields.

It seemed an unthinkably long way, and his burden so heavy he felt he would never get to the house. But at last he was in the stable-yard, and then in the house-yard. He opened the door and went into the house. In the kitchen he laid her down on the hearthrug, and called. The house was empty. But the fire was burning in the grate.

Then again he kneeled to attend to her. She was breathing regularly, her eyes were wide open and as if conscious, but there seemed something missing in her look. She was conscious in herself, but unconscious of her surroundings.

He ran upstairs, took blankets from a bed, and put them before the fire to warm. Then he removed her saturated, earthy-smelling clothing, rubbed her dry with a towel, and wrapped her naked in the blankets. Then he went into the dining-room, to look for spirits. There was a little whisky. He drank a gulp himself, and put some into her mouth.

The effect was instantaneous. She looked full into his face, as if she had been seeing him for some time, and yet had only just become conscious of him.

"Dr. Fergusson?" she said.

"What?" he answered.

He was divesting himself of his coat, intending to find some dry clothing upstairs. He could not bear the smell of the dead, clayey water, and he was mortally afraid for his own health.

"What did I do?" she asked.

"Walked into the pond," he replied. He had begun to shudder like one sick, and could hardly attend to her. Her eyes remained full on him, he seemed to be going dark in his mind, looking back at her helplessly. The shuddering became quieter in him, his life came back to him, dark and unknowing, but strong again.

"Was I out of my mind?" she asked, while her eyes were fixed on him all the time.

"Maybe, for the moment," he replied. He felt quiet, because his strength had come back. The strange fretful strain had left him.

"Am I out of my mind now?" she asked.

"Are you?" he reflected a moment. "No," he answered truthfully, "I don't see that you are." He turned his face aside. He was afraid now, because he felt dazed, and felt dimly that her power was stronger than his, in this issue. And she continued to look at him fixedly all the time. "Can you tell me where I shall find some dry things to put on?" he asked.

"Did you dive into the pond for me?" she asked.

"No," he answered. "I walked in. But I went in overhead as well."

There was silence for a moment. He hesitated. He very much wanted to go upstairs to get into dry clothing. But there was another desire in him. And she seemed to hold him. His will seemed to have gone to sleep, and left him, standing there slack before her. But he felt warm inside himself. He did not shudder at all, though his clothes were sodden on him.

"Why did you?" she asked.

"Because I didn't want you to do such a foolish thing," he said.

"It wasn't foolish," she said, still gazing at him as she lay on the floor, with a sofa cushion under her head. "It was the right thing to do. *I* knew best, then."

"I'll go and shift these wet things," he said. But still he had not the power to move out of her presence, until she sent him. It was as if she had the life of his body in her hands, and he could not extricate himself. Or perhaps he did not want to.

Suddenly she sat up. Then she became aware of her own immediate condition. She felt the blankets about her, she knew her own limbs. For a moment it seemed as if her reason were going. She looked round, with wild eye, as if seeking something. He stood still with fear. She saw her clothing lying scattered.

"Who undressed me?" she asked, her eyes resting full and inevitable on his face.

"I did," he replied, "to bring you round."

For some moments she sat and gazed at him awfully, her lips parted.

"Do you love me, then?" she asked.

He only stood and stared at her, fascinated. His soul seemed to melt.

She shuffled forward on her knees, and put her arms round him, round his legs, as he stood there, pressing her breasts against his knees and thighs, clutching him with strange, convulsive certainty, pressing his thighs against her, drawing him to her face, her throat, as she looked up at him with flaring, humble eyes of transfiguration, triumphant in first possession.

"You love me," she murmured, in strange transport, yearning and triumphant and confident. "You love me. I know you love me, I know."

And she was passionately kissing his knees, through the wet clothing, passionately and indiscriminately kissing his knees, his legs, as if unaware of everything.

He looked down at the tangled wet hair, the wild, bare, animal shoulders. He was amazed, bewildered, and afraid. He had never thought of loving her. He had never wanted to love her. When he rescued her and restored her, he was a doctor, and she was a patient. He had had no single personal thought of her. Nay, this introduction of the personal element was very distasteful to him, a violation of his professional honour. It was horrible to have her there embracing his knees. It was horrible. He revolted from it, violently. And yet—and yet—he had not the power to break away.

She looked at him again, with the same supplication of powerful love, and that same transcendent, frightening light of triumph. In view of the delicate flame which seemed to come from her face like a light, he was powerless. And yet he had never intended to love her. He had never intended. And something stubborn in him could not give way.

"You love me," she repeated, in a murmur of deep, rhapsodic assurance. "You love me."

Her hands were drawing him, drawing him down to her. He was afraid, even a little horrified. For he had, really, no intention of loving her. Yet her hands were drawing him towards her. He put out his hand quickly to steady himself, and grasped her bare shoulder. A flame seemed to burn the hand that grasped her soft shoulder. He had no intention of loving her: his whole will was against his yielding. It was horrible. And yet wonderful was the touch of her shoulders, beautiful the shining of her face. Was she perhaps mad? He had a horror of yielding to her. Yet something in him ached also.

He had been staring away at the door, away from her. But his hand remained on her shoulder. She had gone suddenly very still. He looked down at her. Her eyes were now wide with fear, with doubt, the light was dying from her face, a shadow of terrible greyness was returning. He could not bear the touch of her eyes' question upon him, and the look of death behind the question.

With an inward groan he gave way, and let his heart yield towards her. A sudden gentle smile came on his face. And her eyes, which never left his face, slowly, slowly filled with tears. He watched the strange water rise in her eyes, like some slow fountain coming up. And his heart seemed to burn and melt away in his breast.

He could not bear to look at her any more. He dropped on his knees and caught her head with his arms and pressed her face against his throat. She was very still. His heart, which seemed to have broken, was burning with a kind of agony in his breast. And he felt her slow, hot tears wetting his throat. But he could not move.

He felt the hot tears wet his neck and the hollows of his neck, and he remained motionless, suspended through one of man's eternities. Only now it had become indispensable to him to have her face pressed close to him; he could never let her go again. He could never let her head go away from the close clutch of his arm. He wanted to remain like that for ever, with his heart hurting him in a pain that was also life to him. Without knowing, he was looking down on her damp, soft brown hair.

Then, as it were suddenly, he smelt the horrid stagnant smell of that water. And at the same moment she drew away from him and looked at him. Her eyes were wistful and unfathomable. He was afraid of them, and he fell to kissing her, not knowing what he was doing. He wanted her eyes not to have that terrible, wistful, unfathomable look.

When she turned her face to him again, a faint delicate flush was glowing, and there was again dawning that terrible shining of joy in her eyes, which really terrified him, and yet which he now wanted to see, because he feared the look of doubt still more.

"You love me?" she said, rather faltering.

"Yes." The word cost him a painful effort. Not because it wasn't true. But because it was too newly true, the *saying* seemed to tear open again his newly-torn heart. And he hardly wanted it to be true, even now.

She lifted her face to him, and he bent forward and kissed her on the mouth, gently, with the one kiss that is an eternal pledge. And as he kissed her his heart strained again in his breast. He never intended to love her. But now it was over. He had crossed over the gulf to her, and all that he had left behind had shrivelled and become void.

After the kiss, her eyes again slowly filled with tears. She sat still, away from him, with her face drooped aside, and her hands folded in her lap. The tears fell very slowly. There was complete silence. He too sat there motionless and silent on the hearthrug. The strange pain of his heart that was broken seemed to consume him. That he should love her? That this was love! That he should be ripped open in this way! Him, a doctor! How they would all jeer if they knew! It was agony to him to think they might know.

In the curious naked pain of the thought he looked again to her. She was sitting there drooped into a muse. He saw a tear fall, and his heart flared hot. He saw for the first time that one of her shoulders was quite uncovered, one arm bare, he could see one of her small breasts; dimly, because it had become almost dark in the room.

"Why are you crying?" he asked, in an altered voice.

She looked up at him, and behind her tears the consciousness of her situation for the first time brought a dark look of shame to her eyes.

"I'm not crying, really," she said, watching him, half frightened.

He reached his hand, and softly closed it on her bare arm.

"I love you! I love you!" he said in a soft, low vibrating voice, unlike himself.

She shrank, and dropped her head. The soft, penetrating grip of his hand on her arm distressed her. She looked up at him.

"I want to go," she said. "I want to go and get you some dry things."

"Why?" he said. "I'm all right."

"But I want to go," she said. "And I want you to change your things."

He released her arm, and she wrapped herself in the blanket, looking at him rather frightened. And still she did not rise.

"Kiss me," she said wistfully.

He kissed her, but briefly, half in anger.

Then, after a second, she rose nervously, all mixed up in the blanket. He watched her in her confusion, as she tried to extricate herself and wrap herself up so that she could walk. He watched her relentlessly, as she knew. And as she went, the blanket trailing, and as he saw a glimpse of her feet and her white leg, he tried to remember her as she was when he had wrapped her in the blanket. But then he didn't want to remember, because she had been nothing to him then, and his nature revolted from remembering her as she was when she was nothing to him.

A tumbling, muffled noise from within the dark house startled him. Then he heard her voice:—"There are clothes." He rose and went to the foot of the stairs, and gathered up the garments she had thrown down. Then he came back to the fire, to rub himself down and dress. He grinned at his own appearance when he had finished.

The fire was sinking, so he put on coal. The house was now quite dark, save for the light of a street-lamp that shone in faintly from beyond the holly trees. He lit the gas with matches he found on the mantelpiece. Then he emptied the pockets of his own clothes, and threw all his wet things in a heap into the scullery. After which he gathered up her sodden clothes, gently, and put them in a separate heap on the copper-top in the scullery.

It was six o'clock on the clock. His own watch had stopped. He ought to go back to the surgery. He waited, and still she did not come down. So he went to the foot of the stairs and called:

"I shall have to go."

Almost immediately he heard her coming down. She had on her best dress of black voile, and her hair was tidy, but still damp. She looked at him—and in spite of herself, smiled.

"I don't like you in those clothes," she said.

"Do I look a sight?" he answered.

They were shy of one another.

"I'll make you some tea," she said.

"No, I must go."

"Must you?" And she looked at him again with the wide, strained, doubtful eyes. And again, from the pain of his breast, he knew how he loved her. He went and bent to kiss her, gently, passionately, with his heart's painful kiss.

"And my hair smells so horrible," she murmured in distraction. "And I'm so awful, I'm so awful! Oh, no, I'm too awful." And she broke into bitter, heart-broken sobbing. "You can't want to love me, I'm horrible."

"Don't be silly, don't be silly," he said, trying to comfort her, kissing her, holding her in his arms. "I want you, I want to marry you, we're going to be married, quickly, quickly—tomorrow if I can."

But she only sobbed terribly, and cried:

"I feel awful. I feel awful. I feel I'm horrible to you."

"No, I want you, I want you," was all he answered, blindly, with that terrible intonation which frightened her almost more than her horror lest he should *not* want her.

(1922)

Ezra Pound
(U.S.A., 1885–1972)

Ancient Wisdom, Rather Cosmic

So-shu dreamed,
And having dreamed that he was a bird, a bee, and a butterfly,
He was uncertain why he should try to feel like anything else,

Hence his contentment.

(1916)

In a Station of the Metro

The apparition of these faces in the crowd;
Petals on a wet, black bough.

(1916)

A Pact

I make a pact with you, Walt Whitman—
I have detested you long enough.
I come to you as a grown child
Who has had a pig-headed father;
5   I am old enough now to make friends.
It was you that broke the new wood,
Now is a time for carving.
We have one sap and one root—
Let there be commerce between us.

(1916)

H.D.

[Hilda Doolittle]

(U.S.A., 1886–1961)

Sea Rose

Rose, harsh rose,
marred and with stint of petals,
meagre flower, thin,
sparse of leaf,
5   more precious
than a wet rose
single on a stem—
you are caught in the drift.

Stunted, with small leaf,
10   you are flung on the sand,
you are lifted
in the crisp sand
that drives in the wind.

Can the spice-rose
15   drip such acrid fragrance
hardened in a leaf?

(1916)

Oread

Whirl up, sea—
whirl your pointed pines,
splash your great pines
on our rocks,
5   hurl your green over us,
cover us with your pools of fir.

(1917)

T.S. Eliot

(U.S.A./ENGLAND, 1888–1965)

The Love Song of J. Alfred Prufrock

S'io credesse che mia risposta fosse
A persona che mai tornasse al mondo,
Questa fiamma staria senza piu scosse.
Ma perciocche giammai di questo fondo
Non torno vivo alcun, s'i'odo il vero,
Senza tema d'infamia ti rispondo.

Let us go then, you and I,
When the evening is spread out against the sky
Like a patient etherised upon a table;
Let us go, through certain half-deserted streets,
5   The muttering retreats
Of restless nights in one-night cheap hotels
And sawdust restaurants with oyster-shells:
Streets that follow like a tedious argument
Of insidious intent
10   To lead you to an overwhelming question . . .
Oh, do not ask, "What is it?"
Let us go and make our visit.

In the room the women come and go
Talking of Michelangelo.

15   The yellow fog that rubs its back upon the window-panes,
The yellow smoke that rubs its muzzle on the window-panes
Licked its tongue into the corners of the evening,
Lingered upon the pools that stand in drains,
Let fall upon its back the soot that falls from chimneys,
20   Slipped by the terrace, made a sudden leap,
And seeing that it was a soft October night,
Curled once about the house, and fell asleep.

And indeed there will be time
For the yellow smoke that slides along the street,
25   Rubbing its back upon the window-panes;
There will be time, there will be time
To prepare a face to meet the faces that you meet;
There will be time to murder and create,
And time for all the works and days of hands
30   That lift and drop a question on your plate;

Time for you and time for me,
And time yet for a hundred indecisions,
And for a hundred visions and revisions,
Before the taking of a toast and tea.

35   In the room the women come and go
Talking of Michelangelo.

     And indeed there will be time
To wonder, "Do I dare?" and, "Do I dare?"
Time to turn back and descend the stair,
40   With a bald spot in the middle of my hair—
[They will say: "How his hair is growing thin!"]
My morning coat, my collar mounting firmly to the chin,
My necktie rich and modest, but asserted by a simple pin—
[They will say: "But how his arms and legs are thin!"]
45   Do I dare
Disturb the universe?
In a minute there is time
For decisions and revisions which a minute will reverse.

     For I have known them all already, known them all:—
50   Have known the evenings, mornings, afternoons,
I have measured out my life with coffee spoons;
I know the voices dying with a dying fall
Beneath the music from a farther room.
     So how should I presume?

55   And I have known the eyes already, known them all—
The eyes that fix you in a formulated phrase,
And when I am formulated, sprawling on a pin,
When I am pinned and wriggling on the wall,
Then how should I begin
60   To spit out all the butt-ends of my days and ways?
And how should I presume?
And I have known the arms already, known them all—
Arms that are braceleted and white and bare
[But in the lamplight, downed with light brown hair!]
65   Is it perfume from a dress
That makes me so digress?
Arms that lie along a table, or wrap about a shawl.
     And should I then presume?
     And how should I begin?

          ✿   ✿   ✿   ✿   ✿

70   Shall I say, I have gone at dusk through narrow streets
And watched the smoke that rises from the pipes
Of lonely men in shirt-sleeves, leaning out of windows? . . .

I should have been a pair of ragged claws
Scuttling across the floors of silent seas.

       ✧   ✧   ✧   ✧   ✧

75 And the afternoon, the evening, sleeps so peacefully!
Smoothed by long fingers,
Asleep . . . tired . . . or it malingers,
Stretched on the floor, here beside you and me.
Should I, after tea and cakes and ices,
80 Have the strength to force the moment to its crisis?
But though I have wept and fasted, wept and prayed,
Though I have seen my head [grown slightly bald] brought in upon a platter,
I am no prophet—and here's no great matter;
I have seen the moment of my greatness flicker,
85 And I have seen the eternal Footman hold my coat, and snicker,
And in short, I was afraid.

    And would it have been worth it, after all,
After the cups, the marmalade, the tea,
Among the porcelain, among some talk of you and me,
90 Would it have been worth while,
To have bitten off the matter with a smile,
To have squeezed the universe into a ball
To roll it toward some overwhelming question,
To say: "I am Lazarus, come from the dead,
95 Come back to tell you all, I shall tell you all"—
If one, settling a pillow by her head,
    Should say: "That is not what I meant at all.
    That is not it, at all."

    And would it have been worth it, after all,
100 Would it have been worth while,
After the sunsets and the dooryards and the sprinkled streets,
After the novels, after the teacups, after the skirts that trail along the floor—
And this, and so much more?—
It is impossible to say just what I mean!
105 But as if a magic lantern threw the nerves in patterns on a screen:
Would it have been worth while
If one, settling a pillow or throwing off a shawl,
And turning toward the window, should say:
    "That is not it at all,
110   That is not what I meant, at all."

       ✧   ✧   ✧   ✧   ✧

No! I am not Prince Hamlet, nor was meant to be;
Am an attendant lord, one that will do
To swell a progress, start a scene or two,
Advise the prince; no doubt, an easy tool,
115 Deferential, glad to be of use,
Politic, cautious, and meticulous;
Full of high sentence, but a bit obtuse;
At times, indeed, almost ridiculous—
Almost, at times, the Fool.

120   I grow old . . . I grow old . . .
I shall wear the bottoms of my trousers rolled.

     Shall I part my hair behind? Do I dare to eat a peach?
I shall wear white flannel trousers, and walk upon the beach.
I have heard the mermaids singing, each to each.

125   I do not think that they will sing to me.

     I have seen them riding seaward on the waves
Combing the white hair of the waves blown back
When the wind blows the water white and black.

     We have lingered in the chambers of the sea
130 By sea-girls wreathed with seaweed red and brown
Till human voices wake us, and we drown.

(1915)

The Hollow Men

Mistah Kurtz—he dead.
                   A penny for the Old Guy

I
We are the hollow men
We are the stuffed men
Leaning together
Headpiece filled with straw. Alas!
5 Our dried voices, when
We whisper together
Are quiet and meaningless
As wind in dry grass
Or rats' feet over broken glass
10 In our dry cellar

Shape without form, shade without colour,
Paralysed force, gesture without motion;

    Those who have crossed
With direct eyes, to death's other Kingdom
15 Remember us—if at all—not as lost
Violent souls, but only
As the hollow men
The stuffed men.

            II
Eyes I dare not meet in dreams
20 In death's dream kingdom
These do not appear:
There, the eyes are
Sunlight on a broken column
There, is a tree swinging
25 And voices are
In the wind's singing
More distant and more solemn
Than a fading star.

    Let me be no nearer
30 In death's dream kingdom
Let me also wear
Such deliberate disguises
Rat's coat, crowskin, crossed staves
In a field
35 Behaving as the wind behaves
No nearer—

    Not that final meeting
In the twilight kingdom

            III
This is the dead land
40 This is cactus land
Here the stone images
Are raised, here they receive
The supplication of a dead man's hand
Under the twinkle of a fading star.

45   Is it like this
In death's other kingdom
Waking alone
At the hour when we are
Trembling with tenderness
50 Lips that would kiss
Form prayers to broken stone.

The eyes are not here
There are no eyes here
In this valley of dying stars
55 In this hollow valley
This broken jaw of our lost kingdoms

   In this last of meeting places
We grope together
And avoid speech
60 Gathered on this beach of the tumid river

   Sightless, unless
The eyes reappear
As the perpetual star
Multifoliate rose
65 Of death's twilight kingdom
The hope only
Of empty men.

V

Here we go round the prickly pear
Prickly pear prickly pear
70 *Here we go round the prickly pear*
At five o'clock in the morning.

   Between the idea
And the reality
Between the motion
75 And the act
Falls the Shadow

   For Thine is the Kingdom

   Between the conception
And the creation
80 Between the emotion
And the response
Falls the Shadow

   Life is very long

   Between the desire
85 And the spasm
Between the potency
And the existence
Between the essence
And the descent
90 Falls the Shadow

   For Thine is the Kingdom

        For Thine is
    Life is
    For Thine is the

95 *This is the way the world ends*
    This is the way the world ends
    This is the way the world ends
    Not with a bang but a whimper.
                        (1925)

Journey of the Magi

    'A cold coming we had of it,
    Just the worst time of the year
    For a journey, and such a long journey:
    The ways deep and the weather sharp,
5   The very dead of winter.'
    And the camels galled, sore-footed, refractory,
    Lying down in the melting snow.
    There were times we regretted
    The summer palaces on slopes, the terraces,
10 And the silken girls bringing sherbet.
    Then the camel men cursing and grumbling
    And running away, and wanting their liquor and women,
    And the night-fires going out, and the lack of shelters,
    And the cities hostile and the towns unfriendly
15 And the villages dirty and charging high prices:
    A hard time we had of it.
    At the end we preferred to travel all night,
    Sleeping in snatches,
    With the voices singing in our ears, saying
20 That this was all folly.

        Then at dawn we came down to a temperate valley,
    Wet, below the snow line, smelling of vegetation;
    With a running stream and a water-mill beating the darkness,
    And three trees on the low sky,
25 And an old white horse galloped away in the meadow.
    Then we came to a tavern with vine-leaves over the lintel,
    Six hands at an open door dicing for pieces of silver,
    And feet kicking the empty wine-skins.
    But there was no information, and so we continued
30 And arrived at evening, not a moment too soon
    Finding the place; it was (you may say) satisfactory.

All this was a long time ago, I remember,
And I would do it again, but set down
This set down
35 This: were we led all that way for
Birth or Death? There was a Birth, certainly,
We had evidence and no doubt. I had seen birth and death,
But had thought they were different; this Birth was
Hard and bitter agony for us, like Death, our death.
40 We returned to our places, these Kingdoms,
But no longer at ease here, in the old dispensation,
With an alien people clutching their gods.
I should be glad of another death.

(1927)

Katherine Mansfield

(NEW ZEALAND, 1888–1923)

The Fly

'Y'are very snug in here,' piped old Mr. Woodifield and he peered out of the great, green-leather armchair by his friend the boss's desk as a baby peers out of its pram. His talk was over; it was time for him to be off. But he did not want to go. Since he had retired, since his . . . stroke, the wife and the girls kept him boxed up in the house every day of the week except Tuesday. On Tuesday he was dressed and brushed and allowed to cut back to the City for the day. Though what he did there the wife and girls couldn't imagine. Made a nuisance of himself to his friends, they supposed. . . . Well, perhaps so. All the same, we cling to our last pleasures as the tree clings to its last leaves. So there sat old Woodifield, smoking a cigar and staring almost greedily at the boss, who rolled in his office chair, stout, rosy, five years older than he, and still going strong, still at the helm. It did one good to see him.

Wistfully, admiringly, the old voice added, 'It's snug in here, upon my word!'

'Yes, it's comfortable enough,' agreed the boss, and he flipped the *Financial Times* with a paper-knife. As a matter of fact he was proud of his room; he liked to have it admired, especially by old Woodifield. It gave him a feeling of deep, solid satisfaction to be planted there in the midst of it in full view of that frail old figure in the muffler.

'I've had it done up lately,' he explained, as he had explained for the past—how many?—weeks. 'New carpet,' and he pointed to the bright red carpet with a pattern of large white rings. 'New furniture,' and he nodded towards the massive bookcase and the table with legs like twisted treacle. 'Electric heating!' He waved almost exultantly towards the five transparent, pearly sausages glowing so softly in the tilted copper pan.

But he did not draw old Woodifield's attention to the photograph over the table of a grave-looking boy in uniform standing in one of those spectral photographers' parks with photographers' storm-clouds behind him. It was not new. It had been there for over six years.

'There was something I wanted to tell you,' said old Woodifield, and his eyes grew dim remembering. 'Now what was it? I had it in my mind when I started out this morning.' His hands began to tremble, and patches of red showed above his beard.

Poor old chap, he's on his last pins, thought the boss. And, feeling kindly, he winked at the old man, and said jokingly, 'I tell you what. I've got a little drop of something here that'll do you good before you go out into the cold again. It's beautiful stuff. It wouldn't hurt a child.' He took a key off his watch-chain, unlocked a cupboard below his desk, and drew forth a dark, squat bottle. 'That's the medicine,' said he. 'And the man from whom I got it told me on the strict Q.T. it came from the cellars at Windsor Castle.'

Old Woodifield's mouth fell open at the sight. He couldn't have looked more surprised if the boss had produced a rabbit.

'It's whisky, ain't it?' he piped feebly.

The boss turned the bottle and lovingly showed him the label. Whisky it was.

'D'you know,' said he, peering up at the boss wonderingly, 'they won't let me touch it at home.' And he looked as though he was going to cry.

'Ah, that's where we know a bit more than the ladies,' cried the boss, swooping across for two tumblers that stood on the table with the water-bottle, and pouring a generous finger into each. 'Drink it down. It'll do you good. And don't put any water with it. It's sacrilege to tamper with stuff like this. Ah!' He tossed off his, pulled out his handkerchief, hastily wiped his moustaches, and cocked an eye at old Woodifield, who was rolling his in his chaps.

The old man swallowed, was silent a moment, and then said faintly, 'It's nutty!'

But it warmed him; it crept into his chill old brain—he remembered.

'That was it,' he said, heaving himself out of his chair. 'I thought you'd like to know. The girls were in Belgium last week having a look at poor Reggie's grave, and they happened to come across your boy's. They're quite near each other, it seems.'

Old Woodifield paused, but the boss made no reply. Only a quiver in his eyelids showed that he heard.

'The girls were delighted with the way the place is kept,' piped the old voice. 'Beautifully looked after. Couldn't be better if they were at home. You've not been across, have yer?'

'No, no!' For various reasons the boss had not been across.

'There's miles of it,' quavered old Woodifield, 'and it's all as neat as a garden. Flowers growing on all the graves. Nice broad paths.' It was plain from his voice how much he liked a nice broad path.

The pause came again. Then the old man brightened wonderfully.

'D'you know what the hotel made the girls pay for a pot of jam?' he piped. 'Ten francs! Robbery, I call it. It was a little pot, so Gertrude says, no bigger than a half-crown. And she hadn't taken more than a spoonful when they charged her ten francs. Gertrude brought the pot away with her to teach 'em a lesson. Quite right, too; it's trading on our feelings. They think because we're over there having a look round we're ready to pay anything. That's what it is.' And he turned towards the door.

'Quite right, quite right!' cried the boss, though what was quite right he hadn't the least idea. He came round by his desk, followed the shuffling footsteps to the door, and saw the old fellow out. Woodifield was gone.

For a long moment the boss stayed, staring at nothing, while the grey-haired office messenger, watching him, dodged in and out of his cubby-hole like a dog that expects to be taken for a run. Then: 'I'll see nobody for half an hour, Macey,' said the boss. 'Understand? Nobody at all.'

'Very good, sir.'

The door shut, the firm heavy steps recrossed the bright carpet, the fat body plumped down in the spring chair, and leaning forward, the boss covered his face with his hands. He wanted, he intended, he had arranged to weep. . . .

It had been a terrible shock to him when old Woodifield sprang that remark upon him about the boy's grave. It was exactly as though the earth had opened and he had seen the boy lying there with Woodifield's girls staring down at him. For it was strange. Although over six years had passed away, the boss never thought of the boy except as lying unchanged, unblemished in his uniform, asleep for ever. 'My son!' groaned the boss. But no tears came yet. In the past, in the first months and even years after the boy's death, he had only to say those words to be overcome by such grief that nothing short of a violent fit of weeping could relieve him. Time, he had declared then, he had told everybody, could make no difference. Other men perhaps might recover, might live their loss down, but not he. How was it possible? His boy was an only son. Ever since his birth the boss had worked at building up this business for him; it had no other meaning if it was not for the boy. Life itself had come to have no other meaning. How on earth could he have slaved, denied himself, kept going all those years without the promise for ever before him of the boy's stepping into his shoes and carrying on where he left off?

And that promise had been so near being fulfilled. The boy had been in the office learning the ropes for a year before the war. Every morning they had started off together; they had come back by the same train. And what congratulations he had received as the boy's father! No wonder; he had taken to it marvellously. As to his popularity with the staff, every man jack of them down to old Macey couldn't make enough of the boy. And he wasn't in the least spoilt. No, he was just his bright natural self, with the right word for everybody, with that boyish look and his habit of saying, 'Simply splendid!'"

But all that was over and done with as though it never had been. The day had come when Macey had handed him the telegram that brought the whole place crashing about his head. 'Deeply regret to inform you . . .' And he had left the office a broken man, with his life in ruins.

Six years ago, six years. . . . How quickly time passed! It might have happened yesterday. The boss took his hands from his face; he was puzzled. Something seemed to be wrong with him. He wasn't feeling as he wanted to feel. He decided to get up and have a look at the boy's photograph. But it wasn't a favourite photograph of his; the expression was unnatural. It was cold, even stern-looking. The boy had never looked like that.

At that moment the boss noticed that a fly had fallen into his broad inkpot, and was trying feebly but desperately to clamber out again. Help! help! said those struggling legs. But the sides of the inkpot were wet and slippery; it fell back again and began to swim. The boss took up a pen, picked the fly out of the ink, and shook it on to a piece of blotting-paper. For a fraction of a second it lay still on the dark patch that oozed round it. Then the front legs waved, took hold, and, pulling its small, sodden body up, it began the immense task of cleaning the ink from its wings. Over and under, over and under, went a leg along a wing as the stone goes over and under the scythe. Then there was a pause, while the fly, seeming to stand on the tips of its toes, tried to expand first one wing and then the other. It succeeded at last, and, sitting down, it began, like a minute cat, to clean its face. Now one could imagine that the little front legs rubbed against each other lightly, joyfully. The horrible danger was over; it had escaped; it was ready for life again.

But just then the boss had an idea. He plunged his pen back into the ink, leaned his thick wrist on the blotting-paper, and as the fly tried its wings down came a great heavy blot. What would it make of that? What indeed! The little beggar seemed absolutely cowed, stunned, and afraid to move because of what would happen next. But then, as if painfully, it dragged itself forward. The front legs waved, caught hold, and, more slowly this time, the task began from the beginning.

He's a plucky little devil, thought the boss, and he felt a real admiration for the fly's courage. That was the way to tackle things; that was the right spirit. Never say die; it was only a question of . . . But the fly had again finished its laborious task, and the boss had just time to refill his pen, to shake fair and square on the new-cleaned body yet another dark drop. What about it this time? A painful moment of suspense followed. But behold, the front legs were again waving; the boss felt a rush of relief. He leaned over the fly and said to it tenderly, 'You artful little b . . .' And he actually had the brilliant notion of breathing on it to help the drying process. All the same, there was something timid and weak about its efforts now, and the boss decided that this time should be the last, as he dipped the pen deep into the inkpot.

It was. The last blot fell on the soaked blotting-paper, and the draggled fly lay in it and did not stir. The back legs were stuck to the body; the front legs were not to be seen.

'Come on,' said the boss. 'Look sharp!' And he stirred it with his pen—in vain. Nothing happened or was likely to happen. The fly was dead.

The boss lifted the corpse on the end of the paper-knife and flung it into the waste-paper basket. But such a grinding feeling of wretchedness seized him that he felt positively frightened. He started forward and pressed the bell for Macey.

'Bring me some fresh blotting-paper,' he said sternly, 'and look sharp about it.' And while the old dog padded away he fell to wondering what it was he had been thinking about before. What was it? It was . . . He took out his handkerchief and passed it inside his collar. For the life of him he could not remember.

(1923)

John Crowe Ransom
(U.S.A., 1888–1974)

Bells for John Whiteside's Daughter

There was such speed in her little body,
And such lightness in her footfall,
It is no wonder her brown study
Astonishes us all.

5   Her wars were bruited in our high window.
We looked among orchard trees and beyond
Where she took arms against her shadow,
Or harried unto the pond

The lazy geese, like a snow cloud
10   Dripping their snow on the green grass,
Tricking and stopping, sleepy and proud,
Who cried in goose, Alas,

For the tireless heart within the little
Lady with rod that made them rise
15   From their noon apple-dreams and scuttle
Goose-fashion under the skies!

But now go the bells, and we are ready,
In one house we are sternly stopped
To say we are vexed at her brown study,
20   Lying so primly propped.

(1924)

Wilfred Owen

(ENGLAND, 1893–1918)

Dulce et Decorum Est

Bent double, like old beggars under sacks,
Knock-kneed, coughing like hags, we cursed through sludge,
Till on the haunting flares we turned our backs,
And towards our distant rest began to trudge.
5   Men marched asleep. Many had lost their boots,
But limped on, blood-shod. All went lame, all blind;
Drunk with fatigue; deaf even to the hoots
Of gas-shells dropping softly behind.

Gas! GAS! Quick, boys!—An ecstasy of fumbling,
10   Fitting the clumsy helmets just in time,
But someone still was yelling out and stumbling
And floundering like a man in fire or lime.—
Dim through the misty panes and thick green light,
As under a green sea, I saw him drowning.

15   In all my dreams before my helpless sight
He plunges at me, guttering, choking, drowning.

If in some smothering dreams, you too could pace
Behind the wagon that we flung him in,
And watch the white eyes writhing in his face,
20   His hanging face, like a devil's sick of sin;
If you could hear, at every jolt, the blood
Come gargling from the froth-corrupted lungs,
Obscene as cancer, bitter as the cud
Of vile, incurable sores on innocent tongues,—
25   My friend, you would not tell with such high zest
To children ardent for some desperate glory,
The old Lie: Dulce et decorum est
Pro patria mori.

(1917)

Arms and the Boy

Let the boy try along this bayonet-blade
How cold steel is, and keen with hunger of blood;
Blue with all malice, like a madman's flash;
And thinly drawn with famishing for flesh.

5   Lend him to stroke these blind, blunt bullet-heads
Which long to nuzzle in the hearts of lads,
Or give him cartridges of fine zinc teeth,
Sharp with the sharpness of grief and death.

For his teeth seem for laughing round an apple.
10 There lurk no claws behind his fingers supple;
And God will grow no talons at his heels,
Nor antlers through the thickness of his curls.

                                      (1918)

Strange Meeting

It seemed that out of battle I escaped
Down some profound dull tunnel, long since scooped
Through granites which titanic wars had groined.
Yet also there encumbered sleepers groaned,
5   Too fast in thought or death to be bestirred.
Then, as I probed them, one sprang up, and stared
With piteous recognition in fixed eyes,
Lifting distressful hands as if to bless.
And by his smile, I knew that sullen hall,
10 By his dead smile I knew we stood in Hell.
With a thousand pains that vision's face was grained;
Yet no blood reached there from the upper ground,
And no guns thumped, or down the flues made moan.
"Strange friend," I said, "here is no cause to mourn."
15 "None," said the other, "save the undone years,
The hopelessness. Whatever hope is yours,
Was my life also; I went hunting wild
After the wildest beauty in the world,
Which lies not calm in eyes, or braided hair,
20 But mocks the steady running of the hour,
And if it grieves, grieves richlier than here.
For by my glee might many men have laughed,
And of my weeping something had been left,
Which must die now. I mean the truth untold,
25 The pity of war, the pity war distilled.
Now men will go content with what we spoiled.
Or, discontent, boil bloody, and be spilled.
They will be swift with swiftness of the tigress,
None will break ranks, though nations trek from progress.

30 Courage was mine, and I had mystery,
Wisdom was mine, and I had mastery;
To miss the march of this retreating world
Into vain citadels that are not walled.
Then, when much blood had clogged their chariot-wheels
35 I would go up and wash them from sweet wells,
Even with truths that lie too deep for taint.
I would have poured my spirit without stint
But not through wounds; not on the cess of war.
Foreheads of men have bled where no wounds were.
40 I am the enemy you killed, my friend.
I knew you in this dark; for so you frowned
Yesterday through me as you jabbed and killed.
I parried; but my hands were loath and cold.
Let us sleep now. . . ."

(1918)

E.E. Cummings

(U.S.A., 1894–1962)

Buffalo Bill's

Buffalo Bill's
defunct
   who used to
   ride a watersmooth-silver
5   stallion
and break onetwothreefourfive pigeonsjustlikethat
                       Jesus
he was a handsome man
              and what i want to know is
10 how do you like your blueeyed boy
Mister Death

(1923)

Spring is like a perhaps hand

Spring is like a perhaps hand
(which comes carefully
out of Nowhere)arranging
a window into which people look(while
5 people stare
arranging and changing placing
carefully there a strange
thing and a known thing here)and

changing everything carefully

10   spring is like a perhaps
Hand in a window
(carefully to
and fro moving New and
Old things,while
15   people stare carefully
moving a perhaps
fraction of flower here placing
an inch of air there)and

without breaking anything.

(1925)

"next to of course god america i

"next to of course god america i
love you land of the pilgrims' and so forth oh
say can you see by the dawn's early my
country 'tis of centuries come and go
5   and are no more what of it we should worry
in every language even deafanddumb
thy sons acclaim your glorious name by gorry
by jingo by gee by gosh by gum
why talk of beauty what could be more beau-
10   tiful than these heroic happy dead
who rushed like lions to the roaring slaughter
they did not stop to think they died instead
then shall the voice of liberty be mute?"

He spoke. And drank rapidly a glass of water

(1926)

somewhere i have never travelled, gladly beyond

somewhere i have never travelled, gladly beyond
any experience, your eyes have their silence:
in your most frail gesture are things which enclose me,
or which i cannot touch because they are too near

5   your slightest look easily will unclose me
though i have closed myself as fingers,
you open always petal by petal myself as Spring opens
(touching skilfully, mysteriously) her first rose

or if your wish be to close me, i and
10   my life will shut very beautifully, suddenly,
as when the heart of this flower imagines
the snow carefully everywhere descending;

nothing which we are to perceive in this world equals
the power of your intense fragility: whose texture
15   compels me with the color of its countries,
rendering death and forever with each breathing

(i do not know what it is about you that closes
and opens; only something in me understands
the voice of your eyes is deeper than all roses)
20   nobody, not even the rain, has such small hands

(1931)

anyone lived in a pretty how town

anyone lived in a pretty how town
(with up so floating many bells down)
spring summer autumn winter
he sang his didn't he danced his did.

5   Women and men(both little and small)
cared for anyone not at all
they sowed their isn't they reaped their same
sun moon stars rain

children guessed(but only a few
10   and down they forgot as up they grew
autumn winter spring summer)
that noone loved him more by more

when by now and tree by leaf
she laughed his joy she cried his grief
15   bird by snow and stir by still
anyone's any was all to her

someones married their everyones
laughed their cryings and did their dance
(sleep wake hope and then)they
20   said their revers they slept their dream

stars rain sun moon
(and only the snow can begin to explain
how children are apt to forget to remember
with up so floating many bells down)

25 one day anyone died i guess
    (and noone stooped to kiss his face)
    busy folk buried them side by side
    little by little and was by was

    all by all and deep by deep
30 and more by more they dream their sleep
    noone and anyone earth by april
    wish by spirit and if by yes.

    Women and men(both dong and ding)
    summer autumn winter spring
35 reaped their sowing and went their came
    sun moon stars rain

                            (1940)

W.W.E. Ross
(CANADA, 1894–1966)

Spring Song

One day	in the spring
walking	walking
along	the railroad track
the track	near the town
5 I passed	looking at
a pond	a pond
slimy	of greenish water
greenish	a large pond
From it came	incessantly
10 sounds	sounds
of frogs	frogs piping
piping	frogs in the water
I picked up	I could not see
a stone	any frogs
15 and threw it	I threw a stone
into the pond	into the pond
The stone	it splashed
splashed	a big splash
and the piping	and the sounds
20 of the frogs	the frogs' piping
stopped	

                            (1928)

James Thurber
(U.S.A., 1894–1963)

The Rabbits Who Caused All the Trouble

Within the memory of the youngest child there was a family of rabbits who lived near a pack of wolves. The wolves announced that they did not like the way the rabbits were living. (The wolves were crazy about the way they themselves were living, because it was the only way to live.) One night several wolves were killed in an earthquake and this was blamed on the rabbits, for it is well known that rabbits pound on the ground with their hind legs and cause earthquakes. On another night one of the wolves was killed by a bolt of lightning and this was also blamed on the rabbits, for it is well known that lettuce-eaters cause lightning. The wolves threatened to civilize the rabbits if they didn't behave, and the rabbits decided to run away to a desert island. But the other animals, who lived at a great distance, shamed them, saying, "You must stay where you are and be brave. This is no world for escapists. If the wolves attack you, we will come to your aid, in all probability." So the rabbits continued to live near the wolves and one day there was a terrible flood which drowned a great many wolves. This was blamed on the rabbits, for it is well known that carrot-nibblers with long ears cause floods. The wolves descended on the rabbits, for their own good, and imprisoned them in a dark cave, for their own protection.

When nothing was heard about the rabbits for some weeks, the other animals demanded to know what had happened to them. The wolves replied that the rabbits had been eaten and since they had been eaten the affair was a purely internal matter. But the other animals warned that they might possibly unite against the wolves unless some reason was given for the destruction of the rabbits. So the wolves gave them one. "They were trying to escape," said the wolves, "and, as you know, this is no world for escapists."

Moral: Run, don't walk, to the nearest desert island.

(1940)

Louise Bogan
(U.S.A., 1897–1970)

Women

Women have no wilderness in them,
They are provident instead,
Content in the tight hot cell of their hearts
To eat dusty bread.

5 They do not see cattle cropping red winter grass,
They do not hear
Snow water going down under culverts
Shallow and clear.

They wait, when they should turn to journeys,
10 They stiffen, when they should bend.
They use against themselves that benevolence
To which no man is friend.

They cannot think of so many crops to a field
Or of clean wood cleft by an axe.
15 Their love is an eager meaninglessness
Too tense, or too lax.

They hear in every whisper that speaks to them
A shout and a cry.
As like as not, when they take life over their door-sills
20 They should let it go by.

(1923)

Ernest Hemingway
(U.S.A., 1899–1961)

In Another Country

In the fall the war was always there, but we did not go to it any more. It was cold in the fall in Milan and the dark came very early. Then the electric lights came on, and it was pleasant along the streets looking in the windows. There was much game hanging outside the shops, and the snow powdered in the fur of the foxes and the wind blew their tails. The deer hung stiff and heavy and empty, and small birds blew in the wind and the wind turned their feathers. It was a cold fall and the wind came down from the mountains.

We were all at the hospital every afternoon, and there were different ways of walking across the town through the dusk to the hospital. Two of the ways were alongside canals, but they were long. Always, though, you crossed a bridge across a canal to enter the hospital. There was a choice of three bridges. On one of them a woman sold roasted chestnuts. It was warm, standing in front of her charcoal fire, and the chestnuts were warm afterward in your pocket. The hospital was very old and very beautiful, and you entered through a gate and walked across a courtyard and out a gate on the other side. There were usually funerals starting from the courtyard. Beyond the old hospital were the new brick pavilions, and there we met every afternoon and were all very polite and interested in what was the matter, and sat in the machines that were to make so much difference.

The doctor came up to the machine where I was sitting and said: "What did you like best to do before the war? Did you practise a sport?"

I said: "Yes, football."

"Good," he said. "You will be able to play football again better than ever."

My knee did not bend and the leg dropped straight from the knee to the ankle without a calf, and the machine was to bend the knee and make it move as in riding a tricycle. But it did not bend yet, and instead the machine lurched when it came to the bending part. The doctor said: "That will all pass. You are a fortunate young man. You will play football again like a champion."

In the next machine was a major who had a little hand like a baby's. He winked at me when the doctor examined his hand, which was between two leather straps that bounced up and down and flapped the stiff fingers, and said: "And will I too play football, captain-doctor?" He had been a very great fencer, and before the war the greatest fencer in Italy.

The doctor went to his office in a back room and brought a photograph which showed a hand that had been withered almost as small as the major's, before it had taken a machine course, and after was a little larger. The major held the photograph with his good hand and looked at it very carefully. "A wound?" he asked.

"An industrial accident," the doctor said.

"Very interesting, very interesting," the major said, and handed it back to the doctor.

"You have confidence?"

"No," said the major.

There were three boys who came each day who were about the same age I was. They were all three from Milan, and one of them was to be a lawyer, and one was to be a painter, and one had intended to be a soldier, and after we were finished with the machines, sometimes we walked back together to the Café Cova, which was next door to the Scala. We walked the short way through the communist quarter because we were four together. The people hated us because we were officers, and from a wine-shop some one called out, "A basso gli ufficiali!" as we passed. Another boy who walked with us sometimes and made us five wore a black silk handkerchief across his face because he had no nose then and his face was to be rebuilt. He had gone out to the front from the military academy and been wounded within an hour after he had gone into the front line for the first time. They rebuilt his face, but he came from a very old family and they could never get the nose exactly right. He went to South America and worked in a bank. But this was a long time ago, and then we did not any of us know how it was going to be afterward. We only knew then that there was always the war, but that we were not going to it any more.

We all had the same medals, except the boy with the black silk bandage across his face, and he had not been at the front long enough to get any medals. The tall boy with a very pale face who was to be a lawyer had been a lieutenant of Arditi and had three medals of the sort we each had only one of. He had lived a very long time with death and was a little detached. We were all a little detached, and there was nothing that held us together except that we met every afternoon at the hospital. Although, as we walked to the Cova through the tough part of town, walking in the dark, with light and singing out of the wine-shops, and sometimes having to walk into the street when the men and women would crowd together on the sidewalk so that we would have had to jostle them to get by, we felt held together by there being something that had happened that they, the people who disliked us, did not understand.

We ourselves all understood the Cova, where it was rich and warm and not too brightly lighted, and noisy and smoky at certain hours, and there were always girls at the tables and the illustrated papers on a rack on the wall. The girls at the Cova were very patriotic, and I found that the most patriotic people in Italy were the café girls—and I believe they are still patriotic.

The boys at first were very polite about my medals and asked me what I had done to get them. I showed them the papers, which were written in very beautiful language and full of *fratellanza* and *abnegazione*, but which really said, with the adjectives removed, that I had been given the medals because I was an American. After that their manner changed a little toward me, although I was their friend against outsiders. I was a friend, but I was never really one of them after they had read the citations, because it had been different with them and they had done very different things to get their medals. I had been wounded, it was true; but we all knew that being wounded, after all, was really an accident. I was never ashamed of the ribbons, though, and sometimes, after the cocktail hour, I would imagine myself having done all the things they had done to get their medals; but walking home at night through the empty streets with the cold wind and all the shops closed, trying to keep near the street lights, I knew that I would never have done such things, and I was very much afraid to die, and often lay in bed at night by myself, afraid to die and wondering how I would be when I went back to the front again.

The three with the medals were like hunting-hawks; and I was not a hawk, although I might seem a hawk to those who had never hunted; they, the three, knew better and so we drifted apart. But I stayed good friends with the boy who had been wounded his first day at the front, because he would never know now how he would have turned out; so he could never be accepted either, and I liked him because I thought perhaps he would not have turned out to be a hawk either.

The major, who had been the great fencer, did not believe in bravery, and spent much time while we sat in the machines correcting my grammar. He had complimented me on how I spoke Italian, and we talked together very easily. One day I had said that Italian seemed such an easy language to me that I could not take a great interest in it; everything was so easy to say. "Ah, yes," the major said. "Why, then, do you not take up the use of grammar?" So we took up the use of grammar, and soon Italian was such a difficult language that I was afraid to talk to him until I had the grammar straight in my mind.

The major came very regularly to the hospital. I do not think he ever missed a day, although I am sure he did not believe in the machines. There was a time when none of us believed in the machines, and one day the major said it was all nonsense. The machines were new then and it was we who were to prove them. It was an idiotic idea, he said, "a theory, like another." I had not learned my grammar, and he said I was a stupid impossible disgrace, and he was a fool to have bothered with me. He was a small man and he sat straight up in his chair with his right hand thrust into the machine and looked straight ahead at the wall while the straps thumped up and down with his fingers in them.

"What will you do when the war is over if it is over?" he asked me. "Speak grammatically!"

"I will go to the States."

"Are you married?"

"No, but I hope to be."

"The more of a fool you are," he said. He seemed very angry. "A man must not marry."

"Why, Signor Maggiore?"

"Don't call me 'Signor Maggiore.'"

"Why must not a man marry?"

"He cannot marry. He cannot marry," he said angrily. "If he is to lose everything, he should not place himself in a position to lose that. He should not place himself in a position to lose. He should find things he cannot lose."

He spoke very angrily and bitterly, and looked straight ahead while he talked.

"But why should he necessarily lose it?"

"He'll lose it," the major said. He was looking at the wall. Then he looked down at the machine and jerked his little hand out from between the straps and slapped it hard against his thigh. "He'll lose it," he almost shouted. "Don't argue with me!" Then he called to the attendant who ran the machines. "Come and turn this damned thing off."

He went back into the other room for the light treatment and the massage. Then I heard him ask the doctor if he might use his telephone and he shut the door. When he came back into the room, I was sitting in another machine. He was wearing his cape and had his cap on, and he came directly toward my machine and put his arm on my shoulder.

"I am so sorry," he said, and patted me on the shoulder with his good hand. "I would not be rude. My wife has just died. You must forgive me."

"Oh—" I said, feeling sick for him. "I am *so* sorry."

He stood there biting his lower lip. "It is very difficult," he said. "I cannot resign myself."

He looked straight past me and out through the window. Then he began to cry. "I am utterly unable to resign myself," he said and choked. And then crying, his head up looking at nothing, carrying himself straight and soldierly, with tears on both his cheeks and biting his lips, he walked past the machines and out the door.

The doctor told me that the major's wife, who was very young and whom he had not married until he was definitely invalided out of the war, had died of pneumonia. She had been sick only a few days. No one expected her to die. The major did not come to the hospital for three days. Then he came at the usual hour, wearing a black band on the sleeve of his uniform. When he came back, there were large framed photographs around the wall, of all sorts of wounds before and after they had been cured by the machines. In front of the machine the major used were three photographs of hands like his that were completely restored. I do not know where the doctor got them. I always understood we were the first to use the machines. The photographs did not make much difference to the major because he only looked out of the window.

(1926)

F.R. Scott
(CANADA, 1899–1985)

Laurentian Shield

Hidden in wonder and snow, or sudden with summer,
This land stares at the sun in a huge silence
Endlessly repeating something we cannot hear.
Inarticulate, arctic,
5 Not written on by history, empty as paper,
It leans away from the world with songs in its lakes
Older than love, and lost in the miles.

This waiting is wanting.
It will choose its language
10 When it has chosen its technic,
A tongue to shape the vowels of its productivity.

A language of flesh and of roses.

Now there are pre-words,
Cabin syllables,
15 Nouns of settlement
Slowly forming, with steel syntax,
The long sentence of its exploitation.

The first cry was the hunter, hungry for fur,
And the digger for gold, nomad, no-man, a particle;
20 Then the bold commands of monopoly, big with machines,
Carving its kingdoms out of the public wealth;
And now the drone of the plane, scouting the ice,
Fills all the emptiness with neighbourhood
And links our future over the vanished pole.

25 But a deeper note is sounding, heard in the mines,
The scattered camps and the mills, a language of life,
And what will be written in the full culture of occupation
Will come, presently, tomorrow,
From millions whose hands can turn this rock into children.

(1945)

Bonne Entente

The advantages of living with two cultures
Strike one at every turn,
Especially when one finds a notice in an office building:
'This elevator will not run on Ascension Day';
5 Or reads in the *Montreal Star*:
'Tomorrow being the Feast of the Immaculate Conception,
There will be no collection of garbage in the city';
Or sees on the restaurant menu the bilingual dish:

DEEP APPLE PIE
10 TARTE AUX POMMES PROFONDES

(1953)

Langston Hughes

(U.S.A. 1902–1967)

Theme for English B

The instructor said,

> *Go home and write*
> *a page tonight.*
> *And let that page come out of you—*
> *Then, it will be true.*

5

I wonder if it's that simple?
I am twenty-two, colored, born in Winston-Salem.
I went to school there, then Durham, then here
to this college on the hill above Harlem.

10 I am the only colored student in my class.
The steps from the hill lead down into Harlem,
through a park, then I cross St. Nicholas,
Eighth Avenue, Seventh, and I come to the Y,
the Harlem Branch Y, where I take the elevator

15 up to my room, sit down, and write this page:

It's not easy to know what is true for you or me
at twenty-two, my age. But I guess I'm what
I feel and see and hear, Harlem, I hear you:
hear you, hear me—we two—you, me, talk on this page.

20 (I hear New York, too.) Me—who?

Well, I like to eat, sleep, drink, and be in love.
I like to work, read, learn, and understand life.
I like a pipe for a Christmas present,
or records—Bessie, bop, or Bach.

25 I guess being colored doesn't make me *not* like
the same things other folks like who are other races.
So will my page be colored that I write?

Being me, it will not be white.
But it will be
30   a part of you, instructor.
You are white—
yet a part of me, as I am a part of you.
That's American.
Sometimes perhaps you don't want to be a part of me.
35   Nor do I often want to be a part of you.
But we are, that's true!
As I learn from you,
I guess you learn from me—
although you're older—and white—
40   and somewhat more free.

This is my page for English B.

(1959)

George Orwell
(ENGLAND, 1903–1950)

Politics and the English Language

Most people who bother with the matter at all would admit that the English language is in a bad way, but it is generally assumed that we cannot by conscious action do anything about it. Our civilization is decadent and our language—so the argument runs—must inevitably share in the general collapse. It follows that any struggle against the abuse of language is a sentimental archaism, like preferring candles to electric light or hansom cabs to aeroplanes. Underneath this lies the half-conscious belief that language is a natural growth and not an instrument which we shape for our own purposes.

Now, it is clear that the decline of a language must ultimately have political and economic causes: it is not due simply to the bad influence of this or that individual writer. But an effect can become a cause, reinforcing the original cause and producing the same effect in an intensified form, and so on indefinitely. A man may take to drink because he feels himself to be a failure, and then fail all the more completely because he drinks. It is rather the same thing that is happening to the English language. It becomes ugly and inaccurate because our thoughts are foolish, but the slovenliness of our language makes it easier for us to have foolish thoughts. The point is that the process is reversible. Modern English, especially written English, is full of bad habits which spread by imitation and which can be avoided if one is willing to take the necessary trouble. If one gets rid of these habits one can think more clearly, and to think clearly is a necessary first step towards political regeneration: so that the fight against bad English is not frivolous and is not the exclusive concern of professional writers. I will come back to this presently, and I hope that by that time the meaning of what I have said here will have become clearer. Meanwhile, here are five specimens of the English language as it is now habitually written.

These five passages have not been picked out because they are especially bad—I could have quoted far worse if I had chosen—but because they illustrate various of the mental vices from which we now suffer. They are a little below the average, but are fairly representative samples. I number them so that I can refer back to them when necessary:

(1) I am not, indeed, sure whether it is not true to say that the Milton who once seemed not unlike a seventeenth-century Shelley had not become, out of an experience ever more bitter in each year, more alien [sic] to the founder of that Jesuit sect which nothing could induce him to tolerate.

Professor Harold Laski (Essay in Freedom of Expression)

(2) Above all, we cannot play ducks and drakes with a native battery of idioms which prescribes such egregious collocations of vocables as the Basic *put up with* for *tolerate* or *put at a loss* for *bewilder*.

Professor Lancelot Hogben (Interglossa)

(3) On the one side we have the free personality: by definition it is not neurotic, for it has neither conflict nor dream. Its desires, such as they are, are transparent, for they are just what institutional approval keeps in the forefront of consciousness; another institutional pattern would alter their number and intensity; there is little in them that is natural, irreducible, or culturally dangerous. But *on the other side*, the social bond itself is nothing but the mutual reflection of these self-secure integrities. Recall the definition of love. Is not this the very picture of a small academic? Where is there a place in this hall of mirrors for either personality or fraternity?

Essay on psychology in Politics (New York)

(4) All the 'best people' from the gentlemen's clubs, and all the frantic fascist captains, united in common hatred of Socialism and bestial horror of the rising tide of the mass revolutionary movement, have turned to acts of provocation, to foul incendiarism, to medieval legends of poisoned wells, to legalize their own destruction of proletarian organizations, and rouse the agitated petty-bourgeoisie to chauvinistic fervour on behalf of the fight against the revolutionary way out of the crisis.

Communist pamphlet

(5) If a new spirit *is* to be infused into this old country, there is one thorny and contentious reform which must be tackled, and that is the humanization and galvanization of the B.B.C. Timidity here will bespeak canker and atrophy of the soul. The heart of Britain may be sound and of strong beat, for instance, but the British lion's roar at present is like that of Bottom in Shakespeare's *Midsummer Night's Dream*—as gentle as any sucking dove. A virile new Britain cannot continue indefinitely to be traduced in the eyes or rather ears, of the world by the effete languors of Langham Place, brazenly masquerading as 'standard English'. When the Voice of Britain is heard at nine o'clock, better far and infinitely less ludicrous to hear aitches honestly dropped than the present priggish, inflated, inhibited, school-ma'amish arch braying of blameless bashful mewing maidens!

Letter in Tribune

Each of these passages has faults of its own, but, quite apart from avoidable ugliness, two qualities are common to all of them. The first is staleness of imagery: the other is lack of precision. The writer either has a meaning and cannot express it, or he inadvertently says something else, or he is almost indifferent as to whether his words mean anything or not. This mixture of vagueness and sheer incompetence is the most marked characteristic of modern English prose, and especially of any kind of political writing. As soon as certain topics are raised, the concrete melts into the abstract and no one seems able to think of turns of speech that are not hackneyed: prose consists less and less of *words* chosen for the sake of their meaning, and more and more of *phrases* tacked together like the sections of a prefabricated hen-house. I list below, with notes and examples, various of the tricks by means of which the work of prose-construction is habitually dodged:

DYING METAPHORS. A newly invented metaphor assists thought by evoking a visual image, while on the other hand a metaphor which is technically 'dead' (e.g. *iron resolution*) has in effect reverted to being an ordinary word and can generally be used without loss of vividness. But in between these two classes there is a huge dump of worn-out metaphors which have lost all evocative power and are merely used because they save people the trouble of inventing phrases for themselves. Examples are: *Ring the changes on, take up the cudgels for, toe the line, ride roughshod over, stand shoulder to shoulder with, play into the hands of, no axe to grind, grist to the mill, fishing in troubled waters, on the order of the day, Achilles' heel, swan song, hotbed.* Many of these are used without knowledge of their meaning (what is a 'rift', for instance?), and incompatible metaphors are frequently mixed, a sure sign that the writer is not interested in what he is saying. Some metaphors now current have been twisted out of their original meaning without those who use them even being aware of the fact. For example, *toe the line* is sometimes written *tow the line*. Another example is *the hammer and the anvil*, now always used with the implication that the anvil gets the worst of it. In real life it is always the anvil that breaks the hammer, never the other way about: a writer who stopped to think what he was saying would be aware of this, and would avoid perverting the original phrase.

OPERATORS OR VERBAL FALSE LIMBS. These save the trouble of picking out appropriate verbs and nouns, and at the same time pad each sentence with extra syllables which give it an appearance of symmetry. Characteristic phrases are: *render inoperative, militate against, make contact with, be subjected to, give rise to, give grounds for, have the effect of, play a leading part (role) in, make itself felt, take effect, exhibit a tendency to, serve the purpose of, etc., etc.* The keynote is the elimination of simple verbs. Instead of being a single word, such as *break, stop, spoil, mend, kill*, a verb becomes a *phrase*, made up of a noun or adjective tacked on to some general-purposes verb such as *prove, serve, form, play, render*. In addition, the passive voice is wherever possible used in preference to the active, and noun constructions are used instead of gerunds (*by examination of* instead of *by examining*). The range of verbs is further cut down by means of the *-ize* and *de-* formations, and the banal statements are given an appearance of profundity by means of the *not un-* formation. Simple conjunctions and prepositions are replaced by such phrases as *with respect to, having regard to, the fact that, by dint of, in view of, in the interests of, on the hypothesis that*; and the ends of sentences are saved from anticlimax by such resounding common-places as *greatly to be desired, cannot be left out of account, a development to be expected in the near future, deserving of serious consideration, brought to a satisfactory conclusion*, and so on and so forth.

PRETENTIOUS DICTION. Words like *phenomenon, element, individual* (as noun), *objective, categorical, effective, virtual, basic, primary, promote, constitute, exhibit, exploit, utilize, eliminate, liquidate*, are used to dress up simple statement and give an air of scientific impartiality to biased judgements. Adjectives like *epoch-making, epic, historic, unforgettable, triumphant, age-old, inevitable, inexorable, veritable*, are used to dignify the sordid processes of international politics, while writing that aims at glorifying war usually takes on an archaic colour, its characteristic words being: *realm, throne, chariot, mailed fist, trident, sword, shield, buckler, banner, jackboot, clarion.* Foreign words and expressions such as *cul de sac, ancien régime, deus ex machina, mutatis mutandis, status quo, gleichschaltung, weltanschauung,* are used to give an air of culture and elegance. Except for the useful abbreviations *i.e., e.g.,* and *etc.,* there is no real need for any of the hundreds of foreign phrases now current in English. Bad writers, and especially scientific, political and sociological writers, are nearly always haunted by the notion that Latin or Greek words are grander than Saxon ones, and unnecessary words like *expedite, ameliorate, predict, extraneous, deracinated, clandestine, subaqueous* and hundreds of others constantly gain ground from their Anglo-Saxon opposite numbers.[1] The jargon peculiar to Marxist writing (*hyena, hangman, cannibal, petty bourgeois, these gentry, lacquey, flunkey, mad dog, White Guard,* etc.) consists largely of words and phrases translated from Russian, German or French; but the normal way of coining a new word is to use a Latin or Greek root with the appropriate affix and, where necessary, the *-ize* formation. It is often easier to make up words of this kind (*deregionalize, impermissible, extramarital, non-fragmentatory* and so forth) than to think up the English words that will cover one's meaning. The result, in general, is an increase in slovenliness and vagueness.

MEANINGLESS WORDS. In certain kinds of writing, particularly in art criticism and literary criticism, it is normal to come across long passages which are almost completely lacking in meaning.[2] Words like *romantic, plastic values, human, dead, sentimental, natural vitality,* as used in art criticism, are strictly meaningless, in the sense that they not only do not point to any discoverable object, but are hardly ever expected to do so by the reader. When one critic writes, 'The outstanding feature of Mr X's work is its living quality', while another writes, 'The immediately striking thing about Mr X's work is its peculiar deadness', the reader accepts this as a simple difference of opinion. If words like *black* and *white* were involved, instead of the jargon words *dead* and *living*, he would see at once that language was being used in an improper way. Many political words are similarly abused. The word *Fascism* has now no meaning except in so far as it signifies 'something not desirable'. The words *democracy, socialism, freedom, patriotic, realistic, justice,* have each of them several different meanings which cannot be reconciled with one another. In the case of a word like *democracy*, not only is there no agreed definition but the attempt to make one is resisted from all sides. It is almost universally felt that when we call a country democratic we are praising it: consequently the defenders of every kind of régime claim that it is a democracy, and fear that they might have to stop using the word if it were tied down to any one meaning. Words of this kind are often used in a consciously dishonest way. That is, the person who uses them has his own private definition, but allows his hearer to think he means something quite different. Statements like *Marshal Pétain was a true patriot, The Soviet Press is the freest in the world, The Catholic Church is opposed to persecution,* are almost always

---

[1] An interesting illustration of this is the way in which the English flower names which were in use till very recently are being ousted by Greek ones, *snapdragon* becoming *antirrhinum, forget-me-not* becoming *myosotis,* etc. It is hard to see any practical reason for this change of fashion: it is probably due to an instinctive turning-away from the more homely word and a vague feeling that the Greek word is scientific.

[2] Example: 'Comfort's catholicity of perception and image, strangely Whitmanesque in range, almost the exact opposite in aesthetic compulsion, continues to evoke that trembling atmospheric accumulative hinting at a cruel, an inexorably serene timelessness . . . Wrey Gardiner scores by aiming at simple bull's-eyes with precision. Only they are not so simple, and through this contented sadness runs more than the surface bitter-sweet of resignation.' (*Poetry Quarterly.*)

made with intent to deceive. Other words used in variable meanings, in most cases more or less dishonestly, are: *class, totalitarian, science, progressive, reactionary, bourgeois, equality*.

Now that I have made this catalogue of swindles and perversions, let me give another example of the kind of writing that they lead to. This time it must of its nature be an imaginary one. I am going to translate a passage of good English into modern English of the worst sort. Here is a well-known verse from *Ecclesiastes*:

> I returned and saw under the sun, that the race is not to the swift, nor the battle to the strong, neither yet bread to the wise, nor yet riches to men of understanding, nor yet favour to men of skill; but time and chance happeneth to them all.

Here it is in modern English:

> Objective consideration of contemporary phenomena compels the conclusion that success or failure in competitive activities exhibits no tendency to be commensurate with innate capacity, but that a considerable element of the unpredictable must invariably be taken into account.

This is a parody, but not a very gross one. Exhibit (3), above, for instance, contains several patches of the same kind of English. It will be seen that I have not made a full translation. The beginning and ending of the sentence follow the original meaning fairly closely, but in the middle the concrete illustrations—race, battle, bread—dissolve into the vague phrase 'success or failure in competitive activities'. This had to be so, because no modern writer of the kind I am discussing—no one capable of using phrases like 'objective consideration of contemporary phenomena'—would ever tabulate his thoughts in that precise and detailed way. The whole tendency of modern prose is away from concreteness. Now analyse these two sentences a little more closely. The first contains forty-nine words but only sixty syllables, and all its words are those of everyday life. The second contains thirty-eight words of ninety syllables: eighteen of its words are from Latin roots, and one from Greek. The first sentence contains six vivid images, and only one phrase ('time and chance') that could be called vague. The second contains not a single fresh, arresting phrase, and in spite of its ninety syllables it gives only a shortened version of the meaning contained in the first. Yet without a doubt it is the second kind of sentence that is gaining ground in modern English. I do not want to exaggerate. This kind of writing is not yet universal, and outcrops of simplicity will occur here and there in the worst-written page. Still, if you or I were told to write a few lines on the uncertainty of human fortunes, we should probably come much nearer to my imaginary sentence than to the one from *Ecclesiastes*.

As I have tried to show, modern writing at its worst does not consist in picking out words for the sake of their meaning and inventing images in order to make the meaning clearer. It consists in gumming together long strips of words which have already been set in order by someone else, and making the results presentable by sheer humbug. The attraction of this way of writing is that it is easy. It is easier—even quicker, once you have the habit—to say *In my opinion it is a not unjustifiable assumption that* than to say *I think*. If you use ready-made phrases, you not only don't have to hunt about for words; you also don't have to bother with the rhythms of your sentences, since these phrases are generally so arranged as to be more or less euphonious. When you are composing in a hurry—when you are dictating to a stenographer, for instance, or making a public speech—it is natural to fall into a pretentious, Latinized style. Tags like *a consideration which we should do well to bear in mind* or *a conclusion to which all of us would readily assent* will save many a sentence from coming down with a bump. By using stale metaphors, similes and idioms, you save much mental effort, at the cost of leaving your meaning vague, not only for your reader but for yourself. This is the significance of mixed metaphors. The sole aim of a metaphor is to call up a visual image. When these images clash—as in *The Fascist octopus has sung its swan song, the jackboot is thrown into the melting pot*—it can be taken as certain that the writer is not seeing a mental image of the objects he is naming; in other words he is not really thinking. Look again at the examples I gave at the beginning of this essay. Professor Laski (1) uses five negatives in fifty-three words. One of these is superfluous, making nonsense of the whole passage, and in addition there is the slip *alien* for akin, making further nonsense, and several avoidable pieces of clumsiness which increase the general vagueness. Professor Hogben (2) plays ducks and drakes with a battery which is able to write prescriptions, and, while disapproving of the everyday phrase *put up with*, is unwilling to look *egregious* up in the dictionary and see what it means. (3), if one takes an uncharitable attitude towards it, is simply meaningless: probably one could work out its intended meaning by reading the whole of the article in which it occurs. In (4), the writer knows more or less what he wants to say, but an accumulation of stale phrases chokes him like tea leaves blocking a sink. In (5), words and meaning have almost parted company. People who write in this manner usually have a general emotional meaning—they dislike one thing and want to express solidarity with another—but they are not interested in the detail of what they are saying. A scrupulous writer, in every sentence that he writes, will ask himself at least four questions, thus: What am I trying to say? What words will express it? What image or idiom will make it clearer? Is this image fresh enough to have an effect? And he will probably ask himself two more: Could I put it more shortly? Have I said anything that is avoidably ugly? But you are not obliged to go to all this trouble. You can shirk it by simply throwing your mind open and letting the ready-made phrases come crowding in. They will construct your sentences for you—even think your thoughts for you, to a certain extent—and at need they will perform the important service of partially concealing your meaning even from yourself. It is at this point that the special connection between politics and the debasement of language becomes clear.

In our time it is broadly true that political writing is bad writing. Where it is not true, it will generally be found that the writer is some kind of rebel, expressing his private opinions and not a 'party line'. Orthodoxy, of whatever colour, seems to demand a lifeless, imitative style. The political dialects to be found in pamphlets, leading articles, manifestos, White Papers and the speeches of undersecretaries do, of course, vary from party to party, but they are all alike in that one almost never finds in them a fresh, vivid, home-made turn of speech. When one watches some tired hack on the platform mechanically repeating the familiar phrases—*bestial atrocities, iron heel, bloodstained tyranny, free peoples of the world, stand shoulder to shoulder*—one often has a curious feeling that one is not watching a live human being but some kind of dummy: a feeling which suddenly becomes stronger at moments when the light catches the speaker's spectacles and turns them into blank discs which seem to have no eyes behind them. And this is not altogether fanciful. A speaker who uses that kind of phraseology has gone some distance towards turning himself into a machine. The appropriate noises are coming out of his larynx, but his brain is not involved as it would be if he were choosing his words for himself. If the speech he is making is one that he is accustomed to make over and over again, he may be almost unconscious of what he is saying, as one is when one utters the responses in church. And this reduced state of consciousness, if not indispensable, is at any rate favourable to political conformity.

In our time, political speech and writing are largely the defence of the indefensible. Things like the continuance of British rule in India, the Russian purges and deportations, the dropping of the atom bombs on Japan, can indeed be defended, but only by arguments which are too brutal for most people to face, and which do not square with the professed aims of political parties. Thus political language has to consist largely of euphemism, question-begging and sheer cloudy vagueness. Defenceless villages are bombarded from the air, the inhabitants driven out into the countryside, the cattle machine-gunned, the huts set on fire with incendiary bullets: this is called *pacification*. Millions of peasants are robbed of their farms and sent trudging along the roads with no more than they can carry: this is called *transfer of population* or *rectification of frontiers*. People are imprisoned for years without trial, or shot in the back of the neck or sent to die of scurvy in Arctic lumber camps: this is called *elimination of unreliable elements*. Such phraseology is needed if one wants to name things without calling up mental pictures of them. Consider for instance some comfortable English professor defending Russian totalitarianism. He cannot say outright, 'I believe in killing off your opponents when you can get good results by doing so'. Probably, therefore, he will say something like this:

'While freely conceding that the Soviet régime exhibits certain features which the humanitarian may be inclined to deplore, we must, I think, agree that a certain curtailment of the right to political opposition is an unavoidable concomitant of transitional periods, and that the rigours which the Russian people have been called upon to undergo have been amply justified in the sphere of concrete achievement.'

The inflated style is itself a kind of euphemism. A mass of Latin words falls upon the facts like soft snow, blurring the outlines and covering up all the details. The great enemy of clear language is insincerity. When there is a gap between one's real and one's declared aims, one turns as it were instinctively to long words and exhausted idioms, like a cuttlefish squirting out ink. In our age there is no such thing as 'keeping out of politics'. All issues are political issues, and politics itself is a mass of lies, evasions, folly, hatred and schizophrenia. When the general atmosphere is bad, language must suffer. I should expect to find—this is a guess which I have not sufficient knowledge to verify—that the German, Russian and Italian languages have all deteriorated in the last ten or fifteen years, as a result of dictatorship.

But if thought corrupts language, language can also corrupt thought. A bad usage can spread by tradition and imitation, even among people who should and do know better. The debased language that I have been discussing is in some ways very convenient. Phrases like *a not unjustifiable assumption, leaves much to be desired, would serve no good purpose, a consideration which we should do well to bear in mind*, are a continuous temptation, a packet of aspirins always at one's elbow. Look back through this essay, and for certain you will find that I have again and again committed the very faults I am protesting against. By this morning's post I have received a pamphlet dealing with conditions in Germany. The author tells me that he 'felt impelled' to write it. I open it at random, and here is almost the first sentence that I see: '(The Allies) have an opportunity not only of achieving a radical transformation of Germany's social and political structure in such a way as to avoid a nationalistic reaction in Germany itself, but at the same time of laying the foundations of a co-operative and unified Europe.' You see, he 'feels impelled' to write—feels, presumably, that he has something new to say—and yet his words, like cavalry horses answering the bugle, group themselves automatically into the familiar dreary pattern. This invasion of one's mind by ready-made phrases (*lay the foundations, achieve a radical transformation*) can only be prevented if one is constantly on guard against them, and every such phrase anaesthetizes a portion of one's brain.

I said earlier that the decadence of our language is probably curable. Those who deny this would argue, if they produced an argument at all, that language merely reflects existing social conditions, and that we cannot influence its development by any direct tinkering with words and constructions. So far as the general tone or spirit of a language goes, this may be true, but it is not true in detail. Silly words and expressions have often disappeared, not through any evolutionary process but owing to the conscious action of a minority. Two recent examples were *explore every avenue* and *leave no stone unturned*, which were killed by the jeers of a few journalists. There is a long list of flyblown metaphors which could similarly be got rid of if enough people would interest themselves in the job; and it should also be possible to laugh the *not un-* formation out of existence,[3] to reduce the amount of Latin and Greek in the average sentence, to drive out foreign phrases and strayed scientific words, and, in general, to make pretentiousness unfashionable. But all these are minor points. The defence of the English language implies more than this, and perhaps it is best to start by saying what it *does not* imply.

To begin with it has nothing to do with archaism, with the salvaging of obsolete words and turns of speech, or with the setting up of a 'standard English' which must never be departed from. On the contrary, it is especially concerned with the scrapping of every word or idiom which has outworn its usefulness. It has nothing to do with correct grammar and syntax, which are of no importance so long as one makes one's meaning clear, or with the avoidance of Americanisms, or with having what is called a 'good prose style'. On the other hand it is not concerned with fake simplicity and the attempt to make written English colloquial. Nor does it even imply in every case preferring the Saxon word to the Latin one, though it does imply using the fewest and shortest words that will cover one's meaning. What is above all needed is to let the meaning choose the word, and not the other way about. In prose, the worst thing one can do with words is to surrender to them. When you think of a concrete object, you think wordlessly, and then, if you want to describe the thing you have been visualizing you probably hunt about till you find the exact words that seem to fit it. When you think of something abstract you are more inclined to use words from the start, and unless you make a conscious effort to prevent it, the existing dialect will come rushing in and do the job for you, at the expense of blurring or even changing your meaning. Probably it is better to put off using words as long as possible and get one's meaning as clear as one can through pictures or sensations. Afterwards one can choose—not simply *accept*—the phrases that will best cover the meaning, and then switch round and decide what impression one's words are likely to make on another person. This last effort of the mind cuts out all stale or mixed images, all prefabricated phrases, needless repetitions, and humbug and vagueness generally. But one can often be in doubt about the effect of a word or a phrase, and one needs rules that one can rely on when instinct fails. I think the following rules will cover most cases:

(i) Never use a metaphor, simile or other figure of speech which you are used to seeing in print.

(ii) Never use a long word where a short one will do.

(iii) If it is possible to cut out a word, always cut it out.

(iv) Never use the passive where you can use the active.

(v) Never use a foreign phrase, a scientific word or a jargon word if you can think of an everyday English equivalent.

(vi) Break any of these rules sooner than say anything outright barbarous.

These rules sound elementary, and so they are, but they demand a deep change of attitude in anyone who has grown used to writing in the style now fashionable. One could keep all of them and still write bad English, but one could not write the kind of stuff that I quoted in those five specimens at the beginning of this article.

I have not here been considering the literary use of language, but merely language as an instrument for expressing and not for concealing or preventing thought. Stuart Chase and

---

[3] One can cure oneself of the *not un-* formation by memorizing this sentence: *A not unblack dog was chasing a not unsmall rabbit across a not ungreen field.*

others have come near to claiming that all abstract words are meaningless, and have used this as a pretext for advocating a kind of political quietism. Since you don't know what Fascism is, how can you struggle against Fascism? One need not swallow such absurdities as this, but one ought to recognize that the present political chaos is connected with the decay of language, and that one can probably bring about some improvement by starting at the verbal end. If you simplify your English, you are freed from the worst follies of orthodoxy. You cannot speak any of the necessary dialects, and when you make a stupid remark its stupidity will be obvious, even to yourself. Political language—and with variations this is true of all political parties, from Conservatives to Anarchists—is designed to make lies sound truthful and murder respectable, and to give an appearance of solidity to pure wind. One cannot change this all in a moment, but one can at least change one's own habits, and from time to time one can even, if one jeers loudly enough, send some worn-out and useless phrase—some *jackboot, Achilles' heel, hotbed, melting pot, acid test, veritable inferno* or other lump of verbal refuse—into the dustbin where it belongs.

(1946)

William Plomer
(SOUTH AFRICA, 1903–1973)

The Boer War

> The whip-crack of a Union Jack
> In a stiff breeze (the ship will roll),
> Deft abracadabra drums
> Enchant the patriotic soul—
>
> 5 A grandsire in St James's Street
> Sat at the window of his club,
> His second son, shot through the throat,
> Slid backwards down a slope of scrub,
>
> Gargled his last breaths, one by one by one,
> 10 In too much blood, too young to spill,
> Died difficultly, drop by drop by drop—
> 'By your son's courage, sir, we took the hill.'
>
> They took the hill (Whose hill? What for?)
> But what a climb they left to do!
> 15 Out of that bungled, unwise war
> An alp of unforgiveness grew.

(1932)

The Devil-Dancers

In shantung suits we whites are cool,
Glasses and helmets censoring the glare;
Fever has made our anxious faces pale,
We stoop a little from the load we bear;

5   Grouped in the shadow of the compound wall
We get our cameras ready, sitting pensive;
Keeping our distance and our dignity
We talk and smile, though slightly apprehensive.

The heat strikes upward from the ground,
10 The ground the natives harden with their feet,
The flag is drooping on its bamboo pole,
The middle distance wavers in the heat.

Naked or gaudy, all agog the crowd
Buzzes and glistens in the sun; the sight
15 Dazzles the retina; we remark the smell,
The drums beginning, and the vibrant light.

Now the edge of the jungle rustles. In a hush
The crowd parts. Nothing happens. Then
The dancers stalk adroitly out on stilts,
20 Weirdly advancing, twice as high as men.

Sure as fate, strange as the mantis, cruel
As vengeance in a dream, four bodies hung
In cloaks of rasping grasses, turning
Their tiny heads, the masks besmeared with dung;

25 Each mops and mows, uttering no sound,
Each stately, awkward, giant marionette,
Each printed shadow frightful on the ground
Moving in small distorted silhouette;

The fretful pipes and thinly-crying strings,
30 The mounting expectation of the drums
Excite the nerves, and stretch the muscles taut
Against the climax—but it never comes;

It never comes because the dance must end
And soon the older dancers will be dead;
35 We leave by air tomorrow. How
Can ever these messages by us be read?

These bodies hung with viscera and horns
Move with an incomparable lightness,
And through the masks that run with bullocks' blood
40 Quick eyes aim out, dots of fanatic brightness.

Within the mask the face, and moulded
(As mask to face) within the face the ghost,
As in its chrysalis-case the foetus folded
Of leaf-light butterfly. What matters most

45 When it comes out and we admire its wings
Is to remember where its life began:
Let us take care—that flake of flame may be
A butterfly whose bite can kill a man.

(1936)

Earle Birney
(CANADA, 1904–1995)

Anglosaxon Street

Dawndrizzle ended   dampness steams from
blotching brick and   blank plasterwaste
Faded housepatterns   hoary and finicky
unfold stuttering   stick like a phonograph

5 Here is a ghetto   gotten for goyim
O with care denuded   of nigger and kike
No coonsmell rankles   reeks only cellarrot
attar of carexhaust   catcorpse and cookinggrease
Imperial hearts   heave in this haven
10 Cracks across windows   are welded with slogans
There'll Always Be An England   enhances geraniums
and V's for Victory   vanquish the housefly

Ho! with climbing sun   march the bleached beldames
festooned with shopping bags   farded flatarched
15 bigthewed Saxonwives   stepping over buttrivers
waddling back wienerladen   to suckle smallfry

Hoy! with sunslope   shrieking over hydrants
flood from learninghall   the lean fingerlings
Nordic nobbledcheeked   not all clean of nose
20 leaping Commandowise   into leprous lanes

What! after whistleblow   spewed from wheelboat
after daylong doughtiness   dire handplay
in sewertrench or sandpit   come Saxonthegns
Junebrown Jutekings   jawslack for meat

25 Sit after supper   on smeared doorsteps
   not humbly swearing   hatedeeds on Huns
   profiteers politicians   pacifists Jews

   Then by twobit magic   to muse in movie
   unlock picturehoard   or lope to alehall
30 soaking bleakly   in beer skittleless

   Home again to hotbox   and humid husbandhood
   in slumbertrough adding   sleepily to Anglekin
   Alongside in lanenooks   carling and leman
   caterwaul and clip   careless of Saxonry
35 with moonglow and haste   and a higher heartbeat

   Slumbers now slumtrack   unstinks cooling
   waiting brief for milkmaid   mornstar and worldrise
                                    (Toronto 1942)

The Bear on the Delhi Road

   Unreal   tall as a myth
   by the road the Himalayan bear
   is beating the brilliant air
   with his crooked arms
5 About him two men   bare
   spindly as locusts   leap

   One pulls on a ring
   in the great soft nose   His mate
   flicks   flicks with a stick
10 up at the rolling eyes

   They have not led him here
   down from the fabulous hills
   to this bald alien plain
   and the clamorous world   to kill
15 but simply to teach him to dance

   They are peaceful both   these spare
   men of Kashmir   and the bear
   alive is their living   too
   If   far on the Delhi way
20 around him galvanic they dance
   it is merely to wear   wear
   from his shaggy body the tranced
   wish forever to stay
   only an ambling bear
25 four-footed in berries

It is no more joyous for them
in this hot dust to prance
out of reach of the praying claws
sharpened to paw for ants
30   in the shadows of deodars
It is not easy to free
myth from reality
or rear this fellow up
to lurch   lurch with them
35   in the tranced dancing of men
                    (1962)

Wind-Chimes in a Temple Ruin

This is the moment
    for two glass leaves
dangling dumb
    from the temple eaves
5   This is the instant
    when the sly air breathes
and the tremblers touch
    where no man sees
Who is the moving
10   or moved is no matter
but the birth of the possible
    song in the rafter
that dies as the wind goes
    nudging other
15   broken eaves
    for waiting lovers
                    (Nara 1962)

Patrick Kavanagh
(IRELAND, 1905–1967)

Spring Day

O come all ye tragic poets and sing a stave with me—
Give over T. S. Eliot and also W. B.
We'll sing our way through Stephen's Green where March has never found
In the growing grass a cadence of the verse of Ezra Pound.

5   The University girls are like tulip bulbs behind
More luxurious than ever from Holland was consigned,
Those bulbs will shortly break in flower—rayon, silk and cotton
And our verbal constipation will be totally forgotten.

Philosophy's graveyard—only dead men analyse
10 The reason for existence. Come all you solemn boys
From out your dictionary world and literary gloom—
Kafka's mad, Picasso's sad in Despair's confining room.

O come all darling poets and try to look more happy,
Forget about sexology as you gossip in the cafe;
15 Forget about the books you've read and the inbred verses there
Forget about the Kinsey Report and take a mouthful of air.

The world began this morning, God-dreamt and full of birds,
The fashion shops were glorious with the new collection of words.
And Love was practising phrases in young balladry—
20 Ten thousand years must pass before the birth of Psychology.

O come all ye gallant poets—to know it doesn't matter
Is imagination's message—break out but do not scatter.
Ordinary things wear lovely wings—the peacock's body's common.
O come all ye youthful poets and try to be more human.

(1960)

Samuel Beckett
(IRELAND/FRANCE, 1906–1989)

Catastrophe

for Vaclav Havel

Written in French in 1982. First performed at the Avignon Festival in 1982. First published in the United States in Evergreen Review, 1984.

Director (D).
His female assistant (A).
Protagonist (P).
Luke, in charge of the lighting, offstage (L).

Rehearsal. Final touches to the last scene. Bare stage. A *and* L *have just set the lighting.* D *has just arrived.*

D *in an armchair downstairs audience left. Fur coat. Fur toque to match. Age and physique unimportant.*
A *standing beside him. White overall. Bare head. Pencil on ear. Age and physique unimportant.*
P *midstage standing on a black block 18 inches high. Black wide-brimmed hat. Black dressing-gown to ankles. Barefoot. Head bowed. Hands in pockets. Age and physique unimportant.*

D *and* A *contemplate* P. *Long pause.*

A: [*Finally.*] Like the look of him?

D: So so. [*Pause.*] Why the plinth?

A: To let the stalls see the feet.
    [*Pause.*]

D: Why the hat?

A: To help hide the face.
    [*Pause.*]

D: Why the gown?

A: To have him all black.
    [*Pause.*]

D: What has he on underneath? [A *moves towards* P.] Say it.
    [A *halts.*]

A: His night attire.

D: Colour?

A: Ash.
    [D *takes out a cigar.*]

D: Light. [A *returns, lights the cigar, stands still.* D *smokes.*]
    How's the skull?

A: You've seen it.

D: I forget. [A *moves towards* P.] Say it.
    [A *halts.*]

A: Moulting. A few tufts.

D: Colour?

A: Ash.
    [*Pause.*]

D: Why hands in pockets?

A: To help have him all black.

D: They mustn't.

A: I make a note. [*She takes out a pad, takes pencil, notes.*] Hands exposed.
    [*She puts back pad and pencil.*]

D: How are they? [A *at a loss. Irritably.*] The hands, how are the hands?

A: You've seen them.

D: I forget.

A: Crippled. Fibrous degeneration.

D: Clawlike?

A: If you like.

D: Two claws?

A: Unless he clench his fists.

D: He mustn't.

A: I make a note. [*She takes out pad, takes pencil, notes.*] Hands limp.
    [*She puts back pad and pencil.*]

D: Light. [A *returns, relights the cigar, stands still.* D *smokes.*] Good. Now let's have a
    look. [A *at a loss. Irritably.*] Get going. Lose that gown. [*He consults his chronometer.*]
    Step on it, I have a caucus.
    [A *goes to* P, *takes off the gown.* P *submits, inert.* A *steps back, the gown over her arm.*
    P *in old grey pyjamas, head bowed, fists clenched. Pause.*]

A: Like him better without? [*Pause.*] He's shivering.

D: Not all that. Hat.
  [A *advances, takes off hat, steps back, hat in hand. Pause.*]
A: Like that cranium?
D: Needs whitening.
A: I make a note. [*She takes out pad, takes pencil, notes.*] Whiten cranium.
  [*She puts back pad and pencil.*]
D: The hands. [A *at a loss. Irritably.*] The fists. Get going. [A *advances, unclenches fists, steps back.*] And whiten.
A: I make a note. [*She takes out pad, takes pencil, notes.*] Whiten hands.
  [*She puts back pad and pencil. They contemplate* P.]
D: [*Finally.*] Something wrong. [*Distraught.*] What is it?
A: [*Timidly.*] What if we were . . . were to . . . join them?
D: No harm trying. [A *advances, joins the hands, steps back.*] Higher. [A *advances, raises waist high the joined hands, steps back.*] A touch more. [A *advances, raises breast-high the joined hands.*] Stop! [A *steps back.*] Better. It's coming. Light.
  [A *returns, relights cigar, stands still.* D *smokes.*]
A: He's shivering.
D: Bless his heart.
  [*Pause.*]
A: [*Timidly.*] What about a little . . . a little . . . gag?
D: For God's sake! This craze for explicitation! Every i dotted to death! Little gag!
  For God's sake!
A: Sure he won't utter?
D: Not a squeak. [*He consults his chronometer.*] Just time. I'll go and see how it looks from the house.
  [*Exit* D, *not to appear again.* A *subsides in the armchair, springs to her feet no sooner seated, takes out a rag, wipes vigorously back and seat of chair, discards rag, sits again. Pause.*]
D: [*Off, plaintive.*] I can't see the toes. [*Irritably.*] I'm sitting in the front row of the stalls and can't see the toes.
A: [*Rising.*] I make a note. [*She takes out a pad, takes pencil, notes.*] Raise pedestal.
D: There's a trace of face.
A: I make a note.
  [*She takes out pad, takes pencil, makes to note.*]
D: Down the head. [A *at a loss. Irritably.*] Get going. Down his head. [A *puts back pad and pencil, goes to* P, *bows his bead further, steps back.*] A shade more. [A *advances, bows the bead further.*] Stop! [A *steps back.*] Fine. It's coming. [*Pause.*] Could do with more nudity.
A: I make a note.
  [*She takes out pad, makes to take her pencil.*]
D: Get going! Get going! [A *puts back the pad, goes to* P, *stands irresolute.*] Bare the neck.
  [A *undoes top buttons, parts the flaps, steps back.*] The legs. The shins. [A *advances, rolls up to below knee one trouser-leg, steps back.*] The other. [*Same for other leg, steps back.*] Higher. The knees. [A *advances, rolls up to above knees both trouser-legs, steps back.*] And whiten.
A: I make a note. [*She takes out pad, takes pencil, notes.*] Whiten all flesh.
D: It's coming. Is Luke around?
A: [*Calling.*] Luke! [*Pause. Louder.*] Luke!

L: [*Off, distant.*] I hear you. [*Pause. Nearer.*] What's the trouble now?

A.. Luke's around.

D: Blackout stage.

L: What?

> [A *transmits in technical terms. Fade-out of general light. Light on* P *alone.*
> A *in shadow.*]

D: Just the head.

L: What?

> [A *transmits in technical terms. Fade-out of light on* P's *body. Light on head alone.*
Long pause.]

D: Lovely.

> [*Pause.*]

A: [*Timidly.*] What if he were to . . . were to . . . raise his head . . .
> an instant . . . show his face . . . just an instant.

D: For God's sake! What next? Raise his head? Where do you think we are? In
> Patagonia? Raise his head? For God's sake! [*Pause.*] Good. There's our
> catastrophe. In the bag. Once more and I'm off.

A: [*To* L.] Once more and he's off.

> [*Fade-up of light on* P's *body. Pause. Fade-up of general light.*]

D: Stop! [*Pause.*] Now . . . let 'em have it. [*Fade-out of general light. Pause. Fade-out of
> light on body. Light on head alone. Long pause.*] Terrific! He'll have them on their
> feet. I can hear it from here.

> [*Pause. Distant storm of applause.* P *raises his head, fixes the audience. The
> applause falters, dies.*
>> *Long pause.*
>> *Fade-out of light on face.*]

(1984)

W.H. Auden

(ENGLAND/U.S.A., 1907–1973)

Musée des Beaux Arts

About suffering they were never wrong,
The Old Masters: how well they understood
Its human position; how it takes place
While someone else is eating or opening a window or just walking dully along;
5   How, when the aged are reverently, passionately waiting
For the miraculous birth, there always must be
Children who did not specially want it to happen, skating
On a pond at the edge of the wood:
They never forgot
10 That even the dreadful martyrdom must run its course
Anyhow in a corner, some untidy spot
Where the dogs go on with their doggy life and the torturer's horse
Scratches its innocent behind on a tree.

In Brueghel's *Icarus*, for instance: how everything turns away
15   Quite leisurely from the disaster; the ploughman may
Have heard the splash, the forsaken cry,
But for him it was not an important failure; the sun shone
As it had to on the white legs disappearing into the green
Water; and the expensive delicate ship that must have seen
20   Something amazing, a boy falling out of the sky,
Had somewhere to get to and sailed calmly on.

(1940)

The Unknown Citizen

(To JS/O7/M/378 This Marble Monument Is Erected by the State)

He was found by the Bureau of Statistics to be
One against whom there was no official complaint,
And all the reports on his conduct agree
That, in the modern sense of an old-fashioned word, he was a saint,
5   For in everything he did he served the Greater Community.
Except for the War till the day he retired
He worked in a factory and never got fired,
But satisfied his employers, Fudge Motors Inc.
Yet he wasn't a scab or odd in his views,
10   For his Union reports that he paid his dues,
(Our report on his Union shows it was sound)
And our Social Psychology workers found
That he was popular with his mates and liked a drink.
The Press are convinced that he bought a paper every day
15   And that his reactions to advertisements were normal in every way.
Policies taken out in his name prove that he was fully insured,
And his Health-card shows he was once in hospital but left it cured.
Both Producers Research and High-Grade Living declare
He was fully sensible to the advantages of the Instalment Plan
20   And had everything necessary to the Modern Man,
A phonograph, a radio, a car and a frigidaire.
Our researchers into Public Opinion are content
That he held the proper opinions for the time of year;
When there was peace, he was for peace; when there was war, he went.
25   He was married and added five children to the population,
Which our Eugenist says was the right number for a parent of his generation.
And our teachers report that he never interfered with their education.
Was he free? Was he happy? The question is absurd:
Had anything been wrong, we should certainly have heard.

(1940)

A.D. Hope
(AUSTRALIA 1907-)

Australia

A Nation of trees, drab green and desolate grey
In the field uniform of modern wars,
Darkens her hills, those endless, outstretched paws
Of Sphinx demolished or stone lion worn away.

5   They call her a young country, but they lie:
She is the last of lands, the emptiest,
A woman beyond her change of life, a breast
Still tender but within the womb is dry.

Without songs, architecture, history:
10 The emotions and superstitions of younger lands,
Her rivers of water drown among inland sands,
The river of her immense stupidity

Floods her monotonous tribes from Cairns to Perth.
In them at last the ultimate men arrive
15 Whose boast is not: 'we live' but 'we survive',
A type who will inhabit the dying earth.

And her five cities, like five teeming sores,
Each drains her: a vast parasite robber-state
Where second-hand Europeans pullulate
20 Timidly on the edge of alien shores.

Yet there are some like me turn gladly home
From the lush jungle of modern thought, to find
The Arabian desert of the human mind,
Hoping, if still from the deserts the prophets come,

25 Such savage and scarlet as no green hills dare
Springs in that waste, some spirit which escapes
The learned doubt, the chatter of cultured apes
Which is called civilization over there.

(1939)

Hugh MacLennan

(CANADA, 1907–1990)

On Living in a Cold Country

I was twenty-one before I met a live writer; before I met, one might say, my fate. It was on my first voyage to England, where I was going to study: I had never been away from home before.

It is difficult for me to remember now how naive I was then. I had worked and played hard, and had been equipping myself for twentieth-century life by studying Latin and Greek. I had never been outside the little province of Nova Scotia since the cessation of the period known to the psychologists as childhood amnesia (in my infancy, I'm told, I was in England for several months), and the polyglot passengers aboard that ship fascinated me, for the ship had sailed from New York and her ultimate destination was Antwerp. At Halifax, where I lived, she had stopped for half a day to take on two thousand barrels of apples, two elderly ladies, and myself.

Prowling about the ship after we got to sea, I had observed a sloppily dressed man of indeterminate age lounging in the smoke-room or brooding over the ocean with his elbows on the railing. I could not imagine what his profession was, but the cut of his suit was American—in those days even I could distinguish an American suit from an English one—and his face looked as though some things I had never heard of had sunk into it and stayed there. When he told me he was a writer, I was impressed. When he later informed me that he was engaged on a three-hundred-thousand-word novel about Lincoln, in three sections of equal length, and in three different styles, I was reverent.

"The first section will be in the style of Mark Twain," he explained. "Why? Because that is the only style that fits the mood of Lincoln's youth. The second section"—he paused and assessed me with give-away, spaniel's eyes—"will be in the style of Henry James."

In those days I had heard of Henry James, but only barely.

"You see, Lincoln's middle period was one of doubts, hesitations, and parentheses. He was a Hamlet in Illinois. Shakespeare would have made a success of *Hamlet* if he had written it in novel form in the style of Henry James."

The third section was to be written in the style of a writer I had not even heard about barely; it was to be written in the style of the last chapter of James Joyce's *Ulysses*.

"The choice is obvious," the writer explained. "Lincoln's third period was the presidency, and presidents, by the very nature of their jobs, can't think. They haven't the time. The stuff just pours through them."

I had never heard of this ship-met writer before, and perhaps I have already said enough to explain why I have never heard of him since. Yet he abides with me. I learned more from him about the trade of writing than I learned from any other teacher except Experience herself.

One night over his sixth drink he said that writing would be easy if it weren't for what he called "all the other things that went along with it," and that the chief of these other things were three insoluble problems. "Money," he said, "Women, and Liquor," and he pronounced each word as though a capital letter stood before it.

Much of what he had been saying had sounded strange to me, but this rang a familiar note. I admitted that my father had told me much the same thing the day before I sailed, but had not limited the three problems to writers. According to him, Money, Women, and Liquor were the three problems of every man who ever lived, nor were they (according to him) insoluble. With the first I was to be thrifty; the other two I was entirely to avoid.

The writer observed me gloomily: "If you take that advice, your Oedipus will be screaming before you're thirty."

I told him I had an *Oedipus* in my stateroom, and added guiltily that I ought to be studying it at that particular moment.

"My God," he said, "do you still think Oedipus is a play? But to get back—money you must have for obvious reasons, but too much is worse than too little. A high standard of living invariably produces a low standard of prose. But women and liquor, these are even more essential than money. They're necessary food for your subconscious. You need them to awaken your guilts." After ordering another drink, he sighed: "But the trouble with liquor is it's apt to leave you with nothing else *but* your subconscious. And alcoholic remorse, I'm sorry to say, is an uncreative remorse."

The next morning on deck he was obviously suffering from alcoholic remorse, and as we leaned on the railing and stared down at the yard-wide band of white brine seething along the vessel's flank, he told me he was feeling sorry for me.

"Because you want to be a writer," he said, "and you haven't a chance."

I felt myself flushing, for in those days I never told my love. I pretended that all I wished to be was a scholar.

"What gives you the idea I want to write?" I asked.

"When I meet a man I know will be no good for anything else, I always know he's going to get the bug sooner or later, and probably sooner."

"Well, supposing I do? Why do you say I haven't a chance?"

"You aren't decadent enough. In fact, you're not decadent at all, and as you're twenty-one already, I doubt if you'll become decadent in time for it to matter. Frankly, your country has ruined any chance you might ever have had of becoming a writer."

"What's my country to do with it?"

"It's a cold country. In the entire history of the human race, no important art has ever come out of a cold country."

"But Canada can also get very hot," I protested.

He shook his head. "No. Canada is a cold country because that's what the world believes it is. Wait till you begin talking to editors and you'll remember that I told you so."

Some twenty years later I was talking with an editor and I did remember that he had told me so. By that time I had been writing long enough to be acutely aware of the first of the Three Problems, and this editor belonged to a super-colossal magazine that paid super-colossal fees. I wanted one of those fees to finance six months' work on a novel. While we ate lunch, with a tableful of bilingual lawyers across the aisle discussing a case with Gallic gestures, the editor informed me that what he wanted was "a real, true-to-life piece on Canada". For a subject I could take my pick of Eskimos, trappers, Mounties, or husky dogs, and if I could manage to work all four of them into the same piece, it would be perfect, providing it met the literary standards of his magazine. While we talked, the temperature was ninety degrees, and the editor was feeling it, for he had come north clad in heavy worsteds. Mopping his forehead, he explained that this would be what he called a "duty-piece". His magazine sold several hundred thousand copies in Canada every month, and occasionally the management felt it a duty to print some Canadian material. I must have made a comment about there being no Eskimos, trappers, or husky dogs within fifteen hundred miles of where we were sitting, for he cut me short with a gesture.

"No, they're imperative. In an African duty-piece you stress the heat and the jungle. In an English duty-piece you stress how old everything is. A French duty-piece has got to be romantic, but at the same time we like an angle showing the French are also practical and getting themselves orientated to the up-to-date. But in a Canadian duty-piece you simply have to go heavy on the snow and the cold."

But to return to that morning at sea—for some reason my newly met American writer had taken an interest in me. After saying that he believed in Voltaire's way of dealing with aspiring young authors ("If I had a son who wanted to write, I'd strangle him out of sheer good nature"), he asked me how I'd been living "up there," his notion of Canada being a red-painted roof on top of the North American house.

"Well actually," I told him, "and so much for your idea of my living in a cold country, for the past eleven years I've been living in a tent."

"In a *what*?"

"The first time in eleven years that I've slept between four walls was my first night aboard this ship. Well yes, I suppose it does sound a little odd."

"It sounds *very* odd." His eyes opened wide at me. "Indeed, it sounds so odd that it may indicate possibilities for you. Continue. Tell me about it."

So I told him.

In those days in Halifax the life was not much different from life in a village, even though we had the harbour, the university, the hospitals, the Government House, the curfew gun on the Citadel, and the memory of the explosion which had smashed a third of the town a few years before. Behind every house was some sort of back yard—the word "yard" had probably reached us from New England Loyalists—and most of these had a kitchen garden, a few fruit trees, and a one-horse stable which might or might not have been converted into a one-car garage. In the early 1920s there was still a faint smell of stable behind the houses and a reasonably strong smell of it in the streets. Each yard was separated from its neighbours by a rough board fence on the top of which prowling tom cats sat in the nights and howled at the female cats they knew were inside the houses.

In the summer of my eleventh year I went to a boys' camp where we slept under canvas, and when I returned to Halifax, the weather was so hot I could not sleep well indoors. Heat waves are rare in Nova Scotia, but when they come, the salt humidity sticks to your skin. My father reminded me of a little tent in the basement he had used years ago for fishing trips and he said it was probably mouldy in spots. It was, but I got it out, pitched it in the back yard, installed a battered old hospital cot and a packing case to hold a saucer with a candle in it, and that night I slept beautifully. The next day I told my parents I intended to stay out in the tent until school began.

But when school began on the first of September it was still warm, so I decided to stay out until it got cold. Then in the first week of October the mornings were cool enough, but there was dew on the ripe apples and pears, and waking up in such air was a sensual experience as delicious as any I can remember. I told my parents I intended staying out until it got really cold. Three weeks later I woke to see the tent walls sagging and a foot of snow on the ground. Presumably this was really cold, but I told my parents I had slept so well I would stay out until it got impossibly cold.

It never did. The Canadian climate in the early 1920s had a mean average temperature three to four degrees lower than it has now, and this, meteorologists tell me, represents a substantial differential. Nowadays the temperature seldom drops below zero in Halifax, though the salt humidity of a Maritime climate makes zero feel as cold as twenty-five below on the prairies. But it often got below zero in Halifax when I was a boy, and one night in my first January in the tent the thermometer fell to seventeen below, and the trees cracked like guns in the frost. Once more I slept beautifully, and after that night I decided to remain outside indefinitely.

It seemed perfectly natural to do this. I used to wear in the winters two pairs of flannel pajamas, a pair of woollen socks, and a red beret. When I emerged from the back door in this regalia I carried a hot-water bottle (it was bad the night it broke) to warm the blankets before my own body-heat sustained a modest furnace inside of them. The only part of me that ever got cold in the tent was my nose. And here is an item for anyone who does not already know it: a cold nose is a better sedative than a quarter-grain Seconal.

Phenomena belonging to the science of physics became high poetry on the really cold nights. My breath made snow, real snow. As it issued warm from my nose and mouth, it mounted to the canvas under the ridge-pole and turned into a delicate cloud in the still, frigid air. When it congealed, it was converted into a filmy snow-mist, which descended and settled on top of the bed. Once I woke with a bright orange sun flaring into the tent and found myself warm under a quarter-inch layer of the softest snow I ever saw, each crystal dancing in the eye of that Austerlitz sunrise.

But congealed breath made another problem, an uncomfortable chin. In the vicinity of the mouth, when you sleep out in sub-zero weather, your breath does not turn into snow but into ice, and ice irritates the skin. Having been helpless all my adulthood in the presence of the most elementary technical problem, it gives me a certain satisfaction to relate how I dealt with this one when I was ten years old and resourceful. I asked my mother for an old sheet, cut it cross-wise into strips a foot wide, and each night when I tucked myself in by candle light I laid this length of sheeting under my jaw. Whenever I woke with ice irritating me, I shifted the sheeting to a dry place. After a while this routine became so automatic that I was unconscious of it.

A more serious problem was the one of waking up in the morning.

In those days my family kept a maid from Newfoundland called Sadie, a fisherman's daughter from the little island of Ramea off the southern coast of the Ancient Colony. Ramea is barren, but the water surrounding it is so abundant in codfish that in Cabot's time the density of the cod impeded the motion of his ships. Ramea's climate is a little milder than Labrador's, but some of Sadie's tales of *her* experience of living in a cold country made Halifax seem like a sultry port in a sugar island. Sometimes the salt sea froze out a distance of two miles from the shore of Ramea, and when this happened, if the fishermen wanted food, they had to haul their dories over the treacherous, spongy, salt-water ice to deep water, and then haul them back in the evening with the catch. More than one man Sadie knew was drowned doing things like this. So to her, warmth was a thing you hoarded. When her Newfoundland friends, seamen all, visited her kitchen, the fug was so thick you could barely see through it, for while the men smoked shag in cutty pipes, the stove glowed cherry-red as it brewed the gallons of tea they drank. Happy in a hundred-degree temperature, the Newfoundlanders conversed in a dialect I could hardly understand, for the speech of their outports is the speech that was used by common folk in western England in Shakespeare's time.

Newfoundlanders are polite people, and Sadie never said straight out that I was crazy. But she did say it was no part of her duty to wade through the snow of a zero morning in order to waken a small boy who had a perfectly comfortable room indoors. My mother agreed with her; indeed, I suspect her of hoping that this would settle the matter, for she knew I would never wake up in time for school if left to myself.

However, there was a chandler's shop along the Halifax waterfront which boasted that it sold everything from a needle to an anchor, and displayed in its window an anchor and a sail-maker's needle to prove it. Thither I repaired one afternoon when school was out, and came home lugging a four-pound gong of the kind they used to place on the outside of school walls to ring in the children from recess. This gong I installed inside the tent, and ran a cord from its clapper through a row of pulleys to the kitchen window. After boring a hole through the window-frame, I thrust the cord inside for Sadie to pull. And at seven-thirty the next morning, pull she did—with the vigour of a fisher girl heaving on a halyard.

The noise was appalling, for this was a gong which was meant to be audible for a quarter of a mile. I was out of the tent and inside the house before I was even awake. My father feared the police would intervene if the gong was used again. My mother, ever hopeful, telephoned the neighbours to apologize and to ask if they had been disturbed. She was told by all of them that they were delighted with the gong. They all got up at seven-thirty, and if they could be assured the gong would always ring, they would not have to worry about setting their own alarm clocks.

Now all the problems about sleeping in the tent were solved and I settled in for the years and the seasons that lay ahead. The little bells on the horses pulling milkmen's sleighs, jingling past on the street beyond the fence at six o'clock in the morning, used to reach through the walls of sleep like the bells of elfland. In the foggy springtimes I fell asleep with my ears filled with the groans, snores, and musical clangs of the fog signals and bell-buoys of Halifax harbour. When summer came, I often read by candlelight before falling asleep, and with the passage of seasons and years moved the passage of education and even of history.

I was sleeping in the tent when I learned how to translate the invaluable information that on the second day before the Kalends of June, Caesar moved his camp and marched his legions a distance of ten miles to a place where he made another camp. I was sleeping in the tent when, years later, I made my first acquaintance with communism in the form of Plato's *Republic*. I was in the tent the night when Lindbergh, after having spent the previous day flying over Nova Scotia, was dodging the ice-making clouds over the Atlantic. To the tent I returned at two o'clock in the morning the night Tunney beat Dempsey in Philadelphia, which also happened to be the first night I ever wore a dinner jacket or went to a Government House Ball.

Such was the story I told my writer-friend, and when I had finished I said: "So you see— it wasn't such a cold country after all."

He was silent a while, possibly engrossed in thoughts of Lincoln, probably worrying about his liver, and I felt embarrassed to have spoken so much about myself. But he seemed to have heard, for finally he turned and spoke.

"You'll never go back to that again, of course."

"I don't see why not."

"You must have slept without movement to have gotten away with it. If you'd moved in your sleep, you'd have disturbed the blankets and let in the cold."

"I did sleep without movement."

The spaniel eyes were prophetic: "Well, you have given me clear proof that your days of sleeping without movement are numbered. This avoidance of the house where your parents were sleeping, this compulsive crawling away from their vicinity and *into* that little tent in the back yard—if that doesn't indicate an Oedipus complex of magnitude I don't know what else it indicates. A little while—and remember I told you so—and it will burst out. A little while, and your guilts will make you thrash and writhe in your sleep, and the last thing you'll ever think of doing will be to sleep in the tent with your lost innocence."

He stared out over the sea: "No, I can't help you. You're going to be a writer, all right."

(c. 1961)

Louis MacNeice
(ULSTER 1907–1963)

The Habits

When they put him in rompers the habits
Fanned out to close in, they were dressed
In primary colours and each of them
Carried a rattle and a hypodermic;
5   His parents said it was all for the best.

Next, the barracks of boys: the habits
Slapped him on the back, they were dressed
In pinstripe trousers and carried
A cheque book, a passport, and a sjambok;
10   The master said it was all for the best.

And then came the women: the habits
Pretended to leave, they were dressed
In bittersweet undertones and carried
A Parthian shaft and an affidavit;
15   The adgirl said it was all for the best.

Age became middle: the habits
Made themselves at home, they were dressed
In quilted dressing-gowns and carried
A decanter, a siphon, and a tranquillizer;
20   The computer said it was all for the best.

The age became real: the habits
Outstayed their welcome, they were dressed
In nothing and carried nothing.
He said: If you won't go, I go.
25   The Lord God said it was all for the best.

                                    (1963)

Theodore Roethke

(U.S.A., 1908–1963)

My Papa's Waltz

The whiskey on your breath
Could make a small boy dizzy;
But I hung on like death:
Such waltzing was not easy.

5   We romped until the pans
Slid from the kitchen shelf;
My mother's countenance
Could not unfrown itself.

The hand that held my wrist
10   Was battered on one knuckle;
At every step you missed
My right ear scraped a buckle.

You beat time on my head
With a palm caked hard by dirt,
15   Then waltzed me off to bed
Still clinging to your shirt.

                       (1948)

The Waking

I wake to sleep, and take my waking slow.
I feel my fate in what I cannot fear.
I learn by going where I have to go.

We think by feeling. What is there to know?
5   I hear my being dance from ear to ear.
I wake to sleep, and take my waking slow.

Of those so close beside me, which are you?
God bless the Ground! I shall walk softly there,
And learn by going where I have to go.

10   Light takes the Tree; but who can tell us how?
The lowly worm climbs up a winding stair;
I wake to sleep, and take my waking slow.

Great Nature has another thing to do
To you and me; so take the lively air,
15   And, lovely, learn by going where to go.

This shaking keeps me steady. I should know.
What falls away is always. And is near.
I wake to sleep, and take my waking slow.
I learn by going where I have to go.

(1953)

Some Remarks on Rhythm

What do *I* like? Listen:

> *Hinx, minx, the old witch winks!*
> *The fat begins to fry!*
> *There's nobody home but Jumping Joan,*
> *And father, and mother, and I.*

Now what makes that "catchy," to use Mr. Frost's word? For one thing: the rhythm. Five stresses out of a possible six in the first line, though maybe "old" doesn't take quite as strong a stress as the others. And three—keep noticing that magic number—internal rhymes, *hinx, minx, winks*. And notice too the apparent mysteriousness of the action: something happens right away—the old witch winks and she sets events into motion. The fat begins to fry, literally and symbolically. She commands—no fool witch this one. Notice that the second line, "The fat begins to fry," is absolutely regular metrically. It's all iambs, a thing that often occurs when previous lines are sprung or heavily counterpointed. The author doesn't want to get too far from his base, from his ground beat. The third line varies again with an anapaest and variations in the "o" and "u" sounds. "There's nobody home but Jumping Joan." Then the last line—anapaest lengthening the line out to satisfy the ear, "And father, and mother, and I." Sometimes we are inclined to feel that Mother Goose, or the traditional kind of thing, is almost infallible as memorable speech—the phrase is Auden's. But this is by no means so. There is another version that goes,

> *Hink, mink, the old witch stinks,*
> *The fat begins to fry:*
> *Nobody's home but Jumping Joan,*
> *Jumping Joan and I.*

Well, the whole situation has obviously altered, for the better perhaps from the standpoint of the speaker at least. But in his excitement he has produced a much inferior poem.

First, deleting the "x's" takes some of the force away from the three rhyming words— "Hinx, minx, the old witch winks,"—the triad. What's more, he has become tiresomely naturalistic. "The old witch stinks"—hardly a fresh piece of observation. Stinks is a splendid old word, but here it is a bore. It is a prerogative of old witches to stink: part of their stock in trade as it were, and nobody mentions it. Take the change from minx, which means of course a pert little vixen of a girl, and carries with it overtones of tenderness; or, further back, a wanton, a roaring girl. And the mink—a wonderful little predatory animal with a characteristic odor. But if we keep *that* in mind, the line becomes an olfactory horror. It's some fusty little cave these two have in the absence of father and mother. And *their* absence takes away the real drama from the situation. It's a roll in the hay, and nothing more.

Allow me another I love:

> *I.N. spells IN.*
> *I was in my kitchen*
> *Doin' a bit of stitching.*
> *Old Father Nimble*
> *Came and took my thimble*
> *I got a great big stone,*
> *Hit him on the belly-bone.*
> *O.U.T. spells OUT.*

Here we see how light "i" and short "i" and feminine endings can make for speed, rhythmical quickness, and velocity, and then, with the words following the action, that truly awesome and portentous line with its spondees, "I got a great bíg stóne . . ."; and then the sudden speed-up in the action—the triumphant release from a frustration, I suppose the Freudians would say—"Hit him on the belly-bone./O.U.T. spells out."

Take another, a single line, which is always a test:

Great A, little a, bouncing B.

There are three shifts of pace—it's a triad again, lovely alliteration, the long full vowels combined.

Names themselves can be a love—and half the poem:

Julius Caesar Pompey Green
Wore a jacket of velveteen.

What's my real point by these little examples? It's this: that, while our genius in the language may be essentially iambic, particularly in the formal lyric, much of memorable or passionate speech *is* strongly stressed, irregular, even "sprung," if you will. Now we see that the name itself, the direct address, makes for the memorable, for rhythmical interest; often it makes for an implied dialogue. Take the ridiculous:

Oh father dear, do ships at sea,
Have legs way down below?
Of course they do, you goosey you,
Or else how could they go?

But you may protest, these are the rhythms of children, of folk material, strongly stressed—memorable perhaps, but do they appear in poetry today? The answer is yes, certainly in some poets. For instance, Auden's:

The silly fool, the silly fool
Was sillier in school
But beat the bully as a rule.

The youngest son, the youngest son
Was certainly no wise one
Yet could surprise one.

Or rather, or rather
To be posh, we gather,
One should have no father.

Then the cryptic and elliptical end:

Simple to prove
That deeds indeed
In life succeed
But love in love
And tales in tales
Where no one fails.

Not all Mother-Goosey to be sure. And the "rather-father" rhyme maybe comes from Sam Johnson's:

If the man who turnips cries,
Cry not when his father dies,
'Tis a proof that he had rather
Have a turnip than his father.

Or take an example from myself: "I Need, I Need." In the first section the protagonist, a little boy, is very sad. Then there is a jump-rope section in which two children chant in alternate aggressive dialogue. Then their aggression trails off into something else:

Even steven all is less:
I haven't time for sugar,
Put your finger in your face,
And there will be a booger.

> *A one is a two is*
> *I know what you is:*
> *You're not very nice,—*
> *So touch my toes twice.*

I know you are my nemesis
So bibble where the pebble is.
The Trouble is with No and Yes
As you can see I guess I guess.

> *I wish I was a pifflebob*
> *I wish I was a funny*
> *I wish I had ten thousand hats*
> *And made a lot of money.*

Open a hole and see the sky:
A duck knows something
You and I don't.
Tomorrow is Friday.

> *Not you I need.*
> *Go play with your nose.*
> *Stay in the sun,*
> *Snake-eyes.*

Some of the poems I cherish from the dramatists have heavily pronounced, strongly stressed swat rhythms. They are written to be sung, or maybe danced to. Here from *Ralph Roister Doister*:

I mun be married a Sunday;
I mun be married a Sunday;
Whosoever shall come that way,
> *I mun be married a Sunday.*

Roister Doister is my name;
Roister Doister is my name;
A lusty brute I am the same;
> *I mun be married a Sunday.*

Notice that shift in the second stanza, in tone, and feeling—how it goes into another speed rhythmically.

George Peele, that wonderful poet, abounds in incantatory effects with the same propulsion. Here is the opening of a dialogue:

Fair and fair, and twice so fair,
As fair as any may be,
The fairest shepherd on our green,
A love for any lady.

And later:

And of my love my roundelay,
My merry, merry, merry roundelay,
> *Concludes with Cupid's curse:*
They that do change old love for new,
> *Pray gods they change for worse!*

Repetition in word and phrase and in idea is the very essence of poetry and particularly of *this* kind of poetry. Notice how these poets can and do change the pace, and the change is right, psychologically. We say the command, the hortatory, often makes for the memorable. We're caught up, involved. It is implied we do something, at least vicariously. But it can also be very tricky—it can seem to have a factitious strength. The emotion must be strong and legitimate and not fabricated. Thus when Elinor Wylie writes:

> *Go study to disdain*
> *The frail, the overfine,*

I can't get past the first line. There is no conviction, no natural rhythm of speech. I suppose there must be an element of the startling, or the strange, or the absurd. Yeats is magnificent, often, at getting the right tone, seizing the attention:

> *Call down the hawk from the air;*
> *Let him be hooded or caged . . .*

or:

> *Come swish around, my pretty punk,*
> *And keep me dancing still*
> *That I may stay a sober man*
> *Although I drink my fill.*

Or Donne's

> *So, so, breake off this last lamenting kisse, . . .*

In some more serious poetry we see again how the direct address can pull us up sharply. We are used to this in spoken language. Maybe we hark back to the condition of the child when we are being told. Almost invariably a dramatic situation, some kind of opposition, is indicated. Thus in Charlotte Mew's:

> *Sweetheart, for such a day, one mustn't grudge the score; . . .*

Or Donne's:

> *When by thy scorne, O murderesse, I am dead, . . .*

Or the action itself can be dramatic, as in Herbert's:

> *I struck the board, and cry'd "No more; . . .*

Or the situation can be given dramatically, as in Kunitz's:

> *Within the city of the burning cloud,*
> *Dragging my life behind me in a sack,*
> *Naked I prowl, . . .*

But what about the rhythm and the motion of the poem as a whole? Are there any ways of sustaining it, you may ask? We must keep in mind that rhythm is the entire movement, the flow, the recurrence of stress and unstress that is related to the rhythms of the blood, the rhythms of nature. It involves certainly stress, time, pitch, the texture of the words, the total meaning of the poem.

We've been told that a rhythm is invariably produced by playing against an established pattern. Blake does this admirably in "A Poison Tree":

> *I was angry with my friend,*
> *I told my wrath, my wrath did end.*
> *I was angry with my foe,*
> *I told it not, my wrath did grow.*

The whole poem is a masterly example of variation in rhythm, of playing against meter. It's what Blake called "the bounding line," the nervousness, the tension, the energy in the whole poem. And this is a clue to everything. Rhythm gives us the very psychic energy of the speaker, in one emotional situation at least.

But there are slow rhythms, too, for we're not always emotionally "high." And these, as any practitioner will find, are very difficult to sustain in poetry without boring the reader. Listen to Janet Lewis's "Girl Help":

> Mild and slow and young,
> She moves about the room,
> And stirs the summer dust
> With her wide broom.
>
> In the warm, lofted air,
> Soft lips together pressed,
> Soft wispy hair,
> She stops to rest,
>
> And stops to breathe,
> Amid the summer hum,
> The great white lilac bloom
> Scented with days to come.

Here we see particularly the effect of texture, especially the vowel sounds as well as the effect of the dentates, the "d's" and "t's." The first line sets the pace. It *can't* be said fast: "Mild and slow and young." It's a little vignette, very feminine, absolutely true emotionally—the drowsy adolescent; but the poem is not static: the girl moves, she stirs, she stops to rest, and stops to breathe. And the girl is virtually embraced by the season that is part of herself.

It's nonsense, of course, to think that memorableness in poetry comes solely from rhetorical devices, or the following of certain sound patterns, or contrapuntal rhythmical effects. We all know that poetry is shot through with appeals to the unconsciousness, to the fears and desires that go far back into our childhood, into the imagination of the race. And we know that some words, like *hill, plow, mother, window, bird, fish*, are so drenched with human association, they sometimes can make even bad poems evocative.

I remember the first time I heard Robert Frost read in 1930. Suddenly a line, I think it was from Shakespeare, came into his head. He recited it. "Listen to that," he said. "Just like a *hiss*, just like a *hiss*." It is what Eliot has called "the auditory imagination": the sinuousness, a rhythm like the tail of a fish, a cadence like the sound of the sea or the arbor bees—a droning, a hissing, a sighing. I find it in early Auden:

> Shall memory restore
> The steps and the shore,
> The face and the meeting place;
> Shall the bird live,
> Shall the fish dive,
> And sheep obey
> In a sheep's way;
> Can love remember
> The question and the answer,
> For love recover
> What has been dark and rich and warm all over?

Curiously, we find this primitiveness of the imagination cropping up in the most sophisticated poetry. If we concern ourselves with more primitive effects in poetry, we come inevitably to consideration, I think, of verse that is closer to prose. And here we jump rhythmically to a kind of opposite extreme. For many *strong* stresses, or a playing against an iambic pattern to a loosening up, a longer, more irregular foot, I agree that free verse is a denial in terms. There is, invariably, the ghost of some other form, often blank verse, behind what is written, or the more elaborate rise and fall of the rhythmical prose sentence. Let me point up, to use Mr. Warren's phrase, in a more specific way the difference between the formal poem and the more proselike piece. Mr. Ransom has written his beautiful elegy, "Bells for John Whiteside's Daughter"; I'd like to read "Elegy for Jane" on the same theme, a poem, I'm proud to say, Mr. Ransom first printed.

> *I remember the neckcurls, limp and damp as tendrils;*
> *And her quick look, a sidelong pickerel smile;*
> *And how, once startled into talk, the light syllables leaped for her,*
> *And she balanced in the delight of her thought,*
> *A wren, happy, tail into the wind,*
> *Her song trembling the twigs and small branches.*
> *The shade sang with her;*
> *The leaves, their whispers turned to kissing;*
> *And the mold sang in the bleached valleys under the rose.*
>
> *Oh, when she was sad, she cast herself down into such a pure depth,*
> *Even a father could not find her:*
> *Scraping her cheek against straw;*
> *Stirring the clearest water.*
>
> *My sparrow, you are not here,*
> *Waiting like a fern, making a spiny shadow.*
> *The sides of wet stones cannot console me,*
> *Nor the moss, wound with the last light.*
>
> *If only I could nudge you from this sleep,*
> *My maimed darling, my skittery pigeon.*
> *Over this damp grave I speak the words of my love:*
> *I, with no rights in this matter,*
> *Neither father nor lover.*

But let me indicate one or two technical effects in my little piece. For one thing, the enumeration, the favorite device of the more irregular poem. We see it again and again in Whitman and Lawrence. "I remember," then the listing, the appositions, and the absolute construction. "Her song trembling," etc. Then the last three lines in the stanza lengthen out:

> *The shade sang with her;*
> *The leaves, their whispers turned to kissing;*
> *And the mold sang in the bleached valleys under the rose.*

A kind of continuing triad. In the last two stanzas exactly the opposite occurs, the final lines being,

> *Over this damp grave I speak the words of my love:*
> *I, with no rights in this matter,*
> *Neither father nor lover.*

There is a successive shortening of the line length, an effect I have become inordinately fond of, I'm afraid. This little piece indicates in a way some of the strategies for the poet writing without the support of a formal pattern—he can vary his line length, modulate, he can stretch out the line, he can shorten. It was Lawrence, a master of this sort of poem (I think I quote him more or less exactly) who said, "It all depends on the pause, the natural pause." In other words, the breath unit, the language that is natural to the immediate thing, the particular emotion. Think of what we'd have missed in Lawrence, in Whitman, in Charlotte Mew, or, more lately, in Robert Lowell, if we denied this kind of poem. There are areas of experience in modern life that simply cannot be rendered by either the formal lyric or straight prose. We need the catalogue in our time. We need the eye close on the object, and the poem about the single incident—the animal, the child. We must permit poetry to extend consciousness as far, as deeply, as particularly as it can, to recapture, in Stanley Kunitz's phrase, what it has lost to some extent to prose. We must realize, I think, that the writer in freer forms must have an even greater fidelity to his subject matter than the poet who has the support of form. He must keep his eye on the object, and his rhythm must move as a mind moves, must be imaginatively right, or he is lost. Let me end with a simple and somewhat clumsy example of my own, in which we see a formal device giving energy to the piece, that device being, simply, participial or verbal forms that keep the action going:

Big Wind

Where were the greenhouses going,
Lunging into the lashing
Wind driving water
So far down the river
All the faucets stopped?—
So we drained the manure-machine
For the steam plant,
Pumping the stale mixture
Into the rusty boilers,
Watching the pressure gauge
Waver over to red,
As the seams hissed
And the live steam
Drove to the far
End of the rose-house,
Where the worst wind was,
Creaking the cypress window-frames,
Cracking so much thin glass
We stayed all night,
Stuffing the holes with burlap;
But she rode it out,
That old rose-house,
She hove into the teeth of it,
The core and pith of that ugly storm,
Ploughing with her stiff prow,
Bucking into the wind-waves
That broke over the whole of her,
Flailing her sides with spray,
Flinging long strings of wet across the roof-top,
Finally veering, wearing themselves out, merely
Whistling thinly under the wind vents;
She sailed until the calm morning,
Carrying her full cargo of roses.

(1960)

Sinclair Ross
(CANADA, 1908–1996)

One's a Heifer

My uncle was laid up that winter with sciatica, so when the blizzard stopped and still two of the yearlings hadn't come home with the other cattle, Aunt Ellen said I'd better saddle Tim and start out looking for them.

"Then maybe I'll not be back tonight," I told her firmly. "Likely they've drifted as far as the sandhills. There's no use coming home without them."

I was thirteen, and had never been away like that all night before, but, busy with the breakfast, Aunt Ellen said yes, that sounded sensible enough, and while I ate, hunted up a dollar in silver for my meals.

"Most people wouldn't take it from a lad, but they're strangers up towards the hills. Bring it out independent-like, but don't insist too much. They're more likely to grudge you a feed of oats for Tim."

After breakfast I had to undress again, and put on two suits of underwear and two pairs of thick, home-knitted stockings. It was a clear, bitter morning. After the storm the drifts lay clean and unbroken to the horizon. Distant farm-buildings stood out distinct against the prairie as if the thin sharp atmosphere were a magnifying glass. As I started off Aunt Ellen peered cautiously out of the door a moment through a cloud of steam, and waved a red and white checkered dish-towel. I didn't wave back, but conscious of her uneasiness rode erect, as jaunty as the sheepskin and two suits of underwear would permit.

We took the road straight south about three miles. The calves, I reasoned, would have by this time found their way home if the blizzard hadn't carried them at least that far. Then we started catercornering across fields, riding over to straw-stacks where we could see cattle sheltering, calling at farmhouses to ask had they seen any strays. "Yearlings," I said each time politely. "Red with white spots and faces. The same almost except that one's a heifer and the other isn't."

Nobody had seen them. There was a crust on the snow not quite hard enough to carry Tim, and despite the cold his flanks and shoulders soon were steaming. He walked with his head down, and sometimes, taking my sympathy for granted, drew up a minute for breath.

My spirits, too, began to flag. The deadly cold and the flat white silent miles of prairie asserted themselves like a disapproving presence. The cattle round the straw-stacks stared when we rode up as if we were intruders. The fields stared, and the sky stared. People shivered in their doorways, and said they'd seen no strays.

At about one o'clock we stopped at a farmhouse for dinner. It was a single oat sheaf half thistles for Tim, and fried eggs and bread and tea for me. Crops had been poor that year, they apologized, and though they shook their heads when I brought out my money I saw the woman's eyes light greedily a second, as if her instincts of hospitality were struggling hard against some urgent need. We too, I said, had poor crops lately. That was why it was so important that I find the calves.

We rested an hour, then went on again. "Yearlings," I kept on describing them. "Red with white spots and faces. The same except that one's a heifer and the other isn't."

Still no one had seen them, still it was cold, still Tim protested what a fool I was.

The country began to roll a little. A few miles ahead I could see the first low line of sandhills. "They'll be there for sure," I said aloud, more to encourage myself than Tim. "Keeping straight to the road it won't take a quarter as long to get home again."

But home now seemed a long way off. A thin white sheet of cloud spread across the sky, and though there had been no warmth in the sun the fields looked colder and bleaker without the glitter on the snow. Straw-stacks were fewer here, as if the land were poor, and every house we stopped at seemed more dilapidated than the one before.

A nagging wind rose as the afternoon wore on. Dogs yelped and bayed at us, and sometimes from the hills, like the signal of our approach, there was a thin, wavering howl of a coyote. I began to dread the miles home again almost as much as those still ahead. There were so many cattle straggling across the fields, so many yearlings just like ours. I saw them for sure a dozen times, and as often choked my disappointment down and clicked Tim on again.

And then at last I really saw them. It was nearly dusk, and along with fifteen or twenty other cattle they were making their way towards some buildings that lay huddled at the foot of the sandhills. They passed in single file less than fifty yards away, but when I pricked Tim forward to turn them back he floundered in a snowed-in water-cut. By the time we were out they were a little distance ahead, and on account of the drifts it was impossible to put on a spurt of speed and pass them. All we could do was take our place at the end of the file, and proceed at their pace towards the buildings.

It was about half a mile. As we drew near I debated with Tim whether we should ask to spend the night or start off right away for home. We were hungry and tired, but it was a poor, shiftless-looking place. The yard was littered with old wagons and machinery; the house was scarcely distinguishable from the stables. Darkness was beginning to close in, but there was no light in the windows.

Then as we crossed the yard we heard a shout, "Stay where you are," and a man came running towards us from the stable. He was tall and ungainly, and, instead of the short sheepskin that most farmers wear, had on a long black overcoat nearly to his feet. He seized Tim's bridle when he reached us, and glared for a minute as if he were going to pull me out of the saddle. "I told you to stay out," he said in a harsh, excited voice. "You heard me, didn't you? What do you want coming round here anyway?"

I steeled myself and said, "Our two calves."

The muscles of his face were drawn together threateningly, but close to him like this and looking straight into his eyes I felt that for all their fierce look there was something about them wavering and uneasy. "The two red ones with the white faces," I continued. "They've just gone into the shed over there with yours. If you'll give me a hand getting them out again I'll start for home now right away."

He peered at me a minute, let go the bridle, then clutched it again. "They're all mine," he countered. "I was over by the gate. I watched them coming in."

His voice was harsh and thick. The strange wavering look in his eyes steadied itself for a minute to a dare. I forced myself to meet it and insisted, "I saw them back a piece in the field. They're ours all right. Let me go over a minute and I'll show you."

With a crafty tilt of his head he leered. "You didn't see any calves. And now, if you know what's good for you, you'll be on your way."

"You're trying to steal them," I flared rashly. "I'll go home and get my uncle and the police after you—then you'll see whether they're our calves or not."

My threat seemed to impress him a little. With a shifty glance in the direction of the stable he said, "All right, come along and look them over. Then maybe you'll be satisfied." But all the way across the yard he kept his hand on Tim's bridle, and at the shed made me wait a few minutes while he went inside.

The cattle shed was a lean to on the horse stable. It was plain enough: he was hiding the calves before letting me inside to look around. While waiting for him, however, I had time to reflect that he was a lot bigger and stronger than I was, and that it might be prudent just to keep my eyes open, and not give him too much insolence.

He reappeared carrying a smoky lantern. "All right," he said pleasantly enough, "come in and look around. Will your horse stand, or do you want to tie him?"

We put Tim in an empty stall in the horse stable, then went through a narrow doorway with a bar across it to the cattle shed. Just as I expected, our calves weren't there. There were two red ones with white markings that he tried to make me believe were the ones I had seen, but, positive I hadn't been mistaken, I shook my head and glanced at the doorway we had just come through. It was narrow, but not too narrow. He read my expression and said, "You think they're in there. Come on, then, and look around."

The horse stable consisted of two rows of open stalls with a passage down the centre like an aisle. At the far end were two box-stalls, one with a sick colt in it, the other closed. They were both boarded up to the ceiling, so that you could see inside them only through the doors. Again he read my expression, and with a nod towards the closed one said, "It's just a kind of harness room now. Up till a year ago I kept a stallion."

But he spoke furtively, and seemed anxious to get me away from that end of the stable. His smoky lantern threw great swaying shadows over us; and the deep clefts and triangles of shadow on his face sent a little chill through me, and made me think what a dark and evil face it was.

I was afraid, but not too afraid. "If it's just a harness room," I said recklessly, "why not let me see inside? Then I'll be satisfied and believe you."

He wheeled at my question, and sidled over swiftly to the stall. He stood in front of the door, crouched down a little, the lantern in front of him like a shield. There was a sudden still-ness through the stable as we faced each other. Behind the light from his lantern the darkness hovered vast and sinister. It seemed to hold its breath, to watch and listen. I felt a clutch of fear now at my throat, but I didn't move. My eyes were fixed on him so intently that he seemed to lose substance, to loom up close a moment, then recede. At last he disappeared completely, and there was only the lantern like a hard hypnotic eye.

It held me. It held me rooted, against my will. I wanted to run from the stable, but I wanted even more to see inside the stall. Wanting to see and yet afraid of seeing. So afraid that it was a relief when at last he gave a shame-faced laugh and said, "There's a hole in the floor—that's why I keep the door closed. If you didn't know, you might step into it—twist your foot. That's what happened to one of my horses a while ago."

I nodded as if I believed him, and went back tractably to Tim. But regaining control of myself as I tried the saddle girths, beginning to feel that my fear had been unwarranted, I looked up and said, "It's ten miles home, and we've been riding hard all day. If we could stay a while—have something to eat, and then get started—"

The wavering light came into his eyes again. He held the lantern up to see me better, such a long, intent scrutiny that it seemed he must discover my designs. But he gave a nod finally, as if reassured, brought oats and hay for Tim, and suggested, companionably, "After supper we can have a game of checkers."

Then, as if I were a grown-up, he put out his hand and said, "My name is Arthur Vickers."

Inside the house, rid of his hat and coat, he looked less forbidding. He had a white nervous face, thin lips, a large straight nose, and deep uneasy eyes. When the lamp was lit I fancied I could still see the wavering expression in them, and decided it was what you called a guilty look.

"You won't think much of it," he said apologetically, following my glance around the room. "I ought to be getting things cleaned up again. Come over to the stove. Supper won't take long."

It was a large, low-ceilinged room that for the first moment or two struck me more like a shed or granary than a house. The table in the centre was littered with tools and harness. On a rusty cook-stove were two big steaming pots of bran. Next to the stove stood a grindstone, then a white iron bed covered with coats and horse blankets. At the end opposite the bed, weasel and coyote skins were drying. There were guns and traps on the wall, a horse collar, a pair of rubber boots. The floor was bare and grimy. Ashes were littered around the stove. In a corner squatted a live owl with a broken wing.

He walked back and forth a few times looking helplessly at the disorder, then cleared off the table and lifted the pots of bran to the back of the stove. "I've been mending harness," he explained. "You get careless, living alone like this. It takes a woman anyway."

My presence, apparently, was making him take stock of the room. He picked up a broom and swept for a minute, made an ineffective attempt to straighten the blankets on the bed, brought another lamp out of a cupboard and lit it. There was an ungainly haste to all his movements. He started unbuckling my sheepskin for me, then turned away suddenly to take off his own coat. "Now we'll have supper," he said with an effort at self-possession. "Coffee and beans is all I can give you—maybe a little molasses."

I replied diplomatically that that sounded pretty good. It didn't seem right, accepting hospitality this way from a man trying to steal your calves, but theft, I reflected, surely justified deceit. I held my hands out to the warmth and asked if I could help.

There was a kettle of plain navy beans already cooked. He dipped out enough for our supper into a frying pan, and on top laid rashers of fat salt pork. While I watched that they didn't burn he rinsed off a few dishes. Then he set the sugar and canned milk, butter, molasses, and dark heavy biscuits that he had baked himself the day before. He kept glancing at me so apologetically all the while that I leaned over and sniffed the beans, and said at home I ate a lot of them.

"It takes a woman," he repeated as we sat down to the table. "I don't often have anyone here to eat with me. If I'd known, I'd have cleaned things up a little."

I was too intent on my plateful of beans to answer. All through the meal he sat watching me, but made no further attempts at conversation. Hungry as I was, I noticed that the wavering, uneasy look was still in his eyes. A guilty look, I told myself again, and wondered what I was going to do to get the calves away. I finished my coffee and he continued:

"It's worse even than this in the summer. No time for meals—and the heat and flies. Last summer I had a girl cooking for a few weeks, but it didn't last. Just a cow she was—just a big stupid cow—and she wanted to stay on. There's a family of them back in the hills. I had to send her home."

I wondered should I suggest starting now, or ask to spend the night. Maybe when he's asleep, I thought, I can slip out of the house and get away with the calves. He went on, "You don't know how bad it is sometimes. Weeks on end and no one to talk to. You're not yourself—you're not sure what you're going to say or do."

I remembered hearing my uncle talk about a man who had gone crazy living alone. And this fellow Vickers had queer eyes all right. And there was the live owl over in the corner, and the grindstone standing right beside the bed. "Maybe I'd better go now," I decided aloud. "Tim'll be rested, and it's ten miles home."

But he said no, it was colder now, with the wind getting stronger, and seemed so kindly concerned that I half forgot my fears. "Likely he's just starting to go crazy," I told myself, "and it's only by staying that I'll have a chance to get the calves away."

When the table was cleared and the dishes washed he said he would go out and bed down the stable for the night. I picked up my sheepskin to go with him, but he told me sharply to stay inside. Just for a minute he looked crafty and forbidding as when I first rode up on Tim, and to allay his suspicions I nodded compliantly and put my sheepskin down again. It was better like that anyway, I decided. In a few minutes I could follow him, and perhaps, taking advantage of the shadows and his smoky lantern, make my way to the box-stall unobserved.

But when I reached the stable he had closed the door after him and hooked it from the inside. I walked round a while, tried to slip in by way of the cattle shed, and then had to go back to the house. I went with a vague feeling of relief again. There was still time, I told myself, and it would be safer anyway when he was sleeping.

So that it would be easier to keep from falling asleep myself I planned to suggest coffee again just before we went to bed. I knew that the guest didn't ordinarily suggest such things, but it was no time to remember manners when there was someone trying to steal your calves.

When he came in from the stable we played checkers. I was no match for him, but to encourage me he repeatedly let me win. "It's a long time now since I've had a chance to play," he kept on saying, trying to convince me that his shortsighted moves weren't intentional. "Sometimes I used to ask her to play, but I had to tell her every move to make. If she didn't win she'd upset the board and go off and sulk."

"My aunt is a little like that too," I said. "She cheats sometimes when we're playing cribbage—and, when I catch her, says her eyes aren't good."

"Women talk too much ever to make good checker players. It takes concentration. This one, though, couldn't even talk like anybody else."

After my long day in the cold I was starting to yawn already. He noticed it, and spoke in a rapid, earnest voice, as if afraid I might lose interest soon and want to go to bed. It was important for me too to stay awake, so I crowned a king and said, "Why don't you get someone, then, to stay with you?"

"Too many of them want to do that." His face darkened a little, almost as if warning me. "Too many of the kind you'll never get rid of again. She did, last summer when she was here. I had to put her out."

There was silence for a minute, his eyes flashing, and wanting to placate him I suggested, "She liked you, maybe."

He laughed a moment, harshly. "She liked me all right. Just two weeks ago she came back—walked over with an old suitcase and said she was going to stay. It was cold at home, and she had to work too hard, and she didn't mind even if I couldn't pay her wages."

I was getting sleepier. To keep awake I sat on the edge of the chair where it was uncomfortable and said, "Hadn't you asked her to come?"

His eyes narrowed. "I'd had trouble enough getting rid of her the first time. There were six of them at home, and she said her father thought it time that someone married her."

"Then she must be a funny one," I said. "Everybody knows that the man's supposed to ask the girl."

My remark seemed to please him. "I told you didn't I?" he said, straightening a little, jumping two of my men. "She was so stupid that at checkers she'd forget whether she was black or red."

We stopped playing now. I glanced at the owl in the corner and the ashes littered on the floor, and thought that keeping her would maybe have been a good idea after all. He read it in my face and said, "I used to think that too sometimes. I used to look at her and think nobody knew now anyway and that she'd maybe do. You need a woman on a farm all right. And night after night she'd be sitting there where you are—right there where you are, looking at me, not even trying to play—"

The fire was low, and we could hear the wind. "But then I'd go up in the hills, away from her for a while, and start thinking back the way things used to be, and it wasn't right even for the sake of your meals ready and your house kept clean. When she came back I tried to tell her that, but all the family are the same, and I realized it wasn't any use. There's nothing you can do when you're up against that sort of thing. The mother talks just like a child of ten. When she sees you coming she runs and hides. There are six of them, and it's come out in every one."

It was getting cold, but I couldn't bring myself to go over to the stove. There was the same stillness now as when he was standing at the box-stall door. And I felt the same illogical fear, the same powerlessness to move. It was the way his voice had sunk, the glassy, cold look in his eyes. And they filled me with a vague and overpowering dread. My own voice a whisper, I asked, "And when you wouldn't marry her—what happened then?"

He remained motionless a moment, as if answering silently; then with an unexpected laugh like a breaking dish said, "Why, nothing happened. I just told her she couldn't stay. I went to town for a few days—and when I came back she was gone."

"Has she been back to bother you since?" I asked.

He made a little silo of checkers. "No—she took her suitcase with her."

To remind him that the fire was going down I went over to the stove and stood warming myself. He raked the coals with the lifter and put in poplar, two split pieces for a base and a thick round log on top. I yawned again. He said maybe I'd like to go to bed now, and I shivered and asked him could I have a drink of coffee first. While it boiled he stood stirring the two big pots of bran. The trouble with coffee, I realized, was that it would keep him from getting sleepy too.

I undressed finally and got into bed, but he blew out only one of the lamps, and sat on playing checkers with himself. I dozed a while, then sat up with a start, afraid it was morning already and that I'd lost my chance to get the calves away. He came over and looked at me a minute, then gently pushed my shoulders back on the pillow. "Why don't you come to bed too?" I asked, and he said, "Later I will—I don't feel sleepy yet."

It was like that all night. I kept dozing on and off, wakening in a fright each time to find him still there sitting at his checker board. He would raise his head sharply when I stirred, then tiptoe over to the bed and stand close to me listening till satisfied again I was asleep. The owl kept wakening too. It was down in the corner still where the lamplight scarcely reached, and I could see its eyes go on and off like yellow bulbs. The wind whistled drearily around the house. The blankets smelled like an old granary. He suspected what I was planning to do, evidently, and was staying awake to make sure I didn't get outside.

Each time I dozed I dreamed I was on Tim again. The calves were in sight, but far ahead of us, and with the drifts so deep we couldn't overtake them. Then instead of Tim it was the grindstone I was straddling, and that was the reason, not the drifts, that we weren't making better progress.

I wondered what would happen to the calves if I didn't get away with them. My uncle had sciatica, and it would be at least a day before I could be home and back again with some of the neighbours. By then Vickers might have butchered the calves, or driven them up to a hiding place in the hills where we'd never find them. There was the possibility, too, that Aunt Ellen and the neighbours wouldn't believe me. I dozed and woke—dozed and woke—always he was sitting at the checker board. I could hear the dry tinny ticking of an alarm clock, but from where I was lying couldn't see it. He seemed to be listening to it too. The wind would sometimes creak the house, and then he would give a start and sit rigid a moment with his eyes fixed on the window. It was always the window, as if there was nothing he was afraid of that could reach him by the door.

Most of the time he played checkers with himself, moving his lips, muttering words I couldn't hear, but once I woke to find him staring fixedly across the table as if he had a partner sitting there. His hands were clenched in front of him, there was a sharp, metallic glitter in his eyes. I lay transfixed, unbreathing. His eyes as I watched seemed to dilate, to brighten, to harden like a bird's. For a long time he sat contracted, motionless, as if gathering himself to strike, then furtively he slid his hand an inch or two along the table towards some checkers that were piled beside the board. It was as if he were reaching for a weapon, as if his invisible partner were an enemy. He clutched the checkers, slipped slowly from his chair and straightened. His movements were sure, stealthy, silent like a cat's. His face had taken on a desperate, contorted look. As he raised his hand the tension was unbearable.

It was a long time—a long time watching him the way you watch a finger tightening slowly in the trigger of a gun—and then suddenly wrenching himself to action he hurled the checkers with such vicious fury that they struck the wall and clattered back across the room.

And everything was quiet again. I started a little, mumbled to myself as if half-awakened, lay quite still. But he seemed to have forgotten me, and after standing limp and dazed a minute got down on his knees and started looking for the checkers. When he had them all, he put more wood in the stove, then returned quietly to the table and sat down. We were alone again; everything was exactly as before. I relaxed gradually, telling myself that he'd just been seeing things.

The next time I woke he was sitting with his head sunk forward on the table. It looked as if he had fallen asleep at last, and huddling alert among the bedclothes I decided to watch a minute to make sure, then dress and try to slip out to the stable.

While I watched, I planned exactly every movement I was going to make. Rehearsing it in my mind as carefully as if I were actually doing it, I climbed out of bed, put on my clothes, tiptoed stealthily to the door and slipped outside. By this time, though, I was getting drowsy, and relaxing among the blankets I decided that for safety's sake I should rehearse it still again. I rehearsed it four times altogether, and the fourth time dreamed that I hurried on successfully to the stable.

I fumbled with the door a while, then went inside and felt my way through the darkness to the box-stall. There was a bright light suddenly and the owl was sitting over the door with his yellow eyes like a pair of lanterns. The calves, he told me, were in the other stall with the sick colt. I looked and they were there all right, but Tim came up and said it might be better not to start for home till morning. He reminded me that I hadn't paid for his feed or my own supper yet, and that if I slipped off this way it would mean that I was stealing, too. I agreed, realizing now that it wasn't the calves I was looking for after all, and that I still had to see inside the stall that was guarded by the owl. "Wait here," Tim said, "I'll tell you if he flies away," and without further questioning I lay down in the straw and went to sleep again. . . . When I woke coffee and beans were on the stove already, and though the lamp was still lit I could tell by the window that it was nearly morning.

We were silent during breakfast. Two or three times I caught him watching me, and it seemed his eyes were shiftier than before. After his sleepless night he looked tired and haggard. He left the table while I was still eating and fed raw rabbit to the owl, then came back and drank another cup of coffee. He had been friendly and communicative the night before, but now, just as when he first came running out of the stable in his long black coat, his expression was sullen and resentful. I began to feel that he was in a hurry to be rid of me.

I took my time, however, racking my brains to outwit him still and get the calves away. It looked pretty hopeless now, his eyes on me so suspiciously, my imagination at low ebb. Even if I did get inside the box-stall to see the calves—was he going to stand back then and let me start off home with them? Might it not more likely frighten him, make him do something desperate, so that I couldn't reach my uncle or the police? There was the owl over in the corner, the grindstone by the bed. And with such a queer fellow you could never tell. You could never tell, and you had to think about your own skin too. So I said politely, "Thank you, Mr. Vickers, for letting me stay all night," and remembering what Tim had told me took out my dollar's worth of silver.

He gave a short dry laugh and wouldn't take it. "Maybe you'll come back," he said, "and next time stay longer. We'll go shooting up in the hills if you like—and I'll make a trip to town for things so that we can have better meals. You need company sometimes for a change. There's been no one here now quite a while."

His face softened again as he spoke. There was an expression in his eyes as if he wished that I could stay on. It puzzled me. I wanted to be indignant, and it was impossible. He held my sheepskin for me while I put it on, and tied the scarf around the collar with a solicitude and determination equal to Aunt Ellen's. And then he gave his short dry laugh again, and hoped I'd find my calves all right.

He had been out to the stable before I was awake, and Tim was ready for me, fed and saddled. But I delayed a few minutes, pretending to be interested in his horses and the sick colt. It would be worth something after all, I realized, to get just a glimpse of the calves. Aunt Ellen was going to be sceptical enough of my story as it was. It could only confirm her doubts to hear me say I hadn't seen the calves in the box-stall, and was just pretty sure that they were there.

So I went from stall to stall, stroking the horses and making comparisons with the ones we had at home. The door, I noticed, he had left wide open, ready for me to lead out Tim. He was walking up and down the aisle, telling me which horses were quiet, which to be careful of. I came to a nervous chestnut mare, and realized she was my only chance.

She crushed her hips against the side of the stall as I slipped up to her manger, almost pinning me, then gave her head a toss and pulled back hard on the halter shank. The shank, I noticed, was tied with an easy slip-knot that the right twist and a sharp tug would undo in half a second. And the door was wide open, ready for me to lead out Tim—and standing as she was with her body diagonally, I was for the moment screened from sight.

It happened quickly. There wasn't time to think of consequences. I just pulled the knot, in the same instant struck the mare across the nose. With a snort she threw herself backwards, almost trampling Vickers, then flung up her head to keep from tripping on the shank and plunged outside.

It worked as I hoped it would. "Quick," Vickers yelled to me, "the gate's open—try and head her off"—but instead I just waited till he himself was gone, then leaped to the box-stall.

The door was fastened with two tight-fitting slide-bolts, one so high that I could scarcely reach it standing on my toes. It wouldn't yield. There was a piece of broken whiffle-tree beside the other box-stall door. I snatched it up and started hammering on the pin. Still it wouldn't yield. The head of the pin was small and round, and the whiffle-tree kept glancing off. I was too terrified to pause a moment to take careful aim.

Terrified of the stall though, not of Vickers. Terrified of the stall, yet compelled by a frantic need to get inside. For the moment I had forgotten Vickers, forgotten even the danger of his catching me. I worked blindly, helplessly, as if I were confined and smothering. For a moment I yielded to panic, dropped the piece of whiffle-tree and started kicking at the door. Then, collected again, I forced back the lower bolt, and picking up the whiffle-tree tried to pry the door out a little at the bottom. But I had wasted too much time. Just as I dropped to my knees to peer through the opening Vickers seized me. I struggled to my feet and fought a moment, but it was such a hard, strangling clutch at my throat that I felt myself go limp and blind. In desperation then I kicked him, and with a blow like a reflex he sent me staggering to the floor.

But it wasn't the blow that frightened me. It was the fierce, wild light in his eyes.

Stunned as I was, I looked up and saw him watching me, and, sick with terror, made a bolt for Tim. I untied him with hands that moved incredibly, galvanized for escape. I knew now for sure that Vickers was crazy. He followed me outside, and just as I mounted, seized Tim again by the bridle. For a second or two it made me crazy too. Gathering up the free ends of the rein I lashed him hard across the face. He let go of the bridle and, frightened and excited too now, Tim made a dash across the yard and out of the gate. Deep as the snow was, I kept him galloping for half a mile, pommelling him with my fists, kicking my heels against his sides. Then of his own accord he drew up short for breath, and I looked around to see whether Vickers was following. He wasn't—there was only snow and the hills, his buildings a lonely smudge against the whiteness—and the relief was like a stick pulled out that's been holding up tomato vines or peas. I slumped across the saddle weakly, and till Tim started on again lay there whimpering like a baby.

We were home by noon. We didn't have to cross fields or stop at houses now, and there had been teams on the road packing down the snow so that Tim could trot part of the way and even canter. I put him in the stable without taking time to tie or unbridle him, and ran to the house to tell Aunt Ellen. But I was still frightened, cold and a little hysterical, and it was a while before she could understand how everything had happened. She was silent a minute, indulgent, then helping me off with my sheepskin said kindly, "You'd better forget about it now, and come over and get warm. The calves came home themselves yesterday. Just about an hour after you set out."

I looked up at her. "But the stall, then—just because I wanted to look inside he knocked me down—and if it wasn't the calves in there—"

She didn't answer. She was busy building up the fire and looking at the stew.

(1944)

Ralph Gustafson

(CANADA, 1909–1995)

Of Green Steps and Laundry

The man will put a large-headed nail,
Shiny as silver, into the green step,
Straightening winter's bias and spring
Thaw and his hammer will knock it crooked
5   The bird come obtrusively to the bough above,
And it will have to be done again, and that
Will be important; and she will hang
Blue and white shirts and a patched quilt
On the laundry line that runs from the kitchen
10 Step to the yard telephone pole and sheets
That smell of winter's cold, and the pulley
Each time the line is launched will squeak,
And that will be important; and neither
She nor the man pounding the clear air
15 Fixing the green step with another nail,
Will be aware of the importance, twenty
Years later thought of by him
Who drove nails and saw laundry,
Who thought little of cardinals and clothespins
20 And now loves life, loves life.

(1977)

Partial Argument

Poetry, the only act which separates
Truth from supposition. Atomic
Missive is accurate but supposes. Music
Is pure: F-sharp, F-natural,
5   Without burdens such as "we
Must love one another or die"
Or thirteen million a year are born
In India. The greater art, but
Itself. Poetry, the truth
10   Plus trouble. Let us suppose the polished
Lens discovers black star,
The rocks on the moon are shoved back
A billion years. Does Jack love
Jill?
15   No, I tell you, the poet's
Postulate trembles with extents,
The writing's urgence a doctor's script,
The sculptor's inch, that much comparison.
Kitchen statistics mark the loaf and
20   Knead of bread but I have seen
Coition with belly hunger bitten
Predicted by a verse, the farthest
Decimal relay supposition
And oil from Persia choke birds.
25   "Instinctive integrations" lacking,
The day's absurd; clocks, compassion;
The world's measure taken by honest
Men, an iridio-platinum
Metre at 62°.
30   Words in a poem come together
Implacably as an apple tastes;
A pond, a dog, three boys on skates;
Someone singing or a death.

(1977)

A.M. Klein
(CANADA, 1909–1972)

A Modest Proposal

Many readers no doubt will recall that the great satirist Dean Swift, in seeking to heap ridicule upon his contemporaries, suggested by way of 'modest proposal' a *reductio ad absurdum* of the customs of his fellow-men then current. Having neither the wit nor the Irish of the Dean, it does seem to us, nonetheless, that there is a crying need for such a 'modest proposal' anent the destiny of the Jewish homeland and the fate of Jewish refugees.

It appears that great numbers of the wanderers have willy-nilly taken to the high seas. The *St. Louis* floats upon the Atlantic for two months, freighted with unhappy human cargo. Another ship leaves some Greek port, and arrives in Palestine only to see its passengers interned in a concentration camp. But a little while ago there came to the shores of Erez Israel a ship which Jews in Danzig had bought and manned, and directed to the Holy Land; when they arrived at the Port of Haifa they were towed out of the harbour and left floating along the sea-coast.

Here then is the opportunity for some grim humorist to win himself a place in immortality beside Dean Swift. Let him suggest a homeland for Jews upon the face of the waters!

If there was room for a 'Jewish Territorial Movement,' perhaps a Hebrew Oceanic Society can be organized!

Perhaps, too, the British Government, realizing the error of its ways, will revise the Balfour Declaration, and issue a new one, a liquid one: 'His Majesty's Government views with favour the "floating" of a "National Jewish Homewater," anywhere upon the surface of those waves which Britannia rules, and will use its best endeavours to facilitate the achievement of this proposal, it being clearly understood that nothing will be done to injure the rights of non-Jews in the said waters.'

Upon the issuance of such a proclamation, shiploads of Jews would issue. They would always stay at anchor, a floating state joined, ship to ship, cruiser to cruiser, liner to liner, a floating state.

A couple of years thereafter, as this naval country would begin to prosper, the British Government would send forth a Royal Commission to investigate. The Commission would bring in a report that the Jewish Homewater was not properly docked, and that the Jewish ships were destroying the national independence of the neighboring fish. Tons of pamphlets would then be circulated about the problem of 'the landless fish.' The chairman of the aforementioned Commission would insist, with all the logic he could muster, that the phrase 'nothing will be done to injure the rights of non-Jews,' obviously referred to the local marine life, which apparently did not subscribe to the Mosaic creed.

Ship-building would continue, and the Homewater would expand. Another Commission would be then sent to examine the area of '*Yom Yisroel*' and would look with disapproval upon the 'immigration waves.' Recommendations would be made that there should be a Partition of the waves, the learned Commissioner, indeed, would support his viewpoint by citing from the biography of Moses who performed a similar procedure on the Red Sea.

But the Homewater would still flourish. '*Yom Yisroel Chai!*' would be the slogan of a national Jewry. Whereupon the Colonial Office, completely fed up with the manner in which these *chalutzim* would be making a success even out of water, would begin to study the above-mentioned Declaration again. Finally, it would issue a White Paper, made out of rubber—the better to float with, my child. The gist of this White Paper would be that when the Government promised a Homewater on the surface of those waves which Britannia rules, it really meant a different thing entirely. Instead of 'on the surface,' read, 'at the bottom'; otherwise they stick by all their commitments.

(14 July 1939)

Indian Reservation: Caughnawaga

Where are the braves, the faces like autumn fruit,
who stared at the child from the coloured frontispiece?
And the monosyllabic chief who spoke with his throat?
Where are the tribes, the feathered bestiaries?—
5   Rank Aesop's animals erect and red,
with fur on their names to make all live things kin—
Chief Running Deer, Black Bear, Old Buffalo Head?

Childhood, that wished me Indian, hoped that
one afterschool I'd leave the classroom chalk,
10   the varnish smell, the watered dust of the street,
to join the clean outdoors and the Iroquois track.
Childhood; but always,—as on a calendar,—
there stood that chief, with arms akimbo, waiting
the runaway mascot paddling to his shore.

15   With what strange moccasin stealth that scene is changed!
With French names, without paint, in overalls,
their bronze, like their nobility expunged,—
the men. Beneath their alimentary shawls
sit like black tents their squaws; while for the tourist's
20   brown pennies scattered at the old church door,
the ragged papooses jump, and bite the dust.

Their past is sold in a shop: the beaded shoes,
the sweetgrass basket, the curio Indian,
burnt wood and gaudy cloth and inch-canoes—
25   trophies and scalpings for a traveller's den.
Sometimes, it's true, they dance, but for a bribe;
after a deal don the bedraggled feather
and welcome a white mayor to the tribe.

This is a grassy ghetto, and no home.
30   And these are fauna in a museum kept.
The better hunters have prevailed. The game,
losing its blood, now makes these grounds its crypt.
The animals pale, the shine of the fur is lost,
bleached are their living bones. About them watch
35   as through a mist, the pious prosperous ghosts.

(1948)

Political Meeting

(For Camillien Houde)

On the school platform, draping the folding seats,
they wait the chairman's praise and glass of water.
Upon the wall the agonized Y initials their faith.

Here all are laic; the skirted brothers have gone.
5   Still, their equivocal absence is felt, like a breeze
that gives curtains the sounds of surplices.

The hall is yellow with light, and jocular;
suddenly some one lets loose upon the air
the ritual bird which the crowd in snares of singing

10   catches and plucks, throat, wings, and little limbs.
Fall the feathers of sound, like *alouette's*.
The chairman, now, is charming, full of asides and wit,

building his orators, and chipping off
the heckling gargoyles popping in the hall.
15   (Outside, in the dark, the street is body-tall,

flowered with faces intent on the scarecrow thing
that shouts to thousands the echoing
of their own wishes.) The Orator has risen!

Worshipped and loved, their favourite visitor,
20   a country uncle with sunflower seeds in his pockets,
full of wonderful moods, tricks, imitative talk,

he is their idol: like themselves, not handsome,
not snobbish, not of the *Grande Allée! Un homme!*
Intimate, informal, he makes bear's compliments

25   to the ladies; is gallant; and grins;
goes for the balloon, his opposition, with pins;
jokes also on himself, speaks of himself

in the third person, slings slang, and winks with folklore;
and knows now that he has them, kith and kin.
30   Calmly, therefore, he begins to speak of war,

praises the virtue of being *Canadien,*
of being at peace, of faith, of family,
and suddenly his other voice: *Where are your sons?*

He is tearful, choking tears; but not he
35   would blame the clever English; in their place
he'd do the same; maybe.

Where *are* your sons?
                  The whole street wears one face,
shadowed and grim; and in the darkness rises
40   the body-odour of race.

                                    (1948)

The Rocking Chair

It seconds the crickets of the province. Heard
in the clean lamplit farmhouses of Quebec,—
wooden,—it is no less a national bird;
and rivals, in its cage, the mere stuttering clock.
5   To its time, the evenings are rolled away;
and in its peace the pensive mother knits
contentment to be worn by her family,
grown-up, but still cradled by the chair in which she sits.

It is also the old man's pet, pair to his pipe,
10   the two aids of his arithmetic and plans,
plans rocking and puffing into market-shape;
and it is the toddler's game and dangerous dance.
Moved to the verandah, on summer Sundays, it is,
among the hanging plants, the girls, the boy-friends,
15   sabbatical and clumsy, like the white haloes
dangling above the blue serge suits of the young men.

It has a personality of its own;
is a character (like that old drunk Lacoste,
exhaling amber, and toppling on his pins);
20   it is alive; individual; and no less
an identity than those about it. And
it is tradition. Centuries have been flicked
from its arcs, alternatively flicked and pinned.
It rolls with the gait of St Malo. It is act

25   and symbol, symbol of this static folk
which moves in segments, and returns to base,—
a sunken pendulum: *invoke, revoke*;

loosed yon, leashed hither, motion on no space.
O, like some Anjou ballad, all refrain,
30   which turns about its longing, and seems to move
to make a pleasure out of repeated pain,
its music moves, as if always back to a first love.

                                    (1948)

Dorothy Livesay

(CANADA, 1909–1996)

Bartok and the Geranium

She lifts her green umbrellas
Towards the pane
Seeking her fill of sunlight
Or of rain;
5   Whatever falls
She has no commentary
Accepts, extends,
Blows out her furbelows
Her bustling boughs;

10   And all the while he whirls
Explodes in space,
Never content with this small room;
Not even can he be
Confined to sky
15   But must speed high
From galaxy to galaxy,
Wrench from the stars their momentary calm,
Stir music on the moon.

She's daylight;
20   He is dark.
She's heaven's held breath;
He storms and crackles
Spits with hell's own spark.

Yet in this room, this moment now
25   These together breathe and be:
She, essence of serenity,
He in a mad intensity
Soars beyond sight
Then hurls, lost Lucifer,
30   From heaven's height.
And when he's done, he's out:

She lays a lip against the glass
And preens herself in light.

(1955, 1957)

Wallace Stegner

(CANADA/U.S.A., 1909–1993)

The Town Dump

The town dump of Whitemud, Saskatchewan, could only have been a few years old when I knew it, for the village was born in 1913 and I left there in 1919. But I remember the dump better than I remember most things in that town, better than I remember most of the people. I spent more time with it, for one thing; it had more poetry and excitement in it than people did.

It lay in the southeast corner of town, in a section that was always full of adventure for me. Just there the Whitemud River left the hills, bent a little south, and started its long traverse across the prairie and international boundary to join the Milk. For all I knew, it might have been on its way to join the Alph: simply, before my eyes, it disappeared into strangeness and wonder.

Also, where it passed below the dumpground, it ran through willowed bottoms that were a favorite campsite for passing teamsters, gypsies, sometimes Indians. The very straw scattered around those camps, the ashes of those strangers' campfires, the manure of their teams and saddle horses, were hot with adventurous possibilities.

It was as an extension, a living suburb, as it were, of the dumpground that we most valued those camps. We scoured them for artifacts of their migrant tenants as if they had been archaeological sites full of the secrets of ancient civilizations. I remember toting around for weeks the broken cheek strap of a bridle. Somehow or other its buckle looked as if it had been fashioned in a far place, a place where they were accustomed to flatten the tongues of buckles for reasons that could only be exciting, and where they made a habit of plating the metal with some valuable alloy, probably silver. In places where the silver was worn away the buckle underneath shone dull yellow: probably gold.

It seemed that excitement liked that end of town better than our end. Once old Mrs. Gustafson, deeply religious and a little raddled in the head, went over there with a buckboard full of trash, and as she was driving home along the river she looked and saw a spent catfish, washed in from Cypress Lake or some other part of the watershed, floating on the yellow water. He was two feet long, his whiskers hung down, his fins and tail were limp. He was a kind of fish that no one had seen in the Whitemud in the three or four years of the town's life, and a kind that none of us children had ever seen anywhere. Mrs. Gustafson had never seen one like him either; she perceived at once that he was the devil, and she whipped up the team and reported him at Hoffman's elevator.

We could hear her screeching as we legged it for the river to see for ourselves. Sure enough, there he was. He looked very tired, and he made no great effort to get away as we pushed out a half-sunken rowboat from below the flume, submerged it under him, and brought him ashore. When he died three days later we experimentally fed him to two half-wild cats, but they seemed to suffer no ill effects.

At that same end of town the irrigation flume crossed the river. It always seemed to me giddily high when I hung my chin over its plank edge and looked down, but it probably walked no more than twenty feet above the water on its spidery legs. Ordinarily in summer it carried about six or eight inches of smooth water, and under the glassy hurrying of the little boxed stream the planks were coated with deep sun-warmed moss as slick as frogs' eggs. A boy could sit in the flume with the water walling up against his back, and grab a cross brace above him, and pull, shooting himself sledlike ahead until he could reach the next brace for another pull and another slide, and so on across the river in four scoots.

After ten minutes in the flume he would come out wearing a dozen or more limber black leeches, and could sit in the green shade where darning needles flashed blue, and dragonflies hummed and darted and stopped, and skaters dimpled slack and eddy with their delicate transitory footprints, and there stretch the leeches out one by one while their sucking ends clung and clung, until at last, stretched far out, they let go with a tiny wet *puk* and snapped together like rubber bands. The smell of the river and the flume and the clay cutbanks and the bars of that part of the river was the smell of wolf willow.

But nothing in that end of town was as good as the dumpground that scattered along a little runoff coulee dipping down toward the river from the south bench. Through a historical process that went back, probably, to the roots of community sanitation and distaste for eyesores, but that in law dated from the Unincorporated Towns Ordinance of the territorial government, passed in 1888, the dump was one of the very first community enterprises, almost our town's first institution.

More than that, it contained relics of every individual who had ever lived there, and of every phase of the town's history.

The bedsprings on which the town's first child was begotten might be there; the skeleton of a boy's pet colt; two or three volumes of Shakespeare bought in haste and error from a peddler, later loaned in carelessness, soaked with water and chemicals in a house fire, and finally thrown out to flap their stained eloquence in the prairie wind.

Broken dishes, rusty tinware, spoons that had been used to mix paint; once a box of percussion caps, sign and symbol of the carelessness that most of those people felt about all matters of personal or public safety. We put them on the railroad tracks and were anonymously denounced in the *Enterprise*. There were also old iron, old brass, for which we hunted assiduously, by night conning junkmen's catalogues and the pages of the *Enterprise* to find how much wartime value there might be in the geared insides of clocks or in a pound of tea lead carefully wrapped in a ball whose weight astonished and delighted us. Sometimes the unimaginable outside world reached in and laid a finger on us. I recall that, aged no more than seven, I wrote a St. Louis junk house asking if they preferred their tea lead and tinfoil wrapped in balls, or whether they would rather have it pressed flat in sheets, and I got back a typewritten letter in a window envelope instructing me that they would be happy to have it in any way that was convenient for me. They added that they valued my business and were mine very truly. Dazed, I carried that windowed grandeur around in my pocket until I wore it out, and for months I saved the letter as a souvenir of the wondering time when something strange and distinguished had singled me out.

We hunted old bottles in the dump, bottles caked with dirt and filth, half buried, full of cobwebs, and we washed them out at the horse trough by the elevator, putting in a handful of shot along with the water to knock the dirt loose; and when we had shaken them until our arms were tired, we hauled them off in somebody's coaster wagon and turned them in at Bill Anderson's pool hall, where the smell of lemon pop was so sweet on the dark pool-hall air that I am sometimes awakened by it in the night, even yet.

Smashed wheels of wagons and buggies, tangles of rusty barbed wire, the collapsed perambulator that the French wife of one of the town's doctors had once pushed proudly up the planked sidewalks and along the ditchbank paths. A welter of foul-smelling feathers and coyote-scattered carrion which was all that remained of somebody's dream of a chicken ranch. The chickens had all got some mysterious pip at the same time, and died as one, and the dream lay out there with the rest of the town's history to rustle to the empty sky on the border of the hills.

There was melted glass in curious forms, and the half-melted office safe left from the burning of Bill Day's Hotel. On very lucky days we might find a piece of the lead casing that had enclosed the wires of the town's first telephone system. The casing was just the right size for rings, and so soft that it could be whittled with a jackknife. It was a material that might have made artists of us. If we had been Indians of fifty years before, that bright soft metal would have enlisted our maximum patience and craft and come out as ring and metal and amulet inscribed with the symbols of our observed world. Perhaps there were too many ready-made alternatives in the local drug, hardware, and general stores; perhaps our feeble artistic response was a measure of the insufficiency of the challenge we felt. In any case I do not remember that we did any more with the metal than to shape it into crude seal rings with our initials or pierced hearts carved in them; and these, though they served a purpose in juvenile courtship, stopped something short of art.

The dump held very little wood, for in that country anything burnable got burned. But it had plenty of old iron, furniture, papers, mattresses that were the delight of field mice, and jugs and demijohns that were sometimes their bane, for they crawled into the necks and drowned in the rain water or redeye that was inside.

If the history of our town was not exactly written, it was at least hinted, in the dump. I think I had a pretty sound notion even at eight or nine of how significant was that first institution of our forming Canadian civilization. For rummaging through its foul purlieus I had several times been surprised and shocked to find relics of my own life tossed out there to rot or blow away.

The volumes of Shakespeare belonged to a set that my father had bought before I was born. It had been carried through successive moves from town to town in the Dakotas, and from Dakota to Seattle, and from Seattle to Bellingham, and Bellingham to Redmond, and from Redmond back to Iowa, and from there to Saskatchewan. Then, stained in a stranger's house fire, these volumes had suffered from a house-cleaning impulse and been thrown away for me to stumble upon in the dump. One of the Cratchet girls had borrowed them, a hatchet-faced, thin, eager, transplanted Cockney girl with a frenzy, almost a hysteria, for reading. And yet somehow, through her hands, they found the dump, to become a symbol of how much was lost, how much thrown aside, how much carelessly or of necessity given up, in the making of a new country. We had so few books that I was familiar with them all, and handled them, looked at their pictures, perhaps even read them. They were the lares and penates, part of the skimpy impedimenta of household gods we had brought with us into Latium. Finding those three thrown away was a little like finding my own name on a gravestone.

And yet not the blow that something else was, something that impressed me even more with the dump's close reflection of the town's intimate life. The colt whose picked skeleton lay out there was mine. He had been incurably crippled when dogs chased our mare, Daisy, the morning after she foaled. I had labored for months to make him well; had fed him by hand, curried him, exercised him, adjusted the iron braces that I had talked my father into having made. And I had not known that he would have to be destroyed. One weekend I turned him over to the foreman of one of the ranches, presumably so that he could be cared for. A few days later I found his skinned body, with the braces still on his crippled front legs, lying on the dump.

Not even that, I think, cured me of going there, though our parents all forbade us on pain of cholera or worse to do so. The place fascinated us, as it should have. For this was the kitchen midden of all the civilization we knew; it gave us the most tantalizing glimpses into our lives as well as into those of the neighbors. It gave us an aesthetic distance from which to know ourselves.

The dump was our poetry and our history. We took it home with us by the wagonload, bringing back into town the things the town had used and thrown away. Some little part of what we gathered, mainly bottles, we managed to bring back to usefulness, but most of our gleanings we left lying around barn or attic or cellar until in some renewed fury of spring cleanup our families carted them off to the dump again, to be rescued and briefly treasured by some other boy with schemes for making them useful. Occasionally something we really valued with a passion was snatched from us in horror and returned at once. That happened to the mounted head of a white mountain goat, somebody's trophy from old times and the far Rocky Mountains, that I brought home one day in transports of delight. My mother took one look and discovered that his beard was full of moths.

I remember that goat; I regret him yet. Poetry is seldom useful, but always memorable. I think I learned more from the town dump than I learned from school: more about people, more about how life is lived, not elsewhere but here, not in other times but now. If I were a sociologist anxious to study in detail the life of any community, I would go very early to its refuse piles. For a community may be as well judged by what it throws away—what it has to throw away and what it chooses to—as by any other evidence. For whole civilizations we have sometimes no more of the poetry and little more of the history than this.

(1959)

Elizabeth Bishop

(U.S.A., 1911–1979)

The Unbeliever

He sleeps on the top of a mast.—Bunyan

He sleeps on the top of a mast
with his eyes fast closed.
The sails fall away below him
like the sheets of his bed,
5   leaving out in the air of the night the sleeper's head.

Asleep he was transported there,
asleep he curled
in a gilded ball on the mast's top,
or climbed inside
10   a gilded bird, or blindly seated himself astride.

"I am founded on marble pillars,"
said a cloud. "I never move.
See the pillars there in the sea?"
Secure in introspection
15   he peers at the watery pillars of his reflection.

A gull had wings under his
and remarked that the air
was "like marble." He said: "Up here
I tower through the sky
20 for the marble wings on my tower-top fly."

But he sleeps on the top of his mast
with his eyes closed tight.
The gull inquired into his dream,
which was, "I must not fall.
25 The spangled sea below wants me to fall.
It is hard as diamonds; it wants to destroy us all."

                                        (1946)

Sandpiper

The roaring alongside he takes for granted,
and that every so often the world is bound to shake.
He runs, he runs to the south, finical, awkward,
in a state of controlled panic, a student of Blake.

5   The beach hisses like fat. On his left, a sheet
of interrupting water comes and goes
and glazes over his dark and brittle feet.
He runs, he runs straight through it, watching his toes.

—Watching, rather, the spaces of sand between them,
10 where (no detail too small) the Atlantic drains
rapidly backwards and downwards. As he runs,
he stares at the dragging grains.

The world is a mist. And then the world is
minute and vast and clear. The tide
15 is higher or lower. He couldn't tell you which.
His beak is focussed; he is preoccupied,

looking for something, something, something.
Poor bird, he is obsessed!
The millions of grains are black, white, tan, and gray,
20 mixed with quartz grains, rose and amethyst.

                                        (1965)

Sestina

September rain falls on the house.
In the failing light, the old grandmother
sits in the kitchen with the child
beside the Little Marvel Stove,
5   reading the jokes from the almanac,
laughing and talking to hide her tears.

She thinks that her equinoctial tears
and the rain that beats on the roof of the house
were both foretold by the almanac,
10   but only known to a grandmother.
The iron kettle sings on the stove.
She cuts some bread and says to the child,

It's time for tea now; but the child
is watching the teakettle's small hard tears
15   dance like mad on the hot black stove,
the way the rain must dance on the house.
Tidying up, the old grandmother
hangs up the clever almanac

on its string. Birdlike, the almanac
20   hovers half open above the child,
hovers above the old grandmother
and her teacup full of dark brown tears.
She shivers and says she thinks the house
feels chilly, and puts more wood in the stove.

25   *It was to be*, says the Marvel Stove.
I know what I know, says the almanac.
With crayons the child draws a rigid house
and a winding pathway. Then the child
puts in a man with buttons like tears
30   and shows it proudly to the grandmother.

But secretly, while the grandmother
busies herself about the stove,
the little moons fall down like tears
from between the pages of the almanac
35   into the flower bed the child
has carefully placed in the front of the house.

Time to plant tears, says the almanac.
The grandmother sings to the marvellous stove
and the child draws another inscrutable house.

(1965)

Northrop Frye
(CANADA, 1912-1991)

Symbolism of the Unconscious

If you spend much time in libraries, you will probably have seen long rows of dark green books with gold lettering, published by Macmillan and bearing the name of Frazer. Fifteen of them have the running title of *The Golden Bough*. Then there's *Folklore in the Old Testament*, three volumes. *Totemism and Exogamy*, four volumes. An edition of Pausanias, the traveler who wrote a description of Greece about A.D. 200, six volumes. *The Worship of Nature*, two volumes. *The Fear of the Dead in Primitive Religion*, three volumes. *The Belief in Immortality*, three volumes. These are the biggest lots, but there are many more: editions of Addison's essays and Cowper's letters, two volumes each; editions of several other classical authors; a book of extracts from the Bible; lectures, essays, fugitive pieces. It would take a good many months of hard work, without distractions, to read completely through Frazer.

The man who produced all this was the son of a Scottish Presbyterian minister, born in Glasgow in 1854. He was two years older than Bernard Shaw and not unlike Shaw in physical type: lean and wiry, with a pointed beard and glittering blue eyes. His father wanted him to study law, and in England that's a good profession to choose if you want to do other things. He did qualify as a barrister, but he spent his whole working life in universities, mainly as a fellow of Trinity College, Cambridge, emerging at intervals to collect honorary degrees and decorations. He got a knighthood, the Order of Merit, the Legion of Honor, and a shower of doctorates. He was naturally shy and retiring, said to have been a poor speaker unless he had a script, and, like many shy people, bristly and somewhat intolerant in conversation. Apparently it was Lady Frazer who managed him and helped get him his degrees. She wrote books too, mostly translations from the French. Frazer died in 1941, at eighty-seven, the victim of a Nazi bomb, and Lady Frazer with him.

He was a fine classical scholar who grew up in the later Victorian period, after Darwin had changed the whole direction of science. Anthropology was a new and exciting subject, and for Frazer it threw a flood of light on his classical studies. The Greeks and Romans had been primitives once too, and many things had survived in their religion that were very like the things being reported from the African jungles and the Australian bush. The biblical scholar Robertson Smith had studied primitive Arabian tribes to discover the sort of religion that's concealed in the earliest layers of the Old Testament. He had also worked on a theory that had a great influence on Frazer: that in primitive societies ritual precedes myth: people act out their beliefs first and think up reasons for them afterward. Then again, German scholars following the Grimm brothers, especially a scholar named Mannhardt, were turning up curious customs in the German countryside that seemed to be filling in the outlines of a nature cult centuries older than Christianity. Scholars were taking much the same view of primitive man that primitive man was supposed to have taken of his own life, as a kind of dream in which everything was charged with a mysterious fascination, and they pounced eagerly on anything that had to do with "folk."

Frazer was a professor of social anthropology, yet he never to my knowledge did any real fieldwork and never came much closer than the Cambridge library to primitive societies. He certainly doesn't sound like a man who had any firsthand knowledge of primitive life, or ever wanted to have any. He speaks, for instance, of something being familiar "to the crude intelligence not only of the savage, but of ignorant and dull-witted people everywhere." *The Golden Bough* is really a work of classical scholarship that uses a very large amount of illustrative material from anthropology and folklore. In the course of his classical reading, Frazer came across a custom in Roman life that puzzled him, and as he pondered it, the work of Robertson Smith on the Bible and of Mannhardt in Germany began to suggest hundreds of parallels to it; and finally the puzzling Roman custom became the key to a vast amount of ritual, myth, folklore, superstition, and religious belief all over the world. So it was that his essay on *The Golden Bough*, which first appeared in 1890, had expanded to three volumes by 1900, and into twelve, in the usual format, by 1915—a book of about 4000 pages. The length of the book is the result of the enormous mass of material collected as evidence: if you know only the one-volume abridgment he made in 1922, you haven't really missed much of the main argument. He was a disciple of Darwin in believing that if you were going to be properly scientific, for every statement you had to choke your reader with examples and illustrations, and his text walks over a thick pile carpet of footnotes from Greek and Latin literature, from the Old Testament, which Frazer read in Hebrew, from monographs and periodicals in English, French, German, Italian, and Dutch.

Near Rome, in the time of the Caesars, there was a grove sacred to the goddess Diana, in which there was a runaway slave who was called the priest of the grove and the King of the Wood. When he got there he found his predecessor in charge, and what he had to do was to break a branch off a certain tree, then attack and kill his predecessor. Then he was King of the Wood until some other runaway slave did the same thing to him. Why was there such a custom? That was the question that started Frazer off on the twelve-volume journey that another anthropologist, Malinowski, has called "the greatest scientific Odyssey in modern humanism."

Frazer begins by explaining that magic is the belief that you can affect things either by imitating them or by getting hold of part of them. If you have an enemy, magic suggests that you imitate killing him, say by sticking pins in a wax image of him, or that you get something belonging to him, like a lock of his hair, and then injure that. Primitive tribes take a magical view of their leader or king. As long as he's strong and virile the tribe will hold together and their food supply will be steady: if he gets old and feeble, so will the crops. So magic reasons that a king ought to be killed when his strength fails. It sounds like a funny way of preserving his strength, but the idea is to transfer it to his successor and distribute what's left over to the tribe. Magic assumes that you can get the qualities of something by eating it; so if you want the magic strength of the king, you eat his body and drink his blood.

Out of this pattern of ritual a great number of religions have developed, mostly around the Mediterranean Sea. The central figure is a god conceived in the form of a young man, who represents the fertility of the seasons in general and of the crops in particular. Hence, his body and blood become identified with the two chief products of the crops, bread and wine. At the center of this religion is a ritual representing the death and rebirth of the god, usually lasting three days. The god was called Adonis in Syria, Attis in Asia Minor, Osiris in Egypt, Dionysus in Greece, Balder in the North. There are also a great number of folk customs surviving among the European peasantry that feature similar figures, like the King and Queen of the May. Originally, Frazer thinks, these gods or mythical figures were represented by human beings who were sacrificed, and in peasant customs, even in children's games, there are many mock executions that at one time weren't mock at all.

An immense number of side issues are explored and problems solved, or at any rate fascinating guesses made, in every field of mythology and folklore. There is the "scapegoat" ritual, for instance, where an old man or woman who represents death and sterility is killed or driven away. There is the symbolism springing from the use of a temporary or mock king to serve as a substitute for the real one: he has a brief reign and is then executed, and this figure survives in all the lords of misrule and kings of the carnival in medieval Europe, besides being involved in the mockery of Jesus in the Passion. There is the connection which gives Frazer his title between the branch broken off by the King of the Wood and the golden bough Aeneas broke off before he could visit hell in Virgil's *Aeneid*. Virgil compares the golden bough to the mistletoe, and Frazer thinks it was the mistletoe, regarded as sacred in the ancient *cultus* of Europe.

Some of the side issues spill over into other books. The most important of them is the question of totemism, the identifying of a tribe with a certain animal or plant which is ceremonially eaten at stated times, and which for complicated reasons has been of great importance in developing the structure of primitive societies. Frazer's four volumes on *Totemism and Exogamy* (which means the rule that a man must marry outside his totem clan) are still an important source book for this subject. His other books are mostly in the form of compilations. As a teacher who made hosts of readers familiar with the conceptions of anthropology, Frazer is very important; as a scholar who could apply literary and scientific knowledge to the same problem, he is equally so. But as an architect of modern thought, he has to stand or fall by *The Golden Bough*.

I am not competent to discuss *The Golden Bough* as anthropology because I'm a literary critic, and I don't know any more about anthropology than the next man. Before you ask whatever possessed the CBC to get me to talk about Frazer, I should say that *The Golden Bough* seems to be at present more a book for literary critics than for anthropologists. It is, after all, a study of comparative symbolism, and one would expect that to appeal most to artists, poets, critics, and students of certain aspects of religion. When it first appeared, *The Golden Bough* was called an example of the Covent Garden school of anthropology, meaning that it was full of vegetation, Covent Garden being a market. There doesn't seem to be much of a Covent Garden school of anthropology left. I've just checked through several textbooks on anthropology to see what they said about Frazer. They were respectful enough about him as a pioneer, but it would have taken a Geiger counter to find much influence of *The Golden Bough* in them. Of course, there's a lot of fashion in such matters, but there's also a real problem involved.

Frazer often refers to what he calls the "comparative method." In his early years, tremendous strides had been made in biology through comparative anatomy. Those were the days when there were stories about scientists who could reconstruct a whole skeleton of an unknown animal from one piece of tailbone. In the comparative study of languages, too, a fascinating new world had opened up. But to make valid comparisons you have to know what your primary categories are. If you are studying natural history, no matter how fascinated you may be by anything that has eight legs, you can't just lump together an octopus and a spider and a string quartet. Now it is the anthropologist's business, as I understand it, to study individual cultures: those are his primary categories. So when Frazer compares rituals all over the world without telling us anything about the societies they fit into, he is not doing what many anthropologists, at least at present, have much interest in doing. At the same time, he is doing precisely what the student of symbolism, looking for the recurrence of a certain symbolic theme through all the world's cultures, wants to see done.

To appreciate *The Golden Bough* for what it is we have to see it as a kind of grammar of the human imagination. Its value is in its central idea: every fact in it could be questioned or reassessed without affecting that value. We don't have to assume that once upon a time everybody everywhere used to eat their kings and then gradually evolved slightly less repulsive customs. Frazer's ritual is to be thought of as something latent in the human imagination: it may have been acted out literally sometimes, but it is fundamentally a hypothesis that explains features in rituals, not necessarily the original ritual from which all others have derived. *The Golden Bough* isn't really about what people did in a remote and savage past; it is about what the human imagination does when it tries to express itself about the greatest mysteries, the mysteries of life and death and afterlife. It is a study, in other words, of unconscious symbolism on its social side, and it corresponds to and complements the work that Freud and Jung and others have done in psychology on unconscious symbolism on its individual side, in dreams and the like. It is extraordinary how closely Frazer's patterns fit the psychological ones. Frazer's dying gods are very like the libido figures of Freudian dreams; the old men and women of Frazer's scapegoat rituals correspond to Freud's parental imagos; the temporary kings of the carnival are the social forms of what Freud has studied in the mind as the mechanism of wit.

A ritual, in magic, is done for practical purposes, to make the crops grow, to baffle enemies, to bring rain or sunshine or children. In religion, a ritual expresses certain beliefs and hopes and theories about supernatural beings. The practical results of magic don't work out; religious beliefs disappear or change in the twilight of the gods. But when deprived of both faith and works, the ritual becomes what it really is, something made by the imagination, and a potential work of art. As that, it can grow into drama or romance or fiction or symbolic poetry. Poetry, said Aristotle, is an imitation of nature, and the structures of literature grow out of the patterns that the human mind sees in or imposes on nature, of which the most important are the rhythms of recurrence, the day, the month, the four seasons of the year. Poets can get from Frazer a new sense of what their own images mean, and critics can learn more from him about how the human imagination has responded to nature than from any other modern writer.

For the student of religion, *The Golden Bough* is of immense value in showing the positive importance of myth. Up to Frazer's time, interest in religion was confined mainly to theology or to history, and myth was felt to be just something that wasn't true—something all the *other* religions had. But now we can see more clearly how religion can appeal to the imagination as well as to faith or reason. Frazer's god-eating ritual is a kind of primitive parody of Christianity and shows us how magic and superstition, even in their weirdest forms, can be seen as gropings towards a genuine religious understanding.

In Oxford, Frazer used to be referred to as "the Cambridge fellow who can write," and it is certainly true that he can write. He can take a great inert mass of evidence and with a few selective touches make it into a lively narrative that keeps you turning the pages into the small hours. Of course, people who can't write are not only apt to be jealous of people who can, but often believe quite sincerely that anybody who is readable must be superficial. That is why you get so many sniffy remarks about Frazer's "highly imaginative" or "picturesque" style in books that are a lot harder to get through than his are. But no matter what happens to the subjects he dealt with, Frazer will always be read, because he can be. There are other aspects of his style I don't care so much for. He's fond of relapsing into fine writing, and when he does, he goes in for a kind of languid elegance that reminds one of a heroine of a Victorian novel about to expire with refinement and tight corsets. But for sheer power to organize material he ranks in the first class, with Gibbon or Macaulay, and a more recent encyclopedic writer, Toynbee, has learned a lot from him.

I would not say that Frazer was a great thinker. Like Darwin, he got hold of one tremendous intuition and spent his life documenting it, but apart from that he had a rather commonplace mind. People often believe that if a man spends his time among books he will lose contact with life: actually this very seldom happens, but it is true that Frazer looks at the world through a study window. In all his work I have found only one specific expression of interest in the events of his own day, a letter urging the union of England and France, and even that was published twenty years after it was written. He gives the impression of a Victorian liberal of a somewhat vague and sentimental kind. The theory of evolution popularized the idea that man had developed from lower forms of life, and it was easy to extend that to a theory of progress, to seeing man as still developing out of savagery into higher and higher civilization. A lot of people still think that biological evolution and historical progress are the same thing, and that one is the scientific proof of the other. Frazer thought so too, and he never doubted that man had gone steadily up an escalator from ape-man through savagery to twentieth-century Cambridge.

Now Frazer's "comparative method" is one that puts together myths from the ancient world, customs from contemporary primitive societies, and survivals of ancient beliefs in our own day. Such a method obviously hasn't anything historical about it and can hardly justify him in making any historical statements. But still, there is a historical framework to his book that is provided by his Darwinian escalator. All human societies, he believes, belong at certain points on this escalator, from the lowest, like the African bushmen, to the highest, like us. Societies that are on the same level will behave in pretty much the same way, no matter how far apart they are. This is the principle he relies on when he compares rituals that are vastly remote in time and space. In the final pages of *The Golden Bough*, Frazer ties this theory up. He suggests that there have been three ages of man: an age of magic, an age of religion, and an age of science, the last one just beginning.

Magic, Frazer says, is psychologically much the same thing as science. The magician's aim, like the scientist's, is a practical and secular aim: he believes that nature obeys fixed laws, and he tries to turn those laws to his own advantage. The difference between magic and science is not in attitude, but in the fact that magic is wrong about natural law and science right. Because the magician's notions of nature are crude, magic doesn't work, and so man turns from magic to religion, which for Frazer is a belief in mysterious external powers that man thinks he can either placate or get on his side. It is our job now to outgrow religion—Frazer isn't very explicit about this, but that is clearly what he means—and enter on an age of science, or true magic. In a series of lectures called *Psyche's Task*, he says that many of the fundamentals of civilization today, respect for government, for private property, for marriage, and for human life, grew out of primitive superstition, and all we have to do is separate the superstition in them from their rational sense.

One thinks of G.K. Chesterton's remark about the Victorians who saw the whole of human history in the form of one of their own three-volume novels, sure that they were the third volume and that history was turning out well because it was turning out with them. I imagine that not many scholars today would endorse Frazer's view that magic has always and everywhere preceded religion: it seems clear that magic and religion start off together. If there is any intermediate stage between magic and science, it isn't religion, which is quite distinct from both, but such things as alchemy and astrology. Also, there is a lot in magic—its dependence on tradition and authority, its secrecy, its emotional and dramatic elements—that make it something very different from any kind of rationalism, however crude. And if magic is just wrong science, surely primitive societies have and apply a lot of very sound knowledge of nature, which is scientific according to Frazer's definition—if they didn't they would starve to death.

As for the happy ending of his three-volume novel, outgrowing religion and becoming reasonable and scientific about everything doesn't sound like much of a program for the world in 1958. One person that Frazer seems to have had absolutely no use for was Freud, in spite of the fact that Freud based one of his books, *Totem and Taboo*, on Frazer's work. Maybe this was just prudery, but why should a man handling Frazer's kind of material be prudish? The answer seems clearly to be that Freud's discoveries about what is going on inside civilized man today makes one feel a lot more doubtful about this being an age of reason. For Frazer, it was fine for savages to be brutal and incestuous, but for well-dressed people in the nineteenth century to be full of brutal and incestuous impulses was a reflection on progress. True, Frazer often warns us that our civilization is a very thin veneer on top of what is really savagery and superstition still. But by this he appears to mean that outside the cities and universities there is a countryside full of people who want to sow their fields at the new moon and sacrifice a cat to make the crops grow. It never seems to occur to him that there might be things just as silly and more dangerous in civilization and progress themselves.

It seems a curious trick of fate that made Frazer the influence he is today. He was an old-fashioned agnostic who revolutionized our understanding of religion. He was a devotee of what he thought was a rigorous scientific method who profoundly affected the imagery of modern poetry. He was a believer in progress through reason who has told us more than any other man, except perhaps the Freud he disapproved of, about the symbolism of the unconscious. In a way he's not so much an architect of modern thought as of modern feeling and imagination. But one of the great discoveries of modern thought is that feeling and imagination are inseparably a part of thought, that logic is only one of many forms of symbolism. And that is a discovery Frazer helped to make.

(1959)

Patrick White

(AUSTRALIA, 1912–1990)

Clay

For Barry Humphries and Zoe Caldwell

When he was about five years old some kids asked Clay why his mother had called him that. And he did not know. But began to wonder. He did, in fact, wonder a great deal, particularly while picking the bark off trees, or stripping a flower down to its core of mystery. He too, would ask questions, but more often than not failed to receive the answer because his mother could not bring herself to leave her own train of thought.

Mrs Skerritt said: 'If only your father hadn't died he'd still be putting out the garbage the bin is too much for me the stooping not to mention the weight in anyone short of breath but you Clay I know will be good to your mum and help when you are older stronger only that is still a long way off.'

So that it was Clay's turn not to answer. What could you say, anyway?

Mrs Skerritt said: 'I wouldn't ask anything of anyone but there are certain things of course I wouldn't expect a gentleman to stand up for me in the tram while I have my own two legs only it's the sort of thing a gentleman ought to do and ladies take Mrs Pearl for instance what she expects of her husband and him with the sugar-diabetes too.'

Clay mooned about the house listening to his mother's voice boring additional holes in the fretwork, for fretwork had been Dadda's hobby: there was fretwork just about everywhere, brackets and things, even a lace of fretwork hanging from tabletop and doorway. Stiff. Sometimes while his mother's voice bored and sawed further Clay would break off pieces of the brown fretwork and hide it away under the house. Under the house was full of fretwork finally.

Or he would moon about the terraces of garden, amongst the collapsing lattices, flower-pot shards crackling underfoot, legs slapped by the straps of dark, leathery plants, lungs filled with suffocating bursts of asparagus fern. He would dawdle down to the harbour, with its green smell of sea-lettuce, and the stone wall, scribbled with the white droppings of gulls. The house itself leaned rather far towards the harbour, but had not fallen, because some men had come and shored it up. There it hung, however.

So Clay mooned. And would return often to the photograph. It was as though his child-hood were riveted to the wedding group. There was his father, those thick thighs, rather tight about the serge crutch (unlike the Dadda he remembered lying Incurable in bed), and the influential Mr Stutchbury, and Auntie Ada, and Nellie Watson (who died), and someone else who was killed in action. But it was to his mum that Clay was drawn, before and after all, into the torrential satin of the lap, by the face which had just begun to move out of its fixture of fretted lace. And the shoe. He was fascinated by the white shoe. Sometimes its great boat would float out from the shore of frozen time, into the waters of his imagination, rocking his cargo of almost transparent thoughts.

Once Mrs Skerritt came into the room and caught him at it, though she did not exactly see Clay for looking at herself.

'Ah dear,' she said, 'in the end things is sad.'

She would often half cry, and at such moments her hair would look more than ever like so many lengths of grey string, or on windy days, a tizz of frayed dish-cloth.

On this particular day when she caught Clay looking at the photograph, his throat swelled, and he dared to ask:

'Why is my name Clay, Mum?'

Because by that time he was seven, and the kids were asking worse than ever, and bashing him up (they were afraid that he was different).

'Why,' she said, 'let me think your father wanted Percival that is after Mr Stutchbury but I could not bring myself I said there are so many things you don't do but want take a name a name is yours take pottery I said I've half a mind to try my hand if I can find some feller or lady you never know I may be artistic but didn't because well there isn't the time always so much to do the people who have to be told and who have to be told and then Dadda's incurable illness so I did not do that only thought and thought about it and that I believe is why you was called Clay.'

Then she went out the back to empty the tea-pot on a bed of maidenhair which tingled perpetually with moisture.

So the kids continued to bash Clay up, and ask him why he was called that, and he couldn't tell them, because how could you even when you knew.

There were times when it got extra bad, and once they chased him with a woman's old cast-off shoe. He ran like a green streak, but not fast enough in the end—they caught him at the corner of Plant Street, where he had been born and always lived, and the heel of their old shoe bored for ever in his mind.

Later, when he had let himself in, into the garden of the leaning house, lost amongst collapsing lattices and the yellow fuzz of asparagus fern, he cried a bit for the difference to which he had been born. But smeared his eyes dry at last, and his nose. The light was rising from the bay in all green peacefulness, as if the world of pointed objects did not exist alongside that of the dreamy bridal shoe.

But he did not embark. Not then. His ribs had not subsided yet.

Once Clay dreamed a dream, and came down into the kitchen. He had meant to keep the dream to himself. Then it was too late, he heard, he was telling it to his mum. Even though his mouth was frozen stiff he had to keep on, to tell.

'In this dream,' he said, 'the steps led on down.'

His mum was pushing the rashers around, which went on buckling up in the pan.

'Under the sea,' said Clay. 'It was beautiful.'

He was sorry, but he could not help it.

'Everything drawn out. Hair and things. And weeds. The knotted ones. And the lettucy kind. Some of the fish had beards, Mum, and barked, well, like dogs.'

His mum had put the fried bread on a plate to one side, where the little squares were already stiffening.

'And shells, Mum,' he said, 'all bubbles and echoes as I went on down. It felt good. It felt soft. I didn't have to try. But just floated. Down.'

He could see his mother's behind, how it had begun to quiver, and he dreaded what might happen when he told. There was no avoiding it, though, and his mum went on prodding the bacon in the pan.

'When I got to the bottom,' he said, 'and the steps ended, you should have seen how the sea stretched, over the sand and broken bottles. Everything sort of silvery. I don't remember much else. Except that I found, Mum,' he said.

'What?' she asked.

He dreaded it.

'A cloud, Mum,' he said, 'and it was dead.'

Then Mrs Skerritt turned round, it was dreadful, how she looked. She opened her mouth, but nothing came out at first, only Clay saw the little thing at the back. Raised. When suddenly it began to act like a clapper. She began to cry, she began to create.

'Whatever are you gunna do to me?' she cried, as she pummelled and kneaded the moist grey dough of her cheeks.

'On top of everything else I never ever thought I'd have a freak!'

But Clay could only stand, and receive the blows her voice dealt. It was as though someone had taken a stick and drawn a circle round him. Him at the centre. There was no furniture any more.

The bacon was burning in the pan.

When Mrs Skerritt had thought it over, and used a little eau-de-Cologne, she took him up to McGillivray's. It was late by then, on a Saturday morning too. All the way Clay listened to her breathing and sometimes the sound of her corset. McGillivray was already closing, but agreed to do Mrs Skerritt's lad. McGillivray was kind.

'We want it short short Mr McGillivray please,' Mrs Skerritt said.

As the barber snipped Clay could hear his mum breathing, from where she sat, behind his back, under the coloured picture of the King.

Mr McGillivray did his usual nice job, and was preparing to design the little quiff when Mrs Skerritt choked.

'That is not short Mr McGillivray not what I mean oh no oh dear but it is difficult to explain there is too much involved and I left school when I turned fourteen.'

McGillivray laughed and said: 'Short is not shorn!'

'I don't care,' she said.

Clay could only look at the glass, and suck his cheeks in.

'Short is what I said and mean,' Mrs Skerritt confirmed. 'I was never one for not coming to the point.'

McGillivray was a gentle man, but he too began to breathe, he took the clippers, and shore a path through his subject's hair. He shore, and shore. Till there Clay was. Exposed.

'That suit?' McGillivray asked.

'Thank you,' she said.

So meek.

Then they went home. They crunched over tile asphalt. They were that heavy, both of them.

As they went down the hill towards the turn where the milko's cart had plunged over, Mrs Skerritt said:

'There Clay a person is sometimes driven to things in defence of what we know and love I would not of done this otherwise if not to protect you from yourself because love you will suffer in life if you start talking queer remember it doesn't pay to be different and no one is different without they have something wrong with them.'

Clay touched his prickly hair.

'Let me remind you,' she said, 'that your mum loves you that is why.'

But Clay could no longer believe in love, and the kids bashed him up worse than ever, because his no-hair made him a sort of different different.

'Wot was you in for?' the kids asked, and did windmills on his stubble. 'Old Broad Arrer!' they shouted, and punched.

Actually Clay grew up narrow. He was all knuckle, all wrist. He had those drawn-out arms. He had a greenish skin from living under too many plants. He was long. And his eyes overflowed at dusk, merged with the street lights, and the oil patches on lapping water.

'Are you lonely, Clay?' Mrs Skerritt asked.

'No,' he said. 'Why?'

'I thought perhaps you was lonely you should get out and meet other young people of your own age you should get to know nice girls otherwise it is not normal.'

Then she drew in her chin, and waited.

But Clay stroked his prickly hair. For he went to McGillivray's every so often since it was ordained. When his voice broke the others no longer bashed him up, having problems of their own. The blackheads came, the pimples and moustaches.

Sometimes Mrs Skerritt would cry, sitting on the rotten veranda overlooking the little bay in which cats so often drowned.

'Oh dear Clay,' she cried, 'I am your mother and have a responsibility a double one since Dadda went I will ask Mr Stutchbury but cannot rely totally do you know what you want to do?'

Clay said: 'No.'

'Oh dear,' she moaned worse than ever, 'how did I deserve a silent boy who loves what I would like to know himself perhaps himself.'

In fact Clay did not know what he loved. He would have liked to think it was his mother, though it could have been Dadda. So he would try to remember, but it was only cold yellow skin, and the smell of sick sheets. When he had been forced to approach his father, lying Incurable in the bed, his heart could have tumbled down out of the belfry of his body.

Once his mother, it was evening, clutched his head against her apron, so that she must have pricked her hands.

'You are not my son,' she clanged, 'otherwise you would act different.'

But he could not, did not want to. Sometimes, anyway, at that age, he felt too dizzy from growing.

'How?' his voice asked, or croaked.

But she did not explain. She flung his long body away.

'It's not a matter,' she said, 'that anybody can discuss I will ask Mr Stutchbury to see what we must do and how.'

Mr Stutchbury was so influential, as well as having been a mate of Herb Skerritt's all his life. Mr Stutchbury was something, Mrs Skerritt believed, in the Department of Education, but if she did not clear the matter up, it was because she considered there was not all that necessity.

She bought a T-bone steak, and asked him round.

'What,' she asked, 'should we do with Clay I am a widow as you know and you was his father's friend.'

Mr Stutchbury drew in his moustache.

'We will see,' he said, 'when the time comes.'

Then he folded his moist lips over a piece of yellow fat from the not so tender T-bone steak.

When it was time, Mr Stutchbury thought up a letter to some fellow at the Customs and Excise.

> Dear Archie (he composed)
>
> This is to recommend the son of an old friend. Herb Skerritt, for many years in the Tramways, died in tragic circumstances—of cancer to be precise . . .

(Clay, who of course opened the letter to see, got quite a shock from a word his mother never on any account allowed to be used in the home.)

> . . . it is my duty and wish to further the interests of the above-mentioned boy. In brief, I would esteem it a favour if you could see your way to taking him 'under your wing'. I do not predict wonders of young Skerritt, but am of the·opinion, rather, that he is a decent, average lad. In any event, wonders are not all that desirable, not in the Service anyway. It is the steady hand which pushes the pen a lifetime.
>
> I will not expatiate further, but send you my
>
> Salaams!

The young lady whom Mr Stutchbury had persuaded to type the letter had barely left the room, when his superior called, with the result that he forgot to add as he intended: 'Kindest regards to Mrs Archbold.' Even persons of influence have to consider the ground they tread on.

But Clay Skerritt started at the Customs, because Mr Archbold was not the sort to refuse Mr Stutchbury the favour he asked. So Clay took the ferry, mornings, in the stiff dark suit his mother had chosen. His long thin fingers learned to deal in forms. He carried the papers from tray to tray. In time he grew used to triplicate, and moistened the indelible before writing in his long thin hand the details, and the details.

Clay Skerritt did not complain, and if he was ignored he had known worse. For he was most certainly ignored, by the gentlemen who sat amongst the trays of papers, by the young ladies of the Customs and Excise, who kept their nails so beautifully, who took their personal towels to the toilet, and giggled over private matters and cups of milky tea. If they ever laughed at the junior in particular, at his tricky frame, his pimples, and his stubble of hair, Clay Skerritt was not conscious of it. Why should he be? He was born with inward-looking eyes.

That all was not quite in order, though, he began to gather from his mother.

'When I am gone Clay,' she said—it was the evening the sink got blocked up—'you will remember how your mother was a messer but found she only scraped the dishes into the sink because her mind was otherwise engaged with you Clay your interests always some practical young lady will rectify anything your mother ever did by good intention I would not force you but only advise time is not to be ignored.'

But on days when the wind blew black across the grey water Mrs Skerritt might remark, peering out from the arbours of asparagus fern:

'Some young woman clever with her needle lighter-handed at the pastry-board will make you forget your poor mum well it is the way.'

Her son was bound to ignore what he could not be expected to believe. He would take a look at the wedding group. All so solidly alive, the figures appeared to announce a truth of which he alone could be the arbiter, just as the great white shoe would still put out, into the distance, for destinations of his choice.

His mother, however, continued in her mistaken attempts to celebrate the passing of reality. There was the day she called, her voice intruding amongst the objects which surrounded him:

'Take my grey costume dear up to the dry cleaner at the Junction tomato sauce is fatal when a person is on the stoutish side.'

Clay acted as he had been told. Or the streets were acting round him, and the trams. It was a bright day. Metal sang. The brick homes were no longer surreptitious, but opened up to disclose lives. In one window a woman was looking into her armpit. It made Clay laugh.

At the cleaner's a lady finished a yarn with the young girl. The lady said from alongside her cigarette:

'I'll leave you to it, Marj. I'm gunna make tracks for home and whip me shoes off. My feet are hurting like hell.'

Then the bell.

Clay was still laughing.

The young girl was looking down at the sheets of fresh brown paper, through the smell of cleaning. She herself had a cleaned, pallid skin, with pores.

'What's up?' she asked, as the client continued laughing. She spoke so very flat and polite.

'Nothing,' he said, but added: 'I think perhaps you are like my mother.'

Which was untrue, in a sense, because the girl was flat, still, and colourless, whereas his mother was rotund, voluble, and at least several tones of grey. But Clay had been compelled to say it.

The girl did not reply. She looked down at first, as though he had overstepped the mark. Then she took the costume, and examined the spots of tomato sauce.

'Ready tomorrow,' she said.

'Go on!'

'Why not?' the girl replied. 'We are a One-day.'

But flat and absent she sounded.

Then Clay did not know why, but asked: 'You've got something on your mind.'

She said: 'It's only that the sink got blocked yesterday evening.'

It sounded so terribly grey, and she looking out with that expression of permanence. Then at once he knew he had been right, and that the girl at the dry cleaner's had something of his mother: it was the core of permanence. Then Clay grew excited. For he did not believe in impermanence, not even when his mother attempted to persuade, not even when he watched the clods of earth tumble down on the coffin lid. Not while he was he. So he said: 'Tomorrow.'

It sounded so firm, it was almost today.

Clay got used to Marj just as he had got used to his mum, only differently. They swung hands together, walking over the dead grass of several parks, or staring at animals in cages. They were already living together, that is, their silences intermingled. Each had a somewhat clammy palm. And if Marj spoke there was no necessity to answer, it was so flat, her remarks had the colour of masonite.

Marj said: 'When I have a home of my own, I will turn out the lounge Fridays. I mean, there is a time and place for everything. There are the bedrooms too.'

She said: 'I do like things to be nice.'

And: 'Marriage should be serious.'

How serious, Clay began to see, who had not told his mum.

When at last he did she was drying the apostle spoons, one of which she dropped, and he let her pick it up, on seeing that it was necessary for her to perform some therapeutic act.

'I am so glad Clay,' she said, rather purple, after a pause, 'I cannot wait to see this nice girl we must arrange some we must come to an agree there is no reason why a young couple should not hit it off with the mother-in-law if the home is large it is not so much temperament as the size of the home that causes friction.'

Mrs Skerritt had always known herself to be reasonable.

'And Marj is so like like you, Mum.'

'Eh?' Mrs Skerritt said.

He could not explain that what was necessary for him, for what he had to do, was a continuum. He could not have explained what he had to do, because he did not know, as yet.

All Mrs Skerritt could say was: 'The sooner we see the better we shall know.'

So Clay brought Marj. Their hands were clammier that day. The plants were huge, casting a fuscous tinge on the shored-up house.

Mrs Skerritt looked out of the door.

'Is this,' she said, 'I am not yet not yet ready to see.'

Clay told Marj she must go away, for that day at least, he would send for her, then he took his mother inside.

Mrs Skerritt did not meet Marj again, except in the mirror, in which she saw with something of a shock there is no such thing as permanence.

Shortly after she died of something. They said it was her ticker.

And Clay brought Marj to live in the house in which he had been born and lived. They did not go on a honeymoon, because, as Marj said, marriage should be serious. Clay hoped he would know what to do as they lay in the bed Mum and Dadda had used. Lost in that strange and lumpy acre Clay and Marj listened to each other.

But it was good. He continued going to the Customs. Once or twice he pinched the lobe of Marj's ear.

'What's got into you?' she asked.

He continued going to the Customs. He bought her a Java sparrow in a cage. It was a kind of love poem.

To which Marj replied: 'I wonder if it's gunna scatter its seed on the wall-to-wall. We can always spread a newspaper, though.' And did.

Clay went to the Customs. He sat at his own desk. He used his elbows more than before, because his importance had increased.

'Take this letter away, Miss Venables,' he said. 'There are only two copies. When I expected five. Take it away,' he said.

Miss Venables pouted, but took it away. She, like everybody, saw that something had begun to happen. They would watch Mr Skerritt, and wait for it.

But Marj, she was less expectant. She accepted the houseful of fretwork, the things the mother-in-law had put away—sets of string-coloured doilies for instance, once she came across a stuffed canary in a cardboard box. She did not remark, but accepted. Only once she failed to accept. Until Clay asked:

'What has become of the photo?'

'It is in that cupboard,' she said.

He went and fetched out the wedding group, and stuck it where it had been, on a fretwork table. At least he did not ask why she had put the photo away, and she was glad, because she would not have known what to answer. The bits of your husband you would never know were bad enough, but not to understand yourself was worse.

So Marj stuck to the carpet-sweeper, she was glad of the fluff under the bed, she was glad of the pattern on the lino, the cartons of crispies that she bought—so square. Even light is solid when the paths lead inward. So she listened to the carpet-sweeper.

All this time, she realized, something had been happening to Clay. For one thing his hair had begun to grow. Its long wisps curled like feather behind his ears. He himself, she saw, was not yet used to the silky daring of hair, which formerly had pricked to order.

'Level with the lobes of the ears, Mr McGillivray, please,' Clay would now explain.

McGillivray, who was old by this, and infallibly kind, always refrained from commenting.

So did the gentlemen at the Customs—it was far too strange.

Even the young ladies, who had been prepared to giggle at first, got the shivers for something they did not understand.

Only when the hair had reached as far as Mr Skerritt's shoulders did Mr Archbold send for Clay.

'Is it necessary, Mr Skerritt?' his superior asked, who had the additional protection of a private office.

Clay replied: 'Yes.'

He stood looking.

He was allowed to go away.

His wife Marj decided there is nothing to be surprised at. It is the only solution. Even if the fretwork crackled, she would not hear. Even if the hanging basket sprouted hair instead of fern, she would not see. There were the chops she put in front of her husband always so nicely curled on the plate. Weren't there the two sides of life?

One evening Clay came up out of the terraced garden, where the snails wound, and the sea smells. He stood for some considerable time in front of his parents' wedding group. The great shoe, or boat, or bridge, had never appeared so structural. Looking back he seemed to remember that this was the occasion of his beginning the poem, or novel, or regurgitation, which occupied him for the rest of his life.

Marj was certain that that was the evening he closed the door.

She would lie and call: 'Aren't you gunna come to bed, Clay?'

Or she would stir at the hour when the sheets are greyest, when the air trembles at the withheld threat of aluminium, Marj would ungum her mouth to remark: 'But Clay, the alarm hasn't gone off yet!'

From now on it seemed as though his body never stayed there long enough to warm the impression it left on the bed. She could hardly complain, though. He made love to her twice a year, at Christmas, and at Easter, though sometimes at Easter they might decide against— there was the Royal Agricultural Show, which is so exhausting.

All this is beside the point. It was the sheets of paper which counted, on which Clay wrote, behind the door, of that little room, which his wife failed to remember, it was soon so long since she had been inside. One of the many things Marj Skerritt learned to respect was another person's privacy.

So Clay wrote. At first he occupied himself with objects, the mysterious life which inanimacy contains. For several years in the beginning he was occupied with this.

> '. . . the table standing continues standing its legs so permanent of course you can take
> an axe and swing it cut into the flesh as Poles do every once in a while then the shriek

murder murder but mostly nothing disturbs the maps the childhood journeys on the frozen wave of wooden water no boat whether wood or iron when you come to think satin either ever sails from A to B except in the mind of the passenger so the table standing standing under an electric bulb responds unlikely unless to determination or desperation of a Polish kind . . .'

One night Clay wrote: *'I have never observed a flower-pot intimately until now its hole is fascinating the little down of green moss it is of greater significance than what is within though you can fill it if you decide to if you concentrate long enough. . . .'*

Up till now he had not turned his attention to human beings, though he had been surrounded by them all his life. In actual fact he did not turn his attention to them now, he was intruded on. And Lova was not all that human, or not at first, a presence rather, or sensation of possession.

That night Clay got the hiccups, he was so excited, or nervous. The reverberations were so metallic he failed to hear his wife Marj, her grey voice: 'Aren't you gunna come to bed, Clay?'

Lova was, by comparison, a greenish-yellow, of certain fruits, and plant-flesh.

'*Lova Lova Lova*,' he wrote at first, to try it out.

He liked it so much it surprised him it had not come to him before. He could have sat simply writing the name, but Lova grew more palpable.

'. . . her little conical breasts at times ripening into porepores detachable by sleight of hand or windy days yet so elusive fruit and shoes distributed amongst the grass . . .'

In the beginning Lova would approach from behind glass her skin had that faint hot-house moisture which tingles on the down of ferns, her eyes a ferny brown that complemented his own if he had known. But he knew no more than gestures at first, the floating entanglement of hair in mutual agreement, the slight shiver of skin passing over skin. She would ascend and descend the flights of stone steps, inhabiting for a moment the angles of landings of old moss-upholstered stone. The leaves of the *monstera deliciosa* sieved her at times into a dispersed light. Which he alone knew how to reassemble. On rare occasions their mouths would almost meet, at the bottom of the garden, where the smell of rotting was, and the liquid manure used to stand, which had long since dried up. She was not yet real, and might never be. No. He would make her. But there were the deterrents. The physical discords.

Marj said: 'My hands are that chapped I must ask Mr Todd's advice. You can enjoy a chat with a chemist, doctors are most of them too busy pushing you out.'

And Lova got the herpes. Clay could not look at her at first. As she sat at her own little table, taking the fifteen varieties of pills, forcing them into her pig's snout, Lova would smile still, but it was sad. And soon the sore had become a scab. He could not bring himself to approach. And breath, besides.

For nights and nights Clay could not write a word. Or to be precise, he wrote over several nights:

'. . . a drying and a dying . . .'

If he listened, all he could hear was the rustle of Lova's assorted pills, the ruffling of a single sterile date-palm, the sound of Marj turning in the bed.

Then it occurred to his panic the shored-up house might break open. It was so rotten, so dry. He could not get too quickly round the table, scattering the brittle sheets of paper. Motion detached itself from his feet in the shape of abrupt, leather slippers. Skittering to reach the door.

Clay did not, in fact, because Lova he now saw locking locking locked it, popping the key afterwards down between.

Lova laughed. And Clay stood. The little ripples rose up in her throat, perhaps it was the cold key, and spilled over, out of her mouth, her wet mouth. He knew that the private parts of babies tasted as tender as Lova's mouth.

He had never tried. But suspected he must.

She came to him.

'Bum to you!' Lova said.

She sat in his lap then, and with his free hand he wrote, the first of many white nights:

> 'At last my ryvita has turned to velveeta life is no longer a toast-rack.'

'Golly,' said Lova, 'what it is to be an educated feller! Honest, Clay, it must be a great satisfaction to write, if only to keep one of your hands occupied.'

She laughed again. When he had his doubts. Does every face wear the same expression unless it is your own? He would have liked to look at the wedding group, to verify, but there were all those stairs between, and darkness. All he could hear was the sound of Marj breaking wind. Marj certainly had said at breakfast: 'It is the same. Whatever the manufacturers tell you, that is only to sell the product.'

But Lova said: 'It is different, Clay, as different as kumquats from pommygranates. You are the differentest of all perhaps. I could lap up the cream of your genius.'

She did, in fact, look at moments like a cat crouched in his lap, but would close at once, and open, like a knife.

'I would eat you,' she repeated, baring her pointed teeth, when he had thought them broad and spaced, as in Mum or Marj.

Although he was afraid, he wrote with his free right hand:

> 'I would not trust a razor-blade to any but my own . . .'

When Lova looked it over.

'Shoot!' she said. 'That is what I am!'

He forgot about her for a little, for writing down what he had to write.

> '. . . Lova sat in my lap smelling of crushed carrot tops she has taken the frizz out of her hair but cannot make it smell less green I would not trust her further than without meaning to cast aspersions you can't trust even your own thoughts past midnight . . .'

'Chip Chip Chip chipped off his finger,' Lova said. 'Anyway it begins with C.'

'Oh dear,' C began to cry. 'Oh dear dear dear oh Lova!'

'When does D come in?' she asked.

'D isn't born,' he said, 'and pretty sure won't be. As for A, A is in bed. No,' he corrected. 'A am not.'

Suddenly he wished he was.

He realized he was eye to eye with Lova their lashes grappling together in gummy agreement but melancholy to overflowing. They were poured into each other.

After that, Clay finished, for the night at least, and experienced the great trauma of his little empty room, for Lova had vanished, and there were only the inkstains on his fingers to show that she had ever been there.

There was nothing for it now but to join Marj in the parental bed, where he wondered whether he would ever be able to rise again. He was cold, cold.

Actually Marj turned over and said: 'Clay, I had an argument with Mr Tesoriero over the turnips. I told him you couldn't expect the public to buy them flabby.'

But Clay slept, and in fact he did not rise, not that morning, the first in many years, when the alarm clock scattered its aluminium trays all over the house.

Clay Skerritt continued going to the Customs. They had got used to him by then, even to his hair, the streaks in it.

He realized it was time he went to McGillivray's again, but some young dago came out, and said:

'Nho! Nho! McGillivray gone. Dead. How many years? Five? Six?'

So Clay Skerritt went away.

It was natural enough that it should have happened to McGillivray. Less natural were the substances. The pretending houses. The asphalt which had lifted up.

Then he saw the pointed heel, caught in the crack, wrenching at it. He saw the figure. He saw. He saw.

When she turned round, she said:

'Yes. It's all very well. For you. With square heels. Bum bums.'

Wrenching at her heel all the while.

'But Lova,' he said, putting out his hands.

She was wearing a big-celled honeycomb sweater.

'Oh, yes!' she said.

And laughed.

'If that's how you feel,' he answered.

'If that's how I *feel*!'

His hands were shaking, and might have caught in the oatmeal wool.

'I'm not gunna stand around exchanging words with any long-haired nong in the middle of Military Road. Not on yours!'

'Be reasonable,' he begged.

'What is reasonable?' she asked.

He could not tell. Nor if she had asked: what is love?

'Aren't you going to know me then?' he said.

'I know you,' she said, sort of flat—two boards could not have come together with greater exactitude.

'And it is time,' she said, 'to go.'

Jerking at her stuck heel.

'I've come here for something,' he remembered. 'Was it bird-seed?'

'Was it my Aunt Fanny!'

Then she got her heel free and all the asphalt was crackling up falling around them in scraps of torn black tinkly paper.

If he could only have explained that love cannot be explained.

All the while ladies were going in and out, strings eating into their fingers together with their rings. One lady had an alsatian, a basket suspended from its teeth, it did not even scent the trouble.

It was Saturday morning. Clay went home.

That evening, after they had finished their spaghetti on toast, because they were still paying off the Tecnico, Marj said:

'Clay, I had a dream.'

'No!' he shouted.

Where could he go? There was nowhere now.

Except on the Monday there was the Customs and Excise. He could not get there quick enough. To sharpen his pencils. To move the paper-clips the other side of the ink eraser.

When what he was afraid might happen, happened.

Lova had followed him to the Customs.

The others had not spotted it yet, for it could have been any lady passing the day at the Customs in pursuit of her unlawful goods. Only no lady would have made so straight for Mr Skerritt's desk, nor would she have been growing from her big-celled oatmeal sweater quite so direct as Lova was.

She had those little, pointed, laughing teeth.

'Well,' she opened, 'you didn't reckon on this.'

She was so certain of herself by now, he was afraid she might jump out of her jumper.

He sat looking down, at the letter from Dooley and Mann, Import Agents, re the Bechstein that got lost.

'Listen, Lova,' he advised. 'Not in here. It won't help find the piano.'

'Pianner? A fat lot of pianner! You can't play that one on me.'

'You may be right,' he answered.

'Right!' she said. 'Even if I wasn't. Even if I was flippin' wrong!'

She put her hand-bag on the desk.

'If anyone's gunna play, I'm the one,' she said.

Sure enough the old black upright slid around the corner from behind Archbold's glassed-in office, followed by the little leather-upholstered stool, from which the hair was bursting out. Lova seemed satisfied. She laughed, and when she had sat down, began to dish out the gay sad jazz. Playing and playing. Her little hands were jumping and frolicking on their own. The music playing out of every worm hole in the old, sea-changed piano.

Clay looked up, to see Archbold looking down. Miss Titmuss had taken her personal towel, and was having trouble with her heels as she made her way towards the toilet.

When Lova got up. She was finished. Or not quite. She began to drum with her bum on the greasy, buckled-up rashers of keys of the salt-cured old piano.

'There!' she shouted.

She came and sat on the corner of his desk. She had never been so elastic. It was her rage of breathing. He was unable to avoid the pulse of her suspender, winking at him from her thigh.

One or two other of the Customs officials had begun to notice, he observed, desperately through the side-curtains of his hair.

So he said: 'Look here, Lova, a scene at this stage will make it well nigh impossible for me to remain in the Service. And what will we do without the pension? Marj must be taken into account. I mean to say, it is the prestige as much as the money. Otherwise, we have learnt to do on tea and bread.'

Lova laughed then.

'Ha! *Ha*! HA!'

There is no way of writing it but how it was written on the wall. For it was. It got itself printed up on the wall which ran at right angles to Archbold's office.

Clay sat straight, straight. His adam's apple might not endure it much longer.

'Scenes are so destructive,' he said, or begged.

So his mum had told him.

'If that is what you want,' said Lova, 'you know I was never one for holding up procedure for the sake of filling in a form.'

And she ripped it off the pad from under his nose. Her hands were so naked, and could get a whole lot nakeder. He was afraid he might be answerable.

'I would never suggest,' she shouted, 'that the pisspot was standing right end up when it wasn't.'

But he had to resist, not so much for personal reasons as for the sake of public decorum, for the honour of the Department. He had to protect the paper-clips.

Because their hands were wrestling, troubling the desk. Him and Lova. At any moment the carton might burst open. At any. It happened quite quickly, breathily, ending in the sigh of scatteration.

'I will leave you for now,' she said, getting off the corner of the desk, and pulling down her sweater, which had rucked up.

Almost every one of his colleagues had noticed by this, but all had the decency to avoid passing audible judgment on such a very private situation.

When it was over a little while, Miss Titmuss got down and gathered up the paper-clips, because she was sorry for Mr Skerritt.

He did not wait to thank or explain, but took his hat, treading carefully to by-pass the eyes, and caught the ferry to the other side.

Marj said: 'Aren't you early, Clay? Sit on the veranda a while. I'll bring you a cuppa, and slice of that pound cake, it's still eatable I think.'

So he sat on the veranda, where his mother used to sit and complain, and felt the southerly get inside his neckband, and heard the date-palm starting up. Sparrows gathered cautiously.

Marj said: 'Clay, if you don't eat up, it'll be tea.'

You can always disregard, though, and he went inside the room, which he did not even dread. There she was, sitting in the other chair, in the oatmeal sweater. Her back turned. Naturally.

'Lova,' he began.

Then she came towards him, and he saw that she herself might sink in the waters of time she spread before him cunningly the nets of water smelling of nutmeg over junket the steamy mornings and the rather shivery afternoons.

If he did not resist.

She was just about as resistant as water not the tidal kind but a glad upward plume of water rising and falling back as he put his hands gently lapping lapping. She was so gentle.

Marj began to knock on the door.

'Tea's getting cold, Clay,' she announced.

It was, too. That is the way of things.

'I made you a nice devilled toast.'

She went away, but returned, and held her ear to the dry rot.

'Clay?' she asked. 'Don't you mind?'

Marj did not like to listen at doors because of her regard for privacy.

'Well,' she said, 'I never knew you to act like this.'

It could have been the first time in her life that Marj had opened a door.

Then she began to scream. She began to create. It was unlike her.

She could not see his face because of all that hair. The hair and the boards between them were keeping it a secret.

'This is something I never bargained for,' she cried.

For the blood had spurted out of the leg of the table. Just a little.

And that old shoe. He lay holding a white shoe.

'I never ever saw a shoe!' she moaned. 'Of all the junk she put away, just about every bit of her, and canaries and things, never a shoe!'

As Clay lay.

With that stiff shoe.

'I don't believe it!' Marj cried.

Because everyone knows that what isn't isn't, even when it is.

(1964)

George Barker
(ENGLAND, 1913–1991)

To My Mother

Most near, most dear, most loved and most far,
Under the window where I often found her
Sitting as huge as Asia, seismic with laughter,
Gin and chicken helpless in her Irish hand,
5   Irresistible as Rabelais, but most tender for
The lame dogs and hurt birds that surround her,—
She is a procession no one can follow after
But be like a little dog following a brass band.

She will not glance up at the bomber, or condescend
10   To drop her gin and scuttle to a cellar,
But lean on the mahogany table like a mountain
Whom only faith can move, and so I send
O all my faith, and all my love to tell her
That she will move from mourning into morning.

(1944)

Muriel Rukeyser
(U.S.A., 1913–1980)

The Children's Orchard

In the full sun.   In the fruitfall season.
Against my knees the earth and the bucket, and the soft blue prunes
echoing red   echoing purple   echoing in the silver bucket
sun, and over the flames of earth the sun flies down.

5   Over my head the little trees tremble alive in their black branches
and bare-ribbed boys golden and shouting stoop here to gather the blue,
the wild-red, the dark.   Colors of ripeness in the fruitfall season.
I will remember the last light on the lowest branch.

Will see these trees as they were in spring, wild black rooted in light,
10   root-deep in noon, the piercing yellow noon of mustard-blossom.
Sun breathing on us the scent of heat, richness of air where my hands know
blue, full summer, strong sun.   I tell you harvest.

(1948)

Lewis Thomas
(U.S.A., 1913–1993)

Notes on Punctuation

There are no precise rules about punctuation (Fowler lays out some general advice (as best he can under the complex circumstances of English prose (he points out, for example, that we possess only four stops (the comma, the semicolon, the colon and the period (the question mark and exclamation point are not, strictly speaking, stops; they are indicators of tone (oddly enough, the Greeks employed the semicolon for their question mark (it produces a strange sensation to read a Greek sentence which is a straightforward question: Why weepest thou; (instead of Why weepest thou? (and, of course, there are parentheses (which are surely a kind of punctuation making this whole matter much more complicated by having to count up the left-handed parentheses in order to be sure of closing with the right number (but if the parentheses were left out, with nothing to work with but the stops, we would have considerably more flexibility in the deploying of layers of meaning than if we tried to separate all the clauses by physical barriers (and in the latter case, while we might have more precision and exactitude for our meaning, we would lose the essential flavor of language, which is its wonderful ambiguity)))))))))))).

The commas are the most useful and usable of all the stops. It is highly important to put them in place as you go along. If you try to come back after doing a paragraph and stick them in the various spots that tempt you you will discover that they tend to swarm like minnows into all sorts of crevices whose existence you hadn't realized and before you know it the whole long sentence becomes immobilized and lashed up squirming in commas. Better to use them sparingly, and with affection, precisely when the need for each one arises, nicely, by itself.

I have grown fond of semicolons in recent years. The semicolon tells you that there is still some question about the preceding full sentence; something needs to be added; it reminds you sometimes of the Greek usage. It is almost always a greater pleasure to come across a semicolon than a period. The period tells you that that is that; if you didn't get all the meaning you wanted or expected, anyway you got all the writer intended to parcel out and now you have to move along. But with a semicolon there you get a pleasant little feeling of expectancy; there is more to come; to read on; it will get clearer.

Colons are a lot less attractive, for several reasons: firstly, they give you the feeling of being rather ordered around, or at least having your nose pointed in a direction you might not be inclined to take if left to yourself, and, secondly, you suspect you're in for one of those sentences that will be labeling the points to be made: firstly, secondly and so forth, with the implication that you haven't sense enough to keep track of a sequence of notions without having them numbered. Also, many writers use this system loosely and incompletely, starting out with number one and number two as though counting off on their fingers but then going on and on without the succession of labels you've been led to expect, leaving you floundering about searching for the ninethly or seventeenthly that ought to be there but isn't.

Exclamation points are the most irritating of all. Look! they say, look at what I just said! How amazing is my thought! It is like being forced to watch someone else's small child jumping up and down crazily in the center of the living room shouting to attract attention. If a sentence really has something of importance to say, something quite remarkable, it doesn't need a mark to point it out. And if it is really, after all, a banal sentence needing more zing, the exclamation point simply emphasizes its banality!

Quotation marks should be used honestly and sparingly, when there is a genuine quotation at hand, and it is necessary to be very rigorous about the words enclosed by the marks. If something is to be quoted, the *exact* words must be used. If part of it must be left out because of space limitations, it is good manners to insert three dots to indicate the omission, but it is unethical to do this if it means connecting two thoughts which the original author did not intend to have tied together. Above all, quotation marks should not be used for ideas that you'd like to disown, things in the air so to speak. Nor should they be put in place around cliches; if you want to use a cliché you must take full responsibility for it yourself and not try to fob it off on anon., or on society. The most objectionable misuse of quotation marks, but one which illustrates the dangers of misuse in ordinary prose, is seen in advertising, especially in advertisements for small restaurants, for example "just around the corner," or "a good place to eat." No single, identifiable, citable person ever really said, for the record, "just around the corner," much less "a good place to eat," least likely of all for restaurants of the type that use this type of prose.

The dash is a handy device, informal and essentially playful, telling you that you're about to take off on a different tack but are still in some way connected with the present course—only you have to remember that the dash is there, and either put a second dash at the end of the notion to let the reader know that he's back on course, or else end the sentence, as here, with a period.

The greatest danger in punctuation is for poetry. Here it is necessary to be as economical and parsimonious with commas and periods as with the words themselves, and any marks that seem to carry their own subtle meanings, like dashes and little rows of periods, even semicolons and question marks, should be left out altogether rather than inserted to clog up the thing with ambiguity. A single exclamation point in a poem, no matter what else the poem has to say, is enough to destroy the whole work.

The things I like best in T.S. Eliot's poetry, especially in the *Four Quartets*, are the semicolons. You cannot hear them, but they are there, laying out the connections between the images and the ideas. Sometimes you get a glimpse of a semicolon coming, a few lines farther on, and it is like climbing a steep path through woods and seeing a wooden bench just at a bend in the road ahead, a place where you can expect to sit for a moment, catching your breath.

Commas can't do this sort of thing; they can only tell you how the different parts of a complicated thought are to be fitted together, but you can't sit, not even take a breath, just because of a comma,

(1979)

Randall Jarrell

(U.S.A., 1914–1965)

The Death of the Ball Turret Gunner

From my mother's sleep I fell into the State,
And I hunched in its belly till my wet fur froze.
Six miles from earth, loosed from its dream of life,
I woke to black flak and the nightmare fighters.
5   When I died they washed me out of the turret with a hose.

(1944)

Henry Reed

(ENGLAND, 1914–1986)

Naming of Parts

To-day we have naming of parts. Yesterday,
We had daily cleaning. And to-morrow morning,
We shall have what to do after firing. But to-day,
To-day we have naming of parts. Japonica
5   Glistens like coral in all of the neighbouring gardens,
     And to-day we have naming of parts.

This is the lower sling swivel. And this
Is the upper sling swivel, whose use you will see,
When you are given your slings. And this is the piling swivel,
10   Which in your case you have not got. The branches
Hold in the gardens their silent, eloquent gestures,
     Which in our case we have not got.

This is the safety-catch, which is always released
With an easy flick of the thumb. And please do not let me
15   See anyone using his finger. You can do it quite easy
If you have any strength in your thumb. The blossoms
Are fragile and motionless, never letting anyone see
     Any of them using their finger.

And this you can see is the bolt. The purpose of this
20   Is to open the breech, as you see. We can slide it
Rapidly backwards and forwards: we call this
Easing the spring. And rapidly backwards and forwards
The early bees are assaulting and fumbling the flowers:
     They call it easing the Spring.

25   They call it easing the Spring: it is perfectly easy
If you have any strength in your thumb: like the bolt,
And the breech, and the cocking-piece, and the point of balance,
Which in our case we have not got; and the almond-blossom
Silent in all of the gardens and the bees going backwards and forwards,
30   For to-day we have naming of parts.

(1946)

Dylan Thomas
(WALES, 1914–1953)

The Force That Through the Green Fuse Drives the Flower

The force that through the green fuse drives the flower
Drives my green age; that blasts the roots of trees
Is my destroyer.
And I am dumb to tell the crooked rose
5 My youth is bent by the same wintry fever.

The force that drives the water through the rocks
Drives my red blood; that dries the mouthing streams
Turns mine to wax.
And I am dumb to mouth unto my veins
10 How at the mountain spring the same mouth sucks.

The hand that whirls the water in the pool
Stirs the quicksand; that ropes the blowing wind
Hauls my shroud sail.
And I am dumb to tell the hanging man
15 How of my clay is made the hangman's lime.

The lips of time leech to the fountain head;
Love drips and gathers, but the fallen blood
Shall calm her sores.
And I am dumb to tell a weather's wind
20 How time has ticked a heaven round the stars.

And I am dumb to tell the lover's tomb
How at my sheet goes the same crooked worm.

(1934)

A Refusal to Mourn the Death, by Fire, of a Child in London

Never until the mankind making
Bird beast and flower
Fathering and all humbling darkness
Tells with silence the last light breaking
5 And the still hour
Is come of the sea tumbling in harness

And I must enter again the round
Zion of the water bead
And the synagogue of the ear of corn
10 Shall I let pray the shadow of a sound
Or sow my salt seed
In the least valley of sackcloth to mourn

The majesty and burning of the child's death.
I shall not murder
15 The mankind of her going with a grave truth
Nor blaspheme down the stations of the breath
With any further
Elegy of innocence and youth.

Deep with the first dead lies London's daughter,
20 Robed in the long friends,
The grains beyond age, the dark veins of her mother,
Secret by the unmourning water
Of the riding Thames.
After the first death, there is no other.

(1945)

Fern Hill

Now as I was young and easy under the apple boughs
About the lilting house and happy as the grass was green,
    The night above the dingle starry,
        Time let me hail and climb
5   Golden in the heydays of his eyes,
And honoured among wagons I was prince of the apple towns
And once below a time I lordly had the trees and leaves
        Trail with daisies and barley
    Down the rivers of the windfall light.

10 And as I was green and carefree, famous among the barns
About the happy yard and singing as the farm was home,
    In the sun that is young once only,
        Time let me play and be
    Golden in the mercy of his means,
15 And green and golden I was huntsman and herdsman, the calves
Sang to my horn, the foxes on the hills barked clear and cold,
        And the sabbath rang slowly
    In the pebbles of the holy streams.

All the sun long it was running, it was lovely, the hay
20 Fields high as the house, the tunes from the chimneys, it was air
    And playing, lovely and watery
        And fire green as grass.
    And nightly under the simple stars
As I rode to sleep the owls were beating the farm away,
25 All the moon long I heard, blessed among stables, the nightjars
    Flying with the ricks, and the horses
        Flashing into the dark.

And then to awake, and the farm, like a wanderer white
With the dew, come back, the cock on his shoulder: it was all
30   Shining, it was Adam and maiden,
           The sky gathered again
      And the sun grew round that very day.
So it must have been after the birth of the simple light
In the first, spinning place, the spellbound horses walking warm
35   Out of the whinnying green stable
           On to the fields of praise.

And honoured among foxes and pheasants by the gay house
Under the new made clouds and happy as the heart was long,
      In the sun born over and over,
40   I ran my heedless ways,
        My wishes raced through the house high hay
And nothing I cared, at my sky blue trades, that time allows
In all his tuneful turning so few and such morning songs
      Before the children green and golden
45   Follow him out of grace,

Nothing I cared, in the lamb white days, that time would take me
Up to the swallow thronged loft by the shadow of my hand,
      In the moon that is always rising,
        Nor that riding to sleep
50   I should hear him fly with the high fields
And wake to the farm forever fled from the childless land.
Oh as I was young and easy in the mercy of his means,
       Time held me green and dying
      Though I sang in my chains like the sea.

(1946)

Do Not Go Gentle into That Good Night

Do not go gentle into that good night,
Old age should burn and rave at close of day;
Rage, rage against the dying of the light.

Though wise men at their end know dark is right,
5 Because their words had forked no lightning they
Do not go gentle into that good night.

Good men, the last wave by, crying how bright
Their frail deeds might have danced in a green bay,
Rage, rage against the dying of the light.

10 Wild men who caught and sang the sun in flight,
And learn, too late, they grieved it on its way,
Do not go gentle into that good night.

Grave men, near death, who see with blinding sight
Blind eyes could blaze like meteors and be gay,
15   Rage, rage against the dying of the light.

And you, my father, there on the sad height,
Curse, bless, me now with your fierce tears, I pray.
Do not go gentle into that good night.
Rage, rage against the dying of the light.

(1951)

Judith Wright
(AUSTRALIA, 1915-)

The Beanstalk, Meditated Later

What's fortune, that we pray it may be mild?
The beans I carried home that careless day
I thought were toys, and I a clever child—
but mother scolded, throwing them away:
5   "The subtlest traps have just such pretty bait."
Well, she was right. That beanstalk reached a sky
where giants cheat us. We must skulk and wait
and steal our fortune back to mock them by.

Who was my father? See where that doubt leads—
10   the ladder grew so pat out of our garden
perhaps my mother recognized its seeds.
Giants have trampled earth and asked no pardon—
Well, nor did I. He took our family's gold.
I stole it back and saw the giant die.
15   (Four days to bury him.) Now I've grown old,
but still the giants trample in the sky.

Yes, still I hear them; and I meditate
(old, rich, respected, maudlin—says my son)
upon our generations and our fate.
20   Does each repeat the thing the last has done
though claiming he rejects it? Once I stood
beside my beanstalk—clever boy—and crowed
I'd killed the giant, Tom Thumb whose luck was good;
but now—what farmer saved the seed I sowed?

25 For somewhere still that dizzy ladder grows—
  pathway for tit-for-tat from here to there—
  and what's the traffic on it, no man knows.
  Sometimes I hug my gold in pure despair
  watching my son—my cocky enemy—
30 big, ugly, boastful. It's the giant strain
  come out in him, I think. I watch, and he
  watches me. The gold is in his brain.

  I'll post a proclamation—advertise—
  find that farmer, buy his whole year's crop,
35 burn the lot, and see the last seed dies.
  But one seed—yes—I'll plant. That's for my son.
  I'll send him up it, wait; and when he's crawled
  far enough, I'll lay the axe-blows on
  and send him sprawling where his grandpa sprawled.

              (1966)

At Cooloola

  The blue crane fishing in Cooloola's twilight
  has fished there longer than our centuries.
  He is the certain heir of lake and evening,
  and he will wear their colour till he dies,

5 but I'm a stranger, come of a conquering people.
  I cannot share his calm, who watch his lake,
  being unloved by all my eyes delight in,
  and made uneasy, for an old murder's sake.

  Those dark-skinned people who once named Cooloola
10 knew that no land is lost or won by wars,
  for earth is spirit: the invader's feet will tangle
  in nets there and his blood be thinned by fears.

  Riding at noon and ninety years ago,
  my grandfather was beckoned by a ghost—
15 a black accoutred warrior armed for fighting,
  who sank into bare plain, as now into time past.

  White shores of sand, plumed reed and paperbark,
  clear heavenly levels frequented by crane and swan—
  I know that we are justified only by love,
20 but oppressed by arrogant guilt, have room for none.

  And walking on clean sand among the prints
  of bird and animal, I am challenged by a driftwood spear
  thrust from the water; and, like my grandfather,
  must quiet a heart accused by its own fear.

              (1955)

P.K. Page

(CANADA, 1916–)

The Stenographers

After the brief bivouac of Sunday,
their eyes, in the forced march of Monday to Saturday,
hoist the white flag, flutter in the snow-storm of paper,
haul it down and crack in the mid-sun of temper.

5   In the pause between the first draft and the carbon
they glimpse the smooth hours when they were children—
the ride in the ice-cart, the ice-man's name,
the end of the route and the long walk home;

remember the sea where floats at high tide
10   were sea marrows growing on the scatter-green vine
or spools of grey toffee, or wasps' nests on water;
remember the sand and the leaves of the country.

Bell rings and they go and the voice draws their pencil
like a sled across snow; when its runners are frozen
15   rope snaps and the voice then is pulling no burden
but runs like a dog on the winter of paper.

Their climates are winter and summer—no wind
for the kites of their hearts—no wind for a flight;
a breeze at the most, to tumble them over
20   and leave them like rubbish—the boy-friends of blood.

In the inch of the noon as they move they are stagnant.
The terrible calm of the noon is their anguish;
the lip of the counter, the shapes of the straws
like icicles breaking their tongues, are invaders.

25   Their beds are their oceans—salt water of weeping
the waves that they know—the tide before sleep;
and fighting to drown they assemble their sheep
in columns and watch them leap desks for their fences
and stare at them with their own mirror-worn faces.

30   In the felt of the morning the calico-minded,
sufficiently starched, insert papers, hit keys,
efficient and sure as their adding machines;
yet they weep in the vault, they are taut as net curtains
stretched upon frames. In their eyes I have seen
35   the pin men of madness in marathon trim
race round the track of the stadium pupil.

(1946)

Cook's Mountains

By naming them he made them.
They were there
before he came
but they were not the same.
5 It was his gaze
that glazed each one.
He saw
the Glass House Mountains in his glass.
They shone.

10 And still they shine,
We saw them as we drove—
sudden, surrealist, conical
they rose
out of the rain forest.
15 The driver said,
"Those are the Glass House Mountains up ahead."

And instantly they altered to become
the sum of shape and name.
Two strangenesses united into one
20 more strange than either.
Neither of us now
remembers how they looked before they broke
the light to fragments as the driver spoke.

Like mounds of mica,
25 hive-shaped hothouses,
mountains of mirror glimmering
they form
in diamond panes behind the tree ferns of
the dark imagination,
30 burn and shake
the lovely light of Queensland like a bell
reflecting Cook upon a deck
his tongue
silvered with paradox and metaphor.

(1967)

Poor Bird

. . . looking for something, something, something.
Poor bird, he is obsessed!
The millions of grains are black, white, tan, and gray,
mixed with quartz grains, rose and amethyst.

"Sandpiper," Elizabeth Bishop

From birth, from the first astonishing moment
when he pecked his way out of the shell, pure fluff,
he was looking for something—warmth, food, love
or light, or darkness—we are all the same stuff,
5   all have the same needs: to be one of the flock
or to stand apart, a singular fledgling.
So the search began—the endless search
that leads him onward—a vocation
year in, year out, morning to evening
10   *looking for something, something, something.*

Nothing will stop him. Although distracted
by nest-building, eggs, high winds, high tides
and too short a life-span for him to plan
an intelligent search—still, on he goes
15   with his delicate legs and spillikin feet
and the wish to know what he's almost guessed.
Can't leave it alone, that stretch of sand.
Thinks himself Seurat (pointilliste)
or a molecular physicist.
20   *Poor bird, he is obsessed!*

And just because he has not yet found
what he doesn't know he is searching for
is not a sign he's off the track.
His track is the sedge, the sand, the suck
25   of the undertow, the line of shells.
Nor would he have it another way.
And yet—the nag—is there something else?
Something more, perhaps, or something less.
And though he examine them, day after day
30   *the millions of grains are black, white, tan and gray.*

But occasionally, when he least expects it,
in the glass of a wave a painted fish
like a work of art across his sight
reminds him of something he doesn't know
35   that he has been seeking his whole long life—
something that may not even exist!
Poor bird, indeed! Poor dazed creature!
Yet when his eye is sharp and sideways seeing
oh, *then* the quotidian unexceptional sand is
40   *mixed with quartz grains, rose and amethyst.*

(1994)

Robert Lowell

(U.S.A., 1917–1977)

For the Union Dead

"Relinquunt Omnia Servare Rem Publicam."

The old South Boston Aquarium stands
in a Sahara of snow now. Its broken windows are boarded.
The bronze weathervane cod has lost half its scales.
The airy tanks are dry.

5   Once my nose crawled like a snail on the glass;
my hand tingled
to burst the bubbles
drifting from the noses of the cowed, compliant fish.

My hand draws back. I often sigh still
10   for the dark downward and vegetating kingdom
of the fish and reptile. One morning last March,
I pressed against the new barbed and galvanized

fence on the Boston Common. Behind their cage,
yellow dinosaur steamshovels were grunting
15   as they cropped up tons of mush and grass
to gouge their underworld garage.

Parking spaces luxuriate like civic
sandpiles in the heart of Boston.
A girdle of orange, Puritan-pumpkin colored girders
20   braces the tingling Statehouse,

shaking over the excavations, as it faces Colonel Shaw
and his bell-cheeked Negro infantry
on St. Gaudens' shaking Civil War relief,
propped by a plank splint against the garage's earthquake.

25   Two months after marching through Boston,
half the regiment was dead;
at the dedication,
William James could almost hear the bronze Negroes breathe.

Their monument sticks like a fishbone
30   in the city's throat.
Its Colonel is as lean
as a compass-needle.

He has an angry wrenlike vigilance,
a greyhound's gentle tautness;
35   he seems to wince at pleasure,
and suffocate for privacy.

He is out of bounds now. He rejoices in man's lovely,
peculiar power to choose life and die—
when he leads his black soldiers to death,
40   he cannot bend his back.

On a thousand small town New England greens,
the old white churches hold their air
of sparse, sincere rebellion; frayed flags
quilt the graveyards of the Grand Army of the Republic.

45   The stone statues of the abstract Union Soldier
grow slimmer and younger each year—
wasp-waisted, they doze over muskets
and muse through their sideburns . . .

Shaw's father wanted no monument
50   except the ditch,
where his son's body was thrown
and lost with his "niggers."

The ditch is nearer.
There are no statues for the last war here;
55   on Boylston Street, a commercial photograph
shows Hiroshima boiling

over a Mosler Safe, the "Rock of Ages"
that survived the blast. Space is nearer.
When I crouch to my television set,
60   the drained faces of Negro school-children rise like balloons.

Colonel Shaw
is riding on his bubble,
he waits
for the blessèd break.

65   The Aquarium is gone. Everywhere,
giant finned cars nose forward like fish;
a savage servility
slides by on grease.

                              (1964)

Margaret Avison

(CANADA, 1918–)

Butterfly Bones; or Sonnet Against Sonnets

The cyanide jar seals life, as sonnets move
towards final stiffness. Cased in a white glare
these specimens stare for peering boys, to prove
strange certainties. Plane dogsled and safari
5   assure continuing range. The sweep-net skill,
the patience, learning, leave all living stranger.
Insect—or poem—waits for the fix, the frill
precision can effect, brilliant with danger.
What law and wonder the museum spectres
10   bespeak is cryptic for the shivery wings,
the world cut-diamond-eyed, those eyes' reflectors,
or herbal grass, sunned motes, fierce listening.
Might sheened and rigid trophies strike men blind
like Adam's lexicon locked in the mind?

(1960)

The Swimmer's Moment

For everyone
The swimmer's moment at the whirlpool comes,
But many at that moment will not say,
"This is the whirlpool, then."
5   By their refusal they are saved
From the black pit, and also from contesting
The deadly rapids, and emerging in
The mysterious, and more ample, further waters.
And so their bland-blank faces turn and turn
10   Pale and forever on the rim of suction
They will not recognize.
Of those who dare the knowledge
Many are whirled into the ominous center
That, gaping vertical, seals up
15   For them an eternal boon of privacy,
So that we turn away from their defeat
With a despair, not for their deaths, but for
Ourselves, who cannot penetrate their secret
Nor even guess at the anonymous breadth
20   Where one or two have won:
(The silver reaches of the estuary).

(1960)

Al Purdy

(CANADA, 1918–)

Lament for the Dorsets

(Eskimos extinct in the 14th century A.D.)

Animal bones and some mossy tent rings
scrapers and spearheads   carved ivory swans
all that remains of the Dorset giants
who drove the Vikings back to their long ships
5   talked to spirits of earth and water
—a picture of terrifying old men
so large they broke the backs of bears
so small they lurk behind bone rafters
in the brain of modern hunters
10 among good thoughts and warm things
and come out at night
to spit on the stars

The big men with clever fingers
who had no dogs and hauled their sleds
15 over the frozen northern oceans
awkward giants
              killers of seal
they couldn't compete with little men
who came from the west with dogs
20 Or else in a warm climatic cycle
the seals went back to cold waters
and the puzzled Dorsets scratched their heads
with hairy thumbs around 1350 A.D.
—couldn't figure it out
25 went around saying to each other
plaintively
    "What's wrong? What happened?
    Where are the seals gone?"
And died

30 Twentieth century people
apartment dwellers
executives of neon death
warmakers with things that explode
—they have never imagined us in their future
35 how could we imagine them in the past
squatting among the moving glaciers

six hundred years ago
with glowing lamps?
As remote or nearly
40 as the trilobites and swamps
when coal became
or the last great reptile hissed
at a mammal the size of a mouse
that squeaked and fled

45 Did they ever realize at all
what was happening to them?
Some old hunter with one lame leg
a bear had chewed
sitting in a caribou-skin tent
50 —the last Dorset?
Let's say his name was Kudluk
and watch him sitting there
carving 2-inch ivory swans
for a dead grand-daughter
55 taking them out of his mind
the places in his mind
where pictures are
He selects a sharp stone tool
to gouge a parallel pattern of lines
60 on both sides of the swan
holding it with his left hand
bearing down and transmitting
his body's weight
from brain to arm and right hand
65 and one of his thoughts
turns to ivory
The carving is laid aside
in beginning darkness
at the end of hunger
70 and after a while wind
blows down the tent and snow
begins to cover him

After 600 years
the ivory thought
75 is still warm

                    (1968)

Rosemary Dobson
(AUSTRALIA, 1920–)

The Bystander

I am the one who looks the other way,
In any painting you may see me stand
Rapt at the sky, a bird, an angel's wing,
While others kneel, present the myrrh, receive
5   The benediction from the radiant hand.

I hold the horses while the knights dismount
And draw their swords to fight the battle out;
Or else in dim perspective you may see
My distant figure on the mountain road
10 When in the plains the hosts are put to rout.

I am the silly soul who looks too late,
The dullard dreaming, second from the right.
I hang upon the crowd, but do not mark
(Cap over eyes) the slaughtered Innocents,
15 Or Icarus, his downward-plunging flight.

Once in a Garden—back view only there—
How well the painter placed me, stroke on stroke,
Yet scarcely seen among the flowers and grass—
I heard a voice say, "Eat," and would have turned—
20 I often wonder who it was that spoke.

(1955)

Canberra Morning

Morning: such long shadows
Like low-bellied cats
Creep under parked cars
And out again, stealthily
5 Flattening the grasses.

At the bus-stop
A flock of starlings:
School-children, chatterers,
Swinging haversacks,
10 Pulling ribbons.

The driver's got a book by
Sartre in his pocket,
He wears dark glasses,
Listens moodily
15 To the Top Forty.

Life gets better
As I grow older
Not giving a damn
And looking slantwise
20 At everyone's morning.
(1978)

Gwen Harwood

(AUSTRALIA, 1920–)

Father and Child

I BARN OWL

Daybreak: the household slept.
I rose, blessed by the sun.
A horny fiend, I crept
out with my father's gun.
5 Let him dream of a child
obedient, angel-mild—

old No-Sayer, robbed of power
by sleep. I knew my prize
who swooped home at this hour
10 with daylight-riddled eyes
to his place on a high beam
in our old stables, to dream

light's useless time away.
I stood, holding my breath,
15 in urine-scented hay,
master of life and death,
a wisp-haired judge whose law
would punish beak and claw.

My first shot struck. He swayed,
20 ruined, beating his only
wing, as I watched, afraid
by the fallen gun, a lonely
child who believed death clean
and final, not this obscene

25   bundle of stuff that dropped,
      and dribbled through loose straw
      tangling in bowels, and hopped
      blindly closer. I saw
30   those eyes that did not see
      mirror my cruelty

      while the wrecked thing that could
      not bear the light nor hide
      hobbled in its own blood.
35   My father reached my side,
      gave me the fallen gun.
      "End what you have begun."

      I fired. The blank eyes shone
      once into mine, and slept.
40   I leaned my head upon
      my father's arm, and wept,
      owl-blind in early sun
      for what I had begun.

II   NIGHTFALL

      Forty years, lived or dreamed:
45   what memories pack them home.
      Now the season that seemed
      incredible is come.
      Father and child, we stand
      in time's long-promised land.

50   Since there's no more to taste
      ripeness is plainly all.
      Father, we pick our last
      fruits of the temporal.
      Eighty years old, you take
55   this late walk for my sake.

      Who can be what you were?
      Link your dry hand in mine,
      my stick-thin comforter.
      Far distant suburbs shine
60   with great simplicities.
      Birds crowd in flowering trees,

      sunset exalts its known
      symbols of transience.
      Your passionate face is grown
65   to ancient innocence.
      Let us walk for this hour
      as if death had no power

or were no more than sleep.
Things truly named can never
70 vanish from earth. You keep
a child's delight for ever
in birds, flowers, shivery-grass—
I name them as we pass.

"Be your tears wet?" You speak
75 as if air touched a string
near breaking-point. Your cheek
brushes on mine. Old king,
your marvellous journey's done.
Your night and day are one

80 as you find with your white stick
the path on which you turn
home with the child once quick
to mischief, grown to learn
what sorrows, in the end,
85 no words, no tears can mend.
(1975)

Edwin Morgan

(SCOTLAND, 1920–)

Opening the Cage

14 variations on 14 words
I have nothing to say and I am saying it and that is poetry.
JOHN CAGE

I have to say poetry and is that nothing and am I saying it
I am and I have poetry to say and is that nothing saying it
I am nothing and I have poetry to say and that is saying it
I that am saying poetry have nothing and it is I and to say
5 And I say that I am to have poetry and saying it is nothing
I am poetry and nothing and saying it is to say that I have
To have nothing is poetry and I am saying that and I say it
Poetry is saying I have nothing and I am to say that and it
Saying nothing I am poetry and I have to say that and it is
10 It is and I am and I have poetry saying say that to nothing
It is saying poetry to nothing and I say I have and am that
Poetry is saying I have it and I am nothing and to say that
And that nothing is poetry I am saying and I have to say it
Saying poetry is nothing and to that I say I am and have it
(1968)

Howard Nemerov

(U.S.A., 1920–1991)

The Town Dump

"The art of our necessities is strange,
That can make vile things precious."

A mile out in the marshes, under a sky
Which seems to be always going away
In a hurry, on that Venetian land threaded
With hidden canals, you will find the city
5   Which seconds ours (so cemeteries, too,
Reflect a town from hillsides out of town),
Where Being most Becomingly ends up
Becoming some more. From cardboard tenements,
Windowed with cellophane, or simply tenting
10   In paper bags, the angry mackerel eyes
Glare at you out of stove-in, sunken heads
Far from the sea; the lobster, also, lifts
An empty claw in his most minatory
Of gestures; oyster, crab, and mussel shells
15   Lie here in heaps, savage as money hurled
Away at the gate of hell. If you want results,
These are results.
                            Objects of value or virtue,
However, are also to be picked up here,
Though rarely, lying with bones and rotten meat,
20   Eggshells and mouldy bread, banana peels
No one will skid on, apple cores that caused
Neither the fall of man nor a theory
Of gravitation. People do throw out
The family pearls by accident, sometimes,
25   Not often; I've known dealers in antiques
To prowl this place by night, with flashlights, on
The off-chance of somebody's having left
Derelict chairs which will turn out to be
By Hepplewhite, a perfect set of six
30   Going to show, I guess, that in any sty
Someone's heaven may open and shower down
Riches responsive to the right dream; though
It is a small chance, certainly, that sends
The ghostly dealer, heavy with fly-netting
35   Over his head, across these hills in darkness,
Stumbling in cut-glass goblets, lacquered cups,
And other products of his dreamy midden
Penciled with light and guarded by the flies.

For there are flies, of course. A dynamo
40 Composed, by thousands, of our ancient black
Retainers, hums here day and night, steady
As someone telling beads, the hum becoming
A high whine at any disturbance; then,
Settled again, they shine under the sun
45 Like oil-drops, or are invisible as night,
By night.
                All this continually smoulders,
Crackles, and smokes with mostly invisible fires
Which, working deep, rarely flash out and flare,
50 And never finish. Nothing finishes;
The flies, feeling the heat, keep on the move.

Among the flies, the purifying fires,
The hunters by night, acquainted with the art
Of our necessities, and the new deposits
55 That each day wastes with treasure, you may say
There should be ratios. You may sum up
The results, if you want results. But I will add
That wild birds, drawn to the carrion and flies,
Assemble in some numbers here, their wings
60 Shining with light, their flight enviably free,
Their music marvelous, though sad, and strange.
                                          (1960)

Santa Claus

Somewhere on his travels the strange Child
Picked up with this overstuffed confidence man,
Affection's inverted thief, who climbs at night
Down chimneys, into dreams, with this world's goods.
5   Bringing all the benevolence of money,
He teaches the innocent to want, thus keeps
Our fat world rolling. His prescribed costume,
White flannel beard, red belly of cotton waste,
Conceals the thinness of essential hunger,
10 An appetite that feeds on satisfaction;
Or, pregnant with possessions, he brings forth
Vanity and the void. His name itself
Is corrupted, and even Saint Nicholas, in his turn,
Gives off a faint and reminiscent stench,
15 The merest soupçon, of brimstone and the pit.

Now, at the season when the Child is born
To suffer for the world, suffer the world,
His bloated Other, jovial satellite
And sycophant, makes his appearance also
20   In a glitter of goodies, in a rock candy glare.
Played at the better stores by bums, for money,
This annual savior of the economy
Speaks in the parables of the dollar sign:
Suffer the little children to come to Him.

25   At Easter, he's anonymous again,
Just one of the crowd lunching on Calvary.

(1962)

To David, about His Education

The world is full of mostly invisible things,
And there is no way but putting the mind's eye,
Or its nose, in a book, to find them out,
Things like the square root of Everest
5   Or how many times Byron goes into Texas,
Or whether the law of the excluded middle
Applies west of the Rockies. For these
And the like reasons, you have to go to school
And study books and listen to what you are told,
10   And sometimes try to remember. Though I don't know
What you will do with the mean annual rainfall
On Plato's Republic, or the calorie content
Of the Diet of Worms, such things are said to be
Good for you, and you will have to learn them
15   In order to become one of the grown-ups
Who sees invisible things neither steadily nor whole,
But keeps gravely the grand confusion of the world
Under his hat, which is where it belongs,
And teaches small children to do this in their turn.

(1962)

Learning by Doing

They're taking down a tree at the front door,
The power saw is snarling at some nerves,
Whining at others. Now and then it grunts,
And sawdust falls like snow or a drift of seeds.

5   Rotten, they tell us, at the fork, and one
Big wind would bring it down. So what they do
They do, as usual, to do us good.
Whatever cannot carry its own weight
Has got to go, and so on; you expect
10   To hear them talking next about survival
And the values of a free society.
For in the explanations people give
On these occasions there is generally some
Mean-spirited moral point, and everyone
15   Privately wonders if his neighbors plan
To saw him up before he falls on them.

Maybe a hundred years in sun and shower
Dismantled in a morning and let down
Out of itself a finger at a time
20   And then an arm, and so down to the trunk,
Until there's nothing left to hold on to
Or snub the splintery holding rope around,
and where those big green divagations were
So loftily with shadows interleaved
25   The absent-minded blue rains in on us.

Now that they've got it sectioned on the ground
It looks as though somebody made a plain
Error in diagnosis, for the wood
Looks sweet and sound throughout. You couldn't know,
30   Of course, until you took it down. That's what
Experts are for, and these experts stand round
The giant pieces of tree as though expecting
An instruction booklet from the factory
Before they try to put it back together.

35   Anyhow, there it isn't, on the ground.
Next come the tractor and the crowbar crew
To extirpate what's left and fill the grave.
Maybe tomorrow grass seed will be sown.
There's some mean-spirited moral point in that
40   As well: you learn to bury your mistakes,
Though for a while at dusk the darkening air
Will be with many shadows interleaved,
And pierced with a bewilderment of birds.

(1967)

An Old Colonial Imperialist

To grip through the ground with your feet;
To feel your toes curled around rocks,
Sucking up water; to stand up straight
And tall for a certain time, and after
5   Go off in any direction, so long as it's up;
That's what I call living: standing there.

Tons of water creeping up my stomach,
Immense strain in my many shoulders
Holding their limbs in proclamation;
10   When a starling lands in my hair
I know it; when the hairy woodpecker
Hits me for lice, I know where the lice are.
My patches of lichen itch for centuries,
I do not stoop to scratch; you pay
15   For dignity in this world.
                       Grown old,
I suffer the surgeon's pruning bill,
Cement in my cavities, healing tar
Over my incidental stumps. I go on,
Bending a little in the bigger winds,
20   Waving light airs away, and every fall
I drop the year's familiarity
Of used leaves with a certain contempt.
                       (1967)

Amos Tutuola

(NIGERIA, 1920–)

Ajao and the Active Bone

A long time ago, there lived a man in a small town. His name was Ajao. He was an expert trickster and deceiver and, because of his profession, everyone in the town took him to be the most useless man in the town.

One year, there was a great famine. Within a few month after the famine had started, there was nothing for the people to eat.

One day, as Ajao was wandering about on the outskirts of the town, looking for food to eat, he came upon the shrine of a god. He eagerly entered it with the hope that, at least, there would be a sacrifice and he could satisfy his hunger with it. But to his disappointment there was nothing like a sacrifice, except one old bone which was half stuck into the sand before the god who was the occupant of the shrine.

The bone was not an ordinary one, but a small god.

Unknowing, Ajao ran to the bone and picked it up immediately. As he was about to leave the shrine he heard a horrible caution from one corner of the shrine: 'Eh! Don't take that bone away! It is not an ordinary bone as you suppose it to be! Come and put it back in the very spot you have taken it from!'

Ajao was greatly afraid and confused when he heard this warning. He glanced at every corner of the shrine, but nobody was there except the huge god. Nevertheless, as Ajao had not eaten anything for the past few days, he did not pay heed to the horrible warning. Instead, he stubbornly ran with the bone to his house.

Ajao entered his room and shut the door; then he began to chew the bone greedily. To his surprise, as he was still enjoying it, it fell from his hand. And as he was just stretching his hand to pick it up, the bone became active suddenly. It immediately began to throw itself along the ground.

Ajao began to chase it along, trying to pick it up in order to continue to chew it.

Thus the bone was throwing itself along and along until it left the town and came to a big river which was at a little distance from the town. Instead of stopping on the bank of the river, this wonderful bone flung itself into the river and, without hesitation, it sank.

Ajao jumped in the river as well. He dived, and he continued to chase the bone along the bottom of the river.

After a while, the bone disappeared, and Ajao was carried to the deepest part of the river by the current. To his surprise, within a few seconds, he found himself unexpectedly inside a massive building. The massive building was under the river, and it belonged to the Nymph or Water Spirit who governed the river.

'Who are you?' the Nymph asked, astonished.

'I am the son of man,' Ajao replied with a trembling voice.

'What do you want here, the son of man?' the Nymph shouted.

Ajao fearfully explained. 'Thank you, Nymph. You see, there is a great famine in my town now. So as I was chewing the only bone which I found in a shrine, it mistakenly fell down from my hand. Then it began to throw itself till it flung itself into the river, and I followed it. I simply found myself in this your massive building unexpectedly.'

'Is that so?' The Nymph wondered greatly to see that Ajao was so hungry for food that he chased a bone to her house which was under the river.

'It is so,' Ajao replied painfully.

'All right, take this wooden spoon. When you return to your house, ask it to do your work for you. But never come back to me for anything as from today!' The Nymph gave a wonderful wooden spoon to Ajao which would supply him with every kind of delicious food and drink.

Ajao thanked the Nymph when she gave the wooden spoon to him. Then she told him to sit on a chair, and he had hardly done so when he found himself on the bank of the river. From there he went to his house with the spoon.

As soon as he entered his room, he asked the spoon: 'Do your work now, wooden spoon!' And he had hardly asked thus when the room was full of all kinds of delicious food and drink. Then greedily he and his family ate and drank to their entire satisfaction.

In the following morning, instead of keeping the secret of the wonderful wooden spoon within himself, Ajao went to the king. He told him to invite all the people of the town to his palace.

'For what reason, Ajao, shall I invite all the people to my palace?' The king was suspicious because he knew Ajao as an expert trickster and deceiver.

'I wish to feed them with delicious food and drink!' Ajao replied with pride.

'You, Ajao, want to feed the people of the town with food and drink in this time of great famine? Or you cannot remember what you came to me for?' The king was still mistrustful.

'I say I have enough food and drink to give to all the people!' Ajao confirmed loudly.

The king still doubted. 'But I am afraid, Ajao. Even I as king of this town have not eaten now for over four days. How much stranger it is for a poor person like you to get sufficient food and drink to give to all the people!'

'Your majesty, just do what I am asking you to do,' Ajao said, compelling the king with his sweet voice.

So in the evening the king's bell-ringer announced to the people of the town that they should gather on the assembly ground which was in front of the palace. And immediately all the people gathered on the assembly ground while the king sat in the middle of the crowd of people. All were waiting for Ajao to come.

After a while, Ajao came with the wooden spoon, and in the presence of the people and the king and his chiefs, he commanded the spoon loudly: 'My wooden spoon, do your work now for these people!'

And Ajao had hardly commanded like that when everyone saw the delicious food and drink in front of him or her. Then greedily the people, the king and the chiefs ate and drank as much as they could.

But after a while, when they were intoxicated by the drinks, they started to play so roughly that they did not know when they smashed the wonderful spoon and it split. So the people and Ajao did not think about the spoon. When they became tired, everyone walked sluggishly back to his or her house, with the hope of coming back in the following morning to eat and drink as before.

On the following morning, all the people, the king and the chiefs gathered again on the assembly ground. They were waiting for their breakfast when Ajao arrived. When he came, because he was late, he hastily commanded the wooden spoon to do its usual work. But unfortunately it failed to supply food and drink. He tried all his best, but the spoon could not supply anything because it had split when the people trampled on it the night before.

The people and the king exclaimed angrily, 'You are an expert deceiver, Ajao, as we already know. We believe you have commanded the spoon not to supply food and drink for us!'

'I think it is powerless to supply food and drink as it was split yesternight,' Ajao suggested to the people with fear.

'If it is so, you had better go back to the same Nymph and tell her to give you another spoon,' the people roared impatiently.

'I am sorry, but the Nymph has already warned me not to come back to her for anything again!' Ajao explained.

'Don't deceive or trick us, Ajao!' the king warned Ajao. 'Go back to her and, I believe, she will give you another spoon if you show her the split one. But if you refuse to go back to her, it means you disobey my order. So for that you will be beheaded!' Thus the king forced Ajao to go back.

'Oh, my head!' Ajao exclaimed, beginning to blame himself as he started to return to the Nymph reluctantly. 'If l had known, I should not have told the king anything about the wooden spoon. Instead, I should have been using it secretly for my family and myself.'

When he got to the Nymph, he showed her the split spoon and he explained to her how the people had split it carelessly.

'Oh, is that how you are, the son of man? All right, I will teach all of you sense today. Take this long whip, and it will serve you satisfactorily even better than the wooden spoon!' With great annoyance, the Nymph gave the whip to Ajao.

'But this is a whip,' Ajao said with a doubtful mind. 'And as far as I understand, the only work of a whip is flogging people.'

'No, this whip is not meant so in this case,' the Nymph explained indirectly. 'It can also produce a lovely music to which all of you will dance merrily, and none of you will say goodbye to one another when leaving your assembly ground. Goodbye, son of man.'

Then Ajao thanked her and left in confusion. But he went to his own house first, instead of going to the king and the people. He gathered his family hastily in the room, as they felt all near to dying from hunger. He commanded the whip: 'Do your work now, whip.'

Ajao had hardly commanded the whip when it began to flog him and his family. When it had flogged them severely for nearly one hour, then it stopped flogging them.

'Yes,' Ajao said with grief within himself, 'as the people, the king and his chiefs enjoyed the delicious food and drinks which the wooden spoon supplied yesterday, so they will share the punishment which this whip supplies instead of food and drink!'

Then immediately Ajao took the whip from the floor and went to the assembly ground. The hungry people, the king, and the chiefs were very happy when he returned to them as early as they wanted him to.

Ajao gave the whip to the king. He told him to ask it to do its work, and after that he hastily bolted away.

The king had hardly asked the whip to do its work when it began to flog him and his chiefs and the people. The whip flogged them so severely that not one of them could remember how he or she managed to leave there, and, as the king was running away for his life, his crown fell off his head—but he was unable to wait and take it back.

Thus the whip taught all of the town not to be careless next time.

A few days later, after the king saw that the people had rested their minds, he invited Ajao to his palace. Angrily, he asked Ajao, 'Why did you bring the cruel whip instead of the kindly wooden spoon?'

'Well, you see, that was the right thing that the Nymph gave to me instead of the wooden spoon, and that meant she taught us a lesson: that we must take good care of whatever might be given to us,' Ajao explained calmly.

'Yes, of course, if we were not careless, the wooden spoon would still be serving us—especially at this time when the great famine continues to besiege our town,' the king remarked quietly, when he realized their mistake.

(1990)

Richard Wilbur

(U.S.A., 1921–)

Love Calls Us to the Things of This World

  The eyes open to a cry of pulleys,
And spirited from sleep, the astounded soul
Hangs for a moment bodiless and simple
As false dawn.
      Outside the open window
5 The morning air is all awash with angels.

Some are in bed-sheets, some are in blouses,
Some are in smocks: but truly there they are.
Now they are rising together in calm swells
Of halcyon feeling, filling whatever they wear
10   With the deep joy of their impersonal breathing;

Now they are flying in place, conveying
The terrible speed of their omnipresence, moving
And staying like white water; and now of a sudden
They swoon down into so rapt a quiet
15   That nobody seems to be there.
                                        The soul shrinks
    From all that it is about to remember,
From the punctual rape of every blessed day,
And cries,
            "Oh, let there be nothing on earth but laundry,
Nothing but rosy hands in the rising steam
20   And clear dances done in the sight of heaven."

    Yet, as the sun acknowledges
With a warm look the world's hunks and colors,
The soul descends once more in bitter love
To accept the waking body, saying now
25   In a changed voice as the man yawns and rises,

    "Bring them down from their ruddy gallows;
Let there be clean linen for the backs of thieves;
Let lovers go fresh and sweet to be undone,
And the heaviest nuns walk in a pure floating
30   Of dark habits,
                keeping their difficult balance."

                                            (1956)

Piazza di Spagna, Early Morning

            I can't forget
    How she stood at the top of that long marble stair
    Amazed, and then with a sleepy pirouette
Went dancing slowly down to the fountain-quieted square

5   Nothing upon her face
    But some impersonal loneliness,—not then a girl,
        But as it were a reverie of the place,
            A called-for falling glide and whirl;

        As when a leaf, petal, or thin chip
10   Is drawn to the falls of a pool and, circling a moment above it
            Rides on over the lip—
        Perfectly beautiful, perfectly ignorant of it.

                                            (1956)

Mavis Gallant
(CANADA, 1922–)

From the Fifteenth District

Although an epidemic of haunting, widely reported, spread through the Fifteenth District of our city last summer, only three acceptable complaints were lodged with the police.

Major Emery Travella, 31st Infantry, 1914–18, Order of the Leopard, Military Beech Leaf, Cross of St. Lambert First Class, killed while defusing a bomb in a civilian area 9 June, 1941, Medal of Danzig (posthumous), claims he is haunted by the entire congregation of St. Michael and All Angels on Bartholomew Street. Every year on the Sunday falling nearest the anniversary of his death, Major Travella attends Holy Communion service at St. Michael's, the church from which he was buried. He stands at the back, close to the doors, waiting until all the communicants have returned to their places, before he approaches the altar rail. His intention is to avoid a mixed queue of dead and living, the thought of which is disgusting to him. The congregation sits, hushed and expectant, straining to hear the Major's footsteps (he drags one foot a little). After receiving the Host, the Major leaves at once, without waiting for the Blessing. For the past several years, the Major has noticed that the congregation doubles in size as 9 June approaches. Some of these strangers bring cameras and tape recorders with them; others burn incense under the pews and wave amulets and trinkets in what they imagine to be his direction, muttering pagan gibberish all the while. References he is sure must be meant for him are worked into the sermons: "And he that was dead sat up, and began to speak" (Luke 7:15), or "So Job died, being old and full of days" (Job 42:17). The Major points out that he never speaks and never opens his mouth except to receive Holy Communion. He lived about sixteen thousand and sixty days, many of which he does not remember. On 23 September, 1914, as a young private, he was crucified to a cart wheel for five hours for having failed to salute an equally young lieutenant. One ankle was left permanently impaired.

The Major wishes the congregation to leave him in peace. The opacity of the living, their heaviness and dullness, the moisture of their skin, and the dustiness of their hair are repellant to a man of feeling. It was always his habit to avoid civilian crowds. He lived for six years on the fourth floor in Block E, Stoneflower Gardens, without saying a word to his neighbors or even attempting to learn their names. An affidavit can easily be obtained from the former porter at the Gardens, now residing at the Institute for Victims of Senile Trauma, Fifteenth District.

Mrs. Ibrahim, aged thirty-seven, mother of twelve children, complains about being haunted by Dr. L. Chalmeton of Regius Hospital, Seventh District, and by Miss Alicia Fohrenbach, social investigator from the Welfare Bureau, Fifteenth District. These two haunt Mrs. Ibrahim without respite, presenting for her ratification and approval conflicting and unpleasant versions of her own death.

According to Dr. Chalmeton's account, soon after Mrs. Ibrahim was discharged as incurable from Regius Hospital he paid his patient a professional call. He arrived at a quarter past four on the first Tuesday of April, expecting to find the social investigator, with whom he had a firm appointment. Mrs. Ibrahim was discovered alone, in a windowless room, the walls of which were coated with whitish fungus a quarter of an inch thick, which rose to a height of about forty inches from the floor. Dr. Chalmeton inquired, "Where is the social investigator?" Mrs. Ibrahim pointed to her throat, reminding him that she could not reply. Several dark-eyed children peeped into the room and ran away. "How many are yours?" the Doctor asked. Mrs. Ibrahim indicated six twice with her fingers. "Where do they sleep?" said the Doctor. Mrs. Ibrahim indicated the floor. Dr. Chalmeton said, "What does your husband do for a living?" Mrs. Ibrahim pointed to a workbench on which the Doctor saw several pieces of finely wrought jewelry; he thought it a waste that skilled work had been lavished on what seemed to be plastics and base metals. Dr. Chalmeton made the patient as comfortable as he could, explaining that he could not administer drugs for the relief of pain until the social investigator had signed a receipt for them. Miss Fohrenbach arrived at five o'clock. It had taken her forty minutes to find a suitable parking space: the street appeared to be poor, but everyone living on it owned one or two cars. Dr. Chalmeton, who was angry at having been kept waiting, declared he would not be responsible for the safety of his patient in a room filled with mold. Miss Fohrenbach retorted that the District could not resettle a family of fourteen persons who were foreign-born when there was a long list of native citizens waiting for accommodation. Mrs. Ibrahim had in any case relinquished her right to a domicile in the Fifteenth District the day she lost consciousness in the road and allowed an ambulance to transport her to a hospital in the Seventh. It was up to the hospital to look after her now. Dr. Chalmeton pointed out that housing of patients is not the business of hospitals. It was well known that the foreign poor preferred to crowd together in the Fifteenth, where they could sing and dance in the streets and attend one another's weddings. Miss Fohrenbach declared that Mrs. Ibrahim could easily have moved her bed into the kitchen, which was somewhat warmer and which boasted a window. When Mrs. Ibrahim died, the children would be placed in foster homes, eliminating the need for a larger apartment. Dr. Chalmeton remembers Miss Fohrenbach's then crying, "Oh, why do all these people come here, where nobody wants them?" While he was trying to think of an answer, Mrs. Ibrahim died.

In her testimony, Miss Fohrenbach recalls that she had to beg and plead with Dr. Chalmeton to visit Mrs. Ibrahim, who had been discharged from Regius Hospital without medicines or prescriptions or advice or instructions. Miss Fohrenbach had returned several times that April day to see if the Doctor had arrived. The first thing Dr. Chalmeton said on entering the room was "There is no way of helping these people. Even the simplest rules of hygiene are too complicated for them to follow. Wherever they settle, they spread disease and vermin. They have been responsible for outbreaks of aphthous stomatitis, hereditary hypoxia, coccidioidomycosis, gonorrheal arthritis, and scleroderma. Their eating habits are filthy. They never wash their hands. The virus that attacks them breeds in dirt. We took in the patient against all rules, after the ambulance drivers left her lying in the courtyard and drove off without asking for a receipt. Regius Hospital was built and endowed for ailing Greek scholars. Now it is crammed with unteachable persons who cannot read or write." His cheeks and forehead were flushed, his speech incoherent and blurred. According to the social investigator, he was the epitome of the broken-down, irresponsible old rascals the Seventh District employs in its public services. Wondering at the effect this ranting of his might have on the patient, Miss Fohrenbach glanced at Mrs. Ibrahim and noticed she had died.

Mrs. Ibrahim's version of her death has the social investigator arriving first, bringing Mrs. Ibrahim a present of a wine-colored dressing gown made of soft, quilted silk. Miss Fohrenbach explained that the gown was part of a donation of garments to the needy. Large plastic bags, decorated with a moss rose, the emblem of the Fifteenth District, and bearing the words "Clean Clothes for the Foreign-Born," had been distributed by volunteer workers in the more prosperous streets of the District. A few citizens kept the bags as souvenirs, but most had turned them in to the Welfare Bureau filled with attractive clothing, washed, ironed, and mended, and with missing buttons replaced. Mrs. Ibrahim sat up and put on the dressing gown, and the social investigator helped her button it. Then Miss Fohrenbach changed the bed linen and pulled the bed away from the wall. She sat down and took Mrs. Ibrahim's hand in hers and spoke about a new, sunny flat containing five warm rooms which would soon be available. Miss Fohrenbach said that arrangements had been made to send the twelve Ibrahim children to the mountains for special winter classes. They would be taught history and languages and would learn to ski.

The Doctor arrived soon after. He stopped and spoke to Mr. Ibrahim, who was sitting at his workbench making an emerald patch box. The Doctor said to him, "If you give me your social-security papers, I can attend to the medical insurance. It will save you a great deal of trouble." Mr. Ibrahim answered, "What is social security?" The Doctor examined the patch box and asked Mr. Ibrahim what he earned. Mr. Ibrahim told him, and the Doctor said, "But that is less than the minimum wage." Mr. Ibrahim said, "What is a minimum wage?" The Doctor turned to Miss Fohrenbach, saying, "We really must try and help them." Mrs. Ibrahim died. Mr. Ibrahim, when he understood that nothing could be done, lay face down on the floor, weeping loudly. Then he remembered the rules of hospitality and got up and gave each of the guests a present—for Miss Fohrenbach a belt made of Syriac coins, a copy of which is in the Cairo Museum, and for the Doctor a bracelet of precious metal engraved with pomegranates, about sixteen pomegranates in all, that has lifesaving properties.

Mrs. Ibrahim asks that her account of the afternoon be registered with the police as the true version and that copies be sent to the Doctor and the social investigator, with a courteous request for peace and silence.

Mrs. Carlotte Essling, née Holmquist, complains of being haunted by her husband, Professor Augustus Essling, the philosopher and historian. When they were married, the former Miss Holmquist was seventeen. Professor Essling, a widower, had four small children. He explained to Miss Holmquist why he wanted to marry again. He said, "I must have one person, preferably female, on whom I can depend absolutely, who will never betray me even in her thoughts. A disloyal thought revealed, a betrayal even in fantasy, would be enough to destroy me. Knowing that I may rely upon some one person will leave me free to continue my work without anxiety or distraction." The work was the Professor's lifelong examination of the philosopher Nicolas de Malebranche, for whom he had named his eldest child. "If I cannot have the unfailing loyalty I have described, I would as soon not marry at all," the Professor added. He had just begun work on *Malebranche and Materialism.*

Mrs. Essling recalls that at seventeen this seemed entirely within her possibilities, and she replied something like "Yes, I see," or "I quite understand," or "You needn't mention it again."

Mrs. Essling brought up her husband's four children and had two more of her own, and died after thirty-six years of marriage at the age of fifty-three. Her husband haunts her with proof of her goodness. He tells people that Mrs. Essling was born an angel, lived like an angel, and is an angel in eternity. Mrs. Essling would like relief from this charge. "Angel" is a loose way of speaking. She is astonished that the Professor cannot be more precise. Angels are created, not born. Nowhere in any written testimony will you find a scrap of proof that angels are "good." Some are merely messengers; others have a paramilitary function. All are stupid.

After her death, Mrs. Essling remained in the Fifteenth District. She says she can go nowhere without being accosted by the Professor, who, having completed the last phase of his work *Malebranche and Mysticism,* roams the streets, looking in shopwindows, eating lunch twice, in two different restaurants, telling his life story to waiters and bus drivers. When he sees Mrs. Essling, he calls out, "There you are!" and "What have you been sent to tell me?" and "Is there a message?" In July, catching sight of her at the open-air fruit market on Dulac Street, the Professor jumped off a bus, upsetting barrows of plums and apricots, waving an umbrella as he ran. Mrs. Essling had to take refuge in the cold-storage room of the central market, where, years ago, after she had ordered twenty pounds of raspberries and currants for making jelly, she was invited by the wholesale fruit dealer, Mr. Lobrano, aged twenty-nine, to spend a holiday with him in a charming southern city whose Mediterranean Baroque churches he described with much delicacy of feeling. Mrs. Essling was too startled to reply. Mistaking her silence, Mr. Lobrano then mentioned a northern city containing a Gothic cathedral. Mrs. Essling said that such a holiday was impossible. Mr. Lobrano asked for one good reason. Mrs. Essling was at that moment four months pregnant with her second child. Three stepchildren waited for her out in the street. A fourth stepchild was at home looking after the baby. Professor Essling, working on his *Malebranche and Money*, was at home, too, expecting his lunch. Mrs. Essling realized she could not give Mr. Lobrano one good reason. She left the cold-storage room without another word and did not return to it in her lifetime.

Mrs. Essling would like to be relieved of the Professor's gratitude. Having lived an exemplary life is one thing; to have it thrown up at one is another. She would like the police to send for Professor Essling and tell him so. She suggests that the police find some method of keeping him off the streets. The police ought to threaten him; frighten him; put the fear of the Devil into him. Philosophy has made him afraid of dying. Remind him about how he avoided writing his *Malebranche and Mortality*. He is an old man. It should be easy.

(1978)

Philip Larkin

(ENGLAND, 1922–1985)

Church Going

Once I am sure there's nothing going on
I step inside, letting the door thud shut.
Another church: matting, seats, and stone,
And little books; sprawlings of flowers, cut
5 For Sunday, brownish now; some brass and stuff
Up at the holy end; the small neat organ;
And a tense, musty, unignorable silence,
Brewed God knows how long. Hatless, I take off
My cycle-clips in awkward reverence,

10 Move forward, run my hand around the font.
From where I stand, the roof looks almost new—
Cleaned, or restored? Someone would know: I don't.
Mounting the lectern, I peruse a few
Hectoring large-scale verses, and pronounce
15 'Here endeth' much more loudly than I'd meant.
The echoes snigger briefly. Back at the door
I sign the book, donate an Irish sixpence,
Reflect the place was not worth stopping for.

Yet stop I did: in fact I often do,
And always end much at a loss like this,
Wondering what to look for; wondering, too,
When churches fall completely out of use
What we shall turn them into, if we shall keep
A few cathedrals chronically on show,
Their parchment, plate and pyx in locked cases,
And let the rest rent-free to rain and sheep.
Shall we avoid them as unlucky places?

Or, after dark, will dubious women come
To make their children touch a particular stone;
Pick simples for a cancer; or on some
Advised night see walking a dead one?
Power of some sort or other will go on
In games, in riddles, seemingly at random;
But superstition, like belief, must die,
And what remains when disbelief has gone?
Grass, weedy pavement, brambles, buttress, sky,

A shape less recognisable each week,
A purpose more obscure. I wonder who
Will be the last, the very last, to seek
This place for what it was; one of the crew
That tap and jot and know what rood-lofts were?
Some ruin-bibber, randy for antique,
Or Christmas-addict, counting on a whiff
Of gown-and-bands and organ-pipes and myrrh?
Or will he be my representative,

Bored, uninformed, knowing the ghostly silt
Dispersed, yet tending to this cross of ground
Through suburb scrub because it held unspilt
So long and equably what since is found
Only in separation—marriage, and birth,
And death, and thoughts of these—for whom was built
This special shell? For, though I've no idea
What this accoutred frowsty barn is worth,
It pleases me to stand in silence here;

A serious house on serious earth it is,
In whose blent air all our compulsions meet,
Are recognised, and robed as destinies.
And that much never can be obsolete,
Since someone will forever be surprising
A hunger in himself to be more serious,
And gravitating with it to this ground,
Which, he once heard, was proper to grow wise in,
If only that so many dead lie round.

(1955)

Toads

Why should I let the toad *work*
    Squat on my life?
Can't I use my wit as a pitchfork
    And drive the brute off?

5   Six days of the week it soils
    With its sickening poison—
Just for paying a few bills!
    That's out of proportion.

Lots of folk live on their wits:
10   Lecturers, lispers,
Losels, loblolly-men, louts—
    They don't end as paupers;

Lots of folk live up lanes
    With fires in a bucket,
15   Eat windfalls and tinned sardines—
They seem to like it.

Their nippers have got bare feet,
    Their unspeakable wives
Are skinny as whippets—and yet
20   No one actually *starves*.

Ah, were I courageous enough
    To shout *Stuff your pension*!
But I know, all too well, that's the stuff
    That dreams are made on:

25   For something sufficiently toad-like
    Squats in me, too;
Its hunkers are heavy as hard luck,
    And cold as snow,

And will never allow me to blarney
30   My way to getting
The fame and the girl and the money
    All at one sitting.

I don't say, one bodies the other
    One's spiritual truth;
35   But I do say it's hard to lose either,
    When you have both.

                  (1955)

Eli Mandel

(CANADA, 1922–1992)

The Madwomen of the Plaza de Mayo

They wear white scarves and shawls.
They carry pictures on strings about their necks.
I have seen their faces elsewhere:
in Ereceira, fishermen's wives
5 walking in dark processions
to the sea, its roaring,
women of Ireland
wearing their dark scarves
hearing the echo of guns, bombs

10 Identities
the *desaparecidos*
lost ones
the disappeared

in the Plaza the Presidential Palace
15 reveals soldiers like fences with steel spikes
the rhythm of lost bodies
the rhythm of loss

A soldier is a man who is not a man.
A fence, a spike
20 A nail in somebody's eye.
Lost man.

Why are the women weeping?
For whom do they cry
under the orange moon
25 under the lemon moon of Buenos Aires?

"If only for humanitarian reasons
tell the families of the living
where are they
tell the families of the dead
30 what they need
what they deserve to know."

No one speaks.
The junta says nothing.
The *desaparecidos* remain silent.
35 The moon has no language.

(1981)

Hone Tuwhare

(NEW ZEALAND, 1922–)

A song in praise of a favourite humming-top

I polish your skin. It is that of a woman
    mellowed by the oil of the tarata,
    humming-top. What stable secret do you

    keep locked up in movement, humming-top?
5   skipping away daintily as you do, sidewise
    lurching, nonchalantly coming erect?

Your drowsy sighs lull and beguile the people
    the many, who've come to hear your talk,
    your whizz your buzz your angry bee-stung

10   murmurs—which are simply about nothing
    at all. Ah, see: they're closing in—
    stopping just short of whip range.

Eyeballs plopping like bird's eggs sucked
    deep into your whirlpool, they're surging
15   forward again treading on each other's feet.

Lips stretched tightly over teeth, they grin;
    find throat at last to shout; exclaim.
    O, they will leave finally, when they've

    finished fondling you, cooing over you like
20   a kukupa. I don't like it: each one of them
    a thief's heart gladdened—but covetous.

(1984)

This poem developed from a 'Spell for a wooden humming-top cut out and fashioned from a totara; matai. Woods which alone hum and whine beautifully'. Author unknown. Text in Edward Shortland's Maori Manuscript Notebook 2(b) (MS2), 73, Hocken Library, University of Otago, Dunedin.

Nadine Gordimer

(SOUTH AFRICA, 1923-)

A Writer's Freedom

What is a writer's freedom?

To me it is his right to maintain and publish to the world a deep, intense, private view of the situation in which he finds his society. If he is to work as well as he can, he must take, and be granted, freedom from the public conformity of political interpretation, morals and tastes.

Living when we do, where we do, as we do, 'Freedom' leaps to mind as a political concept exclusively—and when people think of freedom for writers they visualize at once the great mound of burnt, banned and proscribed books our civilisation has piled up; a pyre to which our own country has added and is adding its contribution. The right to be left alone to write what one pleases is not an academic issue to those of us who live and work in South Africa. The private view always has been and always will be a source of fear and anger to proponents of a way of life, such as the white man's in South Africa, that does not bear looking at except in the light of a special self-justificatory doctrine.

All that the writer can do, as a writer, is to go on writing *the truth as he sees it*. That is what I mean by his 'private view' of events, whether they be the great public ones of wars and revolutions, or the individual and intimate ones of daily, personal life.

As to the fate of his books—there comes a time in the history of certain countries when the feelings of their writers are best expressed in this poem, written within the lifetime of many of us, by Bertolt Brecht:

> When the Regime ordered that books with dangerous teachings
> Should be publicly burnt and everywhere
> Oxen were forced to draw carts fulls of books
> To a funeral pyre, an exiled poet,
> One of the best, discovered with fury, when he studied the list
> Of the burned, that his books
> Had been forgotten. He rushed to his writing table
> On wings of anger and wrote a letter to those in power.
> Burn me, he wrote with hurrying pen, burn me!
> Do not treat me in this fashion. Don't leave me out. Have I not
> Always spoken the truth in my books? And now
> You treat me like a liar! I order you:
> Burn me!

We South African writers can understand the desperate sentiments expressed while still putting up the fight to have our books read rather than burnt.

Bannings and banishments are terrible known hazards a writer must face, and many have faced, if the writer belongs where freedom of expression, among other freedoms, is withheld, but sometimes creativity is frozen rather than destroyed. A Thomas Mann survives exile to write a *Doctor Faustus*; a Pasternak smuggles *Doctor Zhivago* out of a ten-year silence; a Solzhenitsyn emerges with his terrible world intact in the map of *The Gulag Archipelago*; nearer our home continent, a Chinua Achebe, writing from America, does not trim his prose to please a Nigerian regime under which he cannot live; a Dennis Brutus grows in reputation abroad while his poetry remains forbidden at home; and a Breyten Breytenbach, after accepting the special dispensation from racialist law which allowed him to visit his home country with a wife who is not white, no doubt accepts the equally curious circumstance that the book he was to write about the visit was to be banned, in due course.

Through all these vicissitudes, real writers go on writing the truth as they see it. And they do not agree to censor themselves . . . You can burn the books, but the integrity of creative artists is not incarnate on paper any more than on canvas—it survives so long as the artist himself cannot be persuaded, cajoled or frightened into betraying it.

All this, hard though it is to live, is the part of the writer's fight for freedom the *world* finds easiest to understand.

There is another threat to that freedom, in any country where political freedom is withheld. It is a more insidious one, and one of which fewer people will be aware. It's a threat which comes from the very strength of the writer's opposition to repression of political freedom. That other, paradoxically wider, composite freedom—the freedom of his private view of life—may be threatened by the very awareness of *what is expected of him*. And often what is expected of him is conformity to an orthodoxy of opposition.

There will be those who regard him as their mouth-piece; people whose ideals, as a human being, he shares, and whose cause, as a human being, is his own. They may be those whose suffering is his own. His identification with, admiration for, and loyalty to these set up a state of conflict within him. His integrity as a human being demands the sacrifice of everything to the struggle put up on the side of free men. His integrity as a writer goes the moment he begins to write what he is told he ought to write.

This is—whether all admit it or not—and will continue to be a particular problem for black writers in South Africa. For them, it extends even to an orthodoxy of vocabulary: the jargon of struggle, derived internationally, is right and adequate for the public platform, the newsletter, the statement from the dock; it is not adequate, it is not deep enough, wide enough, flexible enough, cutting enough, fresh enough for the vocabulary of the poet, the short story writer or the novelist.

Neither is it, as the claim will be made, 'a language of the people' in a situation where certainly it is very important that imaginative writing must not reach an élite only. The jargon of struggle lacks both the inventive pragmatism and the poetry of common speech—those qualities the writer faces the challenge to capture and explore imaginatively, expressing as they do the soul and identity of a people as no thousandth-hand 'noble evocation' of clichés ever could.

The black writer needs his freedom to assert that the idiom of Chatsworth, Dimbaza, Soweto is no less a vehicle for the expression of pride, self-respect, suffering, anger—or anything else in the spectrum of thought and emotion—than the language of Watts or Harlem.

The fact is, even on the side of the angels, a writer has to reserve the right to tell the truth as he sees it, in his own words, without being accused of letting the side down. For as Philip Toynbee has written, 'the writer's gift to the reader is not social zest or moral improvement or love of country, but an enlargement of the reader's apprehension.'

This is the writer's unique contribution to social change. He needs to be left alone, by brothers as well as enemies, to make this gift. And he must make it even against his own inclination.

I need hardly add this does not mean he retreats to an ivory tower. The gift cannot be made from any such place. The other day, Jean-Paul Sartre gave the following definition of the writer's responsibility to his society as an intellectual, after himself having occupied such a position in France for the best part of seventy years: 'He is someone who is faithful to a political and social body but never stops contesting it. Of course, a contradiction may arise between his fidelity and his *contestation*, but that's a fruitful contradiction. If there's fidelity without *contestation*, that's no good: one is no longer a free man.'

When a writer claims these kinds of freedom for himself he begins to understand the real magnitude of his struggle. It is not a new problem and of all the writers who have had to face it, I don't think anyone has seen it as clearly or dealt with it with such uncompromising honesty as the great nineteenth-century Russian, Ivan Turgenev. Turgenev had an immense reputation as a progressive writer. He was closely connected with the progressive movement in Czarist Russia and particularly with its more revolutionary wing headed by the critic Belinsky and afterwards by the poet Nekrasov. With his sketches and stories, people said that Turgenev was continuing the work Gogol had begun of awakening the conscience of the educated classes in Russia to the evils of a political regime based on serfdom.

But his friends, admirers and fellow progressives stopped short, in their understanding of his genius, of the very thing that made him one—his scrupulous reserve of the writer's freedom to reproduce truth and the reality of life even if this truth does not coincide with his own sympathies.

When his greatest novel, *Fathers and Sons*, was published in 1862, he was attacked not only by the right for pandering to the revolutionary nihilists, but far more bitterly by the left, the younger generation themselves, of whom his chief character in the novel, Bazarov, was both prototype and apotheosis. The radicals and liberals, among whom Turgenev himself belonged, lambasted him as a traitor because Bazarov was presented with all the faults and contradictions that Turgenev saw in his own type, in himself, so to speak, and whom he created as he did because—in his own words—'in the given case, life happened to be like that'.

The attacks were renewed after the publication of another novel, *Smoke*, and Turgenev decided to write a series of autobiographical reminiscences which would allow him to reply to his critics by explaining his views on the art of writing, the place of the writer in society, and what the writer's attitude to the controversial problems of his day should be. The result was a series of unpretentious essays that make up a remarkable testament to a writer's creed. Dealing particularly with Bazarov and *Fathers and Sons*, he writes of his critics:

generally speaking {they} have not got quite the right idea of what is taking place in the mind of an author or what exactly his joys and sorrows, his aims, successes and failures are. They do not, for instance, even suspect the pleasure which Gogol mentions and which consists of castigating oneself and one's faults in the imaginary characters one depicts; they are quite sure that all a writer does is to 'develop his ideas' . . . Let me illustrate my meaning by a small example. I am an inveterate and incorrigible Westerner. I have never concealed it and I am not concealing it now. And yet in spite of that it has given me great pleasure to show up in the person of Panshin (in *A House of Gentlefolk*) all the common and vulgar sides of the Westerners: I made the Slavophil Lavretsky 'crush him utterly'. Why did I do it, I who consider the Slavophil doctrine false and futile? Because, *in the given case, life, according to my ideas, happened to be like that*, and what I wanted above all was to be sincere and truthful. In depicting Bazarov's personality, I excluded everything artistic from the range of his sympathies, I made him express himself in harsh and unceremonious tones, not out of an absurd desire to insult the younger generation . . . but simply as a result of my observations . . . My personal predilections had nothing to do with it. But I expect many of my readers will be surprised if I tell them that with the exception of Bazarov's views on art, I share almost all his convictions.

And in another essay, Turgenev sums up regarding what he calls 'the man of real talent': 'The life that surrounds him provides him with the contents of his works; he is its *concentrated reflection*; but he is as incapable of writing a panegyric as a lampoon . . . When all is said and done—that is beneath him. Only those who can do no better submit to a given theme or carry out a programme.'

These conditions about which I have been talking are the special, though common ones of writers beleaguered in the time of the bomb and the colour-bar, as they were in the time of the jack-boot and rubber truncheon, and, no doubt, back through the ages whose shameful symbols keep tally of oppression in the skeleton cupboard of our civilisations.

Other conditions, more transient, less violent, affect the freedom of a writer's mind. What about literary fashion, for example? What about the cycle of the innovator, the imitators, the debasers, and then the bringing forth of an innovator again? A writer must not be made too conscious of literary fashion, any more than he must allow himself to be inhibited by the mandarin if he is to get on with work that is his own. I say 'made conscious' because literary fashion is a part of his working conditions; he can make the choice of rejecting it, but he cannot choose whether it is urged upon him or not by publishers and readers, who do not let him forget he has to eat.

That rare marvel, an innovator, should be received with shock and excitement. And his impact may set off people in new directions of their own. But the next innovator rarely, I would almost say never, comes from his imitators, those who create a fashion in his image. Not all worthwhile writing is an innovation, but I believe it always comes from an individual vision, privately pursued. The pursuit may stem from a tradition, but a tradition implies a choice of influence, whereas a fashion makes the influence of the moment the only one for all who are contemporary with it.

A writer needs all these kinds of freedom, built on the basic one of freedom from censorship. He does not ask for shelter from living, but for exposure to it without possibility of evasion. He is fiercely engaged with life on his own terms, and ought to be left to it, if anything is to come of the struggle. Any government, any society—any vision of a future society—that has respect for its writers must set them as free as possible to write in their own various ways in their own choices of form and language, and according to their own discovery of truth.

Again, Turgenev expresses this best: 'without freedom in the widest sense of the word—in relation to oneself . . . indeed, to one's people and one's history,—a true artist is unthinkable; without that air it is impossible to breathe.'

And I add my last word: In that air alone, commitment and creative freedom become one.

(1975)

Denise Levertov
(U.S.A., 1923–1997)

The Rainwalkers

An old man whose black face
shines golden-brown as wet pebbles
under the streetlamp, is walking
two mongrel dogs of dis-
5   proportionate size, in the rain,
in the relaxed early-evening avenue.

The small sleek one wants to stop,
docile to the imploring soul of the trashbasket,
but the young tall curly one
10   wants to walk on; the glistening sidewalk
entices him to arcane happenings.

Increasing rain. The old bareheaded man
smiles and grumbles to himself.
The lights change: the avenue's
15 endless nave echoes notes of
liturgical red. He drifts

between his dogs' desires.
The three of them are enveloped—
turning now to go crosstown—in their
20 sense of each other, of pleasure,
of weather, of corners,
of leisurely tensions between them
and private silence.

(1959)

The Novel

A wind is blowing. The book being written
shifts, halts, pages
yellow and white drawing apart
and inching together in
5 new tries. A single white half sheet
skims out under the door.

And cramped in their not yet
halfwritten lives, a man and a woman
grimace in pain. Their cat
10 yawning its animal secret,
stirs in the monstrous limbo of erasure.
They live (when they live) in fear

of blinding, of burning, of choking under a
mushroom cloud in the year of the roach.
15 And they want (like us) the eternity
of today, they want this fear to be
struck out at once by a thick black
magic marker, everywhere, every page,

the whole sheets of it crushed, crackling,
20 and tossed in the fire
     and when they were fine ashes
     the stove would cool and be cleaned
     and a jar of flowers would be put to stand
     on top of the stove in the spring light.

25 Meanwhile from page to page they
buy things, acquiring the look of a
full life; they argue, make silence bitter,
plan journeys, move house, implant
despair in each other
30 and then in the nick of time

they save one another with tears,
remorse, tenderness—
hooked on those wonder-drugs.
Yet they do have—
35 don't they—like us—
their days of grace, they

halt, stretch, a vision
breaks in on the cramped grimace,
inscape of transformation.
40 Something sundered begins to knit.
By scene, by sentence, something is rendered
back into life, back to the gods.

(1961)

Louis Simpson

(JAMAICA/U.S.A., 1923–)

My father in the night commanding No

My father in the night commanding No
Has work to do. Smoke issues from his lips;
 He reads in silence.
The frogs are croaking and the streetlamps glow.

5 And then my mother winds the gramophone;
The Bride of Lammermoor begins to shriek—
 Or reads a story
About a prince, a castle and a dragon.

The moon is glittering above the hill.
10 I stand before the gateposts of the King—
 So runs the story—
Of Thule, at midnight when the mice are still.

And I have been in Thule! It has come true—
The journey and the danger of the world,
15 All that there is
To bear and to enjoy, endure and do.

Landscapes, seascapes . . . where have I been led?
The names of cities—Paris, Venice, Rome—
 Held out their arms.
20 A feathered god, seductive, went ahead.

Here is my house. Under a red rose tree
A child is swinging; another gravely plays.
    They are not surprised
That I am here; they were expecting me.

25   And yet my father sits and reads in silence,
My mother sheds a tear, the moon is still,
    And the dark wind
Is murmuring that nothing ever happens.

Beyond his jurisdiction as I move
30   Do I not prove him wrong? And yet, it's true
    They will not change
There, on the stage of terror and of love.

The actors in that playhouse always sit
In fixed positions—father, mother, child
35   With painted eyes.
How sad it is to be a little puppet!

Their heads are wooden. And you once pretended
To understand them! Shake them as you will,
    They cannot speak.
40   Do what you will, the comedy is ended.

Father, why did you work? Why did you weep,
Mother? Was the story so important?
    'Listen!' the wind
Said to the children, and they fell asleep.

(1963)

The Island Mentality

Look through the telescope
see she said

I looked it looked
like a shilling

5   We'll go in the moon
Daddy said

In the twenties
a Moon was a big touring car

2

white sand
10   blue waves
nobody ever
misbehaves

it's nice to live in a British colony
says the Duchess of
15   Cumuppingshire

O to be a
nightingale
now that Endland's
here

20   O I don't know
says the Duke
I think it's a lot of belly rot

blue sand
white waves
25   jolly good chaps
in nigger graves

3

The natives are dancing
Maud come into the garden
and see the people dancing

30   See, that one's a
rooster
and that one's

a horse
It's called John Canoe
35   Peculiar   Of course

(1971)

Nissim Ezekiel

(INDIA, 1924–)

Night of the Scorpion

I remember the night my mother
was stung by a scorpion. Ten hours
of steady rain had driven him
to crawl beneath a sack of rice.
5   Parting with his poison—flash
of diabolic tail in the dark room—
he risked the rain again.
The peasants came like swarms of flies
and buzzed the Name of God a hundred times
10   to paralyse the Evil One.

With candles and with lanterns
throwing giant scorpion shadows
on the mud-baked walls
they searched for him: he was not found.
15 They clicked their tongues.
With every movement that the scorpion made
his poison moved in Mother's blood, they said.
May he sit still, they said.
May the sins of your previous birth
20 be burned away tonight, they said.
May your suffering decrease
the misfortunes of your next birth, they said.
May the sum of evil
balanced in this unreal world
25 against the sum of good
become diminished by your pain.
May the poison purify your flesh
of desire, and your spirit of ambition,
they said, and they sat around
30 on the floor with my mother in the centre,
the peace of understanding on each face.

More candles, more lanterns, more neighbours
more insects, and the endless rain.
My mother twisted through and through
35 groaning on a mat.
My father, sceptic, rationalist,
trying every curse and blessing,
powder, mixture, herb and hybrid.
He even poured a little paraffin
40 upon the bitten toe and put a match to it.
I watched the flame feeding on my mother.
I watched the holy man perform his rites
to tame the poison with an incantation.
After twenty hours
45 it lost its sting.

My Mother only said
Thank God the scorpion picked on me
and spared my children.

(1965)

Janet Frame

(NEW ZEALAND, 1924-)

The Reservoir

It was said to be four or five miles along the gully, past orchards and farms, paddocks filled with cattle, sheep, wheat, gorse, and the squatters of the land who were the rabbits eating like modern sculpture into the hills, though how could we know anything of modern sculpture, we knew nothing but the Warrior in the main street with his wreaths of poppies on Anzac Day, the gnomes weeping in the Gardens because the seagulls perched on their green caps and showed no respect, and how important it was for birds, animals and people, especially children, to show respect!

And that is why for so long We obeyed the command of the grownups and never walked as far as the forbidden Reservoir, but were content to return "tired but happy" (as we wrote in our school compositions), answering the question, Where did you walk today? with a suspicion of blackmail, "Oh, nearly, nearly to the Reservoir!"

The Reservoir was the end of the world; beyond it, you fell; beyond it were paddocks of thorns, strange cattle, strange farms, legendary people whom we would never know or recognize even if they walked among us on a Friday night downtown when we went to follow the boys and listen to the Salvation Army Band and buy a milk shake in the milk bar and then return home to find that everything was all right and safe, that our mother had not run away and caught the night train to the North Island, that our father had not shot himself with worrying over the bills, but had in fact been downtown himself and had bought the usual Friday night treat, a bag of licorice all-sorts and a bag of chocolate roughs, from Woolworth's.

The Reservoir haunted our lives. We never knew one until we came to this town; we had used pump water. But here, in our new house, the water ran from the taps as soon as we turned them on, and if we were careless and left them on, our father would shout, as if the affair were his personal concern, "Do you want the Reservoir to run dry?"

That frightened us. What should we do if the Reservoir ran dry? Would we die of thirst like Burke and Wills in the desert?

"The Reservoir," our mother said, "gives pure water, water safe to drink without boiling it."

The water was in a different class, then, from the creek which flowed through the gully; yet the creek had its source in the Reservoir. Why had it not received the pampering attention of officialdom which strained weed and earth, cockabullies and trout and eels, from our tap water? Surely the Reservoir was not entirely pure?

"Oh no," they said, when we inquired. We learned that the water from the Reservoir had been "treated." We supposed this to mean that during the night men in light-blue uniforms with sacks over their shoulders crept beyond the circle of pine trees which enclosed the Reservoir, and emptied the contents of the sacks into the water, to dissolve dead bodies and prevent the decay of teeth.

Then, at times, there would be news in the paper, discussed by my mother with the neighbors over the back fence. Children had been drowned in the Reservoir.

"No child," the neighbor would say, "ought to be allowed near the Reservoir."

"I tell mine to keep strictly away," my mother would reply.

And for so long we obeyed our mother's command, on our favorite walks along the gully simply following the untreated cast-off creek which we loved and which flowed day and night in our heads in all its detail—the wild sweet peas, boiled-lolly pink, and the mint growing along the banks; the exact spot in the water where the latest dead sheep could be found, and the stink of its bloated flesh and floating wool, an allowable earthy stink which we accepted with pleasant revulsion and which did not prompt the "inky-pinky I smell Stinkie" rhyme which referred to offensive human beings only. We knew where the water was shallow and could be paddled in, where forts could be made from the rocks; we knew the frightening deep places where the eels lurked and the weeds were tangled in gruesome shapes; we knew the jumping places, the mossy stones with their dangers, limitations, and advantages; the sparkling places where the sun trickled beside the water, upon the stones; the bogs made by roaming cattle, trapping some of them to death; their gaunt telltale bones; the little valleys with their new growth of lush grass where the creek had "changed its course," and no longer flowed.

"The creek has changed its course," our mother would say, in a tone which implied terror and a sense of strangeness, as if a tragedy had been enacted.

We knew the moods of the creek, its levels of low-flow, half-high-flow, high-flow which all seemed to relate to interference at its source—the Reservoir. If one morning the water turned the color of clay and crowds of bubbles were passengers on every suddenly swift wave hurrying by, we would look at one another and remark with the fatality and reverence which attends a visitation or prophecy,

"The creek's going on high-flow. They must be doing something at the Reservoir."

By afternoon the creek would be on high-flow, turbulent, muddy, unable to be jumped across or paddled in or fished in, concealing beneath a swelling fluid darkness whatever evil which "they," the authorities, had decided to purge so swiftly and secretly from the Reservoir.

For so long, then, we obeyed our parents, and never walked as far as the Reservoir. Other things concerned us, other curiosities, fears, challenges. The school year ended. I got a prize, a large yellow book the color of cat's mess. Inside it were editions of newspapers, *The Worms' Weekly*, supposedly written by worms, snails, spiders. For the first part of the holidays we spent the time sitting in the long grass of our front lawn nibbling the stalks of shamrock and reading insect newspapers and relating their items to the lives of those living on our front lawn down among the summer-dry roots of the couch, tinkertailor, daisy, dandelion, shamrock, clover, and ordinary "grass." High summer came. The blowsy old red roses shed their petals to the regretful refrain uttered by our mother year after year at the same time, "I should have made potpourri, I have a wonderful recipe for potpourri in Dr. Chase's Book."

Our mother never made the potpourri, She merely quarreled with our father over how to pronounce it.

The days became unbearably long and hot. Our Christmas presents were broken or too boring to care about. Celluloid dolls had loose arms and legs and rifts in their bright pink bodies; the invisible ink had poured itself out in secret messages; diaries frustrating in their smallness (two lines to a day) had been filled in for the whole of the coming year. . . . Days at the beach were tedious, with no room in the bathing sheds so that we were forced to undress in the common room downstairs with its floor patched with wet and trailed with footmarks and sand and its tiny barred window (which made me believe that I was living in the French Revolution).

Rumors circled the burning world. The sea was drying up, soon you could paddle or walk to Australia. Sharks had been seen swimming inside the breakwater; one shark attacked a little boy and bit off his you-know-what.

We swam. We wore bathing togs all day. We gave up cowboys and ranches; and baseball and sledding; and "those games" where we mimicked grown-up life, loving and divorcing each other, kissing and slapping, taking secret paramours when our husband was working out of town. Everything exhausted us. Cracks appeared in the earth; the grass was bled yellow; the ground was littered with beetle shells and snail shells; flies came in from the unofficial rubbish-dump at the back of the house; the twisting flypapers hung from the ceilings; a frantic buzzing filled the room as the flypapers became crowded. Even the cat put out her tiny tongue, panting in the heat.

We realized, and were glad, that school would soon reopen. What was school like? It seemed so long ago, it seemed as if we had never been to school, surely we had forgotten everything we had learned, how frightening, thrilling and strange it would all seem! Where would we go on the first day, who would teach us, what were the names of the new books?

Who would sit beside us, who would be our best friend?

The earth crackled in early-autumn haze and still the February sun dried the world; even at night the rusty sheet of roofing-iron outside by the cellar stayed warm, but with rows of sweat-marks on it; the days were still long, with night face to face with morning and almost nothing in-between but a snatch of turning sleep with the blankets on the floor and the windows wide open to moths with their bulging lamplit eyes moving through the dark and their grandfather bodies knocking, knocking upon the walls.

Day after day the sun still waited to pounce. We were tired, our skin itched, our sunburn had peeled and peeled again, the skin on our feet was hard, there was dust in our hair, our bodies clung with the salt of sea-bathing and sweat, the towels were harsh with salt.

School soon, we said again, and were glad; for lessons gave shade to rooms and corridors; cloakrooms were cold and sunless. Then, swiftly, suddenly, disease came to the town. Infantile Paralysis. Black headlines in the paper, listing the number of cases, the number of deaths. Children everywhere, out in the country, up north, down south, two streets away.

The schools did not reopen. Our lessons came by post, in smudged print on rough white paper; they seemed makeshift and false, they inspired distrust, they could not compete with the lure of the sun still shining, swelling, the world would go up in cinders, the days were too long, there was nothing to do, there was nothing to do; the lessons were dull; in the front room with the navy-blue blind half down the window and the tiny splits of light showing through, and the lesson papers sometimes covered with unexplained blots of ink as if the machine which had printed them had broken down or rebelled, the lessons were even more dull.

Ancient Egypt and the flooding of the Nile!

The Nile, when we possessed a creek of our own with individual flooding!

"Well let's go along the gully, along by the creek," we would say, tired with all these.

Then one day when our restlessness was at its height, when the flies buzzed like bees in the flypapers, and the warped wood of the house cracked its knuckles out of boredom, the need for something to do in the heat, we found once again the only solution to our unrest.

Someone said, "What's the creek on?"

"Half-high flow."

"Good."

So we set out, in our bathing suits, and carrying switches of willow.

"Keep your sun hats on!" our mother called.

All right. We knew. Sunstroke when the sun clipped you over the back of the head, striking you flat on the ground. Sunstroke. Lightning. Even tidal waves were threatening us on this southern coast. The world was full of alarm.

"And don't go as far as the Reservoir!"

We dismissed the warning. There was enough to occupy us along the gully without our visiting the Reservoir. First, the couples. We liked to find a courting couple and follow them and when, as we knew they must do because they were tired or for other reasons, they found a place in the grass and laid down together, we liked to make jokes about them, amongst our-selves. "Just wait for him to kiss her," we would say. "Watch. There. A beaut. Smack."

Often we giggled and lingered even after the couple had observed us. We were waiting for them to do it. Every man and woman did it, we knew that for a fact. We speculated about technical details. Would he wear a frenchie? If he didn't wear a frenchie then she would start having a baby and be forced to get rid of it by drinking gin. Frenchies, by the way, were for sale in Woolworth's. Some said they were fingerstalls, but we knew they were frenchies and sometimes we would go downtown and into Woolworth's just to look at the frenchies for sale. We hung around the counter, sniggering. Sometimes we nearly died laughing, it was so funny.

After we tired of spying on the couples we would shout after them as we went our way.

> Pound, shillings and pence,
> a man fell over the fence,
> he fell on a lady,
> and squashed out a baby,
> pound, shillings and pence!

Sometimes a slight fear struck us—what if a man fell on us like that and squashed out a chain of babies?

Our other pastime along the gully was robbing the orchards, but this summer day the apples were small green hard and hidden by leaves. There were no couples either. We had the gully to ourselves. We followed the creek, whacking our sticks, gossiping and singing, but we stopped, immediately silent, when someone—sister or brother—said, "Let's go to the Reservoir!"

A feeling of dread seized us. We knew, as surely as we knew our names and our address Thirty-three Stour Street Ohau Otago South Island New Zealand Southern Hemisphere The World, that we would some day visit the Reservoir, but the time seemed almost as far away as leaving school, getting a job, marrying.

And then there was the agony of deciding the right time—how did one decide these things?

"We've been told not to, you know," one of us said timidly.

That was me. Eating bread and syrup for tea had made my hair red, my skin too, so that I blushed easily, and the grownups guessed if I told a lie.

"It's a long way," said my little sister.

"Coward!"

But it *was* a long way, and perhaps it would take all day and night, perhaps we would have to sleep there among the pine trees with the owls hooting and the old needle-filled warrens which now reached to the center of the earth where pools of molten lead bubbled, waiting to seize us if we tripped, and then there was the crying sound made by the trees, a sound of speech at its loneliest level where the meaning is felt but never explained, and it goes on and on in a kind of despair, trying to reach a point of understanding.

We knew that pine trees spoke in this way. We were lonely listening to them because we knew we could never help them to say it, whatever they were trying to say, for if the wind who was so close to them could not help them, how could we?

Oh no, we could not spend the night at the Reservoir among the pine trees.

"Billy Whittaker and his gang have been to the Reservoir, Billy Whittaker and the Green Feather gang, one afternoon."

"Did he say what it was like?"

"No, he never said."

"He's been in an iron lung."

That was true. Only a day or two ago our mother had been reminding us in an ominous voice of the fact which roused our envy just as much as our dread, "Billy Whittaker was in an iron lung two years ago. Infantile paralysis."

Some people were lucky. None of us dared to hope that we would ever be surrounded by the glamour of an iron lung; we would have to be content all our lives with paltry flesh lungs.

"Well are we going to the Reservoir or not?"

That was someone trying to sound bossy like our father,—"Well am I to have salmon sandwiches or not, am I to have lunch at all today or not?"

We struck our sticks in the air. They made a whistling sound. They were supple and young. We had tried to make musical instruments out of them, time after time we hacked at the willow and the elder to make pipes to blow our music, but no sound came but our own voices. And why did two sticks rubbed together not make fire? Why couldn't we ever *make* anything out of the bits of the world lying about us?

An airplane passed in the sky. We craned our necks to read the writing on the underwing, for we collected airplane numbers.

The plane was gone, in a glint of sun.

"Are we?" someone said.

"If there's an eclipse you can't see at all. The birds stop singing and go to bed."

"Well are we?"

Certainly we were. We had not quelled all our misgiving, but we set out to follow the creek to the Reservoir.

What is it? I wondered. They said it was a lake. I thought it was a bundle of darkness and great wheels which peeled and sliced you like an apple and drew you toward them with demonic force, in the same way that you were drawn beneath the wheels of a train if you stood too near the edge of the platform. That was the terrible danger when the Limited came rushing in and you had to approach to kiss arriving aunts.

We walked on and on, past wild sweet peas, clumps of curry grass, horse mushrooms, ragwort, gorse, cabbage trees; and then, at the end of the gully, we came to strange territory, fences we did not know, with the barbed wire tearing at our skin and at our skirts put on over our bathing suits because we felt cold though the sun stayed in the sky.

We passed huge trees that lived with their heads in the sky, with their great arms and joints creaking with age and the burden of being trees, and their mazed and linked roots rubbed bare of earth, like bones with the flesh cleaned from them. There were strange gates to be opened or climbed over, new directions to be argued and plotted, notices which said TRESPASSERS WILL BE PROSECUTED BY ORDER. And there was the remote immovable sun shedding without gentleness its influence of burning upon us and upon the town, looking down from its heavens and considering our infantile-paralysis epidemic, and the children tired of holidays and wanting to go back to school with the new stiff books with their crackling pages, the scrubbed ruler with the sun rising on one side amidst the twelfths, tenths, millimeters, the new pencils to be sharpened with the pencil shavings flying in long pickets and light-brown curls scalloped with red or blue; the brown school, the bare floors, the clump clump in the corridors on wet days!

We came to a strange paddock, a bull-paddock with its occupant planted deep in the long grass, near the gate, a jersey bull polished like a wardrobe, burnished like copper, heavy beams creaking in the wave and flow of the grass.

"Has it got a ring through its nose? Is it a real bull or a steer?"

Its nose was ringed which meant that its savagery was tamed, or so we thought; it could be tethered and led; even so, it had once been savage and it kept its pride, unlike the steers who pranced and huddled together and ran like water through the paddocks, made no impression, quarried no massive shape against the sky.

The bull stood alone.

Had not Mr. Bennet been gored by a bull, his own tame bull, and been rushed to Glenham Hospital for thirty-three stitches? Remembering Mr. Bennet we crept cautiously close to the paddock fence, ready to escape.

Someone said, "Look, it's pawing the ground!"

A bull which pawed the ground was preparing for a charge. We escaped quickly through the fence. Then, plucking courage, we skirted the bushes on the far side of the paddock, climbed through the fence, and continued our walk to the Reservoir.

We had lost the creek between deep banks. We saw it now before us, and hailed it with more relief than we felt, for in its hidden course through the bull-paddock it had undergone change, it had adopted the shape, depth, mood of foreign water, foaming in a way we did not recognize as belonging to our special creek, giving no hint of its depth. It seemed to flow close to its concealed bed, not wishing any more to communicate with us. We realized with dismay that we had suddenly lost possession of our creek. Who had taken it? Why did it not belong to us any more? We hit our sticks in the air and forgot our dismay. We grew cheerful.

Till someone said that it was getting late, and we reminded one another that during the day the sun doesn't seem to move, it just remains pinned with a drawing pin against the sky, and then, while you are not looking, it suddenly slides down quick as the chopped-off head of a golden eel, into the sea, making everything in the world go dark.

"That's only in the tropics!"

We were not in the tropics. The divisions of the world in the atlas, the different colored cubicles of latitude and longitude fascinated us.

"The sand freezes in the desert at night. Ladies wear bits of sand. . . ."

"grains . . ."

"grains or bits of sand as necklaces, and the camels . . ."

"with necks like snails . . ."

"with horns, do they have horns?"

"Minnie Stocks goes with boys. . . ."

"I know who your boy is, I know who your boy is. . . ."

>   Waiting by the garden gate,
>   Waiting by the garden gate . . .

"We'll never get to the Reservoir!"

"Whose idea was it?"

"I've strained my ankle!"

Someone began to cry. We stopped walking.

"I've strained my ankle!"

There was an argument.

"It's not strained, it's sprained."

"strained."

"sprained."

"All right sprained then. I'll have to wear a bandage, I'll have to walk on crutches. . . ."

"I had crutches once. Look. I've got a scar where I fell off my stilts. It's a white scar, like a centipede. It's on my shins."

"Shins! Isn't it a funny word? Shins. Have you ever been kicked in the shins?"

"shins, funnybone . . ."

"It's humerus . . ."

"knuckles . . ."

"a sprained ankle . . ."

"a strained ankle . . ."

"a whitlow, an ingrown toenail the roots of my hair warts spinal meningitis infantile paralysis . . ."

"Infantile paralysis, Infantile paralysis you have to be wheeled in a chair and wear irons on your legs and your knees knock together. . . ."

"Once you're in an iron lung you can't get out, they lock it, like a cage. . . ."

"You go in the amberlance . . ."

"*ambulance* . . ."

"amberlance . . ."

"ambulance to the hostible . . ."

"the *hospital*, an *amberlance to the hospital* . . ."

"Infantile Paralysis . . ."

"Friar's Balsam! Friar's Balsam!"

"Baxter's Lung Preserver, Baxter's Lung Preserver!"

"Syrup of Figs, California Syrup of Figs!"

"The creek's going on high-flow!"

Yes, there were bubbles on the surface, and the water was turning muddy. Our doubts were dispelled. It was the same old creek, and there, suddenly, just ahead, was a plantation of pine trees, and already the sighing sound of it reached our ears and troubled us. We approached it, staying close to the banks of our newly claimed creek, until once again the creek deserted us, flowing its own private course where we could not follow, and we found ourselves among the pine trees, a narrow strip of them, and beyond lay a vast surface of sparkling water, dazzling our eyes, its center chopped by tiny gray waves. Not a lake, nor a river, nor a sea.

"The Reservoir!"

The damp smell of the pine needles caught in our breath. There were no birds, only the constant sighing of the trees. We could see the water clearly now; it lay, except for the waves beyond the shore, in an almost perfect calm which we knew to be deceptive—else why were people so afraid of the Reservoir? The fringe of young pines on the edge, like toy trees, sub-jected to the wind, sighed and told us their sad secrets. In the Reservoir there was an appear-ance of neatness which concealed a disarray too frightening to be acknowledged except, without any defense, in moments of deep sleep and dreaming. The little sparkling innocent waves shone now green, now gray, petticoats, lettuce leaves; the trees sighed, and told us to be quiet, hush-sh, as if something were sleeping and should not be disturbed—perhaps that was what the trees were always telling us, to hush-sh in case we disturbed something which must never ever be awakened?

What was it? Was it sleeping in the Reservoir? Was that why people were afraid of the Reservoir?

Well we were not afraid of it, oh no, it was only the Reservoir, it was nothing to be afraid of, it was just a flat Reservoir with a fence around it, and trees, and on the far side a little house (with wheels inside?), and nothing to be afraid of.

"The Reservoir, The Reservoir!"

A noticeboard said DANGER, RESERVOIR.

Overcome with sudden glee we climbed through the fence and swung on the lower branches of the trees, shouting at intervals, gazing possessively and delightedly at the sheet of water with its wonderful calm and menace,

"The Reservoir! The Reservoir! The Reservoir!"

We quarreled again about how to pronounce and spell the word.

Then it seemed to be getting dark—or was it that the trees were stealing the sunlight and keeping it above their heads? One of us began to run. We all ran, suddenly, wildly, not caring about our strained or sprained ankles, through the trees out into the sun where the creek, but it was our creek no longer, waited for us. We wished it were our creek, how we wished it were our creek! We had lost all account of time. Was it nearly night? Would darkness overtake us, would we have to sleep on the banks of the creek that did not belong to us any more, among the wild sweet peas and the tussocks and the dead sheep? And would the eels come up out of the creek, as people said they did, and on their travels through the paddocks would they change into people who would threaten us and bar our way, TRESPASSERS WILL BE PROSECUTED, standing arm in arm in their black glossy coats, swaying, their mouths open, ready to swallow us? Would they ever let us go home, past the orchards, along the gully? Perhaps they would give us Infantile Paralysis, perhaps we would never be able to walk home, and no one would know where we were, to bring us an iron lung with its own special key!

We arrived home, panting and scratched. How strange! The sun was still in the same place in the sky!

The question troubled us, "Should we tell?"

The answer was decided for us. Our mother greeted us as we went in the door with, "You haven't been long away, kiddies. Where have you been? I hope you didn't go anywhere near the Reservoir."

Our father looked up from reading his newspapers.

"Don't let me catch you going near the Reservoir!"

We said nothing. How out-of-date they were! They were actually afraid!

(1963)

Robert Creeley

(U.S.A., 1926-)

The Whip

I spent a night turning in bed,
my love was a feather, a flat

sleeping thing. She was
very white

5 and quiet and above us on
the roof, there was another woman I

also loved, had
addressed myself to in

a fit she
10 returned. That

encompasses it. But now I was
lonely, I yelled,

but what is that? Ugh,
she said, beside me, she put

15 her hand on
my back, for which act

I think to say this
wrongly.

(1962)

The Window

Position is where you
put it, where it is,
did you, for example, that

large tank there, silvered,
5   with the white church alongside, lift

all that, to what
purpose? How
heavy the slow

10 world is with
everything put
in place. Some

man walks by, a
car beside him on
15 the dropped

road, a leaf of
yellow color is
going to

fall. It
20 all drops into
place. My

face is heavy
with the sight. I can
feel my eye breaking.

(1967)

Allen Ginsberg

(U.S.A., 1926–1997)

A Supermarket in California

What thoughts I have of you tonight, Walt Whitman, for I walked down the sidestreets under the trees with a headache self-conscious looking at the full moon.

In my hungry fatigue, and shopping for images, I went into the neon fruit supermarket, dreaming of your enumerations!

What peaches and what penumbras! Whole families shopping at night! Aisles full of husbands! Wives in the avocados, babies in the tomatoes!—and you, Garcia Lorca, what were you doing down by the watermelons?

I saw you, Walt Whitman, childless, lonely old grubber, poking among the meats in the refrigerator and eyeing the grocery boys.

5   I heard you asking questions of each: Who killed the pork chops? What price bananas? Are you my Angel?

I wandered in and out of the brilliant stacks of cans following you, and followed in my imagination by the store detective.

We strode down the open corridors together in our solitary fancy tasting artichokes, possessing every frozen delicacy, and never passing the cashier.

Where are you going, Walt Whitman? The doors close in an hour. Which way does your beard point tonight?

(I touch your book and dream of our odyssey in the supermarket and feel absurd.)

10   Will we walk all night through solitary streets? The trees add shade to shade, lights out in the houses, we'll both be lonely.

Will we stroll dreaming of the lost America of love past blue automobiles in driveways, home to our silent cottage?

Ah, dear father, graybeard, lonely old courage-teacher, what America did you have when Charon quit poling his ferry and you got out on a smoking bank and stood watching the boat disappear on the black waters of Lethe?

(Berkeley 1955)

Elizabeth Jennings

(ENGLAND, 1926–)

The Settlers

A land once questioned only by the sea
Which carried pebbles off as property,
And spoken to by bird or animal
Or a weight of wind trespassing a little,
5   But now the water throws explorers up
Whose eyes possess and hearts begin to settle.

Climate becomes a privilege for them
Offered to later visitors like love,
And all the corn cut down and packed away
10   Loses the sun a little and casts off
The lash of wind. The complete natural kingdom
Is tamed and ruled, even the sea discouraged.

And the rebellion of an earthquake shaking
The crops awry, throwing the houses down,
15   Killing a few, finds only the next morning
Bruised dreamers planning and the workmen taking
The broken bricks to build another town.

And men who come to meditate a mountain
Are tamed too by the dwellers here and offered
20   Weather for happiness, children to show
The white church in the market-place, the fountain
That mocks the uncouth sea. They go away
Ignorant that they alone are undiscovered.

(1953)

Attempted Suicides

We have come back.
Do not be surprised if we blink our eyes
If we stare oddly
If we hide in corners.
5   It is we, not you, who should show surprise.

For everything looks strange.
Roofs are made of paper
Hands are muslin
Babies look eatable.
10   There has been too much change.

And where do we come from?
Where did the pills take us,
The gas,
The water left pouring?
15 Limbo? Hell? Mere forgetfulness?

It was a lost moment,
There were no dreams,
There was simply the beyond-endurance
And then the coming-to
20 To you and you and you and you.

Do not ask us,
As if we were Lazarus,
What it was like.
We never got far enough.
25 Now we touch ourselves and feel strange.
We have a whole world to arrange.

(1966)

Margaret Laurence

(CANADA, 1926–1987)

Horses of the Night

I never knew I had distant cousins who lived up north, until Chris came down to Manawaka to go to high school. My mother said he belonged to a large family, relatives of ours, who lived at Shallow Creek, up north. I was six, and Shallow Creek seemed immeasurably far, part of a legendary winter country where no leaves grow and where the breath of seals and polar bears snuffled out steamily and turned to ice.

"Could plain people live there?" I asked my mother, meaning people who were not Eskimos. "Could there be a farm?"

"How do you mean?" she said, puzzled. "I told you. That's where they live. On the farm, Uncle Wilf—that was Chris's father, who died a few years back—he got the place as a homestead, donkey's years ago."

"But how could they grow anything? I thought you said it was up north."

"Mercy," my mother said, laughing, "it's not *that* far north, Vanessa. It's about a hundred miles beyond Galloping Mountain. You be nice to Chris, now, won't you? And don't go asking him a whole lot of questions the minute he steps inside the door."

How little my mother knew of me, I thought. Chris had been fifteen. He could be expected to feel only scorn towards me. I detested the fact that I was so young. I did not think I would be able to say anything at all to him.

"What if I don't like him?"

"What if you don't?" my mother responded sharply. "You're to watch your manners, and no acting up, understand? It's going to be quite difficult enough without that."

"Why does he have to come here, anyway?" I demanded crossly. "Why can't he go to school where he lives?"

"Because there isn't any high school up there," my mother said. "I hope he gets on well here, and isn't too homesick. Three years is a long time. It's very good of your grandfather to let him stay at the Brick House."

She said this last accusingly, as though she suspected I might be thinking differently. But I had not thought of it one way or another. We were all having dinner at the Brick House because of Chris's arrival. It was the end of August, and sweltering. My grandfather's house looked huge and cool from the outside, the high low-sweeping spruce trees shutting out the sun with their dusky out-fanned branches. But inside it wasn't cool at all. The woodstove in the kitchen was going full blast, and the whole place smelled of roasting meat.

Grandmother Connor was wearing a large mauve apron. I thought it was a nicer colour than the dark bottle-green of her dress, but she believed in wearing sombre shades lest the spirit give way to vanity, which in her case was certainly not much of a risk. The apron came up over her shapeless bosom and obscured part of her cameo brooch, the only jewellery she ever wore, with its portrait of a fiercely bearded man whom I imagined to be either Moses or God.

"Isn't it nearly time for them to be getting here, Beth?" Grandmother Connor asked.

"Train's not due until six," my mother said. "It's barely five-thirty, now. Has father gone to the station already?"

"He went an hour ago," my grandmother said.

"He would," my mother commented.

"Now, now, Beth," my grandmother cautioned and soothed.

At last the front screen door was hurled open and Grandfather Connor strode into the house, followed by a tall lanky boy. Chris was wearing a white shirt, a tie, grey trousers. I thought, unwillingly, that he looked handsome. His face was angular, the bones showing through the brown skin. His grey eyes were slightly slanted, and his hair was the colour of couchgrass at the end of summer when it has been bleached to a light yellow by the sun. I had not planned to like him, not even a little, but somehow I wanted to defend him when I heard what my mother whispered to my grandmother before they went into the front hall.

"Heavens, look at the shirt and trousers—must've been his father's, the poor kid."

I shot out into the hall ahead of my mother, and then stopped and stood there.

"Hi, Vanessa," Chris said.

"How come you knew who I was?" I asked.

"Well, I knew your mother and dad only had one of a family, so I figured you must be her," he replied, grinning.

The way he spoke did not make me feel I had blundered. My mother greeted him warmly but shyly. Not knowing if she were expected to kiss him or to shake hands, she finally did neither. Grandmother Connor, however, had no doubts. She kissed him on both cheeks and then held him at arm's length to have a proper look at him.

"Bless the child," she said.

Coming from anyone else, this remark would have sounded ridiculous, especially as Chris was at least a head taller. My grandmother was the only person I have ever known who could say such things without appearing false.

"I'll show you your room, Chris," my mother offered.

Grandfather Connor, who had been standing in the living room doorway in absolute silence, looking as granite as a statue in the cemetery, now followed Grandmother out to the kitchen.

"Train was forty minutes late," he said weightily.

"What a shame," my grandmother said. "But I thought it wasn't due until six, Timothy."

"Six!" my grandfather cried. "That's the mainline train. The local's due at five-twenty."

This was not correct, as both my grandmother and I knew. But neither of us contradicted him.

"What on earth are you cooking a roast for, on a night like this?" my grandfather went on. "A person could fry an egg on the sidewalk, it's that hot. Potato salad would've gone down well."

Privately I agreed with this opinion, but I could never permit myself to acknowledge agreement with him on anything. I automatically and emotionally sided with Grandmother in all issues, not because she was inevitably right but because I loved her.

"It's not a roast," my grandmother said mildly. "It's mock-duck. The stove's only been going for an hour. I thought the boy would be hungry after the trip."

My mother and Chris had come downstairs and were now in the living room. I could hear them there, talking awkwardly, with pauses.

"Potato salad," my grandfather declaimed, "would've been plenty good enough. He'd have been lucky to get it, if you ask me anything. Wilf's family hasn't got two cents to rub together. It's me that's paying for the boy's keep."

The thought of Chris in the living room, and my mother unable to explain, was too much for me. I sidled over to the kitchen door, intending to close it. But my grandmother stopped me.

"No," she said, with unexpected firmness. "Leave it open, Vanessa."

I could hardly believe it. Surely she couldn't want Chris to hear? She herself was always able to move with equanimity through a hurricane because she believed that a mighty fortress was her God. But the rest of us were not like that, and usually she did her best to protect us. At the time I felt only bewilderment. I think now that she must have realised Chris would have to learn the Brick House sooner or later, and he might as well start right away.

I had to go into the living room. I had to know how Chris would take my grandfather. Would he, as I hoped, be angry and perhaps even speak out? Or would he, meekly, only be embarrassed?

"Wilf wasn't much good, even as a young man," Grandfather Connor was trumpeting. "Nobody but a simpleton would've taken up a homestead in a place like that. Anybody could've told him that land's no use for a thing except hay."

Was he going to remind us again how well he had done in the hardware business? Nobody had ever given him a hand, he used to tell me. I am sure he believed that this was true. Perhaps it even was true.

"If the boy takes after his father, it's a poor lookout for him," my grandfather continued.

I felt the old rage of helplessness. But as for Chris—he gave no sign of feeling anything. He was sitting on the big wing-backed sofa that curled into the bay window like a black and giant seashell. He began to talk to me, quite easily, just as though he had not heard a word my grandfather was saying.

This method proved to be the one Chris always used in any dealings with my grandfather. When the bludgeoning words came, which was often, Chris never seemed, like myself, to be holding back with a terrible strained force for fear of letting go and speaking out and having the known world unimaginably fall to pieces. He would not argue or defend himself, but he did not apologise, either. He simply appeared to be absent, elsewhere. Fortunately there was very little need for response, for when Grandfather Connor pointed out your shortcomings, you were not expected to reply.

But this aspect of Chris was one which I noticed only vaguely at the time. What won me was that he would talk to me and wisecrack as though I were his same age. He was—although I didn't know the phrase then—a respecter of persons.

On the rare evenings when my parents went out, Chris would come over to mind me. These were the best times, for often when he was supposed to be doing his homework, he would make fantastic objects for my amusement, or his own—pipecleaners twisted into the shape of wildly prancing midget men, or an old set of Christmas-tree lights fixed onto a puppet theatre with a red velvet curtain that really pulled. He had skill in making miniature things of all kinds. Once for my birthday he gave me a leather saddle no bigger than a matchbox, which he had sewn himself, complete in every detail, stirrups and horn, with the criss-cross lines that were the brand name of his ranch, he said, explaining it was a reference to his own name.

"Can I go to Shallow Creek sometime?" I asked one evening.

"Sure. Some summer holidays, maybe. I've got a sister about your age. The others are all grownup."

I did not want to hear. His sisters—for Chris was the only boy—did not exist for me, not even as photographs, because I did not want them to exist. I wanted him to belong only here. Shallow Creek existed, though, no longer filled with ice mountains in my mind but as some beckoning country beyond all ordinary considerations.

"Tell me what it's like there, Chris."

"My gosh, Vanessa, I've told you before, about a thousand times."

"You never told me what your house is like."

"Didn't I? Oh well—it's made out of trees grown right there beside the lake."

"Made out of trees? Gee. Really?"

I could see it. The trees were still growing, and the leaves were firmly and greenly on them. The branches had been coaxed into formations of towers and high-up nests where you could look out and see for a hundred miles or more.

"That lake, you know," Chris said. "It's more like an inland sea. It goes on for ever and ever amen, that's how it looks. And you know what? Millions of years ago, before there were any human beings at all, that lake was full of water monsters. All different kinds of dinosaurs. Then they all died off. Nobody knows for sure why. Imagine them—all those huge creatures, with necks like snakes, and some of them had hackles on their heads, like a rooster's comb only very tough, like hard leather. Some guys from Winnipeg came up a few years back, there, and dug up dinosaur bones, and found footprints in the rocks."

"Footprints in the *rocks*?"

"The rocks were mud, see, when the dinosaurs went trampling through, but after trillions of years the mud turned into stone and there were these mighty footprints with the claws still showing. Amazing, eh?"

I could only nod, fascinated and horrified. Imagine going swimming in those waters. What if one of the creatures had lived on?

"Tell me about the horses," I said.

"Oh, them. Well, we've got these two riding horses. Duchess and Firefly. I raised them, and you should see them. Really sleek, know what I mean? I bet I could make racers out of them."

He missed the horses, I thought with selfish satisfaction, more than he missed his family. I could visualise the pair, one sorrel and one black, swifting through all the meadows of summer.

"When can I go, Chris?"

"Well, we'll have to see. After I get through high school, I won't be at Shallow Creek much."

"Why not?"

"Because," Chris said, "what I am going to be is an engineer, civil engineer. You ever seen a really big bridge, Vanessa? Well, I haven't either, but I've seen pictures. You take the Golden Gate Bridge in San Francisco, now. Terrifically high—all those thin ribs of steel, joined together to go across this very wide stretch of water. It doesn't seem possible, but it's there. That's what engineers do. Imagine doing something like that, eh?"

I could not imagine it. It was beyond me.

"Where will you go?" I asked. I did not want to think of his going anywhere.

"Winnipeg, to college," he said with assurance.

The Depression did not get better, as everyone had been saying it would. It got worse, and so did the drought. That part of the prairies where we lived was never dustbowl country. The farms around Manawaka never had a total crop failure, and afterwards, when the drought was over, people used to remark on this fact proudly, as though it had been due to some virtue or special status, like the Children of Israel being afflicted by Jehovah but never in real danger of annihilation. But although Manawaka never knew the worst, what it knew was bad enough. Or so I learned later. At the time I saw none of it. For me, the Depression and drought were external and abstract, malevolent gods whose names I secretly learned although they were concealed from me, and whose evil I sensed only superstitiously, knowing they threatened us but not how or why. What I really saw was only what went on in our family.

"He's done quite well all through, despite everything," my mother said. She sighed, and I knew she was talking about Chris.

"I know," my father said. "We've been over all this before, Beth. But quite good just isn't good enough. Even supposing he managed to get a scholarship, which isn't likely, it's only tuition and books. What about room and board? Who's going to pay for that? Your father?"

"I see I shouldn't have brought up the subject at all," my mother said in an aloof voice.

"I'm sorry," my father said impatiently. "But you know, yourself, he's the only one who might possibly—"

"I can't bring myself to ask Father about it, Ewen, I simply cannot do it."

"There wouldn't be much point in asking," my father said, "when the answer is a foregone conclusion. He feels he's done his share, and actually, you know, Beth, he has, too. Three years, after all. He may not have done it gracefully, but he's done it."

We were sitting in the living room, and it was evening. My father was slouched in the grey armchair that was always his, My mother was slenderly straight-backed in the blue chair in which nobody else ever sat. I was sitting on the footstool, beige needlepoint with mathematical roses, to which I had staked my own claim. This seating arrangement was obscurely satisfactory to me, perhaps because predictable, like the three bears. I was pretending to be colouring into a scribbler on my knee, and from time to time my lethargic purple crayon added a feather to an outlandish swan. To speak would be to invite dismissal. But their words forced questions in my head.

"Chris isn't going away, is he?"

My mother swooped, shocked at her own neglect.

"My heavens—are you still up, Vanessa? What am l thinking of?"

"Where is Chris going?"

"We're not sure yet," my mother evaded, chivvying me up the stairs. "We'll see."

He would not go, I thought. Something would happen, miraculously, to prevent him. He would remain, with his long loping walk and his half-slanted grey eyes and his talk that never excluded me. He would stay right here. And soon, because I desperately wanted to, and because every day mercifully made me older, quite soon I would be able to reply with such a lightning burst of knowingness that it would astound him, when he spoke of the space or was it some black sky that never ended anywhere beyond this earth. Then I would not be innerly belittled for being unable to figure out what he would best like to hear. At that good and imagined time, I would not any longer be limited. I would not any longer be young.

I was nine when Chris left Manawaka. The day before he was due to go, I knocked on the door of his room in the Brick House.

"Come in," Chris said. "I'm packing. Do you know how to fold socks, Vanessa?"

"Sure. Of course."

"Well, get folding on that bunch there, then."

I had come to say goodbye, but I did not want to say it yet. I got to work on the socks. I did not intend to speak about the matter of college, but the knowledge that I must not speak about it made me uneasy. I was afraid I would blurt out a reference to it in my anxiety not to. My mother had said, "He's taken it amazingly well—he doesn't even mention it, so we mustn't either."

"Tomorrow night you'll be in Shallow Creek," I ventured.

"Yeh." He did not look up. He went on stuffing clothes and books into his suitcase.

"I bet you'll be glad to see the horses, eh?" I wanted him to say he didn't care about the horses any more and that he would rather stay here.

"It'll be good to see them again," Chris said. "Mind handing over those socks now, Vanessa? I think I can just squash them in at the side here. Thanks. Hey, look at that, will you? Everything's in. Am I an expert packer or am I an expert packer?"

I sat on his suitcase for him so it would close, and then he tied a piece of rope around it because the lock wouldn't lock.

"Ever thought what it would be like to be a traveller, Vanessa?" he asked.

I thought of Richard Halliburton, taking an elephant over the Alps and swimming illicitly in the Taj Mahal lily pool by moonlight.

"It would be keen," I said, because this was the word Chris used to describe the best possible: "That's what I'm going to do someday."

He did not say, as for a moment I feared he might, that girls could not be travellers.

"Why not?" he said. "Sure you will, if you really want to. I got this theory, see, that anybody can do anything at all, anything, if they really set their minds to it. But you have to have this total concentration. You have to focus on it with your whole mental powers, and not let it slip away by forgetting to hold it in your mind. If you hold it in your mind, like, then it's real, see? You take most people, now. They can't concentrate worth a darn."

"Do you think I can?" I enquired eagerly, believing that this was what he was talking about.

"What?" he said. "Oh—sure. Sure I think you can. Naturally."

Chris did not write after he left Manawaka. About a month later we had a letter from his mother. He was not at Shallow Creek. He had not gone back. He had got off the northbound train at the first stop after Manawaka, cashed in his ticket, and thumbed a lift with a truck to Winnipeg. He had written to his mother from there, but had given no address. She had not heard from him since. My mother read Aunt Tess's letter aloud to my father. She was too upset to care whether I was listening or not.

"I can't think what possessed him, Ewen. He never seemed irresponsible. What if something should happen to him? What if he's broke? What do you think we should do?"

"What can we do? He's nearly eighteen. What he does is his business. Simmer down, Beth, and let's decide what we're going to tell your father."

"Oh Lord," my mother said. "There's that to consider, of course."

I went out without either of them noticing. I walked to the hill at the edge of the town, and down into the valley where the scrub oak and poplar grew almost to the banks of the Wachakwa River. I found the oak where we had gone last autumn, in a gang, to smoke cigarettes made of dried leaves and pieces of newspaper. I climbed to the lowest branch and stayed there for a while.

I was not consciously thinking about Chris. I was not thinking of anything. But when at last I cried, I felt relieved afterwards and could go home again.

Chris departed from my mind, after that, with a quickness that was due to the other things that happened. My Aunt Edna, who was a secretary in Winnipeg, returned to Manawaka to live because the insurance company cut down on staff and she could not find another job. I was intensely excited and jubilant about her return, and could not see why my mother seemed the opposite, even though she was as fond of Aunt Edna as I was. Then my brother Roderick was born, and that same year Grandmother Connor died. The strangeness, the unbelievability, of both these events took up all of me.

When I was eleven, almost two years after Chris had left, he came back without warning. I came home from school and found him sitting in our living room. I could not accept that I had nearly forgotten him until this instant. Now that he was present, and real again, I felt I had betrayed him by not thinking of him more.

He was wearing a navy-blue serge suit. I was old enough now to notice that it was a cheap one and had been worn a considerable time. Otherwise, he looked the same, the same smile, the same knife-boned face with no flesh to speak of, the same unresting eyes.

"How come you're here?" I cried. "Where have you been, Chris?"

"I'm a traveller," he said. "Remember?"

He was a traveller all right. One meaning of the word *traveller* in our part of the world, was a travelling salesman. Chris was selling vacuum cleaners. That evening he brought out his line and showed us. He went through his spiel for our benefit, so we could hear how it sounded.

"Now look, Beth," he said, turning the appliance on and speaking loudly above its moaning roar, "see how it brightens up this old rug of yours? Keen, eh?"

"Wonderful," my mother laughed, "Only we can't afford one."

"Oh well—" Chris said quickly, "I'm not trying to sell one to you. I'm only showing you. Listen, I've only been in this job a month, but I figure this is really a going thing. I mean, it's obvious, isn't it? You take all those old wire carpet-beaters of yours, Beth. You could kill yourself over them and your carpet isn't going to look one-tenth as good as it does with this."

"Look, I don't want to seem—" my father put in, "but, hell, they're not exactly a new invention, and we're not the only ones who can't afford—"

"This is a pretty big outfit, you know?" Chris insisted. "Listen, I don't plan to stay, Ewen. But a guy could work at it for a year or so, and save—right? Lots of guys work their way through university like that."

I needed to say something really penetrating, something that would show him I knew the passionate truth of his conviction.

"I bet—" I said, "I bet you'll sell a thousand, Chris."

Two years ago, this statement would have seemed self-evident, unquestionable. Yet now, when I had spoken, I knew that I did not believe it.

The next time Chris visited Manawaka, he was selling magazines. He had the statistics worked out. If every sixth person in town would get a subscription to *Country Guide*, he could make a hundred dollars in a month. We didn't learn how he got on. He didn't stay in Manawaka a full month. When he turned up again, it was winter. Aunt Edna phoned.

"Nessa? Listen, kiddo, tell your mother she's to come down if it's humanly possible. Chris is here, and Father's having fits."

So in five minutes we were scurrying through the snow, my mother and I, with our over-shoes not even properly done up and our feet getting wet. We need not have worried. By the time we reached the Brick House, Grandfather Connor had retired to the basement, where he sat in the rocking chair beside the furnace, making occasional black pronouncements like a subterranean oracle. These loud utterances made my mother and aunt wince, but Chris didn't seem to notice any more than he ever had. He was engrossed in telling us about the mechanism he was holding. It had a cranker handle like an old-fashioned sewing machine.

"You attach the ball of wool here, see? Then you set this little switch here, and adjust this lever, and you're away to the races. Neat, eh?"

It was a knitting machine. Chris showed us the finished products. The men's socks he had made were coarse wool, one pair in grey heather and another in maroon. I was impressed.

"Gee—can I do it, Chris?"

"Sure. Look, you just grab hold of the handle right here."

"Where did you get it?" my mother asked.

"I've rented it. The way I figure it, Beth, I can sell these things at about half the price you'd pay in a store, and they're better quality."

"Who are you going to sell them to?" Aunt Edna enquired.

"You take all these guys who do outside work—they need heavy socks all year round, not just in winter. I think this thing could be quite a gold mine."

"Before I forget," my mother said, "how's your mother and the family keeping?"

"They're okay," Chris said in a restrained voice. "They're not short of hands, if that's what you mean, Beth. My sisters have their husbands there."

Then he grinned, casting away the previous moment, and dug into his suitcase.

"Hey, I haven't shown you—these are for you, Vanessa, and this pair is for Roddie."

My socks were cherry-coloured. The very small ones for my brother were turquoise.

Chris only stayed until after dinner, and then he went away again.

After my father died, the whole order of life was torn. Nothing was known or predictable any longer. For months I lived almost entirely within myself, so when my mother told me one day that Chris couldn't find any work at all because there were no jobs and so he had gone back to Shallow Creek to stay, it made scarcely any impression on me. But that summer, my mother decided I ought to go away for a holiday. She hoped it might take my mind off my father's death. What, if anything, was going to take her mind off his death, she did not say.

"Would you like to go to Shallow Creek for a week or so?" she asked me. "I could write to Chris's mother."

Then I remembered, all in a torrent, the way I had imagined it once, when he used to tell me about it—the house fashioned of living trees, the lake like a sea where monsters had dwelt, the grass that shone like green wavering light while the horses flew in the splendour of their pride.

"Yes," I said. "Write to her."

The railway did not go through Shallow Creek, but Chris met me at Challoner's Crossing. He looked different, not only thinner, but—what was it? Then I saw that it was the fact that his face and neck were tanned red-brown, and he was wearing denims, farm pants, and a blue plaid shirt open at the neck. I liked him like this. Perhaps the change was not so much in him as in myself, now that I was thirteen. He looked masculine in a way I had not been aware of, before.

"C'mon, kid," he said. "The limousine's over here."

It was a wagon and two horses, which was what I had expected, but the nature of each was not what I had expected. The wagon was a long and clumsy one, made of heavy planking, and the horses were both plough horses, thick in the legs, and badly matched as a team. The mare was short and stout, matronly. The gelding was very tall and gaunt, and he limped.

"Allow me to introduce you," Chris said. "Floss—Trooper—this is Vanessa."

He did not mention the other horses, Duchess and Firefly, and neither did I, not all the fortnight I was there. I guess I had known for some years now, without realising it, that the pair had only ever existed in some other dimension.

Shallow Creek wasn't a town. It was merely a name on a map. There was a grade school a few miles away, but that was all. They had to go to Challoner's Crossing for their groceries. We reached the farm, and Chris steered me through the crowd of aimless cows and wolfish dogs in the yard, while I flinched with panic.

It was perfectly true that the house was made out of trees. It was a fair-sized but elderly shack, made out of poplar poles and chinked with mud. There was an upstairs, which was not so usual around here, with three bedrooms, one of which I was to share with Chris's sister, Jeannie, who was slightly younger than I, a pallid-eyed girl who was either too shy to talk or who had nothing to say. I never discovered which, because I was so reticent with her myself, wanting to push her away, not to recognise her, and at the same time experiencing a shocked remorse at my own unacceptable feelings.

Aunt Tess, Chris's mother, was severe in manner and yet wanting to be kind, worrying over it, making tentative overtures which were either ignored or repelled by her older daughters and their monosyllabic husbands. Youngsters swam in and out of the house like shoals of nameless fishes. I could not see how so many people could live here, under the one roof, but then I learned they didn't. The married daughters had their own dwelling places, nearby, but some kind of communal life was maintained. They wrangled endlessly but they never left one another alone, not even for a day.

Chris took no part at all, none. When he spoke, it was usually to the children, and they would often follow him around the yard or to the barn, not pestering but just trailing along in clusters of three or four. He never told them to go away. I liked him for this but it bothered me, too. I wished he would return his sisters' bickering for once, or tell them to clear out, or even yell at one of the kids. But he never did. He closed himself off from squabbling voices just as he used to do with Grandfather Connor's spearing words.

The house had no screens on the doors or windows, and at meal times the flies were so numerous you could hardly see the food for the iridescent-winged blue-black bodies squirming all over it. Nobody noticed my squeamishness except Chris, and he was the only one from whom I really wanted to conceal it.

"Fan with your hand," he murmured.

"It's okay," I said quickly.

For the first time in all the years we had known each other, we could not look the other in the eye. Around the table the children stabbed and snivelled, until Chris's older sister, driven frantic, shrieked, *Shut up shut up shut up*. Chris began asking me about Manawaka then, as though nothing were going on around him.

They were due to begin haying, and Chris announced that he was going to camp out in the bluff near the hayfields. To save himself the long drive in the wagon each morning, he explained, but I felt this wasn't the real reason.

"Can I go, too?" I begged. I could not bear the thought of living in the house with all the others who were not known to me, and Chris not here.

"Well, I don't know—"

"Please. Please, Chris. I won't be any trouble. I promise."

Finally he agreed. We drove out in the big hayrack, its slatted sides rattling, its old wheels jolting metallically. The road was narrow and dirt, and around it the low bushes grew, wild rose and blueberry and wolf willow with silver leaves. Sometimes we would come to a bluff of pale-leaved poplar trees, and once a red-winged blackbird flew up out of the branches and into the hot dusty blue of the sky.

Then we were there. The hayfields lay beside the lake. It was my first view of the water which had spawned saurian giants so long ago. Chris drove the hayrack through the fields of high coarse grass and on down almost to the lake's edge, where there was no shore but only the green rushes like floating meadows in which the open lake stretched, deep, green-grey, out and out, beyond sight.

No human word could be applied. The lake was not lonely or untamed. These words relate to people, and there was nothing of people here. There was no feeling about the place. It existed in some world in which man was not yet born. I looked at the grey reaches of it and felt threatened. It was like the view of God which I had held since my father's death. Distant, indestructible, totally indifferent.

Chris had jumped down off the hayrack.

"We're not going to camp *here*, are we?" I asked and pleaded.

"No. I just want to let the horses drink. We'll camp up there in the bluff."

I looked. "It's still pretty close to the lake, isn't it?"

"Don't worry," Chris said, laughing. "You won't get your feet wet."

"I didn't mean that."

Chris looked at me.

"I know you didn't," he said, "But let's learn to be a little tougher, and not let on, eh? It's necessary."

Chris worked through the hours of sun, while I lay on the half-formed stack of hay and looked up at the sky. The blue air trembled and spun with the heat haze and the hay on which I was lying held the scents of grass and dust and wild mint.

In the evening, Chris took the horses to the lake again, and then he drove the hayrack to the edge of the bluff and we spread out our blankets underneath it. He made a fire and we had coffee and a tin of stew, and then we went to bed. We did not wash, and we slept in our clothes. It was only when I was curled up uncomfortably with the itching blanket around me that I felt a sense of unfamiliarity at being here, with Chris only three feet away, a self-consciousness I would not have felt even the year before. I do not think he felt this sexual strangeness. If he wanted me not to be a child—and he did—it was not with the wish that I would be a woman. It was something else.

"Are you asleep, Vanessa?" he asked.

"No. I think I'm lying on a tree root."

"Well, shift yourself, then," he said. "Listen, kid, I never said anything before, because I didn't really know what to say, but—you know how I felt about your dad dying, and that, don't you?"

"Yes," I said chokingly. "It's okay. I know."

"I used to talk with Ewen sometimes. He didn't see what I was driving at, mostly, but he'd always listen, you know? You don't find many guys like that."

We were both silent for a while.

"Look," Chris said finally. "Ever notice how much brighter the stars are when you're completely away from any houses? Even the lamps up at the farm, there, make enough of a glow to keep you from seeing properly like you can out here. What do they make you think about, Vanessa?"

"Well—"

"I guess most people don't give them much thought at all, except maybe to say—*very pretty*—or like that. But the point is, they aren't like that. The stars and planets, in themselves, are just not like that, not *pretty*, for heaven's sake. They're gigantic—some of them burning—imagine those worlds tearing through space and made of pure fire. Or the ones that are absolutely dead—just rock or ice and no warmth in them. There must be some, though, that have living creatures. You wonder what *they* could look like, and what they feel. We won't ever get to know. But somebody will know, someday. I really believe that. Do you ever think about this kind of thing at all?"

He was twenty-one. The distance between us was still too great. For years I had wanted to be older so I might talk with him, but now I felt unready.

"Sometimes," I said, hesitantly, making it sound like *Never*.

"People usually say there must be a God," Chris went on, "because otherwise how did the universe get here? But that's ridiculous. If the stars and planets go on to infinity, they could have existed forever, for no reason at all. Maybe they weren't ever created. Look—what's the alternative? To believe in a God who is brutal. What else could He be? You've only got to look anywhere around you. It would be an insult to Him to believe in a God like that. Most people don't like talking about this kind of thing—it embarrasses them, you know? Or else they're not interested. I don't mind. I can always think about things myself. You don't actually need anyone to talk to. But about God, though—if there's a war, like it looks there will be, would people claim that was planned? What kind of a God would pull a trick like that? And yet, you know, plenty of guys would think it was a godsend, and who's to say they're wrong? It would be a job, and you'd get around and see places."

He paused, as though waiting for me to say something. When I did not, he resumed.

"Ewen told me about the last war, once. He hardly ever talked about it, but this once he told me about seeing the horses in the mud, actually going under, you know? And the way their eyes looked when they realised they weren't going to get out. Ever seen horses' eyes when they're afraid, I mean really berserk with fear, like in a bush-fire? Ewen said a guy tended to concentrate on the horses because he didn't dare think what was happening to the men. Including himself. Do you ever listen to the news at all, Vanessa?"

"I—"

I could only feel how foolish I must sound, still unable to reply as I would have wanted, comprehendingly. I felt I had failed myself utterly. I could not speak even the things I knew. As for the other things, the things I did not know, I resented Chris's facing me with them. I took refuge in pretending to be asleep, and after a while Chris stopped talking.

Chris left Shallow Creek some months after the war began, and joined the Army. After his basic training he was sent to England. We did not hear from him until about a year later, when a letter arrived for me.

"Vanessa—what's wrong?" my mother asked.

"Nothing."

"Don't fib," she said firmly. "What did Chris say in his letter, honey?"

"Oh—not much."

She gave me a curious look and then she went away. She would never have demanded to see the letter. I did not show it to her and she did not ask about it again.

Six months later my mother heard from Aunt Tess. Chris had been sent home from England and discharged from the Army because of a mental breakdown. He was now in the provincial mental hospital and they did not know how long he would have to remain there. He had been violent, before, but now he was not violent. He was, the doctors had told his mother, passive.

Violent. I could not associate the word with Chris, who had been so much the reverse. I could not bear to consider what anguish must have catapulted him into that even greater anguish. But the way he was now seemed almost worse. How might he be? Sitting quite still, wearing the hospital's grey dressing-gown, the animation gone from his face?

My mother cared about him a great deal, but her immediate thought was not for him.

"When I think of you, going up to Shallow Creek that time," she said, "and going out camping with him, and what might have happened—"

I, also, was thinking of what might have happened. But we were not thinking of the same thing. For the first time I recognised, at least a little, the dimensions of his need to talk that night. He must have understood perfectly well how impossible it would be, with a thirteen-year-old. But there was no one else. All his life's choices had grown narrower and narrower. He had been forced to return to the alien lake of home, and when finally he saw a means of getting away, it could only be into a turmoil which appalled him and which he dreaded even more than he knew. I had listened to his words, but I had not really heard them, not until now. It would not have made much difference to what happened, but I wished it were not too late to let him know.

Once when I was on holiday from college, my mother got me to help her clean out the attic. We sifted through boxes full of junk, old clothes, school-books, bric-a-brac that once had been treasures. In one of the boxes I found the miniature saddle that Chris had made for me a long time ago.

"Have you heard anything recently?" I asked, ashamed that I had not asked sooner.

She glanced up at me. "Just the same. It's always the same. They don't think there will be much improvement."

Then she turned away.

"He always used to seem so—hopeful. Even when there was really nothing to be hopeful about. That's what I find so strange. He *seemed* hopeful, didn't you think?"

"Maybe it wasn't hope," I said.

"How do you mean?"

I wasn't certain myself. I was thinking of all the schemes he'd had, the ones that couldn't possibly have worked, the unreal solutions to which he'd clung because there were no others, the brave and useless strokes of fantasy against a depression that was both the world's and his own.

"I don't know," I said. "I just think things were always more difficult for him than he let on, that's all. Remember the letter?"

"Yes."

"Well—what it said was that they could force his body to march and even to kill, but what they didn't know was that he'd fooled them. He didn't live inside it any more."

"Oh Vanessa—" my mother said. "You must have suspected right then."

"Yes, but—"

I could not go on, could not say that the letter seemed only the final heartbreaking extension of that way he'd always had of distancing himself from the absolute unbearability of battle.

I picked up the tiny saddle and turned it over in my hand.

"Look. His brand, the name of his ranch. The CrissCross."

"What ranch?" my mother said, bewildered.

"The one where he kept his racing horses. Duchess and Firefly."

Some words came into my head, a single line from a poem I had once heard. I knew it referred to a lover who did not want the morning to come, but to me it had another meaning, a different relevance.

Slowly, slowly, horses of the night—

The night must move like this for him, slowly, all through the days and nights. I could not know whether the land he journeyed through was inhabited by terrors, the old monster-kings of the lake, or whether he had discovered at last a way for himself to make the necessary dream perpetual.

I put the saddle away once more, gently and ruthlessly, back into the cardboard box.

(1970)

John Ashberry

(U.S.A., 1927–)

The Instruction Manual

As I sit looking out of a window of the building
I wish I did not have to write the instruction manual on the uses of a new metal.
I look down into the street and see people, each walking with an inner peace,
And envy them—they are so far away from me!
5 Not one of them has to worry about getting out this manual on schedule.
And, as my way is, I begin to dream, resting my elbows on the desk and
        leaning out of the window a little,
Of dim Guadalajara! City of rose-colored flowers!
City I wanted most to see, and most did not see, in Mexico!
But I fancy I see, under the press of having to write the instruction manual,
10 Your public square, city, with its elaborate little bandstand!
The band is playing *Scheherazade* by Rimsky-Korsakov.
Around stand the flower girls, handing out rose- and lemon-colored flowers,
Each attractive in her rose-and-blue striped dress (Oh! such shades of rose and blue),
And nearby is the little white booth where women in green serve you green
        and yellow fruit.
15 The couples are parading; everyone is in a holiday mood.
First, leading the parade, is a dapper fellow
Clothed in deep blue. On his head sits a white hat
And he wears a mustache, which has been trimmed for the occasion.
His dear one, his wife, is young and pretty; her shawl is rose, pink, and white.
20 Her slippers are patent leather, in the American fashion,

And she carries a fan, for she is modest, and does not want the crowd to see
      her face too often.
But everybody is so busy with his wife or loved one
I doubt they would notice the mustachioed man's wife.
Here come the boys! They are skipping and throwing little things on the sidewalk
25 Which is made of gray tile. One of them, a little older, has a toothpick in his teeth.
He is silenter than the rest, and affects not to notice the pretty young girls in white.
But his friends notice them, and shout their jeers at the laughing girls.
Yet soon all this will cease, with the deepening of their years,
And love bring each to the parade grounds for another reason.
30 But I have lost sight of the young fellow with the toothpick.
Wait—there he is on the other side of the bandstand,
Secluded from his friends, in earnest talk with a young girl
Of fourteen or fifteen. I try to hear what they are saying
But it seems they are just mumbling something—shy words of love, probably.
35 She is slightly taller than he, and looks quietly down into his sincere eyes.
She is wearing white. The breeze ruffles her long fine black hair against her
      olive cheek.
Obviously she is in love. The boy, the young boy with the toothpick, he is in
      love too;
His eyes show it. Turning from this couple,
I see there is an intermission in the concert.
40 The paraders are resting and sipping drinks through straws
(The drinks are dispensed from a large glass crock by a lady in dark blue),
And the musicians mingle among them, in their creamy white uniforms, and talk
About the weather, perhaps, or how their kids are doing at school.
Let us take this opportunity to tiptoe into one of the side streets.
45 Here you may see one of those white houses with green trim
That are so popular here. Look—I told you!
It is cool and dim inside, but the patio is sunny.
An old woman in gray sits there, fanning herself with a palm leaf fan.
She welcomes us to her patio, and offers us a cooling drink.
50 "My son is in Mexico City," she says. "He would welcome you too
If he were here. But his job is with a bank there.
Look, here is a photograph of him."
And a dark-skinned lad with pearly teeth grins out at us from the worn leather frame.
We thank her for her hospitality, for it is getting late
55 And we must catch a view of the city, before we leave, from a good high place.
That church tower will do—the faded pink one, there against the fierce blue
      of the sky. Slowly we enter.
The caretaker, an old man dressed in brown and gray, asks us how long we
      have been in the city, and how we like it here.
His daughter is scrubbing the steps—she nods to us as we pass into the
      tower.
Soon we have reached the top, and the whole network of the city extends before us.

60 There is the rich quarter, with its houses of pink and white, and its
                 crumbling, leafy terraces.
There is the poorer quarter, its homes a deep blue.
There is the market, where men are selling hats and swatting flies
And there is the public library, painted several shades of pale green and beige.
Look! There is the square we just came from, with the promenaders.
65 There are fewer of them, now that the heat of the day has increased,
But the young boy and girl still lurk in the shadows of the bandstand.
And there is the home of the little old lady—
She is still sitting in the patio, fanning herself.
How limited, but how complete withal, has been our experience of Guadalajara!
70 We have seen young love, married love, and the love of an aged mother for
                 her son.
We have heard the music, tasted the drinks, and looked at colored houses.
What more is there to do, except stay? And that we cannot do.
And as a last breeze freshens the top of the weathered old tower, I turn my gaze
Back to the instruction manual which has made me dream of Guadalajara.

                                                                    (1956)

W.S. Merwin
(U.S.A., 1927-)

In the Winter of My Thirty-Eighth Year

It sounds unconvincing to say *When I was young*
Though I have long wondered what it would be like
To be me now
No older at all it seems from here
5   As far from myself as ever

Waking in fog and rain and seeing nothing
I imagine all the docks have died in the night
Now no one is looking I could choose my age
It would be younger I suppose so I am older
10   It is there at hand I could take it
Except for the things I think I would do differently
They keep coming between they are what I am
They have taught me little I did not know when I was young

There is nothing wrong with my age now probably
15   It is how I have come to it
Like a thing I kept putting off as I did my youth

There is nothing the matter with speech
Just because it lent itself
To my uses

20   Of course there is nothing the matter with the stars
It is my emptiness among them
While they drift farther away in the invisible morning

(1967)

When the War is Over

When the war is over
We will be proud of course the air will be
Good for breathing at last
The water will have been improved the salmon
5   And the silence of heaven will migrate more perfectly
The dead will think the living are worth it we will know
Who we are
And we will all enlist again

(1967)

Phyllis Webb
(CANADA, 1927–)

Marvell's Garden

Marvell's garden, that place of solitude,
is not where I'd choose to live
yet is the fixed sundial
that turns me round
5   unwillingly
in a hot glade
as closer, closer I come to contradiction
to the shade green within the green shade.

The garden where Marvell scorned love's solicitude—
10   that dream—and played instead an arcane solitaire,
shuffling his thoughts like shadowy chance
across the shrubs of ecstasy,
and cast the myths away to flowering hours
as yes, his mind, that sea, caught at green
15   thoughts shadowing a green infinity.

And yet Marvell's garden was not Plato's
garden—and yet—he did care more for the form
of things than for the thing itself—
ideas and visions,
20   resemblances and echoes,
things seeming and being
not quite what they were.

That was his garden, a kind of attitude
struck out of an earth too carefully attended,
25   wanting to be left alone.
And I don't blame him for that.
God knows, too many fences fence us out
and his garden closed in on Paradise.

On Paradise! When I think of his hymning
30   Puritans in the Bermudas, the bright oranges
lighting up that night! When I recall
his rustling tinsel hopes
beneath the cold decree of steel,
Oh, I have wept for some new convulsion
35   to tear together this world and his.

But then I saw his luminous plumèd Wings
prepared for flight,
and then I heard him singing glory
in a green tree,
40   and then I caught the vest he'd laid aside
all blest with fire.

And I have gone walking slowly in
his garden of necessity
leaving brothers, lovers, Christ
45   outside my walls
where they have wept without
and I within.

                                   (1956)

The Days of the Unicorns

I remember when the unicorns
roved in herds through the meadow
behind the cabin, and how they would
lately pause, tilting their jewelled
5 horns to the falling sun as we shared
the tensions of private property
and the need to be alone.

Or as we walked along the beach
a solitary delicate beast
10 might follow on his soft paws
until we turned and spoke the words
to console him.

It seemed they were always near
ready to show their eyes and stare
15 us down, standing in their creamy
skins, pink tongues out
for our benevolence.

As if they knew that always beyond
and beyond the ladies were weaving them
20 into their spider looms.

I knew where they slept
and how the grass was bent
by their own wilderness
and I pitied them.

25 It was only yesterday, or seems
like only yesterday when we could
touch and turn and they came
perfectly real into our fictions.
But they moved on with the courtly sun
30 grazing peacefully beyond the story
horns lowering and lifting and
lowering.

I know this is scarcely credible now
as we cabin ourselves in cold
35 and the motions of panic
and our cells destroy each other
performing music and extinction
and the great dreams pass on
to the common good.

(1980)

Author's Note: "'paws': dream overlap of lion and unicorn."

Richard Selzer
(U.S.A., 1928–)

The Knife

One holds the knife as one holds the bow of a cello or a tulip—by the stem. Not palmed nor gripped nor grasped, but lightly, with the tips of the fingers. The knife is not for pressing. It is for drawing across the field of skin. Like a slender fish, it waits, at the ready, then, go! It darts, followed by a fine wake of red. The flesh parts, falling away to yellow globules of fat. Even now, after so many times, I still marvel at its power—cold, gleaming, silent. More, I am still struck with a kind of dread that it is I in whose hand the blade travels, that my hand is its vehicle, that yet again this terrible steel-bellied thing and I have conspired for a most unnatural purpose, the laying open of the body of a human being.

A stillness settles in my heart and is carried to my hand. It is the quietude of resolve layered over fear. And it is this resolve that lowers us, my knife and me, deeper and deeper into the person beneath, it is an entry into the body that is nothing like a caress; still, it is among the gentlest of acts. Then stroke and stroke again, and we are joined by other instruments, hemostats and forceps, until the wound blooms with strange flowers whose looped handles fall to the sides in steely array.

There is sound, the tight click of clamps fixing teeth into severed blood vessels, the snuffle and gargle of the suction machine clearing the field of blood for the next stroke, the litany of monosyllables with which one prays his way down and in: *clamp, sponge, suture, tie, cut*. And there is color. The green of the cloth, the white of the sponges, the red and yellow of the body. Beneath the fat lies the fascia, the tough fibrous sheet encasing the muscles. It must be sliced and the red beef of the muscles separated. Now there are retractors to hold apart the wound. Hands move together, part, weave. We are fully engaged, like children absorbed in a game or the craftsmen of some place like Damascus.

Deeper still. The peritoneum, pink and gleaming and membranous, bulges into the wound. It is grasped with forceps, and opened. For the first time we can see into the cavity of the abdomen. Such a primitive place. One expects to find drawings of buffalo on the walls. The sense of trespassing is keener now, heightened by the world's light illuminating the organs, their secret colors revealed—maroon and salmon and yellow. The vista is sweetly vulnerable at this moment, a kind of welcoming. An arc of the liver shines high and on the right, like a dark sun. It laps over the pink sweep of the stomach, from whose lower border the gauzy omentum is draped, and through which veil one sees, sinuous, slow as just-fed snakes, the indolent coils of the intestine.

You turn aside to wash your gloves. It is a ritual cleansing. One enters this temple doubly washed. Here is man as microcosm, representing in all his parts the earth, perhaps the universe.

I must confess that the priestliness of my profession has ever been impressed on me. In the beginning there are vows, taken with all solemnity. Then there is the endless harsh novitiate of training, much fatigue, much sacrifice. At last one emerges as celebrant, standing close to the truth lying curtained in the Ark of the body. Not surplice and cassock but mask and gown are your regalia. You hold no chalice, but a knife. There is no wine, no wafer. There are only the facts of blood and flesh.

And if the surgeon is like a poet, then the scars you have made on countless bodies are like verses into the fashioning of which you have poured your soul. I think that if years later I were to see the trace from an old incision of mine, I should know it at once, as one recognizes his pet expressions.

But mostly you are a traveler in a dangerous country, advancing into the moist and jungly cleft your hands have made. Eyes and ears are shuttered from the land you left behind; mind empties itself of all other thought. You are the root of groping fingers. It is a fine hour for the fingers, their sense of touch so enhanced. The blind must know this feeling. Oh, there is risk everywhere. One goes lightly. The spleen. No! No! Do not touch the spleen that lurks below the left leaf of the diaphragm, a manta ray in a coral cave, its bloody tongue protruding. One poke and it might rupture, exploding with sudden hemorrhage. The filmy omentum must not be torn, the intestine scraped or denuded. The hand finds the liver, palms it, fingers running along its sharp lower edge, admiring. Here are the twin mounds of the kidneys, the apron of the omentum hanging in front of the intestinal coils. One lifts it aside and the fingers dip among the loops, searching, mapping territory, establishing boundaries. Deeper still, and the womb is touched, then held like a small muscular bottle—the womb and its earlike appendages, the ovaries. How they do nestle in the cup of a man's hand, their power all dormant. They are frailty itself.

There is a hush in the room. Speech stops. The hands of the others, assistants and nurses, are still. Only the voice of the patient's respiration remains. It is the rhythm of a quiet sea, the sound of waiting. Then you speak, slowly, the terse entries of a Himalayan climber reporting back.

"The stomach is okay. Greater curvature clean. No sign of ulcer. Pylorus, duodenum fine. Now comes the gallbladder. No stones. Right kidney, left, all right. Liver . . . uh-oh."

Your speech lowers to a whisper, falters, stops for a long, long moment, then picks up again at the end of a sigh that comes through your mask like a last exhalation.

"Three big hard ones in the left lobe, one on the right. Metastatic deposits. Bad, bad. Where's the primary? Got to be coming from somewhere."

The arm shifts direction and the fingers drop lower and lower into the pelvis—the body impaled now upon the arm of the surgeon to the hilt of the elbow.

"Here it is."

The voice goes flat, all business now.

"Tumor in the sigmoid colon, wrapped all around it, pretty tight. We'll take out a sleeve of the bowel. No colostomy. Not that, anyway. But, God, there's a lot of it down there. Here, you take a feel."

You step back from the table, and lean into a sterile basin of water, resting on stiff arms, while the others locate the cancer. . . .

What is it, then, this thing, the knife, whose shape is virtually the same as it was three thousand years ago, but now with its head grown detachable? Before steel, it was bronze. Before bronze, stone—then back into unremembered time. Did man invent it or did the knife precede him here, hidden under ages of vegetation and hoofprints, lying in wait to be discovered, picked up, used?

The scalpel is in two parts, the handle and the blade. Joined, it is six inches from tip to tip. At one end of the handle is a narrow notched prong upon which the blade is slid, then snapped into place. Without the blade, the handle has a blind, decapitated look. It is helpless as a trussed maniac. But slide on the blade, click it home, and the knife springs instantly to life. It is headed now, edgy, leaping to mount the fingers for the gallop to its feast.

Now is the moment from which you have turned aside, from which you have averted your gaze, yet toward which you have been hastened. Now the scalpel sings along the flesh again, its brute run unimpeded by germs or other frictions. It is a slick slide home, a barracuda spurt, a rip of embedded talon. One listens, and almost hears the whine—nasal, high, delivered through that gleaming metallic snout. The flesh splits with its own kind of moan. It is like the penetration of rape.

The breasts of women are cut off, arms and legs sliced to the bone to make ready for the saw, eyes freed from sockets, intestines lopped. The hand of the surgeon rebels. Tension boils through his pores, like sweat. The flesh of the patient retaliates with hemorrhage, and the blood chases the knife wherever it is withdrawn.

Within the belly a tumor squats, toadish, fungoid. A gray mother and her brood. The only thing it does not do is croak. It too is hacked from its bed as the carnivore knife lips the blood, turning in it in a kind of ecstasy of plenty, a gluttony after the long fast. It is just for this that the knife was created, tempered, heated, its violence beaten into paper-thin force.

At last a little thread passed into the wound and tied. The monstrous booming fury is stilled by a tiny thread. The tempest is silenced. The operation is over. On the table, the knife lies spent, on its side, the bloody meal smear-dried upon its flanks. The knife rests.

And waits.

(1976)

Anne Sexton
(U.S.A., 1928–1974)

Cinderella

You always read about it:
the plumber with twelve children
who wins the Irish Sweepstakes.
From toilets to riches.
5   That story.

Or the nursemaid,
some luscious sweet from Denmark
who captures the oldest son's heart.
From diapers to Dior.
10 That story.

Or a milkman who serves the wealthy,
eggs, cream, butter, yogurt, milk,
the white truck like an ambulance
who goes into real estate
15 and makes a pile.
From homogenized to martinis at lunch.

Or the charwoman
who is on the bus when it cracks up
and collects enough from the insurance.
20 From mops to Bonwit Teller.
That story.

Once
the wife of a rich man was on her deathbed
and she said to her daughter Cinderella:
25 Be devout. Be good. Then I will smile
down from heaven in the seam of a cloud.
The man took another wife who had
two daughters, pretty enough
but with hearts like blackjacks.
30 Cinderella was their maid.
She slept on the sooty hearth each night
and walked around looking like Al Jolson.
Her father brought presents home from town,
jewels and gowns for the other women
35 but the twig of a tree for Cinderella.
She planted that twig on her mother's grave
and it grew to a tree where a white dove sat.
Whenever she wished for anything the dove
would drop it like an egg upon the ground.
40 The bird is important, my dears, so heed him.

Next came the ball, as you all know.
It was a marriage market.
The prince was looking for a wife.
All but Cinderella were preparing
45 and gussying up for the big event.
Cinderella begged to go too.
Her stepmother threw a dish of lentils
into the cinders and said: Pick them
up in an hour and you shall go.
50 The white dove brought all his friends;
all the warm wings of the fatherland came,
and picked up the lentils in a jiffy.
No, Cinderella, said the stepmother,
you have no clothes and cannot dance.
55 That's the way with stepmothers.

Cinderella went to the tree at the grave
and cried forth like a gospel singer:
Mama! Mama! My turtledove,
send me to the prince's ball!
60 The bird dropped down a golden dress
and delicate little gold slippers.
Rather a large package for a simple bird.
So she went. Which is no surprise.
Her stepmother and sisters didn't
65 recognize her without her cinder face
and the prince took her hand on the spot
and danced with no other the whole day.

As nightfall came she thought she'd better
get home. The prince walked her home
70 and she disappeared into the pigeon house
and although the prince took an axe and broke
it open she was gone. Back to her cinders.
These events repeated themselves for three days.
However on the third day the prince
75 covered the palace steps with cobbler's wax
and Cinderella's shoe stuck upon it.

Now he would find whom the shoe fit
and find his strange dancing girl for keeps.
He went to their house and the two sisters
80 were delighted because they had lovely feet.
The eldest went into a room to try the slipper on
but her big toe got in the way so she simply
sliced it off and put on the slipper.
The prince rode away with her until the white dove
85 told him to look at the blood pouring forth.
That is the way with amputations.
They don't just heal up like a wish.
The other sister cut off her heel
but the blood told as blood will.
90 The prince was getting tired.
He began to feel like a shoe salesman.
But he gave it one last try.
This time Cinderella fit into the shoe
like a love letter into its envelope.

95 At the wedding ceremony
the two sisters came to curry favor
and the white dove pecked their eyes out.
Two hollow spots were left
like soup spoons.

100 Cinderella and the prince
lived, they say, happily ever after,
like two dolls in a museum case
never bothered by diapers or dust,
never arguing over the timing of an egg,
105 never telling the same story twice,
never getting a middle-aged spread,
their darling smiles pasted on for eternity.
Regular Bobbsey Twins.
That story.

                                        (1971)

Adrienne Rich

(U.S.A., 1929–)

When We Dead Awaken: Writing as Re-Vision

The Modern Language Association is both marketplace and funeral parlor for the professional study of Western literature in North America. Like all gatherings of the professions, it has been and remains a "procession of the sons of educated men" (Virginia Woolf): a congeries of old-boys' networks, academicians rehearsing their numb canons in sessions dedicated to the literature of white males, junior scholars under the lash of "publish or perish" delivering papers in the bizarrely lit drawing-rooms of immense hotels: a ritual competition veering between cynicism and desperation.

However, in the interstices of these gentlemanly rites (or, in Mary Daly's words, on the boundaries of this patriarchal space),° some feminist scholars, teachers, and graduate students, joined by feminist writers, editors, and publishers, have for a decade been creating more subversive occasions, challenging the sacredness of the gentlemanly canon, sharing the rediscovery of buried works by women, asking women's questions, bringing literary history and criticism back to life in both senses. The Commission on the Status of Women in the Profession was formed in 1969, and held its first public event in 1970. In 1971 the Commission asked Ellen Peck Killoh, Tillie Olsen, Elaine Reuben, and myself, with Elaine Hedges as moderator, to talk on "The Woman Writer in the Twentieth Century." The essay that follows was written for that forum, and later published, along with the other papers from the forum and workshops, in an issue of *College English* edited by Elaine Hedges ("Women Writing and Teaching," vol. 34, no. 1, October 1972). With a few revisions, mainly updating, it was reprinted in *American Poets* in 1976, edited by William Heyen (New York: Bobbs-Merrill, 1976). That later text is the one published here.

The challenge flung by feminists at the accepted literary canon, at the methods of teaching it, and at the biased and astigmatic view of male "literary scholarship," has not diminished in the decade since the first Women's Forum; it has become broadened and intensified more recently by the challenges of black and lesbian feminists pointing out that feminist literary criticism itself has overlooked or held back from examining the work of black women and lesbians. The dynamic between a political vision and the demand for a fresh vision of literature is clear: without a growing feminist movement, the first inroads of feminist scholarship could not have been made; without the sharpening of a black feminist consciousness, black women's writing would have been left in limbo between misogynist black male critics and white feminists still struggling to unearth a white women's tradition; without an articulate lesbian/feminist movement, lesbian writing would still be lying in that closet where many of us used to sit reading forbidden books "in a bad light."

Much, much more is yet to be done; and university curricula have of course changed very little as a result of all this. What is changing is the availability of knowledge, of vital texts, the visible effects on women's lives of seeing, hearing our wordless or negated experience affirmed and pursued further in language.

✿   ✿   ✿   ✿   ✿

° Mary Daly, *Beyond God the Father* (Boston: Beacon, 1971), pp. 40–41.

Ibsen's *When We Dead Awaken* is a play about the use that the male artist and thinker—in the process of creating culture as we know it—has made of women, in his life and in his work; and about a woman's slow struggling awakening to the use to which her life has been put. Bernard Shaw wrote in 1900 of this play:

[Ibsen] shows us that no degradation ever devized or permitted is as disastrous as this degradation; that through it women can die into luxuries for men and yet can kill them; that men and women are becoming conscious of this; and that what remains to be seen as perhaps the most interesting of all imminent social developments is what will happen "when we dead awaken."[1]

It's exhilarating to be alive in a time of awakening consciousness; it can also be confusing, disorienting, and painful. This awakening of dead or sleeping consciousness has already affected the lives of millions of women, even those who don't know it yet. It is also affecting the lives of men, even those who deny its claims upon them. The argument will go on whether an oppressive economic class system is responsible for the oppressive nature of male/female relations, or whether, in fact, patriarchy—the domination of males—is the original model of oppression on which all others are based. But in the last few years the women's movement has drawn inescapable and illuminating connections between our sexual lives and our political institutions. The sleepwalkers are coming awake, and for the first time this awakening has a collective reality; it is no longer such a lonely thing to open one's eyes.

Re-vision—the act of looking back, of seeing with fresh eyes, of entering an old text from a new critical direction—is for women more than a chapter in cultural history: it is an act of survival. Until we can understand the assumptions in which we are drenched we cannot know ourselves. And this drive to self-knowledge, for women, is more than a search for identity: it is part of our refusal of the self-destructiveness of male-dominated society. A radical critique of literature, feminist in its impulse, would take the work first of all as a clue to how we live, how we have been living, how we have been led to imagine ourselves, how our language has trapped as well as liberated us, how the very act of naming has been till now a male prerogative, and how we can begin to see and name—and therefore live—afresh. A change in the concept of sexual identity is essential if we are not going to see the old political order reassert itself in every new revolution. We need to know the writing of the past, and know it differently than we have ever known it; not to pass on a tradition but to break its hold over us.

For writers, and at this moment for women writers in particular, there is the challenge and promise of a whole new psychic geography to be explored. But there is also a difficult and dangerous walking on the ice, as we try to find language and images for a consciousness we are just coming into, and with little in the past to support us. I want to talk about some aspects of this difficulty and this danger.

Jane Harrison, the great classical anthropologist, wrote in 1914 in a letter to her friend Gilbert Murray:

By the by, about "Women," it has bothered me often—why do women never want to write poetry about Man as a sex—why is Woman a dream and a terror to man and not the other way around?. . . Is it mere convention and propriety, or something deeper?[2]

---

[1] G.B. Shaw, *The Quintessence of Ibsenism* (New York: Hill & Wang, 1922), p. 139.

[2] J.G. Stewart, *Jane Ellen Harrison: A Portrait from Letters* (London: Merlin, 1959), p. 140.

I think Jane Harrison's question cuts deep into the myth-making tradition, the romantic tradition; deep into what women and men have been to each other; and deep into the psyche of the woman writer. Thinking about that question, I began thinking of the work of two twentieth-century women poets, Sylvia Plath and Diane Wakoski. It strikes me that in the work of both Man appears as, if not a dream, a fascination and a terror; and that the source of the fascination and the terror is, simply, Man's power—to dominate, tyrannize, choose, or reject the woman. The charisma of Man seems to come purely from his power over her and his control of the world by force, not from anything fertile or life-giving in him. And, in the work of both these poets, it is finally the woman's sense of *herself*—embattled, possessed—that gives the poetry its dynamic charge, its rhythms of struggle, need, will, and female energy. Until recently this female anger and this furious awareness of the Man's power over her were not available materials to the female poet, who tended to write of Love as the source of her suffering, and to view that victimization by Love as an almost inevitable fate. Or, like Marianne Moore and Elizabeth Bishop, she kept sexuality at a measured and chiseled distance in her poems.

One answer to Jane Harrison's question has to be that historically men and women have played very different parts in each others' lives. Where woman has been a luxury for man, and has served as the painter's model and the poet's muse, but also as comforter, nurse, cook, bearer of his seed, secretarial assistant, and copyist of manuscripts, man has played a quite different role for the female artist. Henry James repeats an incident which the writer Prosper Mérimée described, of how, while he was living with George Sand,

he once opened his eyes, in the raw winter dawn, to see his companion, in a dressing-gown, on her knees before the domestic hearth, a candlestick beside her and a red *madras* round her head, making bravely, with her own hands the fire that was to enable her to sit down betimes to urgent pen and paper. The story represents him as having felt that the spectacle chilled his ardor and tried his taste; her appearance was unfortunate, her occupation an inconsequence, and her industry a reproof—the result of all which was a lively irritation and an early rupture.[3]

The specter of this kind of male judgment, along with the misnaming and thwarting of her needs by a culture controlled by males, has created problems for the woman writer: problems of contact with herself, problems of language and style, problems of energy and survival.

In rereading Virginia Woolf's *A Room of One's Own* (1929) for the first time in some years, I was astonished at the sense of effort, of pains taken, of dogged tentativeness, in the tone of that essay. And I recognized that tone. I had heard it often enough, in myself and in other women. It is the tone of a woman almost in touch with her anger, who is determined not to appear angry, who is *willing* herself to be calm, detached, and even charming in a roomful of men where things have been said which are attacks on her very integrity. Virginia Woolf is addressing an audience of women, but she is acutely conscious—as she always was—of being overheard by men: by Morgan and Lytton and Maynard Keynes and for that matter by her father, Leslie Stephen.[4] She drew the language out into an exacerbated thread in her

---

[3] Henry James, "Notes on Novelists," in *Selected Literary Criticism of Henry James*, Morris Shapira, ed. (London: Heinemann, 1963), pp. 157–58.

[4] A.R., 1978: This intuition of mine was corroborated when, early in 1978, I read the correspondence between Woolf and Dame Ethel Smyth (Henry W. and Albert A. Berg Collection, The New York Public Library, Astor, Lenox and Tilden Foundations); in a letter dated June 8, 1933, Woolf speaks of having kept her own personality out of *A Room of One's Own* lest she not be taken seriously: ". . . how personal, so will they say, rubbing their hands with glee, women always are; *I even hear them as I write.*" (Italics mine.)

determination to have her own sensibility yet protect it from those masculine presences. Only at rare moments in that essay do you hear the passion in her voice; she was trying to sound as cool as Jane Austen, as Olympian as Shakespeare, because that is the way the men of the culture thought a writer should sound.

No male writer has written primarily or even largely for women, or with the sense of women's criticism as a consideration when he chooses his materials, his theme, his language. But to a lesser or greater extent, every woman writer has written for men even when, like Virginia Woolf, she was supposed to be addressing women. If we have come to the point when this balance might begin to change, when women can stop being haunted, not only by "convention and propriety" but by internalized fears of being and saying themselves, then it is an extraordinary moment for the woman writer—and reader.

I have hesitated to do what I am going to do now, which is to use myself as an illustration. For one thing, it's a lot easier and less dangerous to talk about other women writers. But there is something else. Like Virginia Woolf, I am aware of the women who are not with us here because they are washing the dishes and looking after the children. Nearly fifty years after she spoke, that fact remains largely unchanged. And I am thinking also of women whom she left out of the picture altogether—women who are washing other people's dishes and caring for other people's children, not to mention women who went on the streets last night in order to feed their children. We seem to be special women here, we have liked to think of ourselves as special, and we have known that men would tolerate, even romanticize us as special, as long as our words and actions didn't threaten their privilege of tolerating or rejecting us and our work according to *their* ideas of what a special woman ought to be. An important insight of the radical women's movement has been how divisive and how ultimately destructive is this myth of the special woman, who is also the token woman. Every one of us here in this room has had great luck— we are teachers, writers, academicians; our own gifts could not have been enough, for we all know women whose gifts are buried or aborted. Our struggles can have meaning and our privileges—however precarious under patriarchy—can be justified only if they can help to change the lives of women whose gifts—and whose very being—continue to be thwarted and silenced.

My own luck was being born white and middle-class into a house full of books, with a father who encouraged me to read and write. So for about twenty years I wrote for a particular man, who criticized and praised me and made me feel I was indeed "special." The obverse side of this, of course, was that I tried for a long time to please him, or rather, not to displease him. And then of course there were other men—writers, teachers—the Man, who was not a terror or a dream but a literary master and a master in other ways less easy to acknowledge. And there were all those poems about women, written by men: it seemed to be a given that men wrote poems and women frequently inhabited them. These women were almost always beautiful, but threatened with the loss of beauty, the loss of youth—the fate worse than death. Or, they were beautiful and died young, like Lucy and Lenore. Or, the woman was like Maud Gonne, cruel and disastrously mistaken, and the poem reproached her because she had refused to become a luxury for the poet.

A lot is being said today about the influence that the myths and images of women have on all of us who are products of culture. I think it has been a peculiar confusion to the girl or woman who tries to write because she is peculiarly susceptible to language. She goes to poetry or fiction looking for her way of being in the world, since she too has been putting words and images together; she is looking eagerly for guides, maps, possibilities; and over and over in the "words' masculine persuasive force" of literature she comes up against something that negates everything she is about: she meets the image of Woman in books written by men. She finds a terror and a dream, she finds a beautiful pale face, she finds La Belle Dame Sans Merci, she finds Juliet or Tess or Salomé, but precisely what she does not find is that absorbed, drudging, puzzled, sometimes inspired creature, herself, who sits at a desk trying to put words together.

So what does she do? What did I do? I read the older women poets with their peculiar keenness and ambivalence: Sappho, Christina Rossetti, Emily Dickinson, Elinor Wylie, Edna Millay, H.D. I discovered that the woman poet most admired at the time (by men) was Marianne Moore, who was maidenly, elegant, intellectual, discreet. But even in reading these women I was looking in them for the same things I had found in the poetry of men, because I wanted women poets to be the equals of men, and to be equal was still confused with sounding the same.

I know that my style was formed first by male poets: by the men I was reading as an undergraduate—Frost, Dylan Thomas, Donne, Auden, MacNeice, Stevens, Yeats. What I chiefly learned from them was craft.[5] But poems are like dreams: in them you put what you don't know you know. Looking back at poems I wrote before I was twenty-one, I'm startled because beneath the conscious craft are glimpses of the split I even then experienced between the girl who wrote poems, who defined herself in writing poems, and the girl who was to define herself by her relationships with men. "Aunt Jennifer's Tigers" (1951), written while I was a student, looks with deliberate detachment at this split.[6]

> Aunt Jennifer's tigers stride across a screen,
> Bright topaz denizens of a world of green.
> They do not fear the men beneath the tree;
> They pace in sleek chivalric certainty.
>
> Aunt Jennifer's fingers fluttering through her wool
> Find even the ivory needle hard to pull.
> The massive weight of Uncle's wedding band
> Sits heavily upon Aunt Jennifer's hand.
>
> When Aunt is dead, her terrified hands will lie
> Still ringed with ordeals she was mastered by.
> The tigers in the panel that she made
> Will go on striding, proud and unafraid.

In writing this poem, composed and apparently cool as it is, I thought I was creating a portrait of an imaginary woman. But this woman suffers from the opposition of her imagination, worked out in tapestry, and her life-style, "ringed with ordeals she was mastered by." It was important to me that Aunt Jennifer was a person as distinct from myself as possible—distanced by the formalism of the poem, by its objective, observant tone—even by putting the woman in a different generation.

In those years formalism was part of the strategy—like asbestos gloves, it allowed me to handle materials I couldn't pick up barehanded. A later strategy was to use the persona of a man, as I did in "The Loser" (1958):

---

[5] A.R., 1978: Yet I spent months, at sixteen, memorizing and writing imitations of Millay's sonnets; and in notebooks of that period I find what are obviously attempts to imitate Dickinson's metrics and verbal compression. I knew H.D. only through anthologized lyrics; her epic poetry was not then available to me.

[6] A.R., 1978: Texts of poetry quoted herein can be found in A.R., *Poems Selected and New: 1950–1974* (New York: Norton, 1975).

A man thinks of the woman he once loved: first, after her
wedding, and then nearly a decade later.

I

I kissed you, bride and lost, and went
home from that bourgeois sacrament,
your cheek still tasting cold upon
my lips that gave you benison
with all the swagger that they knew—
as losers somehow learn to do.

Your wedding made my eyes ache; soon
the world would be worse off for one
more golden apple dropped to ground
without the least protesting sound,
and you would windfall lie, and we
forget your shimmer on the tree.

Beauty is always wasted: if
not Mignon's song sung to the deaf,
at all events to the unmoved.
A face like yours cannot be loved
long or seriously enough.
Almost, we seem to hold it off.

II

Well, you are tougher than I thought.
Now when the wash with ice hangs taut
this morning of St. Valentine,
I see you strip the squeaking line,
your body weighed against the load,
and all my groans can do no good.

Because you are still beautiful,
though squared and stiffened by the pull
of what nine windy years have done.
You have three daughters, lost a son.
I see all your intelligence
flung into that unwearied stance.

My envy is of no avail.
I turn my head and wish him well
who chafed your beauty into use
and lives forever in a house
lit by the friction of your mind.
You stagger in against the wind.

    I finished college, published my first book by a fluke, as it seemed to me, and broke off a love affair. I took a job, lived alone, went on writing, fell in love. I was young, full of energy, and the book seemed to mean that others agreed I was a poet. Because I was also determined to prove that as a woman poet I could also have what was then defined as a "full" woman's life, I plunged in my early twenties into marriage and had three children before I was thirty. There was nothing overt in the environment to warn me: these were the fifties, and in reaction to the earlier wave of feminism, middle-class women were making careers of domestic perfection, working to send their husbands through professional schools, then retiring to raise large families. People were moving out to the suburbs, technology was going to be the answer to everything, even sex; the family was in its glory. Life was extremely private; women were isolated from each other by the loyalties of marriage. I have a sense that women didn't talk to each other much in the fifties—not about their secret emptinesses, their frustrations. I went on trying to write; my second book and first child appeared in the same month. But by the time that book came out I was already dissatisfied with those poems, which seemed to me mere exercises for poems I hadn't written. The book was praised, however, for its "gracefulness"; I had a marriage and a child. If there were doubts, if there were periods of dull depression or active despairing, these could only mean that I was ungrateful, insatiable, perhaps a monster.

About the time my third child was born, I felt that I had either to consider myself a failed woman and a failed poet, or try to find some synthesis by which to understand what was happening to me. What frightened me most was the sense of drift, of being pulled along on a current which called itself my destiny, but in which I seemed to be losing touch with whoever I had been, with the girl who had experienced her own will and energy almost ecstatically at times, walking around a city or riding a train at night or typing in a student room. In a poem about my grandmother I wrote (of myself): "A young girl, thought sleeping, is certified dead" ("Halfway"). I was writing very little, partly from fatigue, that female fatigue of suppressed anger and loss of contact with my own being; partly from the discontinuity of female life with its attention to small chores, errands, work that others constantly undo, small children's constant needs. What I did write was unconvincing to me; my anger and frustration were hard to acknowledge in or out of poems because in fact I cared a great deal about my husband and my children. Trying to look back and understand that time I have tried to analyze the real nature of the conflict. Most, if not all, human lives are full of fantasy—passive daydreaming which need not be acted on. But to write poetry or fiction, or even to think well, is not to fantasize, or to put fantasies on paper. For a poem to coalesce, for a character or an action to take shape, there has to be an imaginative transformation of reality which is in no way passive. And a certain freedom of the mind is needed—freedom to press on, to enter the currents of your thought like a glider pilot, knowing that your motion can be sustained, that the buoyancy of your attention will not be suddenly snatched away. Moreover, if the imagination is to transcend and transform experience it has to question, to challenge, to conceive of alternatives, perhaps to the very life you are living at that moment. You have to be free to play around with the notion that day might be night, love might be hate; nothing can be too sacred for the imagination to turn into its opposite or to call experimentally by another name. For writing is re-naming. Now, to be maternally with small children all day in the old way, to be with a man in the old way of marriage, requires a holding-back, a putting-aside of that imaginative activity, and demands instead a kind of conservatism. I want to make it clear that I am *not* saying that in order to write well, or think well, it is necessary to become unavailable to others, or to become a devouring ego. This has been the myth of the masculine artist and thinker; and I do not accept it. But to be a female human being trying to fulfill traditional female functions in a traditional way *is* in direct conflict with the subversive function of the imagination. The word traditional is important here. There must be ways, and we will be finding out more and more about them, in which the energy of creation and the energy of relation can be united. But in those years I always felt the conflict as a failure of love in myself. I had thought I was choosing a full life: the life available to most men, in which sexuality, work, and parenthood could coexist. But I felt, at twenty-nine, guilt toward the people closest to me, and guilty toward my own being.

I wanted, then, more than anything, the one thing of which there was never enough: time to think, time to write. The fifties and early sixties were years of rapid revelations: the sit-ins and marches in the South, the Bay of Pigs, the early antiwar movement, raised large questions—questions for which the masculine world of the academy around me seemed to have expert and fluent answers. But I needed to think for myself—about pacifism and dissent and violence, about poetry and society, and about my own relationship to all these things. For about ten years I was reading in fierce snatches, scribbling in notebooks, writing poetry in fragments; I was looking desperately for clues, because if there were no clues then I thought I might be insane. I wrote in a notebook about this time:

Paralyzed by the sense that there exists a mesh of relationships—e.g., between my anger at the children, my sensual life, pacifism, sex (I mean sex in its broadest significance, not merely sexual desire)—an interconnectedness which, if I could see it, make it valid, would give me back myself, make it possible to function lucidly and passionately. Yet I grope in and out among these dark webs.

I think I began at this point to feel that politics was not something "out there" but something "in here" and of the essence of my condition.

In the late fifties I was able to write, for the first time, directly about experiencing myself as a woman. The poem was jotted in fragments during children's naps, brief hours in a library, or at 3:00 A.M. after rising with a wakeful child. I despaired of doing any continuous work at this time. Yet I began to feel that my fragments and scraps had a common consciousness and a common theme, one which I would have been very unwilling to put on paper at an earlier time because I had been taught that poetry should be "universal," which meant, of course, nonfemale. Until then I had tried very much *not* to identify myself as a female poet. Over two years I wrote a ten-part poem called "Snapshots of a Daughter-in-Law" (1958–1960), in a longer looser mode than I'd ever trusted myself with before. It was an extraordinary relief to write that poem. It strikes me now as too literary, too dependent on allusion; I hadn't found the courage yet to do without authorities, or even to use the pronoun "I"—the woman in the poem is always "she." One section of it, No. 2, concerns a woman who thinks she is going mad; she is haunted by voices telling her to resist and rebel, voices which she can hear but not obey.

2

Banging the coffee-pot into the sink
she hears the angels chiding, and looks out
past the raked gardens to the sloppy sky.
Only a week since They said: *Have no patience.*

The next time it was: *Be insatiable.*
Then: *Save yourself; others you cannot save.*
Sometimes she's let the tapstream scald her arm,
a match burn to her thumbnail,

or held her hand above the kettle's snout
right in the woolly steam. They are probably angels,
since nothing hurts her anymore, except
each morning's grit blowing into her eyes.

The poem "Orion," written five years later, is a poem of reconnection with a part of myself I had felt I was losing—the active principle, the energetic imagination, the "half-brother" whom I projected, as I had for many years, into the constellation Orion. It's no accident that the words "cold and egotistical" appear in this poem, and are applied to myself.

Far back when I went zig-zagging
through tamarack pastures
you were my genius, you
my cast-iron Viking, my helmed
lion-heart king in prison.
Years later now you're young

my fierce half-brother, staring
down from that simplified west
your breast open, your belt dragged down
by an oldfashioned thing, a sword
the last bravado you won't give over
though it weighs you down as you stride

and the stars in it are dim
and maybe have stopped burning.
But you burn, and I know it;
as I throw back my head to take you in
an old transfusion happens again:
divine astronomy is nothing to it.

Indoors I bruise and blunder,
break faith, leave ill enough
alone, a dead child born in the dark.
Night cracks up over the chimney,
pieces of time, frozen geodes
come showering down in the grate.

A man reaches behind my eyes
and finds them empty
a woman's head turns away
from my head in the mirror
children are dying my death
and eating crumbs of my life.

Pity is not your forte.
Calmly you ache up there
pinned aloft in your crow's nest,
my speechless pirate!
You take it all for granted
and when I look you back

it's with a starlike eye
shooting its cold and egotistical spear
where it can do least damage.
Breathe deep! No hurt, no pardon
out here in the cold with you
you with your back to the wall.

The choice still seemed to be between "love"—womanly, maternal love, altruistic love—a love defined and ruled by the weight of an entire culture; and egotism—a force directed by men into creation, achievement, ambition, often at the expense of others, but justifiably so. For weren't they men, and wasn't that their destiny as womanly, selfless love was ours? We know now that the alternatives are false ones—that the word "love" is itself in need of re-vision.

There is a companion poem to "Orion," written three years later, in which at last the woman in the poem and the woman writing the poem become the same person. It is called "Planetarium," and it was written after a visit to a real planetarium, where I read an account of the work of Caroline Herschel, the astronomer, who worked with her brother William, but whose name remained obscure, as his did not.

Thinking of Caroline Herschel, 1750–1848, astronomer, sister of William; and others

A woman in the shape of a monster
a monster in the shape of a woman
the skies are full of them

a woman   "in the snow
among the Clocks and instruments
or measuring the ground with poles"

in her 98 years to discover
8 comets

she whom the moon ruled
like us
levitating into the night sky
riding the polished lenses

Galaxies of women, there
doing penance for impetuousness
ribs chilled
in those spaces   of the mind

An eye,
     "virile, precise and absolutely certain"
     from the mad webs of Uranisborg

                         encountering the NOVA

every impulse of light exploding
from the core
as life flies out of us

          Tycho whispering at last
          "Let me not seem to have lived in vain"

What we see, we see
and seeing is changing

the light that shrivels a mountain
and leaves a man alive

Heartbeat of the pulsar
heart sweating through my body

The radio impulse
pouring in from Taurus

          I am bombarded yet   I stand

I have been standing all my life in the
direct path of a battery of signals
the most accurately transmitted most
untranslateable language in the universe
I am a galactic cloud so deep   so involuted that a light wave could take 15
years to travel through me   And has
taken   I am an instrument in the shape
of a woman trying to translate pulsations
into images   for the relief of the body
and the reconstruction of the mind.

In closing I want to tell you about a dream I had last summer. I dreamed I was asked to read
my poetry at a mass women's meeting, but when I began to read, what came out were the lyrics
of a blues song. I share this dream with you because it seemed to me to say something about the
problems and the future of the woman writer, and probably of women in general. The awakening
of consciousness is not like the crossing of a frontier—one step and you are in another country.
Much of woman's poetry has been of the nature of the blues song: a cry of pain, of victimization,
or a lyric of seduction.[7] And today, much poetry by women—and prose for that matter—is
charged with anger. I think we need to go through that anger, and we will betray our own reality
if we try, as Virginia Woolf was trying, for an objectivity, a detachment, that would make us sound
more like Jane Austen or Shakespeare. We know more than Jane Austen or Shakespeare knew:
more than Jane Austen because our lives are more complex, more than Shakespeare because we
know more about the lives of women—Jane Austen and Virginia Woolf included.

Both the victimization and the anger experienced by women are real, and have real
sources, everywhere in the environment, built into society, language, the structures of
thought. They will go on being tapped and explored by poets, among others. We can neither
deny them, nor will we rest there. A new generation of women poets is already working out
of the psychic energy released when women begin to move out towards what the feminist
philosopher Mary Daly has described as the "new space" on the boundaries of patriarchy.[8]
Women are speaking to and of women in these poems, out of a newly released courage to
name, to love each other, to share risk and grief and celebration.

To the eye of a feminist, the work of Western male poets now writing reveals a deep, fatal-
istic pessimism as to the possibilities of change, whether societal or personal, along with a
familiar and threadbare use of women (and nature) as redemptive on the one hand, threatening on the other; and a new tide of phallocentric sadism and overt woman-hating which
matches the sexual brutality of recent films. "Political" poetry by men remains stranded amid
the struggles for power among male groups; in condemning U.S. imperialism or the Chilean
junta the poet can claim to speak for the oppressed while remaining, as male, part of a system
of sexual oppression. The enemy is always outside the self, the struggle somewhere else. The
mood of isolation, self-pity, and self-imitation that pervades "nonpolitical" poetry suggests that
a profound change in masculine consciousness will have to precede any new male poetic—or
other—inspiration. The creative energy of patriarchy is fast running out; what remains is its
self-generating energy for destruction. As women, we have our work cut out for us.

(1971)

---

[7] A.R., 1978: When I dreamed that dream, was I wholly ignorant of the tradition of Bessie Smith and
other women's blues lyrics which transcended victimization to sing of resistance and independence?

[8] Mary Daly, *Beyond God the Father: Towards a Philosophy of Women's Liberation* (Boston: Beacon, 1973).

Chinua Achebe

(NIGERIA, 1930–)

Girls at War

The first time their paths crossed nothing happened. That was in the first heady days of war-like preparation when thousands of young men (and sometimes women too) were daily turned away from enlistment centres because far too many of them were coming forward burning with readiness to bear arms in defence of the exciting new nation.

The second time they met was at a check-point at Awka. Then the war started and was slowly moving southwards from the distant northern sector. He was driving from Onitsha to Enugu and was in a hurry. Although intellectually he approved of thorough searches at road-blocks, emotionally he was always offended whenever he had to submit to them. He would probably not admit it but the feeling people got was that if you were put through a search then you could not really be one of the big people. Generally he got away without a search by pronouncing in his deep, authoritative voice: "Reginald Nwankwo, Ministry of Justice." That almost always did it. But sometimes either through ignorance or sheer cussedness the crowd at the odd check-point would refuse to be impressed. As happened now at Awka. Two constables carrying heavy Mark 4 rifles were watching distantly from the roadside leaving the actual searching to local vigilantes.

"I am in a hurry," he said to the girl who now came up to his car. "My name is Reginald Nwankwo, Ministry of Justice."

"Good afternoon, sir. I want to see your boot."

"Oh Christ! What do you think is in the boot?"

"I don't know, sir."

He got out of the car in suppressed rage, stalked to the back, opened the boot and holding the lid up with his left hand motioned with the right as if to say: After you!

"Are you satisfied?" he demanded.

"Yes, sir. Can I see your pigeon-hole?"

"Christ Almighty!"

"Sorry to delay you, sir. But you people gave us this job to do."

"Never mind. You are damn right. It's just that I happen to be in a hurry. But never mind. That's the glove-box. Nothing there as you can see."

"All right, sir, close it." Then she opened the rear door and bent down to inspect under the seats. It was then he took the first real look at her, starting from behind. She was a beautiful girl in a breasty blue jersey, khaki jeans and canvas shoes with the new-style hair-plait which gave a girl a defiant look and which they called—for reasons of their own—"air force base"; and she looked vaguely familiar.

"I am all right, sir," she said at last meaning she was through with her task. "You don't recognize me?"

"No. Should I?"

"You gave me a lift to Enugu that time I left my school to go and join the militia."

"Ah, yes, you were the girl. I told you, didn't I, to go back to school because girls were not required in the militia. What happened?"

"They told me to go back to school or join the Red Cross."

"You see I was right. So, what are you doing now?"

"Just patching up with Civil Defence."

"Well, good luck to you. Believe me you are a great girl."

That was the day he finally believed there might be something in this talk about revolution. He had seen plenty of girls and women marching and demonstrating before now. But somehow he had never been able to give it much thought. He didn't doubt that the girls and the women took themselves seriously; they obviously did. But so did the little kids who marched up and down the streets at the time drilling with sticks and wearing their mothers' soup bowls for steel helmets. The prime joke of the time among his friends was the contingent of girls from a local secondary school marching behind a banner: WE ARE IMPREGNABLE!

But after that encounter at the Awka check-point he simply could not sneer at the girls again, nor at the talk of revolution, for he had seen it in action in that young woman whose devotion had simply and without self-righteousness convicted him of gross levity. What were her words? We are doing the work you asked us to do. She wasn't going to make an exception even for one who once did her a favour. He was sure she would have searched her own father just as rigorously.

When their paths crossed a third time, at least eighteen months later, things had got very bad. Death and starvation having long chased out the headiness of the early days, now left in some places blank resignation, in others a rock-like, even suicidal, defiance. But surprisingly enough there were many at this time also who had no other desire than to corner whatever good things were still going and to enjoy themselves to the limit. For such people a strange normalcy had returned to the world. All those nervous check-points disappeared. Girls became girls once more and boys boys. It was a tight, blockaded and desperate world but none the less a world—with some goodness and some badness and plenty of heroism which, however, happened most times far, far below the eye-level of the people in this story—in out-of-the-way refugee camps, in the damp tatters, in the hungry and bare-handed courage of the first line of fire.

Reginald Nwankwo lived in Owerri then. But that day he had gone to Nkwerri in search of relief. He had got from Caritas in Owerri a few heads of stock-fish, some tinned meat, and the dreadful American stuff called Formula Two which he felt certain was some kind of animal feed. But he always had a vague suspicion that not being a Catholic put one at a disadvantage with Caritas. So he went now to see an old friend who ran the WCC depot at Nkwerri to get other items like rice, beans and that excellent cereal commonly called Gabon gari.

He left Owerri at six in the morning so as to catch his friend at the depot where he was known never to linger beyond 8.30 for fear of air-raids. Nwankwo was very fortunate that day. The depot had received on the previous day large supplies of new stock as a result of an unusual number of plane landings a few nights earlier. As his driver loaded tins and bags and cartons into his car the starved crowds that perpetually hung around relief centres made crude, ungracious remarks like "War Can Continue!" meaning the WCC! Somebody else shouted "Irevolu!" and his friends replied "shum!" "Irevolu!" "shum!" "Isofeli?" "shum!" "Isofeli?" "Mba!"

Nwankwo was deeply embarrassed not by the jeers of this scarecrow crowd of rags and floating ribs but by the independent accusation of their wasted bodies and sunken eyes. Indeed he would probably have felt much worse had they said nothing, simply looked on in silence, as his boot was loaded with milk, and powdered egg and oats and tinned meat and stock-fish. By nature such singular good fortune in the midst of a general desolation was certain to embarrass him. But what could he do? He had a wife and four children living in the remote village of Ogbu and completely dependent on what relief he could find and send them. He couldn't abandon them to kwashiokor. The best he could do—and did do as a matter of fact—was to make sure that whenever he got sizeable supplies like now he made over some of it to his driver, Johnson, with a wife and six, or was it seven? children and a salary of ten pounds a month when gari in the market was climbing to one pound per cigarette cup. In such a situation one could do nothing at all for crowds; at best one could try to be of some use to one's immediate neighbours. That was all.

On his way back to Owerri a very attractive girl by the roadside waved for a lift. He ordered the driver to stop. Scores of pedestrians, dusty and exhausted, some military, some civil, swooped down on the car from all directions.

"No, no, no," said Nwankwo firmly. "It's the young woman I stopped for. I have a bad tyre and can only take one person. Sorry."

"My son, please," cried one old woman in despair, gripping the door-handle.

"Old woman, you want to be killed?" shouted the driver as he pulled away, shaking her off. Nwankwo had already opened a book and sunk his eyes there. For at least a mile after that he did not even look at the girl until she finding, perhaps, the silence too heavy said:

"You've saved me today. Thank you."

"Not at all. Where are you going?"

"To Owerri. You don't recognize me?"

"Oh yes, of course. What a fool I am . . . You are . . ."

"Gladys."

"That's right, the militia girl. You've changed, Gladys. You were always beautiful of course, but now you are a beauty queen. What do you do these days?"

"I am in the Fuel Directorate."

"That's wonderful."

It was wonderful, he thought, but even more it was tragic. She wore a high-tinted wig and a very expensive skirt and low-cut blouse. Her shoes, obviously from Gabon, must have cost a fortune. In short, thought Nwankwo, she had to be in the keep of some well-placed gentle-man, one of those piling up money out of the war.

"I broke my rule today to give you a lift. I never give lifts these days."

"Why?"

"How many people can you carry? It is better not to try at all. Look at that old woman."

"I thought you would carry her."

He said nothing to that and after another spell of silence Gladys thought maybe he was offended and so added: "Thank you for breaking your rule for me." She was scanning his face, turned slightly away. He smiled, turned, and tapped her on the lap.

"What are you going to Owerri to do?"

"I am going to visit my girl friend."

"Girl friend? You sure?"

"Why not? . . . If you drop me at her house you can see her. Only I pray God she hasn't gone on weekend today; it will be serious."

"Why?"

"Because if she is not at home I will sleep on the road today."

"I pray to God that she is not at home."

"Why?"

"Because if she is not at home I will offer you bed and breakfast . . . What is that?" he asked the driver who had brought the car to an abrupt stop. There was no need for an answer. The small crowd ahead was looking upwards. The three scrambled out of the car and stumbled for the bush, necks twisted in a backward search of the sky. But the alarm was false. The sky was silent and clear except for two high-flying vultures. A humorist in the crowd called them

Fighter and Bomber and everyone laughed in relief. The three climbed into their car again and continued their journey.

"It is much too early for raids," he said to Gladys, who had both her palms on her breast as though to still a thumping heart. "They rarely come before ten o'clock."

But she remained tongue-tied from her recent fright. Nwankwo saw an opportunity there and took it at once.

"Where does your friend live?"

"250 Douglas Road."

"Ah! that's the very centre of town—a terrible place. No bunkers, nothing. I won't advise you to go there before 6 p.m.; it's not safe. If you don't mind I will take you to my place where there is a good bunker and then as soon as it is safe, around six, I shall drive you to your friend. How's that?"

"It's all right," she said lifelessly. "I am so frightened of this thing. That's why I refused to work in Owerri. I don't even know who asked me to come out today."

"You'll be all right. We are used to it."

"But your family is not there with you?"

"No," he said. "Nobody has his family there. We like to say it is because of air-raids but I can assure you there is more to it. Owerri is a real swinging town and we live the life of gay bachelors."

"That is what I have heard."

"You will not just hear it; you will see it today. I shall take you to a real swinging party. A friend of mine, a Lieutenant-Colonel, is having a birthday party. He's hired the Sound Smashers to play. I'm sure you'll enjoy it."

He was immediately and thoroughly ashamed of himself. He hated the parties and frivolities to which his friends clung like drowning men. And to talk so approvingly of them because he wanted to take a girl home! And this particular girl too, who had once had such beautiful faith in the struggle and was betrayed (no doubt about it) by some man like him out for a good time. He shook his head sadly.

"What is it?" asked Gladys.

"Nothing. Just my thoughts."

They made the rest of the journey to Owerri practically in silence.

She made herself at home very quickly as if she was a regular girl friend of his. She changed into a house dress and put away her auburn wig.

"That is a lovely hair-do. Why do you hide it with a wig?"

"Thank you," she said leaving his question unanswered for a while. Then she said: "Men are funny."

"Why do you say that?"

"You are now a beauty queen," she mimicked.

"Oh, that! I mean every word of it." He pulled her to him and kissed her. She neither refused nor yielded fully, which he liked for a start. Too many girls were simply too easy those days. War sickness, some called it.

He drove off a little later to look in at the office and she busied herself in the kitchen helping his boy with lunch. It must have been literally a look-in, for he was back within half an hour, rubbing his hands and saying he could not stay away too long from his beauty queen.

As they sat down to lunch she said: "You have nothing in your fridge."

"Like what?" he asked, half-offended.

"Like meat," she replied undaunted.

"Do you still eat meat?" he challenged.

"Who am I? But other big men like you eat."

"I don't know which big men you have in mind. But they are not like me. I don't make money trading with the enemy or selling relief or . . ."

"Augusta's boy friend doesn't do that. He just gets foreign exchange."

"How does he get it? He swindles the government—that's how he gets foreign exchange, whoever he is. Who is Augusta, by the way?"

"My girl friend."

"I see."

"She gave me three dollars last time which I changed to forty-five pounds. The man gave her fifty dollars."

"Well, my dear girl, I don't traffic in foreign exchange and I don't have meat in my fridge. We are fighting a war and I happen to know that some young boys at the front drink gari and water once in three days."

"It is true," she said simply. "Monkey de work, baboon de chop."

"It is not even that; it is worse," he said, his voice beginning to shake. "People are dying every day. As we talk now somebody is dying."

"It is true," she said again.

"Plane!" screamed his boy from the kitchen.

"My mother!" screamed Gladys. As they scuttled towards the bunker of palm stems and red earth, covering their heads with their hands and stooping slightly in their flight, the entire sky was exploding with the clamour of jets and the huge noise of homemade anti-aircraft rockets.

Inside the bunker she clung to him even after the plane had gone and the guns, late to start and also to end, had all died down again.

"It was only passing," he told her, his voice a little shaky. "It didn't drop anything. From its direction I should say it was going to the war front. Perhaps our people are pressing them. That's what they always do. Whenever our boys press them, they send an SOS to the Russians and Egyptians to bring the planes." He drew a long breath.

She said nothing, just clung to him. They could hear his boy telling the servant from the next house that there were two of them and one dived like this and the other dived like that.

"I see dem well well," said the other with equal excitement. "If no to say de ting de kill porson e for sweet for eye. To God."

"Imagine!" said Gladys, finding her voice at last. She had a way, he thought, of conveying with a few words or even a single word whole layers of meaning. Now it was at once her astonishment as well as reproof, tinged perhaps with grudging admiration for people who could be so light-hearted about these bringers of death.

"Don't be so scared," he said. She moved closer and he began to kiss her and squeeze her breasts. She yielded more and more and then fully. The bunker was dark and unswept and might harbour crawling things. He thought of bringing a mat from the main house but reluctantly decided against it. Another plane might pass and send a neighbour or simply a chance passer-by crashing into them. That would be only slightly better than a certain gentleman in another air-raid who was seen in broad daylight fleeing his bedroom for his bunker starknaked pursued by a woman in a similar state!

Just as Gladys had feared, her friend was not in town. It would seem her powerful boy friend had wangled for her a flight to Libreville to shop. So her neighbours thought anyway.

"Great!" said Nwankwo as they drove away. "She will come back on an arms plane loaded with shoes, wigs, pants, bras, cosmetics and what have you, which she will then sell and make thousands of pounds. You girls are really at war, aren't you?"

She said nothing and he thought he had got through at last to her. Then suddenly she said, "That is what you men want us to do."

"Well," he said, "here is one man who doesn't want you to do that. Do you remember that girl in khaki jeans who searched me without mercy at the check-point?"

She began to laugh.

"That is the girl I want you to become again. Do you remember her? No wig. I don't even think she had any earrings . . ."

"Ah, na lie-o. I had earrings."

"All right. But you know what I mean."

"That time done pass. Now everybody want survival. They call it number six. You put your number six; I put my number six. Everything all right."

The Lieutenant-Colonel's party turned into something quite unexpected. But before it did things had been going well enough. There was goat-meat, some chicken and rice and plenty of home-made spirits. There was one fiery brand nicknamed "tracer" which indeed sent a flame down your gullet. The funny thing was looking at it in the bottle it had the innocent appearance of an orange drink. But the thing that caused the greatest stir was the bread—one little roll for each person! It was the size of a golf-ball and about the same consistency too! But it was real bread. The band was good too and there were many girls. And to improve matters even further two white Red Cross people soon arrived with a bottle of Courvoisier and a bottle of Scotch! The party gave them a standing ovation and then scrambled to get a taste. It soon turned out from his general behaviour, however, that one of the white men had probably drunk too much already. And the reason it would seem was that a pilot he knew well had been killed in a crash at the airport last night, flying in relief in awful weather.

Few people at the party had heard of the crash by then. So there was an immediate damping of the air. Some dancing couples went back to their seats and the band stopped. Then for some strange reason the drunken Red Cross man just exploded.

"Why should a man, a decent man, throw away his life. For nothing! Charley didn't need to die. Not for this stinking place. Yes, everything stinks here. Even these girls who come here all dolled up and smiling, what are they worth? Don't I know? A head of stock-fish, that's all, or one American dollar and they are ready to tumble into bed."

In the threatening silence following the explosion one of the young officers walked up to him and gave him three thundering slaps—right! left! right!—pulled him up from his seat and (there were things like tears in his eyes) shoved him outside. His friend, who had tried in vain to shut him up, followed him out and the silenced party heard them drive off. The officer who did the job returned dusting his palms.

"Fucking beast!" said he with an impressive coolness. And all the girls showed with their eyes that they rated him a man and a hero.

"Do you know him?" Gladys asked Nwankwo.

He didn't answer her. Instead he spoke generally to the party:

"The fellow was clearly drunk," he said.

"I don't care," said the officer. "It is when a man is drunk that he speaks what is on his mind."

"So you beat him for what was on his mind," said the host, "that is the spirit, Joe."

"Thank you, sir," said Joe, saluting.

"His name is Joe," Gladys and the girl on her left said in unison, turning to each other.

At the same time Nwankwo and a friend on the other side of him were saying quietly, very quietly, that although the man had been rude and offensive what he had said about the girls was unfortunately the bitter truth, only he was the wrong man to say it.

When the dancing resumed Captain Joe came to Gladys for a dance. She sprang to her feet even before the word was out of his mouth. Then she remembered immediately and turned round to take permission from Nwankwo. At the same time the Captain also turned to him and said, "Excuse me."

"Go ahead," said Nwankwo, looking somewhere between the two.

It was a long dance and he followed them with his eyes without appearing to do so. Occasionally a relief plane passed overhead and somebody immediately switched off the lights saying it might be the Intruder. But it was only an excuse to dance in the dark and make the girls giggle, for the sound of the Intruder was well known.

Gladys came back feeling very self-conscious and asked Nwankwo to dance with her. But he wouldn't. "Don't bother about me," he said, "I am enjoying myself perfectly sitting here and watching those of you who dance."

"Then let's go," she said, "if you won't dance."

"But I never dance, believe me. So please enjoy yourself."

She danced next with the Lieutenant-Colonel and again with Captain Joe, and then Nwankwo agreed to take her home.

"I am sorry. I didn't dance," he said as they drove away.

"But I swore never to dance as long as this war lasts."

She said nothing.

"When I think of somebody like that pilot who got killed last night. And he had no hand whatever in the quarrel. All his concern was to bring us food . . ."

"I hope that his friend is not like him," said Gladys.

"The man was just upset by his friend's death. But what I am saying is that with people like that getting killed and our own boys suffering and dying at the war fronts I don't see why we should sit around throwing parties and dancing."

"You took me there," said she in final revolt. "They are your friends. I don't know them before."

"Look, my dear, I am not blaming you. I am merely telling you why I personally refuse to dance. Anyway, let's change the subject . . . Do you still say you want to go back tomorrow? My driver can take you early enough on Monday morning for you to go to work. No? All right, just as you wish. You are the boss."

She gave him a shock by the readiness with which she followed him to bed and by her language.

"You want to shell?" she asked. And without waiting for an answer said, "Go ahead but don't pour in troops!"

He didn't want to pour in troops either and so it was all right. But she wanted visual assurance and so he showed her.

One of the ingenious economies taught by the war was that a rubber condom could be used over and over again. All you had to do was wash it out, dry it and shake a lot of talcum powder over it to prevent its sticking; and it was as good as new. It had to be the real British thing, though, not some of the cheap stuff they brought in from Lisbon which was about as strong as a dry cocoyam leaf in the harmattan.

He had his pleasure but wrote the girl off. He might just as well have slept with a prostitute, he thought. It was clear as daylight to him now that she was kept by some army officer. What a terrible transformation in the short period of less than two years! Wasn't it a miracle that she still had memories of the other life, that she even remembered her name? If the affair of the drunken Red Cross man should happen again now, he said to himself, he would stand up beside the fellow and tell the party that here was a man of truth. What a terrible fate to befall a whole generation! The mothers of tomorrow!

By morning he was feeling a little better and more generous in his judgements. Gladys, he thought, was just a mirror reflecting a society that had gone completely rotten and maggotty at the centre. The mirror itself was intact; a lot of smudge but no more. All that was needed was a clean duster. "I have a duty to her," he told himself, "the little girl that once revealed to me our situation. Now she is in danger, under some terrible influence."

He wanted to get to the bottom of this deadly influence. It was clearly not just her good-time girl friend, Augusta, or whatever her name was. There must be some man at the centre of it, perhaps one of these heartless attack-traders who traffic in foreign currencies and make their hundreds of thousands by sending young men to hazard their lives bartering looted goods for cigarettes behind enemy lines, or one of those contractors who receive piles of money daily for food they never deliver to the army. Or perhaps some vulgar and cowardly army officer full of filthy barrack talk and fictitious stories of heroism. He decided he had to find out. Last night he had thought of sending his driver alone to take her home. But no, he must go and see for himself where she lived. Something was bound to reveal itself there. Something on which he could anchor his saving operation. As he prepared for the trip his feeling towards her softened with every passing minute. He assembled for her half of the food he had received at the relief centre the day before. Difficult as things were, he thought, a girl who had something to eat would be spared, not all, but some of the temptation. He would arrange with his friend at the WCC to deliver something to her every fortnight.

Tears came to Gladys's eyes when she saw the gifts. Nwankwo didn't have too much cash on him but he got together twenty pounds and handed it over to her.

"I don't have foreign exchange, and I know this won't go far at all, but . . ."

She just came and threw herself at him, sobbing. He kissed her lips and eyes and mumbled something about victims of circumstance, which went over her head. In deference to him, he thought with exultation, she had put away her high-tinted wig in her bag.

"I want you to promise me something," he said.

"What?"

"Never use that expression about shelling again."

She smiled with tears in her eyes. "You don't like it? That's what all the girls call it."

"Well, you are different from all the girls. Will you promise?"

"O.K."

Naturally their departure had become a little delayed. And when they got into the car it refused to start. After poking around the engine the driver decided that the battery was flat. Nwankwo was aghast. He had that very week paid thirty-four pounds to change two of the cells and the mechanic who performed it had promised him six months' service. A new battery, which was then running at two hundred and fifty pounds, was simply out of the question. The driver must have been careless with something, he thought.

"It must be because of last night," said the driver.

"What happened last night?" asked Nwankwo sharply, wondering what insolence was on the way. But none was intended.

"Because we use the head light."

"Am I supposed not to use my light then? Go and get some people and try pushing it." He got out again with Gladys and returned to the house while the driver went over to neighbouring houses to seek the help of other servants.

After at least half an hour of pushing it up and down the street, and a lot of noisy advice from the pushers, the car finally spluttered to life shooting out enormous clouds of black smoke from the exhaust.

It was eight-thirty by his watch when they set out. A few miles away a disabled soldier waved for a lift.

"Stop!" screamed Nwankwo. The driver jammed his foot on the brakes and then turned his head towards his master in bewilderment.

"Don't you see the soldier waving? Reverse and pick him up!"

"Sorry, sir," said the driver. "I don't know Master wan to pick him."

"If you don't know you should ask. Reverse back."

The soldier, a mere boy, in filthy khaki drenched in sweat lacked his right leg from the knee down. He seemed not only grateful that a car should stop for him but greatly surprised. He first handed in his crude wooden crutches which the driver arranged between the two front seats, then painfully he levered himself in.

"Thank sir," he said turning his neck to look at the back and completely out of breath.

"I am very grateful, Madame, thank you."

"The pleasure is ours," said Nwankwo. "Where did you get your wound?"

"At Azumini, sir. On tenth of January."

"Never mind. Everything will be all right. We are proud of you boys and will make sure you receive your due reward when it is all over."

"I pray God, sir."

They drove on in silence for the next half-hour or so. Then as the car sped down a slope towards a bridge somebody screamed—perhaps the driver, perhaps the soldier—"They have come!" The screech of the brakes merged into the scream and the shattering of the sky over-head. The doors flew open even before the car had come to a stop and they were fleeing blindly to the bush. Gladys was a little ahead of Nwankwo when they heard through the drowning tumult the soldier's voice crying: "Please come and open for me!" Vaguely he saw Gladys stop; he pushed past her shouting to her at the same time to come on. Then a high whistle descended like a spear through the chaos and exploded in a vast noise and motion that smashed up everything. A tree he had embraced flung him away through the bush. Then another terrible whistle starting high up and ending again in a monumental crash of the world; and then another, and Nwankwo heard no more.

He woke up to human noises and weeping and the smell and smoke of a charred world. He dragged himself up and staggered towards the source of the sounds.

From afar he saw his driver running towards him in tears and blood. He saw the remains of his car smoking and the entangled remains of the girl and the soldier. And he let out a piercing cry and fell down again.

(1972)

Bruce Dawe

(AUSTRALIA, 1930–)

Life-Cycle

For Big Jim Phelan

When children are born in Victoria
they are wrapped in the club-colours, laid in beribboned cots,
having already begun a lifetime's barracking.

Carn, they cry, Carn . . . feebly at first
5   while parents playfully tussle with them
for possession of a rusk: Ah, he's a little Tiger! (And they are . . .)

Hoisted shoulder-high at their first League game
they are like innocent monsters who have been years swimming
towards the daylight's roaring empyrean

10   Until, now, hearts shrapnelled with rapture,
they break surface and are forever lost,
their minds rippling out like streamers

In the pure flood of sound, they are scarfed with light, a voice
like the voice of God booms from the stands
15   Ooohh you bludger and the covenant is sealed.

Hot pies and potato-crisps they will eat,
they will forswear the Demons, cling to the Saints
and behold their team going up the ladder into Heaven,

And the tides of life will be the tides of the home-team's fortunes
20   —the reckless proposal after the one-point win,
the wedding and honeymoon after the grand-final . . .

They will not grow old as those from more northern States grow old,
for them it will always be three-quarter-time
with the scores level and the wind advantage in the final term,

25   That passion persisting, like a race-memory, through the welter of seasons,
enabling old-timers by boundary-fences to dream of resurgent lions
and centaur-figures from the past to replenish continually the present,

So that mythology may be perpetually renewed
and Chicken Smallhorn return like the maize-god
30   in a thousand shapes, the dancers changing

But the dance forever the same—the elderly still
loyally crying Carn . . . Carn . . . (if feebly) unto the very end,
having seen in the six-foot recruit from Eaglehawk their hope of salvation.

(1968)

Ted Hughes

(ENGLAND, 1930–1998)

The Thought-Fox

I imagine this midnight moment's forest:
Something else is alive
Beside the clock's loneliness
And this blank page where my fingers move.

5   Through the window I see no star:
Something more near
Though deeper within darkness
Is entering the loneliness:

Cold, delicately as the dark snow
10   A fox's nose touches twig, leaf;
Two eyes serve a movement, that now
And again now, and now, and now

Sets neat prints into the snow
Between trees, and warily a lame
15   hadow lags by stump and in hollow
Of a body that is bold to come

Across clearings, an eye,
A widening deepening greenness,
Brilliantly, concentratedly,
20   Coming about its own business

Till, with a sudden sharp hot stink of fox
It enters the dark hole of the head.
The window is starless still; the clock ticks,
The page is printed.

(1957)

Wodwo

What am I? Nosing here, turning leaves over
Following a faint stain on the air to the river's edge
I enter water. What am I to split
The glassy grain of water looking upward I see the bed
5   Of the river above me upside down very clear
What am I doing here in mid-air? Why do I find
this frog so interesting as I inspect its most secret
interior and make it my own? Do these weeds

know me and name me to each other have they
10   seen me before, do I fit in their world? I seem
separate from the ground and not rooted but dropped
out of nothing casually I've no threads
fastening me to anything I can go anywhere
I seem to have been given the freedom
15   of this place what am I then? And picking
bits of bark off this rotten stump gives me
no pleasure and it's no use so why do I do it
me and doing that have coincided very queerly
But what shall I be called am I the first
20   have I an owner what shape am I what
shape am I am I huge if I go
to the end on this way past these trees and past these trees
till I get tired that's touching one wall of me
for the moment if I sit still how everything
25   stops to watch me I suppose I am the exact centre
but there's all this what is it roots
roots roots roots and here's the water
again very queer but I'll go on looking

(1967)

Night Arrival of Sea-Trout

Honeysuckle hanging her fangs.
Foxglove rearing her open belly.
Dogrose touching the membrane.

Through the dew's mist, the oak's mass
5   Comes plunging, tossing dark antlers.

Then a shattering
Of the river's hole, where something leaps out—

An upside-down, buried heaven
Snarls, moon-mouthed, and shivers.
10   Summer dripping stars, biting at the nape.
Lobworms coupling in saliva
Earth singing under her breath.

And out in the hard corn a horned god
Running and leaping
15   With a bat in his drum.

(1983)

Derek Walcott

(ST. LUCIA/TRINIDAD, 1930–)

A Far Cry from Africa

A wind is ruffling the tawny pelt
Of Africa. Kikuyu, quick as flies
Batten upon the bloodstreams of the veldt.
Corpses are scattered through a paradise.
5   But still the worm, colonel of carrion, cries:
'Waste no compassion on these separate dead'
Statistics justify and scholars seize
The salients of colonial policy.
What is that to the white child hacked in bed?
10   To savages, expendable as Jews?

Threshed out by beaters, the long rushes break
In a white dust of ibises whose cries
Have wheeled since civilization's dawn
From the parched river or beast-teeming plain;
15   The violence of beast on beast is read
As natural law, but upright man
Seeks his divinity with inflicting pain.

Delirious as these worried beasts, his wars
Dance to the tightened carcass of a drum,
20   While he calls courage still, that native dread
Of the white peace contracted by the dead.

Again brutish necessity wipes its hands
Upon the napkin of a dirty cause, again
A waste of our compassion, as with Spain.
25   The gorilla wrestles with the superman.

I who am poisoned with the blood of both,
Where shall I turn, divided to the vein?
I who have cursed
The drunken officer of British rule, how choose
30   Between this Africa and the English tongue I love?
Betray them both, or give back what they give?
How can I face such slaughter and be cool?
How can I turn from Africa and live?

(1962)

Gros-Ilet

From this village, soaked like a grey rag in salt water,
a language came, garnished with conch shells,
with a suspicion of berries in its armpits
and elbows like flexible oars. Every ceremony commenced
5   in the troughs, in the middens, at the daybreak and the daydark funerals
attended by crabs. The odours were fortified
by the sea. The anchor of the islands went deep
but was always clear in the sand. Many a shark,
and often the ray, whose wings are as wide as sails,
10 rose with insomniac stare from the wavering corals,
and a fisherman held up a catfish like a tendrilled head.
And the night with its certain, inextinguishable candles
was like All Souls' Night upside down, the way a bat keeps
its own view of the world. So their eyes looked down, amused,
15 on us, and found we were walking strangely,
and wondered about our sense of balance, how we slept
as if we were dead, how we confused
dreams with ordinary things like nails, or roses,
how rocks aged quickly with moss,
20 the sea made furrows that had nothing to do with time,
and the sand started whirlwinds with nothing to do at all,
and the shadows answered to the sun alone.
And sometimes, like the top of an old tire,
the black rim of a porpoise. Elpenor, you
25 who broke your arse, drunk, tumbling down the bulkhead,
and the steersman who sails, like the ray under the breathing waves,
keep moving, there is nothing here for you.
There are different candles and customs here, the dead
are different. Different shells guard their graves.
30 There are distinctions beyond the paradise
of our horizon. This is not the grape-purple Aegean.
There is no wine here, no cheese, the almonds are green,
the sea grapes bitter, the language is that of slaves.

(1987)

Jay Macpherson

(CANADA, 1931–)

The Boatman

You might suppose it easy
For a maker not too lazy
To convert the gentle reader to an Ark:
But it takes a willing pupil
5   To admit both gnat and camel
—Quite an eyeful, all the crew that must embark.

After me when comes the deluge
And you're looking round for refuge
From God's anger pouring down in gush and spout,
10   Then you take the tender creature
—You remember, that's the reader—
And you pull him through his navel inside out.

That's to get his beasts outside him,
For they've got to come aboard him,
15   As the best directions have it, two by two.
When you've taken all their tickets
And you've marched them through his sockets,
Let the tempest bust Creation: heed not you.

For you're riding high and mighty
20   In a gale that's pushing ninety
With a solid bottom under you—that's his.
Fellow flesh affords a rampart,
And you've got along for comfort
All the world there ever shall be, was, and is.

(1957)

The Fisherman

The world was first a private park
Until the angel, after dark,
Scattered afar to wests and easts
The lovers and the friendly beasts.

5   And later still a home-made boat
Contained Creation set afloat,
No rift nor leak that might betray
The creatures to a hostile day.

But now beside the midnight lake
10   One single fisher sits awake
And casts and fights and hauls to land
A myriad forms upon the sand.

Old Adam on the naming-day
Blessed each and let it slip away:
15 The fisher of the fallen mind
Sees no occasion to be kind,

But on his catch proceeds to sup;
Then bends, and at one slurp sucks up
The lake and all that therein is
20 To slake that hungry gut of his,

Then whistling makes for home and bed
As the last morning breaks in red;
But God the Lord with patient grin
Lets down his hook and hoicks him in.

(1957)

Alice Munro

(CANADA, 1931–)

Boys and Girls

My father was a fox farmer. That is, he raised silver foxes, in pens; and in the fall and early winter, when their fur was prime, he killed them and skinned them and sold their pelts to the Hudson's Bay Company or the Montreal Fur Traders. These companies supplied us with heroic calendars to hang, one on each side of the kitchen door. Against a background of cold blue sky and black pine forests and treacherous northern rivers, plumed adventurers planted the flags of England or of France; magnificent savages bent their backs to the portage.

For several weeks before Christmas, my father worked after supper in the cellar of our house. The cellar was white-washed, and lit by a hundred-watt bulb over the worktable. My brother Laird and I sat on the top step and watched. My father removed the pelt inside-out from the body of the fox, which looked surprisingly small, mean and rat-like, deprived of its arrogant weight of fur. The naked, slippery bodies were collected in a sack and buried at the dump. One time the hired man, Henry Bailey, had taken a swipe at me with this sack, saying, "Christmas present!" My mother thought that was not funny. In fact she disliked the whole pelting operation—that was what the killing, skinning, and preparation of the furs was called—and wished it did not have to take place in the house. There was the smell. After the pelt had been stretched inside-out on a long board my father scraped away delicately, removing the little clotted webs of blood vessels, the bubbles of fat; the smell of blood and animal fat, with the strong primitive odour of the fox itself, penetrated all parts of the house. I found it reassuringly seasonal, like the smell of oranges and pine needles.

"Henry Bailey suffered from bronchial troubles. He would cough and cough until his narrow face turned scarlet, and his light blue, derisive eyes filled up with tears; then he took the lid off the stove, and, standing well back, shot out a great clot of phlegm—hsss—straight into the heart of the flames. We admired him for this performance and for his ability to make his stomach growl at will, and for his laughter, which was full of high whistlings and gurglings and involved the whole faulty machinery of his chest. It was sometimes hard to tell what he was laughing at, and always possible that it might be us.

After we had been sent to bed we could still smell fox and still hear Henry's laugh, but these things, reminders of the warm, safe, brightly lit downstairs world, seemed lost and diminished, floating on the stale cold air upstairs. We were afraid at night in the winter. We were not afraid of *outside* though this was the time of year when snowdrifts curled around our house like sleeping whales and the wind harassed us all night, coming up from the buried fields, the frozen swamp, with its old bugbear chorus of threats and misery. We were afraid of *inside*, the room where we slept. At this time the upstairs of our house was not finished. A brick chimney went up one wall. In the middle of the floor was a square hole, with a wooden railing around it; that was where the stairs came up. On the other side of the stairwell were the things that nobody had any use for any more—a soldiery roll of linoleum, standing on end, a wicker baby carriage, a fern basket, china jugs and basins with cracks in them, a picture of the Battle of Balaclava, very sad to look at. I had told Laird, as soon as he was old enough to understand such things, that bats and skeletons lived over there; whenever a man escaped from the county jail, twenty miles away, I imagined that he had somehow let himself in the window and was hiding behind the linoleum. But we had rules to keep us safe. When the light was on, we were safe as long as we did not step off the square of worn carpet which defined our bedroom-space; when the light was off no place was safe but the beds themselves. I had to turn out the light kneeling on the end of my bed, and stretching as far as I could to reach the cord.

In the dark we lay on our beds, our narrow life rafts, and fixed our eyes on the faint light coming up the stairwell, and sang songs. Laird sang "Jingle Bells," which he would sing any time, whether it was Christmas or not, and I sang "Danny Boy." I loved the sound of my own voice, frail and supplicating, rising in the dark. We could make out the tall frosted shapes of the windows now, gloomy and white. When I came to the part, *When I am dead, as dead I well may be*—a fit of shivering caused not by the cold sheets but by pleasurable emotion almost silenced me. *You'll kneel and say, an Ave there above me*—What was an Ave? Every day I forgot to find out.

Laird went straight from singing to sleep. I could hear his long, satisfied, bubbly breaths. Now for the time that remained to me, the most perfectly private and perhaps the best time of the whole day, I arranged myself tightly under the covers and went on with one of the stories I was telling myself from night to night. These stories were about myself, when I had grown a little older; they took place in a world that was recognizably mine, yet one that presented opportunities for courage, boldness and self-sacrifice, as mine never did. I rescued people from a bombed building (it discouraged me that the real war had gone on so far away from Jubilee). I shot two rabid wolves who were menacing the schoolyard (the teachers cowered terrified at my back). I rode a fine horse spiritedly down the main street of Jubilee, acknowledging the townspeople's gratitude for some yet-to-be-worked-out piece of heroism (nobody ever rode a horse there, except King Billy in the Orangemen's Day parade). There was always riding and shooting in these stories, though I had only been on a horse twice— bareback because we did not own a saddle—and the second time I had slid right around and dropped under the horse's feet; it had stepped placidly over me. I really was learning to shoot, but I could not hit anything yet, not even tin cans on fence posts.

Alive, the foxes inhabited a world my father made for them. It was surrounded by a high guard fence, like a medieval town, with a gate that was padlocked at night. Along the streets of this town were ranged large, sturdy pens. Each of them had a real door that a man could go through, a wooden ramp along the wire, for the foxes to run up and down on, and a kennel—something like a clothes chest with airholes—where they slept and stayed in winter and had their young. There were feeding and watering dishes attached to the wire in such a way that they could be emptied and cleaned from the outside. The dishes were made of old tin cans, and the ramps and kennels of odds and ends of old lumber. Everything was tidy and ingenious; my father was tirelessly inventive and his favourite book in the world was *Robinson Crusoe*. He had fitted a tin drum on a wheelbarrow, for bringing water down to the pens. This was my job in summer, when the foxes had to have water twice a day. Between nine and ten o'clock in the morning, and again after supper, I filled the drum at the pump and trundled it down through the barnyard to the pens, where I parked it, and filled my watering can and went along the streets. Laird came too, with his little cream and green gardening can, filled too full and knocking against his legs and slopping water on his canvas shoes. I had the real watering can, my father's, though I could only carry it three-quarters full.

The foxes all had names, which were printed on a tin plate and hung beside their doors. They were not named when they were born, but when they survived the first year's pelting and were added to the breeding stock. Those my father had named were called names like Prince, Bob, Wally and Betty. Those I had named were called Star or Turk, or Maureen or Diana. Laird named one Maud after a hired girl we had when he was little, one Harold after a boy at school, and one Mexico, he did not say why.

Naming them did not make pets out of them, or anything like it. Nobody but my father ever went into the pens, and he had twice had blood-poisoning from bites. When I was bringing them their water they prowled up and down on the paths they had made inside their pens, barking seldom—they saved that for nighttime, when they might get up a chorus of community frenzy—but always watching me, their eyes burning, clear gold, in their pointed, malevolent faces. They were beautiful for their delicate legs and heavy, aristocratic tails and the bright fur sprinkled on dark down their backs—which gave them their name—but especially for their faces, drawn exquisitely sharp in pure hostility, and their golden eyes.

Besides carrying water I helped my father when he cut the long grass, and the lamb's quarter and flowering money-musk, that grew between the pens. He cut with the scythe and I raked into piles. Then he took a pitchfork and threw fresh-cut grass all over the top of the pens, to keep the foxes cooler and shade their coats, which were browned by too much sun. My father did not talk to me unless it was about the job we were doing. In this he was quite different from my mother, who, if she was feeling cheerful, would tell me all sorts of things—the name of a dog she had had when she was a little girl, the names of boys she had gone out with later on when she was grown up, and what certain dresses of hers had looked like—she could not imagine now what had become of them. Whatever thoughts and stories my father had were private, and I was shy of him and would never ask him questions. Nevertheless I worked willingly under his eyes, and with a feeling of pride. One time a feed salesman came down into the pens to talk to him and my father said, "Like to have you meet my new hired man." I turned away and raked furiously, red in the face with pleasure.

"Could of fooled me," said the salesman. "I thought it was only a girl."

After the grass was cut, it seemed suddenly much later in the year. I walked on stubble in the earlier evening, aware of the reddening skies, the entering silences, of fall. When I wheeled the tank out of the gate and put the padlock on, it was almost dark. One night at this time I saw my mother and father standing talking on the little rise of ground we called the gangway, in front of the barn. My father had just come from the meathouse; he had his stiff bloody apron on, and a pail of cut-up meat in his hand.

It was an odd thing to see my mother down at the barn. She did not often come out of the house unless it was to do something—hang out the wash or dig potatoes in the garden. She looked out of place, with her bare lumpy legs, not touched by the sun, her apron still on and damp across the stomach from the supper dishes. Her hair was tied up in a kerchief, wisps of it falling out. She would tie her hair up like this in the morning, saying she did not have time to do it properly, and it would stay tied up all day. It was true, too; she really did not have time. These days our back porch was piled with baskets of peaches and grapes and pears, bought in town, and onions and tomatoes and cucumbers grown at home, all waiting to be made into jelly and jam and preserves, pickles and chili sauce. In the kitchen there was a fire in the stove all day, jars clinked in boiling water, sometimes a cheesecloth bag was strung on a pole between two chairs, straining blue-black grape pulp for jelly. I was given jobs to do and I would sit at the table peeling peaches that had been soaked in the hot water, or cutting up onions, my eyes smarting and streaming. As soon as I was done I ran out of the house, trying to get out of earshot before my mother thought of what she wanted me to do next. I hated the hot dark kitchen in summer, the green blinds and the flypapers, the same old oilcloth table and wavy mirror and bumpy linoleum. My mother was too tired and preoccupied to talk to me, she had no heart to tell about the Normal School Graduation Dance; sweat trickled over her face and she was always counting under her breath, pointing at jars, dumping cups of sugar. It seemed to me that work in the house was endless, dreary and peculiarly depressing; work done out of doors, and in my father's service, was ritualistically important.

I wheeled the tank up to the barn, where it was kept, and I heard my mother saying, "Wait till Laird gets a little bigger, then you'll have a real help."

What my father said I did not hear. I was pleased by the way he stood listening, politely as he would to a salesman or a stranger, but with an air of wanting to get on with his real work. I felt my mother had no business down here and I wanted him to feel the same way. What did she mean about Laird? He was no help to anybody. Where was he now? Swinging himself sick on the swing, going around in circles, or trying to catch caterpillars. He never once stayed with me till I was finished.

"And then I can use her more in the house," I heard my mother say. She had a dead-quiet, regretful way of talking about me that always made me uneasy. "I just get my back turned and she runs off. It's not like I had a girl in the family at all."

I went and sat on a feed bag in the corner of the barn, not wanting to appear when this conversation was going on. My mother, I felt, was not to be trusted. She was kinder than my father and more easily fooled, but you could not depend on her, and the real reasons for the things she said and did were not to be known. She loved me, and she sat up late at night making a dress of the difficult style I wanted, for me to wear when school started, but she was also my enemy. She was always plotting. She was plotting now to get me to stay in the house more, although she knew I hated it (*because* she knew I hated it) and keep me from working for my father. It seemed to me she would do this simply out of perversity, and to try her power. It did not occur to me that she could be lonely, or jealous. No grown-up could be; they were too fortunate. I sat and kicked my heels monotonously against a feedbag, raising dust, and did not come out till she was gone.

At any rate, I did not expect my father to pay any attention to what she said. Who could imagine Laird doing my work—Laird remembering the padlock and cleaning out the watering-dishes with a leaf on the end of a stick, or even wheeling the tank without it tumbling over? It showed how little my mother knew about the way things really were.

I have forgotten to say what the foxes were fed. My father's bloody apron reminded me. They were fed horsemeat. At this time most farmers still kept horses, and when a horse got too old to work, or broke a leg or got down and would not get up, as they sometimes did, the owner would call my father, and he and Henry went out to the farm in the truck. Usually they shot and butchered the horse there, paying the farmer from five to twelve dollars. If they had already too much meat on hand, they would bring the horse back alive, and keep it for a few days or weeks in our stable, until the meat was needed. After the war the farmers were buying tractors and gradually getting rid of horses altogether, so it sometimes happened that we got a good healthy horse, that there was just no use for any more. If this happened in the winter we might keep the horse in our stable till spring, for we had plenty of hay and if there was a lot of snow—and the plow did not always get our road cleared—it was convenient to be able to go to town with a horse and cutter.

The winter I was eleven years old we had two horses in the stable. We did not know what names they had had before, so we called them Mack and Flora. Mack was an old black workhorse, sooty and indifferent. Flora was a sorrel mare, a driver. We took them both out in the cutter. Mack was slow and easy to handle. Flora was given to fits of violent alarm, veering at cars and even at other horses, but we loved her speed and high-stepping, her general air of gallantry and abandon. On Saturdays we went down to the stable and as soon as we opened the door on its cosy, animal-smelling darkness Flora threw up her head, rolled her eyes, whinnied despairingly and pulled herself through a crisis of nerves on the spot. It was not safe to go into her stall; she would kick.

This winter also I began to hear a great deal more on the theme my mother had sounded when she had been talking in front of the barn. I no longer felt safe. It seemed that in the minds of the people around me there was a steady undercurrent of thought, not to be deflected, on this one subject. The word *girl* had formerly seemed to me innocent and unburdened, like the word *child*; now it appeared that it was no such thing. A girl was not, as I had supposed, simply what I was; it was what I had to become. It was a definition, always touched with emphasis, with reproach and disappointment. Also it was a joke on me.

Once Laird and I were fighting, and for the first time ever I had to use all my strength against him; even so, he caught and pinned my arm for a moment, really hurting me. Henry saw this, and laughed, saying, "Oh, that there Laird's gonna show you, one of these days!" Laird was getting a lot bigger. But I was getting bigger too.

My grandmother came to stay with us for a few weeks and I heard other things. "Girls don't slam doors like that." "Girls keep their knees together when they sit down." And worse still, when I asked some questions, "That's none of girls' business." I continued to slam the doors and sit as awkwardly as possible, thinking that by such measures I kept myself free.

When spring came, the horses were let out in the barnyard. Mack stood against the barn wall trying to scratch his neck and haunches, but Flora trotted up and down and reared at the fences, clattering her hooves against the rails. Snow drifts dwindled quickly, revealing the hard grey and brown earth, the familiar rise and fall of the ground, plain and bare after the fantastic landscape of winter. There was a great feeling of opening-out, of release. We just wore rubbers now, over our shoes; our feet felt ridiculously light. One Saturday we went out to the stable and found all the doors open, letting in the unaccustomed sunlight and fresh air. Henry was there, just idling around looking at his collection of calendars which were tacked up behind the stalls in a part of the stable my mother had probably never seen.

"Come to say goodbye to your old friend Mack?" Henry said. "Here, you give him a taste of oats." He poured some oats into Laird's cupped hands and Laird went to feed Mack. Mack's teeth were in bad shape. He ate very slowly, patiently shifting the oats around in his mouth, trying to find a stump of a molar to grind it on. "Poor old Mack," said Henry mournfully. "When a horse's teeth's gone, he's gone. That's about the way."

"Are you going to shoot him today?" I said. Mack and Flora had been in the stable so long I had almost forgotten they were going to be shot.

Henry didn't answer me. Instead he started to sing in a high, trembly, mocking-sorrowful voice, *Oh there's no more work, for poor Uncle Ned, he's gone where the good darkies go*. Mack's thick, blackish tongue worked diligently at Laird's hand. I went out before the song was ended and sat down on the gangway.

I had never seen them shoot a horse, but I knew where it was done. Last summer Laird and I had come upon a horse's entrails before they were buried. We had thought it was a big black snake, coiled up in the sun. That was around in the field that ran up beside the barn. I thought that if we went inside the barn, and found a wide crack or a knothole to look through, we would be able to see them do it. It was not something I wanted to see; just the same, if a thing really happened, it was better to see it, and know.

My father came down from the house, carrying the gun.

"What are you doing here?" he said.

"Nothing."

"Go on up and play around the house."

He sent Laird out of the stable. I said to Laird, "Do you want to see them shoot Mack?" and without waiting for an answer led him around to the front door of the barn, opened it carefully, and went in. "Be quiet or they'll hear us," I said. We could hear Henry and my father talking in the stable, then the heavy, shuffling steps of Mack being backed out of his stall.

In the loft it was cold and dark. Thin, crisscrossed beams of sunlight fell through the cracks. The hay was low. It was a rolling country, hills and hollows, slipping under our feet. About four feet up was a beam going around the walls. We piled hay up in one corner and I boosted Laird up and hoisted myself. The beam was not very wide; we crept along it with our hands flat on the barn walls. There were plenty of knotholes, and I found one that gave me the view I wanted—a corner of the barnyard, the gate, part of the field. Laird did not have a knothole and began to complain.

I showed him a widened crack between two boards. "Be quiet and wait. If they hear you you'll get us in trouble."

My father came in sight carrying the gun. Henry was leading Mack by the halter. He dropped it and took out his cigarette papers and tobacco; he rolled cigarettes for my father and himself. While this was going on Mack nosed around in the old, dead grass along the fence. Then my father opened the gate and they took Mack through. Henry led Mack away from the path to a patch of ground and they talked together, not loud enough for us to hear. Mack again began searching for a mouthful of fresh grass, which was not to be found. My father walked away in a straight line, and stopped short at a distance which seemed to suit him. Henry was walking away from Mack too, but sideways, still negligently holding on to the halter. My father raised the gun and Mack looked up as if he had noticed something and my father shot him.

Mack did not collapse at once but swayed, lurched sideways and fell, first on his side; then he rolled over on his back and, amazingly, kicked his legs for a few seconds in the air. At this Henry laughed, as if Mack had done a trick for him. Laird, who had drawn a long, groaning breath of surprise when the shot was fired, said out loud, "He's not dead." And it seemed to me it might be true. But his legs stopped, he rolled on his side again, his muscles quivered and sank. The two men walked over and looked at him in a businesslike way; they bent down and examined his forehead where the bullet had gone in, and now I saw his blood on the brown grass.

"Now they just skin him and cut him up," I said. "Let's go." My legs were a little shaky and I jumped gratefully down into the hay. "Now you've seen how they shoot a horse," I said in a congratulatory way, as if I had seen it many times before. "Let's see if any barn cat's had kittens in the hay." Laird jumped. He seemed young and obedient again. Suddenly I remembered how, when he was little, I had brought him into the barn and told him to climb the ladder to the top beam. That was in the spring, too, when the hay was low. I had done it out of a need for excitement, a desire for something to happen so that I could tell about it. He was wearing a little bulky brown and white checked coat, made down from one of mine. He went all the way up, just as I told him, and sat down on the top beam with the hay far below him on one side, and the barn floor and some old machinery on the other. Then I ran screaming to my father, "Laird's up on the top beam!" My father came, my mother came, my father went up the ladder talking very quietly and brought Laird down under his arm, at which my mother leaned against the ladder and began to cry. They said to me, "Why weren't you watching him?" but nobody ever knew the truth. Laird did not know enough to tell. But whenever I saw the brown and white checked coat hanging in the closet, or at the bottom of the rag bag, which was where it ended up, I felt a weight in my stomach, the sadness of unexorcized guilt.

I looked at Laird who did not even remember this, and I did not like the look on his thin, winter-pale face. His expression was not frightened or upset, but remote, concentrating. "Listen," I said, in an unusually bright and friendly voice, "you aren't going to tell, are you?"

"No," he said absently.

"Promise."

"Promise," he said. I grabbed the hand behind his back to make sure he was not crossing his fingers. Even so, he might have a nightmare; it might come out that way. I decided I had better work hard to get all thoughts of what he had seen out of his mind—which, it seemed to me, could not hold very many things at a time. I got some money I had saved and that afternoon we went into Jubilee and saw a show, with Judy Canova, at which we both laughed a great deal. After that I thought it would be all right.

Two weeks later I knew they were going to shoot Flora. I knew from the night before, when I heard my mother ask if the hay was holding out all right, and my father said, "Well, after to-morrow there'll just be the cow, and we should be able to put her out to grass in another week." So I knew it was Flora's turn in the morning.

This time I didn't think of watching it. That was something to see just one time. I had not thought about it very often since, but sometimes when I was busy, working at school, or standing in front of the mirror combing my hair and wondering if I would be pretty when I grew up, the whole scene would flash into my mind: I would see the easy, practised way my father raised the gun, and hear Henry laughing when Mack kicked his legs in the air. I did not have any great feeling of horror and opposition, such as a city child might have had; I was too used to seeing the death of animals as a necessity by which we lived. Yet I felt a little ashamed, and there was a new wariness, a sense of holding-off, in my attitude to my father and his work.

It was a fine day, and we were going around the yard picking up tree branches that had been torn off in winter storms. This was something we had been told to do, and also we wanted to use them to make a teepee. We heard Flora whinny, and then my father's voice and Henry's shouting, and we ran down to the barnyard to see what was going on.

The stable door was open. Henry had just brought Flora out, and she had broken away from him. She was running free in the barnyard, from one end to the other. We climbed up on the fence. It was exciting to see her running, whinnying, going up on her hind legs, prancing and threatening like a horse in a Western movie, an unbroken ranch horse, though she was just an old driver, an old sorrel mare. My father and Henry ran after her and tried to grab the dangling halter. They tried to work her into a corner, and they had almost succeeded when she made a run between them, wild-eyed, and disappeared around the corner of the barn. We heard the rails clatter down as she got over the fence, and Henry yelled, "She's into the field now!"

That meant she was in the long L-shaped field that ran up by the house. If she got around the center, heading towards the lane, the gate was open; the truck had been driven into the field this morning. My father shouted to me, because I was on the other side of the fence, nearest the lane, "Go shut the gate!"

I could run very fast. I ran across the garden, past the tree where our swing was hung, and jumped across a ditch into the lane. There was the open gate. She had not got out, I could not see her up on the road; she must have run to the other end of the field. The gate was heavy. I lifted it out of the gravel and carried it across the roadway. I had it half-way across when she came in sight, galloping straight towards me. There was just time to get the chain on. Laird came scrambling through the ditch to help me.

Instead of shutting the gate, I opened it as wide as I could. I did not make any decision to do this, it was just what I did. Flora never slowed down; she galloped straight past me, and Laird jumped up and down, yelling, "Shut it, shut it!" even after it was too late. My father and Henry appeared in the field a moment too late to see what I had done. They only saw Flora heading for the township road. They would think I had not got there in time.

They did not waste any time asking about it. They went back to the barn and got the gun and the knives they used, and put these in the truck; then they turned the truck around and came bouncing up the field toward us. Laird called to them, "Let me go too, let me go too!" and Henry stopped the truck and they took him in. I shut the gate after they were all gone.

I supposed Laird would tell. I wondered what would happen to me. I had never disobeyed my father before, and I could not understand why I had done it. Flora would not really get away. They would catch up with her in the truck. Or if they did not catch her this morning somebody would see her and telephone us this afternoon or tomorrow. There was no wild country here for her to run to, only farms. What was more, my father had paid for her, we needed the meat to feed the foxes, we needed the foxes to make our living. All I had done was make more work for my father who worked hard enough already. And when my father found out about it he was not going to trust me any more; he would know that I was not entirely on his side. I was on Flora's side, and that made me no use to anybody, not even to her. Just the same, I did not regret it; when she came running at me and I held the gate open, that was the only thing I could do.

I went back to the house, and my mother said, "What's all the commotion?" I told her that Flora had kicked down the fence and got away. "Your poor father," she said, "now he'll have to go chasing over the countryside. Well, there isn't any use planning dinner before one." She put up the ironing board. I wanted to tell her, but thought better of it and went upstairs and sat on my bed.

Lately I had been trying to make my part of the room fancy, spreading the bed with old lace curtains, and fixing myself a dressing-table with some leftovers of cretonne for a skirt. I planned to put up some kind of barricade between my bed and Laird's, to keep my section separate from his. In the sunlight, the lace curtains were just dusty rags. We did not sing at night any more. One night when I was singing Laird said, "You sound silly," and I went right on but the next night I did not start. There was not so much need to anyway, we were no longer afraid. We knew it was just old furniture over there, old jumble and confusion. We did not keep to the rules. I still stayed awake after Laird was asleep and told myself stories, but even in these stories something different was happening, mysterious alterations took place. A story might start off in the old way, with a spectacular danger, a fire or wild animals, and for a while I might rescue people; then things would change around, and instead, somebody would be rescuing me. It might be a boy from our class at school, or even Mr. Campbell, our teacher, who tickled girls under the arms. And at this point the story concerned itself at great length with what I looked like—how long my hair was, and what kind of dress I had on; by the time I had these details worked out the real excitement of the story was lost.

It was later than one o'clock when the truck came back. The tarpaulin was over the back, which meant there was meat in it. My mother had to heat dinner up all over again. Henry and my father had changed from their bloody overalls into ordinary working overalls in the barn, and they washed their arms and necks and faces at the sink, and splashed water on their hair and combed it. Laird lifted his arm to show off a streak of blood. "We shot old Flora," he said, "and cut her up in fifty pieces."

"Well I don't want to hear about it," my mother said. "And don't come to my table like that."

My father made him go and wash the blood off.

We sat down and my father said grace and Henry pasted his chewing-gum on the end of his fork, the way he always did; when he took it off he would have us admire the pattern. We began to pass the bowls of steaming, overcooked vegetables. Laird looked across the table at me and said proudly, distinctly, "Anyway it was her fault Flora got away."

"What?" my father said.

"She could of shut the gate and she didn't. She just open' it up and Flora run out."

"Is that right?" my father said.

Everybody at the table was looking at me. I nodded, swallowing food with great difficulty. To my shame, tears flooded my eyes.

My father made a curt sound of disgust. "What did you do that for?"

I did not answer. I put down my fork and waited to be sent from the table, still not looking up.

But this did not happen. For some time nobody said anything, then Laird said matter-of-factly, "She's crying."

"Never mind," my father said. He spoke with resignation, even good humour, the words which absolved and dismissed me for good. "She's only a girl," he said.

I didn't protest that, even in my heart. Maybe it was true.

(1968)

George MacBeth

(SCOTLAND/IRELAND, 1932–1992)

Owl

    is my favourite. Who flies
    like a nothing through the night,
    who-whoing. Is a feather
    duster in leafy corners ring-a-rosy-ing
5   boles of mice. Twice

    you hear him call. Who
    is he looking for? You hear
    him hoovering over the floor
    of the wood. O would you be gold
10   rings in the driving skull

if you could? Hooded and
vulnerable by the winter suns
owl looks. Is the grain of bark
in the dark. Round beaks are at
15 work in the pellety nest,

resting. Owl is an eye
in the barn. For a hole
in the trunk owl's blood
is to blame. Black talons in the
20 petrified fur! Cold walnut hands

on the case of the brain! In the reign
of the chicken owl comes like
a god. Is a goad in
the rain to the pink eyes,
25 dripping. For a meal in the day

flew, killed, on the moor. Six
mouths are the seed of his
arc in the season. Torn meat
from the sky. Owl lives
30 by the claws of his brain. On the branch

in the sever of the hand's
twigs owl is a backward look.
Flown wind in the skin. Fine
rain in the bones. Owl breaks
35 like the day. Am an owl, am an owl.

(1965)

Marshall

It occurred to Marshall
that if he were a vegetable, he'd
be a bean. Not
one of your thin, stringy
5 green beans, or your

dry, marbly
Burlotti beans. No, he'd be
a broad bean,
a rich, nutritious,
10 meaningful bean,

alert for advantages,
inquisitive with potatoes,
mixing with every kind
and condition of vegetable,
15 and a good friend

to meat and lager. Yes, he'd
leap from his huge
rough pod with a loud
popping sound
20   into the pot: always

in hot water
and out of it with a soft
heart inside
his horny carapace. He'd
25   carry the whole

world's hunger on
his broad shoulders, green
with best butter
or brown with gravy. And if
30   some starving Indian saw his

flesh bleeding
when the gas was turned on
or the knife went in
he'd accept the homage and prayers,
35   and become a god, and die like a man,

which, as things were, wasn't so easy.
(1968)

Sylvia Plath
(U.S.A., 1932-1963)

The Colossus

I shall never get you put together entirely,
Pieced, glued, and properly jointed.
Mule-bray, pig-grunt and bawdy cackles
Proceed from your great lips.
5   It's worse than a barnyard.

Perhaps you consider yourself an oracle,
Mouthpiece of the dead, or of some god or other.
Thirty years now I have laboured
To dredge the silt from your throat.
10   I am none the wiser.

Scaling little ladders with gluepots and pails of lysol
I crawl like an ant in mourning
Over the weedy acres of your brow
To mend the immense skull-plates and clear
15   The bald, white tumuli of your eyes.

A blue sky out of the Oresteia
Arches above us. O father, all by yourself
You are pithy and historical as the Roman Forum.
I open my lunch on a hill of black cypress.
20   Your fluted bones and acanthine hair are littered

In their old anarchy to the horizon-line.
It would take more than a lightning-stroke
To create such a ruin.
Nights, I squat in the cornucopia
25   Of your left ear, out of the wind,

Counting the red stars and those of plum-colour.
The sun rises under the pillar of your tongue.
My hours are married to shadow.
No longer do I listen for the scrape of a keel
30   On the blank stones of the landing.

                                                        (1960)

You're

Clownlike, happiest on your hands,
Feet to the stars, and moon-skulled,
Gilled like a fish. A common-sense
Thumbs-down on the dodo's mode.
5   Wrapped up in yourself like a spool,
Trawling your dark as owls do.
Mute as a turnip from the Fourth
Of July to All Fools' Day,
O high-riser, my little loaf.

10   Vague as fog and looked for like mail.
Farther off than Australia.
Bent-backed Atlas, our travelled prawn.
Snug as a bud and at home
Like a sprat in a pickle jug.
15   A creel of eels, all ripples.
Jumpy as a Mexican bean.
Right, like a well-done sum.
A clean slate, with your own face on.

                                                        (1965)

C.K. Stead

(NEW ZEALAND, 1932–)

Poem to Suppose the Bird

    Suppose the bird ruffled below your pines
    This fine wet shining evening, he sings suppose
    Familiarly strange. A note it is that knows
    Its variations mean just what they are
5   Supposed to mean: this one, suppose, the hedge,
    That one the compost heap, and this the patch
    Your mower cut last spring and made his thatch.
    Then each, then each he sings, and each suppose
    Indifferently the same must represent
10 Its time, its place, some shady happening,
    Sunny accomplishment, or just a thing
    Unnamed suppose.
                He seems a clownish bird
    Not sad not happy that the sun declines
15 His best inflexion for the voiceless pines
    But sings supposing out what life he knows
    Below your pines the ruffled bird suppose.

                          (1972)

John Updike

(U.S.A., 1932–)

Beer Can

This seems to be an era of gratuitous inventions and negative improvements. Consider the beer can. It was beautiful—as beautiful as the clothespin, as inevitable as the wine bottle, as dignified and reassuring as the fire hydrant. A tranquil cylinder of delightfully resonant metal, it could be opened in an instant, requiring only the application of a handy gadget freely dispensed by every grocer. Who can forget the small, symmetrical thrill of those two triangular punctures, the dainty *pffff*, the little crest of suds that foamed eagerly in the exultation of release? Now we are given, instead, a top beetling with an ugly, shmoo-shaped "tab," which, after fiercely resisting the tugging, bleeding fingers of the thirsty man, threatens his lips with a dangerous and hideous hole. However, we have discovered a way to thwart Progress, usually so unthwartable. *Turn the beer can upside down and open the bottom.* The bottom is still the way the top used to be. True, this operation gives the beer an unsettling jolt, and the sight of a consistently inverted beer can might make people edgy, not to say queasy. But the latter difficulty could be eliminated if manufacturers would design cans that looked the same whichever end was up, like playing cards. What we need is Progress with an escape hatch.

(1964)

Edward Lucie-Smith

(JAMAICA/ENGLAND, 1933–)

Imperialists in Retirement

'I have done the state some service', Othello

Tender each to the other, gentle
 But not to the world which has just now
Snatched back its gifts. Oh fallen, fallen
 From your proconsular state! I watch
5 Perhaps too closely, with too much
 Easy pity, the old man's loving
Protective gesture—the old woman
 Accepting the arm of a blind man,
Leaning upon it. I look around
10 At the faded chintz, at china chipped
By so many packings, unpackings.

I listen, too. This part is not so
 Easy. He is not resigned. He cries
Aloud for the state he kept. He wants
15 Privilege still and power, the long
Moonlit nights of the steamship voyage
 Out to a new appointment. Whisky
And bridge and talk of what's to be done—
 The phrase again: 'They're children, really.'
20 And he beats with feeble hands against
 The immovable door of blindness,
The shut door of the years. 'Live in the
 Past,' he says. 'That's the thing. Live in the
Past.' And his wife soothes him, as one would
25 A child when it's nearly his bedtime.
'One mustn't grumble,' she says. 'Times change.'

Her hands are reddened and swollen I
    Notice, saying goodnight. Her head shakes.
She stumbles a little in rising.
30   Tonight she washes up. Tomorrow
She will scrub their kitchen on her knees.
    I see, as we go, the look of love
From her to him blind. Then the door shuts.

                     (1964)

Alden Nowlan

(CANADA, 1933-1983)

The Bull Moose

Down from the purple mist of trees on the mountain,
lurching through forests of white spruce and cedar,
stumbling through tamarack swamps
came the bull moose
5 to be stopped at last by a pole-fenced pasture.

Too tired to turn or, perhaps, aware
there was no place left to go, he stood with the cattle.
They, scenting the musk of death, seeing his great head
like the ritual mask of a blood god, moved to the other end
10 of the field, and waited.

The neighbours heard of it, and by afternoon
cars lined the road. The children teased him
with alder switches and he gazed at them
like an old, tolerant collie. The women asked
15 if he could have escaped from a Fair.

The oldest man in the parish remembered seeing
a gelded moose yoked with an ox for plowing.
The young men snickered and tried to pour beer
down his throat, while their girl friends took their pictures.

20 And the bull moose let them stroke his tick-ravaged flanks,
let them pry open his jaws with bottles, let a giggling girl
plant a little purple cap
of thistles on his head.

When the wardens came, everyone agreed it was a shame
25 to shoot anything so shaggy and cuddlesome.
He looked like the kind of pet
women put to bed with their sons.

So they held their fire. But just as the sun dropped in the river
the bull moose gathered his strength
30   like a scaffolded king, straightened and lifted his horns
so that even the wardens backed away as they raised their rifles.
When he roared, people ran to their cars. All the young men
leaned on their automobile horns as he toppled.

(1962)

David Malouf

(AUSTRALIA, 1934–)

A Charm against the Dumps

Shoo! be far off! fly
on owl's-wing feather-duster
be sucked into the belly
of Hoover go swirling
5   down plug-hole you

Bumbo lord of the dumps lord
of toothache and hay fever
of thumbnail by hammer
blackened spent matches
10   nose-bleeds razor-nicks

and all you left-handed
dialers of wrong numbers
stammerers stumblers
and tittle-tats madcap
15   demons at the wheel

the charm against your sullen
mischief is sneezing
at sunshine cold keys
slipped between skin and sweater
20   or counting to ten

but best of all Bumbo
lord of the dumps is shouting
so loud under the blankets
you tumble out ears ringing
25   the right side of the bed

(1974)

Audre Lorde
(U.S.A., 1934–1992)

The Day They Eulogized Mahalia

The day they eulogized Mahalia
the echoes of her big voice stilled
and the mourners found her
singing out from their sisters' mouths
5   from their mothers' toughness
from the funky dust in the corners
of Sunday church pews
sweet and dry and simple
and that hated Sunday morning fussed-over feeling
10   the songs
singing out from their mothers' toughness
would never threaten the lord's retribution
anymore.

Now she was safe
15   acceptable   that big Mahalia
Chicago turned all out
to show her that they cared
but her eyes were closed
And although Mahalia loved our music
20   nobody sang her favorite song
and while we talked about
what a hard life she had known
and wasn't it too bad Sister Mahalia
didn't have it easier earlier
25   SIX BLACK CHILDREN
BURNED TO DEATH IN A DAY CARE CENTER
on the South Side
kept in a condemned house
for lack of funds
30   firemen found their bodies
like huddled lumps of charcoal
with silent mouths wide open.

Small and without song
six Black children found a voice in flame
35   the day the city eulogized Mahalia.

(1971)

A Trip on the Staten Island Ferry

Dear Jonno
there are pigeons who nest
on the Staten Island Ferry
and raise their young
5   between the moving decks
and never touch
ashore.

Every voyage is a journey.

Cherish this city
10   left you by default
include it in your daydreams
there are still   secrets
in the streets
even I have not discovered
15   who knows if the old men
shining shoes on the Staten Island Ferry
carry their world   in that box
slung across their shoulders
if they share their lunch
20   with the birds flying
back and forth
on an endless journey
if they ever find their way
back home.

(1973)

Wole Soyinka

(NIGERIA, 1934–)

"No!" He Said

(for Nelson Mandela)

Shorn of landmarks, glued to a sere promontory,
The breakers sought to crush his head,
To flush the black will of his race
Back in tidal waves, to flesh-trade centuries,
5   Bile-slick beyond beachcombing, beyond
Salvage operations but—no, he said.

Sea urchins stung his soul. Albino eels
Searched the cortex of his heart,
His hands thrust high to exorcise
10   Visions of lost years, slow parade of isolation's
Ghosts. Still they came, seducers of a moment's
Slack in thought, but—no, he said.

And they saw his hands were clenched.
Blood oozed from a thousand pores. A lonely
15   Fisher tensed against the oilcloth of new dawns,
Hand over hand he hauled. The harvest strained.
Cords turned writhing hawsers in his hands. "Let go!"
The tempters cried, but—no, he said.

Count the passing ships. Whose argosies
20   Stretch like golden beads on far horizons? Those are
Their present ease, your vanished years. Castaway,
Minnows roost in the hold of that doomed ship
You launched in the eye of storms. Your mast is seaweed
On which pale plankton feed, but—no, he said.

25   Are you bigger than Nkomati? Blacker
Than hands that signed away a continent for ease?
Lone matador with broken paddle for a lance,
Are you the Horn? The Cape? Sequinned
Constellation of the Bull for tide-tossed
30   Castaways on pallid sands? No, he said.

The axis of the world has shifted. Even the polar star
Loses its fixity, nudged by man-made planets.
The universe has shrunk. History reechoes as
We plant new space flags of a master race.
35   You are the afterburn of our crudest launch.
The stars disown you, but—no, he said.

Your tongue is salt swollen, a mute keel
Upended on the seabed of forgotten time.
The present breeds new tasks, same taskmasters.
40   On that star planet of our galaxy, code-named Bantustan,
They sieve rare diamonds from moon dust. In choice reserves,
Venerably pastured, you . . . but—no, he said.

That ancient largesse on the mountaintop
Shrinks before our gift's munificence, an offer even
45   Christ, second-come, could not refuse. Be ebony mascot
On the flagship of our space fleet, still
Through every turbulence, spectator of our Brave New World.
Come, Ancient Mariner, but—no, he said—

No! I am no prisoner of this rock, this island,
50   No ash spew on Milky Ways to conquests old or new.
I am this rock, this island. I toiled,
Precedent on this soil, as in the great dark whale
Of time, Black Hole of the galaxy. Its maw
Turns steel-wrought epochs plankton—yes—and
55   Vomits out new worlds.

In and out of time warp, I am that rock
In the black hole of the sky.

                  (1988)

Zulfikar Ghose
(INDIA/PAKISTAN/U.S.A., 1935–)

Come, Sailor

      Not by journeying,
Odysseus (since to you the Mediterranean's
currents are erratic, violent mysteries),
     not fresh explorations
5   now amidst the swollen seas,
Odysseus, will bring back the heart-soothing

      vision, nor will the hills
again be purple near the town that was once
home; and sooner will the extinct birds rise
10   in imagined migrations
        before your startled eyes
than your searching discover the particles

      of dust become again
compacted into masonry, the walls and domes
15   of fallen cities. Open gutters and sewers
     ran out of those kingdoms
        whose golden towers
only are remembered, and the fields of yellow corn

      were sometimes black
20   with locusts. The hills of Rome, the isles
of Greece, even there, Odysseus. And still,
     when you stand beside the sails
        and look down at the tall
waves shouldering your ship, there, Odysseus, like

25   a drowned sailor
a body floats, its face yours and mine. Compulsive,
this voyaging—as if the next calm will settle
    the sea-spray and drive
      away the clouds until
30   the horizon offers the choice of a natural harbour

    where intermingled come
scents of thyme and rosemary, or a clearer
perspective of the ocean's routes, each one
    an illusion that nearer
35   is that vision
which makes sons slam doors on their parents' home.

    Chill breezes catalogue
again autumn's severities; the sky hurries eastward
and the gulls ride a swifter wind. The seas
40   twitch, and again the voice you heard
      in ancient mythologies
calls: Come, sailor, journey towards the cold fog.

                              (1972)

The Remove

The Sikh from Ambala in East Punjab,
India, formerly in the British Empire,
the Muslim from Sialkot in West Punjab,
Pakistan, formerly British India,
5   the Sikh boy and the Muslim boy are two
of twenty such Sikhs and Muslims
from East Punjab and West Punjab, which
formerly were the Punjab,
standing together in assembly, fearfully
10 miming the words of a Christian hymn.

Later, their firework voices explode
in Punjabi until Mr Iqbal—
which can be a Sikh name or a Muslim name,
Mohammed Iqbal or Iqbal *Singh*—
15 who comes from Jullundur in East Punjab
but near enough to the border to be almost
West Punjab, who is a specialist in
the archaic intonations of the *Raj*,
until the three-piece-suited Mr Iqbal
20 gives a stiff-collared voice to his
Punjab command to shut their thick wet
lips on the scattering sparks of their
white Secondary Modern teeth.

Mr Iqbal has come to London to teach
25 English to Punjabi Sikhs and Muslims
and has pinned up in his class pictures
of Gandhi and Jinnah, Nehru and Ayub
in case the parents come to ask in Punjabi
how the kids are doing in English.

30 And so: twenty years after
the Union Jack came down on Delhi
and the Punjab became East Punjab and
West Punjab and the Sikhs did not like it
and the Muslims did not like the Sikhs
35 not liking it and they killed each other
not by the hundred nor by the thousand
but by the hundred thousand, here then
is Mr Iqbal with his remove class of
twenty Punjabis, some Sikh and some Muslim,
40 in a Secondary Modern School in London,
all of them trying to learn English.

Back home the fastidious guardians of freedom,
the Sikh army and the Muslim army, convinced
that East is East and West is West etcetera,
45 periodically accuse each other of aggression.

(1972)

Joy Kogawa

(CANADA, 1935–)

Obasan

She is sitting at the kitchen table when I come in. She is so deaf now that my knocking does not rouse her and when she sees me she is startled.

'O,' she says, and the sound is short and dry as if there is no energy left to put any inflection into her voice. She begins to rise but falters and her hands outstretched in greeting, fall to the table. She says my name as a question.

I put my shoulder bag down, remove the mud-caked boots and stand before her.

'Obasan,' I say loudly and take her hands. My aunt is not one for hugs and kisses.

She peers into my face. 'O,' she says again.

I nod in reply. We stand for a long time in silence. I open my mouth to ask, 'Did he suffer very much?' but the question feels pornographic.

'Everyone dies some day,' she says eventually. She tilts her head to the side as if it's all too heavy inside.

I hang my jacket on a coat peg and sit beside her.

The house is familiar but has shrunk over the years and is even more cluttered than I remember. The wooden table is covered with a plastic table cloth over a blue and while cloth. Along one edge are African violets in profuse bloom, salt and pepper shakers, a soya sauce bottle, an old radio, a non-automatic toaster, a small bottle full of toothpicks. She goes to the stove and turns on the gas flame under the kettle.

'Everyone dies some day,' she says again and looks in my direction, her eyes unclear and sticky with a gum-like mucus. She pours the tea. Tiny twigs and bits of popcorn circle in the cup.

When I last saw her nine years ago, she told me her tear ducts were clogged. I have never seen her cry. Her mouth is filled with a gummy saliva as well. She drinks warm water often because her tongue sticks to the roof of her false plate.

'Thank you,' I say, taking the cup in both hands.

Uncle was disoriented for weeks, my cousin's letter told me. Towards the end he got dizzier and dizzier and couldn't move without clutching things. By the time they got him to the hospital, his eyes were rolling.

'I think he was beginning to see everything upside down again,' she wrote, 'the way we see when we are born.' Perhaps for Uncle, everything had started reversing and he was growing top to bottom, his mind rooted in an upstairs attic of humus and memory, groping backwards through cracks and walls to a moist cellar. Down to water. Down to the underground sea.

Back to the fishing boat, the ocean, the skiff moored off Vancouver Island where he was born. Like Moses, he was an infant of the waves, rocked to sleep by the lap lap and 'Nen, nen, korori', his mother's voice singing the ancient Japanese lullaby. His father, Japanese crafts-man, was also a son of the sea which had tossed and coddled his boatbuilding ancestors for centuries. And though he had crossed the ocean from one island as a stranger coming to an island of strangers, it was the sea who was his constant landlord. His fellow tenants, the Songhee Indians of Esquimalt, and the fishermen, came from up and down the BC coast to his workshop in Victoria, to watch, to barter, and to buy.

In the framed family photograph hanging above the sideboard, Grandfather sits on a chair with his short legs not quite square on the floor. A long black cape hangs from his shoulders. His left hand clutches a pair of gloves and the top of a cane. On a pedestal beside him is a top hat, open end up. Uncle stands slightly to his right, and behind, with his hand like Napoleon's in his vest. Sitting to their left is Grandmother in a lace and velvet suit with my mother in her arms. They all look in different directions, carved and rigid with their expressionless Japanese faces and their bodies pasted over with Rule Britannia. There's not a ripple out of place.

And then there is the picture, not framed, not on display, showing Uncle as a young man smiling and proud in front of an exquisitely detailed craft. Not a fishing boat, not an ordinary yacht—a creation of many years and many winter evenings—a work of art. Uncle stands, happy enough for the attention of the camera, eager to pass on the message that all is well. That forever and ever all is well.

But many things happen. There is the voice of the RCMP officer saying, 'I'll keep that one,' and laughing as he cuts through the water. 'Don't worry, I'll make good use of her.' The other boats are towed away and left to rot. Hundreds of Grandfather's boats belonging to hundreds of fishermen.

The memories are drowned in a whirlpool of protective silence. 'For the sake of the children,' it is whispered over and over. 'Kodomo no tame.'

And several years later, sitting in a shack on the edge of a sugar beet field in southern Alberta, Obasan is watching her two young daughters with their school books doing home-work in the light of a coal oil lamp. Her words are the same. 'Kodomo no tame.' For their sakes, they will survive the dust and the wind, the gumbo, the summer oven sun. For their sakes, they will work in the fields, hoeing, thinning acres of sugar beets, irrigating, topping, harvesting.

'We must go back,' Uncle would say on winter evenings, the ice thick on the windows. But later, he became more silent.

'*Nen nen.*' Rest, my dear uncle. The sea is severed from your veins. You have been cut loose.

They were feeding him intravenously for two days, the tubes sticking into him like grafting on a tree. But Death won against the medical artistry.

'Obasan, will you be all right?' I ask.

She clears her throat and wipes dry skin off her lips but does not speak. She rolls a bit of dried up jam off the table cloth. She isn't going to answer.

The language of grief is silence. She knows it well, its idioms, its nuances. She's had some of the best tutors available. Grief inside her body is fat and powerful. An almighty tapeworm.

Over the years, Grief has roamed like a highwayman down the channels of her body with its dynamite and its weapons blowing up every moment of relief that tried to make its way down the road. It grew rich off the unburied corpses inside her body.

Grief acted in mysterious ways, its melancholy wonders to perform. When it had claimed her kingdom fully, it admitted no enemies and no vengeance. Enemies belonged in a corridor of experience with sense and meaning, with justice and reason. Her Grief knew nothing of these and whipped her body to resignation until the kingdom was secure. But inside the fortress, Obasan's silence was that of a child bewildered.

'What will you do now?' I ask.

What choices does she have? Her daughters, unable to rescue her or bear the silent rebuke of her suffering, have long since fled to the ends of the earth. Each has lived a life in perpetual flight from the density of her inner retreat—from the rays of her inverted sun sucking in their lives with the voracious appetite of a dwarf star. Approaching her, they become balls of liquid metal—mercurial—unpredictable in their moods and sudden departures. Especially for the younger daughter, departure is as necessary as breath. What metallic spider is it in her night that hammers a constant transformation, lacing open doors and windows with iron bars.

'What will you do?' I repeat.

She folds her hands together. I pour her some more tea and she bows her thanks. I take her hands in mine, feeling the silky wax texture.

'Will you come and stay with us?' Are there any other words to say? Her hands move under mine and I release them. Her face is motionless. 'We could leave in a few days and come back next month.'

'The plants. . . .'

'Neighbours can water them.'

'There is trouble with the house,' she says. 'This is an old house. If I leave. . . .'

'Obasan,' I say nodding, 'it is your house.'

She is an old woman. Every homemade piece of furniture, each pot holder and child's paper doily, is a link in her lifeline. She has preserved in shelves and in cupboards, under layers of clothing in closets—a daughter's rubber ball, colouring books, old hats, children's dresses. The items are endless. Every short stub pencil, every cornflake box stuffed with paper bags and old letters is of her ordering. They rest in the corners of the house like parts of her body, hair cells, skin tissue, food particles, tiny specks of memory. This house is now her blood and bones.

She is all old women in every hamlet in the world. You see her on a street corner in a village in southern France, in her black dress and her black stockings. She is squatting on stone steps in a Mexican mountain village. Everywhere she stands as the true and rightful owner of the earth, the bearer of love's keys to unknown doorways, to a network of astonishing tunnels, the possessor of life's infinite personal details.

'I am old,' she says.

These are the words my grandmother spoke that night in the house in Victoria. Grandmother was too old then to understand political expediency, race riots, the yellow peril. I was too young.

She stands up slowly, 'Something in the attic for you,' she says. We climb the narrow stairs one step at a time carrying a flashlight with us. Its dull beam reveals mounds of cardboard boxes, newspapers, magazines, a trunk. A dead sparrow lies in the nearest corner by the eaves.

She attempts to lift the lid of the trunk. Black fly corpses fall to the floor. Between the wooden planks, more flies fill the cracks. Old spider webs hang like blood clots, thick and black from the rough angled ceiling.

Our past is as clotted as old webs hung in dark attics, still sticky and hovering, waiting for us to adhere and submit or depart. Or like a spider with its skinny hairy legs, the past skitters out of the dark, spinning and netting the air, ready to snap us up and ensnare our thoughts in old and complex perceptions. And when its feasting is complete, it leaves its victims locked up forever, dangling like hollowed out insect skins, a fearful calligraphy, dry reminders that once there was life flitting about in the weather.

But occasionally a memory that refuses to be hollowed out, to be categorized, to be identified, to be explained away, comes thudding into the web like a giant moth. And in the daylight, what's left hanging there, ragged and shredded is a demolished fly trap, and beside it a bewildered eight-legged spinning animal.

My dead refuse to bury themselves. Each story from the past is changed and distorted, altered as much by the present as the present is shaped by the past. But potent and pervasive as a prairie dust storm, memory and dream seep and mingle through cracks, settling on furniture, into upholstery. The attic and the living room encroach onto each other, deep into their invisible places.

I sneeze and dust specks pummel across the flashlight beam. Will we all be dust in the end—a jumble of faces and lives compressed and powdered into a few lines of statistics—fading photographs in family albums, the faces no longer familiar, the clothing quaint, the anecdotes lost?

I use the flashlight to break off a web and lift the lid of the trunk. A strong whiff of mothballs assaults us. The odour of preservation. Inside, there are bits of lace and fur, a 1920s nightgown, a shoe box, red and white striped socks. She sifts through the contents, one by one.

'That's strange,' she says several times.

'What are you looking for?' I ask.

'Not here. It isn't here.'

She turns to face me in the darkness. 'That's strange,' she says and leaves her questions enclosed in silence.

I pry open the folds of a cardboard box. The thick dust slides off like chocolate icing sugar—antique pollen. Grandfather's boat building tools are wrapped in heavy cloth. These are all he brought when he came to this country wearing a western suit, western shoes, a round black hat. Here is the plane with a wooden handle which he worked by pulling it towards him. A fundamental difference in workmanship—to pull rather than push. Chisels, hammer, a mallet, a thin pointed saw, the handle extending from the blade like that of a kitchen knife.

'What will you do with these?' I ask.

'The junk in the attic,' my cousin's letter said, 'should be burned. When I come there this summer, I'll have a big bonfire. It's a fire trap. I've taken the only things that are worth keeping.'

Beneath the box of tools is a pile of *Life* magazines dated in the 1950s. A subscription maintained while the two daughters were home. Beside the pile is another box containing shoe boxes, a metal box with a disintegrating elastic band, several chocolate boxes. Inside the metal box are pictures, duplicates of some I have seen in our family albums. Obasan's wedding photo—her mid-calf dress hanging straight down from her shoulders, her smile glued on. In the next picture, Uncle is a child wearing a sailor suit.

The shoe box is full of documents.

Royal Canadian Mounted Police, Vancouver, BC, March 4, 1942. A folded mimeographed paper authorizes Uncle as the holder of a numbered Registration Card to leave a Registered Area by truck for Vernon where he is required to report to the local Registrar of Enemy Aliens, not later than the following day. It is signed by the RCMP superintendent.

Uncle's face, young and unsmiling looks up at me from the bottom right hand corner of a wallet size ID card. 'The bearer whose photograph and specimen of signature appear hereon, has been duly registered in compliance with the provisions of Order-in-Council PC 117.' A purple stamp underneath states 'Canadian Born'. His thumb print appears on the back with marks of identification specified—scar on back of right hand.

There is a letter from the Department of the Secretary of State. Office of the Custodian. Japanese Evacuation Section. 506 Royal Bank Bldg. Hastings and Granville, Vancouver, BC.

Dear Sir.

Dear Uncle. With whom were you corresponding and for what did you hope? That the enmity would cease? That you could return to your boats? I have grown tired, Uncle, of seeking the face of the enemy hiding in the thick forests of the past. You were not the enemy. The police who came to your door were not the enemy. The men who rioted against you were not the enemy. The Vancouver alderman who said 'Keep BC White' was not the enemy. The men who drafted the Order-in-Council were not the enemy. He does not wear a uniform or sit at a long meeting table. The man who read your timid letter, read your polite request, skimmed over your impossible plea, was not your enemy. He had an urgent report to complete. His wife was ill. The phone rang all the time. The senior staff was meeting in two hours. The secretary was spending too much time over coffee breaks. There were a billion problems to attend to. Injustice was the only constant in a world of flux. There were moments when expedience demanded decisions which would later be judged unjust. Uncle, he did not always know what he was doing. You too did not have an all compassionate imagination. He was just doing his job. I am just doing my work, Uncle. We are all just doing our jobs.

My dear dead Uncle. Am I come to unearth our bitterness that our buried love too may revive?

'Obasan, what shall we do with these?'

She has been waiting at the top of the stairs, holding the railing with both hands. I close the shoe box and replace the four interlocking flaps of the cardboard box. With one hand I shine the flashlight and with the other, guide her as I precede her slowly down the stairs. Near the bottom she stumbles and I hold her small body upright.

'Thank you, thank you,' she says. This is the first time my arms have held her. We walk slowly through the living room and back to the kitchen. Her lips are trembling as she sits on the wooden stool.

Outside, the sky of the prairie spring is painfully blue. The trees are shooting out their leaves in the fierce wind, the new branches elastic as whips. The sharp-edged clarity is insistent as trumpets.

But inside, the rooms are muted. Our inner trees, our veins, are involuted, cocooned, webbed. The blood cells in the trunks of our bodies, like tiny specks of light, move in a sluggish river. It is more a potential than an actual river—an electric liquid—the current flowing in and between us, between our generations. Not circular, as in a whirlpool, or climactic and tidal as in fountains or spray—but brooding. Bubbling. You expect to hear barely audible pip-pip electronic tones, a pre-concert tuning up behind the curtains in the darkness. Towards the ends of our branches and fingertips, tiny human-shaped flames or leaves break off and leap towards the shadows. My arms are suffused with a suppressed urge to hold.

At the edges of our flesh is a hint of a spiritual osmosis, an eagerness within matter, waiting to brighten our dormant neurons, to entrust our stagnant cells with movement and dance.

Obasan drinks her tea and makes a shallow scratching sound in her throat. She shuffles to the door and squats beside the boot tray. With a putty knife, she begins to scrape off the thick clay like mud that sticks to my boots.

(1981)

Carol Shields
(U.S.A./CANADA, 1935-)

Mrs. Turner Cutting the Grass

Oh, Mrs. Turner is a sight cutting the grass on a hot afternoon in June! She climbs into an ancient pair of shorts and ties on her halter top and wedges her feet into crepe-soled sandals and covers her red-gray frizz with Gord's old golf cap—Gord is dead now, ten years ago, a seizure on a Saturday night while winding the mantel clock.

The grass flies up around Mrs. Turner's knees. Why doesn't she use a catcher, the Saschers next door wonder. Everyone knows that leaving the clippings like that is bad for the lawn. Each fallen blade of grass throws a minute shadow which impedes growth and repair. The Saschers themselves use their clippings to make compost which they hope one day will be ripe as the good manure that Sally Sascher's father used to spread on his fields down near Emerson Township.

Mrs. Turner's carelessness over the clippings plucks away at Sally, but her husband Roy is far more concerned about the Killex that Mrs. Turner dumps on her dandelions. It's true that in Winnipeg the dandelion roots go right to the middle of the earth, but Roy is patient and persistent in pulling them out, knowing exactly how to grasp the coarse leaves in his hand and how much pressure to apply. Mostly they come up like corks with their roots intact. And he and Sally are experimenting with new ways to cook dandelion greens, believing as they do that the components of nature are arranged for a specific purpose—if only that purpose can be divined.

In the early summer Mrs. Turner is out every morning by ten with her sprinkling can of chemical killer, and Roy, watching from his front porch, imagines how this poison will enter the ecosystem and move by quick capillary surges into his fenced vegetable plot, newly seeded now with green beans and lettuce. His children, his two little girls aged two and four—that they should be touched by such poison makes him morose and angry. But he and Sally so far have said nothing to Mrs. Turner about her abuse of the planet because they're hoping she'll go into an old-folks home soon or maybe die, and then all will proceed as it should.

High-school girls on their way home in the afternoon see Mrs. Turner cutting her grass and are mildly, momentarily repelled by the lapped, striated flesh on her upper thighs. At her age. Doesn't she realize? Every last one of them is intimate with the vocabulary of skin care and knows that what has claimed Mrs. Turner's thighs is the enemy called cellulite, but they can't understand why she doesn't take the trouble to hide it. It makes them queasy; it makes them fear for the future.

The things Mrs. Turner doesn't know would fill the Saschers' new compost pit, would sink a ship, would set off a tidal wave, would make her want to kill herself. Back and forth, back and forth she goes with the electric lawn mower, the grass flying out sideways like whiskers. Oh, the things she doesn't know! She has never heard, for example, of the folk-rock recording star Neil Young, though the high school just around the corner from her house happens to be the very school Neil Young attended as a lad. His initials can actually be seen carved on one of the desks, and a few of the teachers say they remember him, a quiet fellow of neat appearance and always very polite in class. The desk with the initials N.Y. is kept in a corner of Mr. Pring's homeroom, and it's considered lucky—despite the fact that the renowned singer wasn't a great scholar—to touch the incised letters just before an exam. Since it's exam time now, the second week of June, the girls walking past Mrs. Turner's front yard (and shuddering over her display of cellulite) are carrying on their fingertips the spiritual scent, the essence, the fragrance, the aura of Neil Young, but Mrs. Turner is as ignorant of that fact as the girls are that she, Mrs. Turner, possesses a first name—which is Geraldine.

Not that she's ever been called Geraldine. Where she grew up in Boissevain, Manitoba, she was known always—the Lord knows why—as Girlie Fergus, the youngest of the three Fergus girls and the one who got herself in hot water. Her sister Em went to normal school and her sister Muriel went to Brandon to work at Eatons, but Girlie got caught one night—she was nineteen—in a Boissevain hotel room with a local farmer, married, named Gus MacGregor. It was her father who got wind of where she might be and came banging on the door, shouting and weeping, "Girlie, Girlie, what have you done to me?"

Girlie had been working in the Boissevain Dairy since she'd left school at sixteen and had a bit of money saved up, and so, a week after the humiliation in the local hotel, she wrote a farewell note to the family, crept out of the house at midnight and caught the bus to Winnipeg. From there she got another bus down to Minneapolis, then to Chicago and finally New York City. The journey was endless and wretched, and on the way across Indiana and Ohio and Pennsylvania she saw hundreds and hundreds of towns whose unpaved streets and narrow blinded houses made her fear some conspiratorial, punishing power had carried her back to Boissevain. Her father's soppy-stern voice sang and sang in her ears as the wooden bus rattled its way eastward. It was summer, 1930.

New York was immense and wonderful, dirty, perilous and puzzling. She found herself longing for a sight of real earth which she assumed must lie somewhere beneath the tough pavement. On the other hand, the brown flat-roofed factories with their little windows tilted skyward pumped her full of happiness, as did the dusty trees, when she finally discovered them, lining the long avenues. Every last person in the world seemed to be outside, walking around, filling the streets, and every corner breezed with noise and sunlight. She had to pinch herself to believe this was the same sunlight that filtered its way into the rooms of the house back in Boissevain, fading the curtains but nourishing her mother's ferns. She sent postcards to Em and Muriel that said, "Don't worry about me. I've got a job in the theater business."

It was true. For eight and a half months she was an usherette in the Lamar Movie Palace in Brooklyn. She loved her perky maroon uniform, the way it fit on her shoulders, the way the strips of crinkly gold braid outlined her figure. With a little flashlight in hand she was able to send streams of light across the furry darkness of the theater and onto the plum-colored aisle carpet. The voices from the screen talked on and on. She felt after a time that their resonant declarations and tender replies belonged to her.

She met a man named Kiki her first month in New York and moved in with him. His skin was as black as ebony. *As black as ebony*—that was the phrase that hung like a ribbon on the end of his name, and it's also the phrase she uses, infrequently, when she wants to call up his memory, though she's more than a little doubtful about what *ebony* is. It may be a kind of stone, she thinks, something round and polished that comes out of a deep mine.

Kiki was a good-hearted man, though she didn't like the beer he drank, and he stayed with her, willingly, for several months after she had to stop working because of the baby. It was the baby itself that frightened him off, the way it cried probably. Leaving fifty dollars on the table, he slipped out one July afternoon when Girlie was shopping, and went back to Troy, New York, where he'd been raised.

Her first thought was to take the baby and get on a bus and go find him, but there wasn't enough money, and the thought of the baby crying all the way on the hot bus made her feel tired. She was worried about the rent and about the little red sores in the baby's ears—it was a boy, rather sweetly formed, with wonderful smooth feet and hands. On a murderously hot night, a night when the humidity was especially bad, she wrapped him in a clean piece of sheeting and carried him all the way to Brooklyn Heights where the houses were large and solid and surrounded by grass. There was a house on a corner she particularly liked because it had a wide front porch (like those in Boissevain) with a curved railing—and parked on the porch, its brake on, was a beautiful wicker baby carriage. It was here she placed her baby, giving one last look to his sleeping face, as round and calm as the moon. She walked home, taking her time, swinging her legs. If she had known the word *foundling*—which she didn't—she would have bounded along on its rhythmic back, so airy and wide did the world seem that night.

Most of these secrets she keeps locked away inside her mottled thighs or in the curled pinkness of her genital flesh. She has no idea what happened to Kiki, whether he ever went off to Alaska as he wanted to or whether he fell down a flight of stone steps in the silverware factory in Troy, New York, and died of head injuries before his 30th birthday. Or what happened to her son—whether he was bitten that night in the baby carriage by a rabid neighborhood cat or whether he was discovered the next morning and adopted by the large, loving family who lived in the house. As a rule, Girlie tries not to think about the things she can't even guess at. All she thinks is that she did the best she could under the circumstances.

In a year she saved enough money to take the train home to Boissevain. She took with her all her belongings, and also gifts for Em and Muriel, boxes of hose, bottles of apple-blossom cologne, phonograph records. For her mother she took an embroidered apron and for her father a pipe made of curious gnarled wood. "Girlie, my Girlie," her father said, embracing her at the Boissevain station. Then he said, "Don't ever leave us again," in a way that frightened her and made her resolve to leave as quickly as possible.

But she didn't go so far the second time around. She and Gordon Turner—he was, for all his life, a tongue-tied man, though he did manage a proper proposal—settled down in Winnipeg, first in St. Boniface where the rents were cheap and then Fort Rouge and finally the little house in River Heights just around the corner from the high school. It was her husband, Gord, who planted the grass that Mrs. Turner now shaves in the summertime. It was Gord who trimmed and shaped the caragana hedge and Gord who painted the little shutters with the cut-out hearts. He was a man who loved every inch of his house, the wide wooden steps, the oak door with its glass inset, the radiators and the baseboards and the snug sash windows. And he loved every inch of his wife, Girlie, too, saying to her once and only once that he knew about her past (meaning Gus

MacGregor and the incident in the Boissevain Hotel), and that as far as he was concerned the slate had been wiped clean. Once he came home with a little package in his pocket; inside was a diamond ring, delicate and glittering. Once he took Girlie on a picnic all the way up to Steep Rock, and in the woods he took off her dress and underthings and kissed every part of her body.

After he died, Girlie began to travel. She was far from rich, as she liked to say, but with care she could manage one trip every spring.

She has never known such ease. She and Em and Muriel have been to Disneyland and as well as Disneyworld. They've been to Europe, taking a sixteen-day trip through seven countries. The three of them have visited the south and seen the famous antebellum houses of Georgia, Alabama and Mississippi, after which they spent a week in the city of New Orleans. They went to Mexico one year and took pictures of Mayan ruins and queer shadowy gods cut squarely from stone. And three years ago they did what they swore they'd never have the nerve to do: they got on an airplane and went to Japan.

The package tour started in Tokyo where Mrs. Turner ate, on her first night there, a chrysanthemum fried in hot oil. She saw a village where everyone earned a living by making dolls and another village where everyone made pottery. Members of the tour group, each holding up a green flag so their tour leader could keep track of them, climbed on a little train, zoomed off to Osaka where they visited an electronics factory, and then went to a restaurant to eat uncooked fish. They visited more temples and shrines than Mrs. Turner could keep track of. Once they stayed the night in a Japanese hotel where she and Em and Muriel bedded down on floor mats and little pillows stuffed with cracked wheat, and woke up, laughing, with backaches and shooting pains in their legs.

That was the same day they visited the Golden Pavilion in Kyoto. The three-storied temple was made of wood and had a roof like a set of wings and was painted a soft old flaky gold. Everybody in the group took pictures—Em took a whole roll—and bought postcards; everybody, that is, except a single tour member, the one they all referred to as the Professor.

The Professor traveled without a camera, but jotted notes almost continuously into a little pocket scribbler. He was bald, had a trim body and wore Bermuda shorts, sandals and black nylon socks. Those who asked him learned that he really was a professor, a teacher of English poetry in a small college in Massachusetts. He was also a poet who, at the time of the Japanese trip, had published two small chap-books based mainly on the breakdown of his marriage. The poems, sadly, had not caused much stir.

It grieved him to think of that paltry, guarded nut-like thing that was his artistic reputation. His domestic life had been too cluttered; there had been too many professional demands; the political situation in America had drained him of energy—these were the thoughts that buzzed in his skull as he scribbled and scribbled, like a man with a fever, in the back seat of a tour bus traveling through Japan.

Here in this crowded, confused country he discovered simplicity and order and something spiritual, too, which he recognized as being authentic. He felt as though a flower, something like a lily, only smaller and tougher, had unfurled in his hand and was nudging along his fountain pen. He wrote and wrote, shaken by catharsis, but lulled into a new sense of his powers.

Not surprisingly, a solid little book of poems came out of his experience. It was published soon afterwards by a well-thought-of Boston publisher who, as soon as possible, sent him around the United States to give poetry readings.

Mostly the Professor read his poems in universities and colleges where his book was already listed on the Contemporary Poetry course. He read in faculty clubs, student centers, classrooms, gymnasiums and auditoriums, and usually, part way through a reading, someone or other would call from the back of the room, "Give us your Golden Pavilion poem."

He would have preferred to read his Fuji meditation or the tone poem on the Inner Sea, but he was happy to oblige his audiences, though he felt "A Day At The Golden Pavilion" was a somewhat light piece, even what is sometimes known on the circuit as a 'crowd pleaser.' People (admittedly they were mostly undergraduates) laughed out loud when they heard it; he read it well, too, in a moist, avuncular, amateur actor's voice, reminding himself to pause frequently, to look upward and raise an ironic eyebrow.

The poem was not really about the Golden Pavilion at all, but about three midwestern lady tourists who, while viewing the temple and madly snapping photos, had talked incessantly and in loud, flat-bottomed voices about knitting patterns, indigestion, sore feet, breast lumps, the cost of plastic raincoats and a previous trip they'd made together to Mexico. They had wondered, these three—noisily, repeatedly—who back home in Manitoba should receive a postcard, what they'd give for an honest cup of tea, if there was an easy way to remove stains from an electric coffee maker, and where they would go the following year—Hawaii? They were the three furies, the three witches, who for vulgarity and tastelessness formed a shattering counterpoint to the Professor's own state of transcendence. He had been affronted, angered, half-crazed.

One of the sisters, a little pug of a woman, particularly stirred his contempt, she of the pink pantsuit, the red toenails, the grapefruity buttocks, the overly bright souvenirs, the garish Mexican straw bag containing Dentyne chewing gum, aspirin, breath mints, sun goggles, envelopes of saccharine, and photos of her dead husband standing in front of a squat, ugly house in Winnipeg. This defilement she had spread before the ancient and exquisitely proportioned Golden Pavilion of Kyoto, proving—and here the Professor's tone became grave—proving that sublime beauty can be brought to the very doorway of human eyes, ears and lips and remain unperceived.

When he comes to the end of "A Day At The Golden Pavilion" there is generally a thoughtful half second of silence, then laughter and applause. Students turn in their seats and exchange looks with their fellows. They have seen such unspeakable tourists themselves. There was Old Auntie Marigold or Auntie Flossie. There was that tacky Mrs. Shannon with her rouge and her jewelry. They know—despite their youth they know—the irreconcilable distance between taste and banality. Or perhaps that's too harsh; perhaps it's only the difference between those who know about the world and those who don't.

It's true Mrs. Turner remembers little about her travels. She's never had much of a head for history or dates; she never did learn, for instance, the difference between a Buddhist temple and a Shinto shrine. She gets on a tour bus and goes and goes, and that's all there is to it. She doesn't know if she's going north or south or east or west. What does it matter? She's having a grand time. And she's reassured, always, by the sameness of the world. She's never heard the word *commonality*, but is nevertheless fused with its sense. In Japan she was made as happy to see carrots and lettuce growing in the fields as she was to see sunlight, years earlier, pouring into the streets of New York City. Everywhere she's been she's seen people eating and sleeping and working and making things with their hands and urging things to grow. There have been cats and dogs, fences and bicycles and telephone poles, and objects to buy and take care of; it is amazing, she thinks, that she can understand so much of the world and that it comes to her as easily as bars of music floating out of a radio.

Her sisters have long forgotten about her wild days. Now the three of them love to sit on tour buses and chatter away about old friends and family members, their stern father and their mother who never once took their part against him. Muriel carries on about her children (a son in California and a daughter in Toronto) and she brings along snaps of her grandchildren to pass round. Em has retired from school teaching and is a volunteer in the Boissevain

Local History Museum, to which she has donated several family mementos: her father's old carved pipe and her mother's wedding veil and, in a separate case, for all the world to see, a white cotton garment labeled "Girlie Fergus' Underdrawers, handmade, trimmed with lace, circa 1918." If Mrs. Turner knew the word irony she would relish this. Even without knowing the word *irony*, she relishes it.

The professor from Massachusetts has won an important international award for his book of poems; translation rights have been sold to a number of foreign publishers; and recently his picture appeared in the *New York Times*, along with a lengthy quotation from "A Day At The Golden Pavilion." How providential, some will think, that Mrs. Turner doesn't read the *New York Times* or attend poetry readings, for it might injure her deeply to know how she appears in certain people's eyes, but then there are so many things she doesn't know.

In the summer as she cuts the grass, to and fro, to and fro, she waves to everyone she sees. She waves to the high-school girls who timidly wave back. She hollers hello to Sally and Roy Sascher and asks them how their garden is coming on. She cannot imagine that anyone would wish her harm. All she's done is live her life. The green grass flies up in the air, a buoyant cloud swirling about her head. Oh, what a sight is Mrs. Turner cutting her grass and how, like an ornament, she shines.

(1985)

Daryl Hine
(CANADA, 1936–)

Bluebeard's Wife

Impatiently she tampered with the locks,
One by one she opened all the doors;
The music boxes and the cuckoo clocks
Stopped in alarm; dust settled on the floors
5   Like apprehensive footsteps. Then the stores
Of silence were exposed to her soft touch:
Mute diamonds and still exquisite ores.
She had not thought the squalid world had such
Treasure to proffer, nor so easy, nor so much.

10   She did not listen to the hinges' groans,
Complaints in metal, warnings in the wood,
But room by room progressed from precious stones
To tears, and at each secret understood,
Exclaimed, amused, "How simple!" or "How good!"
15   As she took up some fragile, painted jar.
Throughout the palace doors and windows stood
Whether in dread or sympathy ajar
Upon a pale horizon seeming very far.

The open doors of summer afternoons,
20 The scented air that passes in and out
Ferrying insects, humming with the tunes
That nature sings unheard! She could not doubt
She was unseen, no one was about,
The servants all had gone—she wondered where:
25 The calm within was dead as that without,
And all about her breathed the stealthy air.
She knew she was alone, that no one else was there.

Now she attained the room of artifice.
Not a thing that grew there but was made:
30 Venetian glass that counterfeited ice
So close it seemed to melt, and green brocade,
The wind's most subtle movements in a glade.
Nothing was modern, everything was old,
And yet it was not true that they should fade
35 Though time and fashion dim the emerald.
Each was at once an image and a deathless mould.

Dazzled, she shut the door, but through the next
Saw greater good than any she had seen:
A window open on the sacred text
40 Of natural things, whose number had not been
Created or conceived, nor did they mean
Other than what they were, splendid and strange.
One leaf is like another, and between
Them all the worlds of difference range;
45 The world is not destroyed and does not cease to change.

The final door resisted all her strength,
No key would fit, the bars and bolts stuck fast.
But there she pried and worried, till at length
She opened it, knowing it was the last.
50 *They* hung on hooks, their finery surpassed
Each her predecessor's, in their lives
Less fortunate than she. There hung the past,
Putrid and crowned. And thinking, 'Love survives
The grave,' she stepped inside to join the other wives.

(1969)

Ngũgĩ wa Thiong'o

(KENYA, 1936–)

From *Decolonising the Mind*

III

I was born into a large peasant family: father, four wives and about twenty-eight children. I also belonged, as we all did in those days, to a wider extended family and to the community as a whole.

We spoke Gĩkũyũ as we worked in the fields. We spoke Gĩkũyũ in and outside the home. I can vividly recall those evenings of storytelling around the fireside. It was mostly the grown-ups telling the children but everybody was interested and involved. We children would re-tell the stories the following day to other children who worked in the fields picking the pyrethrum flowers, tea-leaves or coffee beans of our European and African landlords.

The stories, with mostly animals as the main characters, were all told in Gĩkũyũ. Hare, being small, weak but full of innovative wit and cunning, was our hero. We identified with him as he struggled against the brutes of prey like lion, leopard, hyena. His victories were our victories and we learnt that the apparently weak can outwit the strong. We followed the animals in their struggle against hostile nature—drought, rain, sun, wind—a confrontation often forcing them to search for forms of co-operation. But we were also interested in their struggles amongst themselves, and particularly between the beasts and the victims of prey. These twin struggles, against nature and other animals, reflected real-life struggles in the human world.

Not that we neglected stories with human beings as the main characters. There were two types of characters in such human-centred narratives: the species of truly human beings with qualities of courage, kindness, mercy, hatred of evil, concern for others; and a man-eat-man two-mouthed species with qualities of greed, selfishness, individualism and hatred of what was good for the larger co-operative community. Co-operation as the ultimate good in a community was a constant theme. It could unite human beings with animals against ogres and beasts of prey, as in the story of how dove, after being fed with castor-oil seeds, was sent to fetch a smith working far away from home and whose pregnant wife was being threatened by these man-eating two-mouthed ogres.

There were good and bad story-tellers. A good one could tell the same story over and over again, and it would always be fresh to us, the listeners. He or she could tell a story told by someone else and make it more alive and dramatic. The differences really were in the use of words and images and the inflexion of voices to effect different tones.

We therefore learnt to value words for their meaning and nuances. Language was not a mere string of words. It had a suggestive power well beyond the immediate and lexical meaning. Our appreciation of the suggestive magical power of language was reinforced by the games we played with words through riddles, proverbs, transpositions of syllables, or through nonsensical but musically arranged words. So we learnt the music of our language on top of the content. The language, through images and symbols, gave us a view of the world, but it had a beauty of its own. The home and the field were then our pre-primary school but what is important, for this discussion, is that the language of our evening teach-ins, and the language of our immediate and wider community, and the language of our work in the fields were one.

And then I went to school, a colonial school, and this harmony was broken. The language of my education was no longer the language of my culture. I first went to Kamaandura, missionary run, and then to another called Maanguuน run by nationalists grouped around the Gĩkũyũ Independent and Karinga Schools Association. Our language of education was still Gĩkũyũ. The very first time I was ever given an ovation for my writing was over a composition in Gĩkũyũ. So for my first four years there was still harmony between the language of my formal education and that of the Limuru peasant community.

It was after the declaration of a state of emergency over Kenya in 1952 that all the schools run by patriotic nationalists were taken over by the colonial regime and were placed under District Education Boards chaired by Englishmen. English became the language of my formal education. In Kenya, English became more than a language: it was *the* language, and all the others had to bow before it in deference.

Thus one of the most humiliating experiences was to be caught speaking Gĩkũyũ in the vicinity of the school. The culprit was given corporal punishment—three to five strokes of the cane on bare buttocks—or was made to carry a metal plate around the neck with inscriptions such as I AM STUPID or I AM A DONKEY. Sometimes the culprits were fined money they could hardly afford. And how did the teachers catch the culprits? A button was initially given to one pupil who was supposed to hand it over to whoever was caught speaking his mother tongue. Whoever had the button at the end of the day would sing who had given it to him and the ensuing process would bring out all the culprits of the day. Thus children were turned into witch-hunters and in the process were being taught the lucrative value of being a traitor to one's immediate community.

The attitude to English was the exact opposite: any achievement in spoken or written English was highly rewarded; prizes, prestige, applause; the ticket to higher realms. English became the measure of intelligence and ability in the arts, the sciences, and all the other branches of learning. English became *the* main determinant of a child's progress up the ladder of formal education.

As you may know, the colonial system of education in addition to its apartheid racial demarcation had the structure of a pyramid: a broad primary base, a narrowing secondary middle, and an even narrower university apex. Selections from primary into secondary were through an examination, in my time called Kenya African Preliminary Examination, in which one had to pass six subjects ranging from Maths to Nature Study and Kiswahili. All the papers were written in English. Nobody could pass the exam who failed the English language paper no matter how brilliantly he had done in the other subjects. I remember one boy in my class of 1954 who had distinctions in all subjects except English, which he had failed. He was made to fail the entire exam. He went on to become a turn boy in a bus company. I who had only passes but a credit in English got a place at the Alliance High School, one of the most elitist institutions for Africans in colonial Kenya. The requirements for a place at the University, Makerere University College, were broadly the same: nobody could go on to wear the undergraduate red gown, no matter how brilliantly they had performed in all the other subjects unless they had a credit—not even a simple pass!—in English. Thus the most coveted place in the pyramid and in the system was only available to the holder of an English language credit card. English was the official vehicle and the magic formula to colonial elitedom.

Literary education was now determined by the dominant language while also reinforcing that dominance. Orature (oral literature) in Kenyan languages stopped. In primary school I now read simplified Dickens and Stevenson alongside Rider Haggard. Jim Hawkins, Oliver Twist, Tom Brown—not Hare, Leopard and Lion—were now my daily companions in the world of imagination. In secondary school, Scott and G.B. Shaw vied with more Rider

Haggard, John Buchan, Alan Paton, Captain W.E. Johns. At Makerere I read English: from Chaucer to T.S. Eliot with a touch of Graham Greene.

Thus language and literature were taking us further and further from ourselves to other selves, from our world to other worlds.

What was the colonial system doing to us Kenyan children? What were the consequences of, on the one hand, this systematic suppression of our languages and the literature they carried, and on the other the elevation of English and the literature it carried? To answer those questions, let me first examine the relationship of language to human experience, human culture, and the human perception of reality.

IV

Language, any language, has a dual character: it is both a means of communication and a carrier of culture. Take English. It is spoken in Britain and in Sweden and Denmark. But for Swedish and Danish people English is only a means of communication with non-Scandinavians. It is not a carrier of their culture. For the British, and particularly the English, it is additionally, and inseparably from its use as a tool of communication, a carrier of their culture and history. Or take Swahili in East and Central Africa. It is widely used as a means of communication across many nationalities. But it is not the carrier of a culture and history of many of those nationalities. However in parts of Kenya and Tanzania, and particularly in Zanzibar, Swahili is inseparably both a means of communication and a carrier of the culture of those people to whom it is a mother-tongue.

Language as communication has three aspects or elements. There is first what Karl Marx once called the language of real life, the element basic to the whole notion of language, its origins and development: that is, the relations people enter into with one another in the labour process, the links they necessarily establish among themselves in the act of a people, a community of human beings, producing wealth or means of life like food, clothing, houses. A human community really starts its historical being as a community of co-operation in production through the division of labour; the simplest is between man, woman and child within a household; the more complex divisions are between branches of production such as those who are sole hunters, sole gatherers of fruits or sole workers in metal. Then there are the most complex divisions such as those in modern factories where a single product, say a shirt or a shoe, is the result of many hands and minds. Production is co-operation, is communication, is language, is expression of a relation between human beings and it is specifically human.

The second aspect of language as communication is speech and it imitates the language of real life, that is communication in production. The verbal signposts both reflect and aid communication or the relation established between human beings in the production of their means of life. Language as a system of verbal signposts makes that production possible. The spoken word is to relations between human beings what the hand is to the relations between human beings and nature. The hand through tools mediates between human beings and nature and forms the language of real life: spoken words mediate between human beings and form the language of speech.

The third aspect is the written signs. The written word imitates the spoken. Where the first two aspects of language as communication through the hand and the spoken word historically evolved more or less simultaneously, the written aspect is a much later historical development. Writing is representation of sounds with visual symbols, from the simplest knot among shepherds to tell the number in a herd or the hieroglyphics among the Agĩkũyũ gicaandi singers and poets of Kenya, to the most complicated and different letter and picture writing systems of the world today.

In most societies the written and the spoken languages are the same, in that they represent each other: what is on paper can be read to another person and be received as that language which the recipient has grown up speaking. In such a society there is broad harmony for a child between the three aspects of language as communication. His interaction with nature and with other men is expressed in written and spoken symbols or signs which are both a result of that double interaction and a reflection of it. The association of the child's sensibility is with the language of his experience of life.

But there is more to it: communication between human beings is also the basis and process of evolving culture. In doing similar kinds of things and actions over and over again under similar circumstances, similar even in their mutability, certain patterns, moves, rhythms, habits, attitudes, experiences and knowledge emerge. Those experiences are handed over to the next generation and become the inherited basis for their further actions on nature and on themselves. There is a gradual accumulation of values which in time become almost self-evident truths governing their conception of what is right and wrong, good and bad, beautiful and ugly, courageous and cowardly, generous and mean in their internal and external relations. Over a time this becomes a way of life distinguishable from other ways of life. They develop a distinctive culture and history. Culture embodies those moral, ethical and aesthetic values, the set of spiritual eyeglasses, through which they come to view themselves and their place in the universe. Values are the basis of a people's identity, their sense of particularity as members of the human race. All this is carried by language. Language as culture is the collective memory bank of a people's experience in history. Culture is almost indistinguishable from the language that makes possible its genesis, growth, banking, articulation and indeed its transmission from one generation to the next.

Language as culture also has three important aspects. Culture is a product of the history which it in turn reflects. Culture in other words is a product and a reflection of human beings communicating with one another in the very struggle to create wealth and to control it. But culture does not merely reflect that history, or rather it does so by actually forming images or pictures of the world of nature and nurture. Thus the second aspect of language as culture is as an image-forming agent in the mind of a child. Our whole conception of ourselves as a people, individually and collectively, is based on those pictures and images which may or may not correctly correspond to the actual reality of the struggles with nature and nurture which produced them in the first place. But our capacity to confront the world creatively is dependent on how those images correspond or not to that reality, how they distort or clarify the reality of our struggles. Language as culture is thus mediating between me and my own self; between my own self and other selves; between me and nature. Language is mediating in my very being. And this brings us to the third aspect of language as culture. Culture transmits or imparts those images of the world and reality through the spoken and the written language, that is through a specific language. In other words, the capacity to speak, the capacity to order sounds in a manner that makes for mutual comprehension between human beings is universal. This is the universality of language, a quality specific to human beings. It corresponds to the universality of the struggle against nature and that between human beings. But the particularity of the sounds, the words, the word order into phrases and sentences, and the specific manner, or laws, of their ordering is what distinguishes one language from another. Thus a specific culture is not transmitted through language in its universality but in its particularity as the language of a specific community with a specific history. Written literature and orature are the main means by which a particular language transmits the images of the world contained in the culture it carries.

Language as communication and as culture are then products of each other. Communication creates culture: culture is a means of communication. Language carries culture, and culture carries, particularly through orature and literature, the entire body of values by which we come to perceive ourselves and our place in the world. How people perceive themselves affects how they look at their culture, at their politics and at the social production of wealth, at their entire relationship to nature and to other beings. Language is thus inseparable from ourselves as a community of human beings with a specific form and character, a specific history, a specific relationship to the world.

V

So what was the colonialist imposition of a foreign language doing to us children?

The real aim of colonialism was to control the people's wealth: what they produced, how they produced it, and how it was distributed; to control, in other words, the entire realm of the language of real life. Colonialism imposed its control of the social production of wealth through military conquest and subsequent political dictatorship. But its most important area of domination was the mental universe of the colonised, the control, through culture, of how people perceived themselves and their relationship to the world. Economic and political control can never be complete or effective without mental control. To control a people's culture is to control their tools of self-definition in relationship to others.

For colonialism this involved two aspects of the same process: the destruction or the deliberate undervaluing of a people's culture, their art, dances, religions, history, geography, education, orature and literature, and the conscious elevation of the language of the coloniser. The domination of a people's language by the languages of the colonising nations was crucial to the domination of the mental universe of the colonised.

Take language as communication. Imposing a foreign language, and suppressing the native languages as spoken and written, were already breaking the harmony previously existing between the African child and the three aspects of language. Since the new language as a means of communication was a product of and was reflecting the 'real language of life' elsewhere, it could never as spoken or written properly reflect or imitate the real life of that community. This may in part explain why technology always appears to us as slightly external, *their* product and not *ours*. The word 'missile' used to hold an alien far-away sound until I recently learnt its equivalent in Gĩkũyũ, *ngurukuhĩ* and it made me apprehend it differently. Learning, for a colonial child, became a cerebral activity and not an emotionally felt experience.

But since the new, imposed languages could never completely break the native languages as spoken, their most effective area of domination was the third aspect of language as communication, the written. The language of an African child's formal education was foreign. The language of the books he read was foreign. The language of his conceptualisation was foreign. Thought, in him, took the visible form of a foreign language. So the written language of a child's upbringing in the school (even his spoken language within the school compound) became divorced from his spoken language at home. There was often not the slightest relationship between the child's written world, which was also the language of his schooling, and the world of his immediate environment in the family and the community. For a colonial child, the harmony existing between the three aspects of language as communication was irrevocably broken. This resulted in the disassociation of the sensibility of that child from his natural and social environment, what we might call colonial alienation. The alienation became reinforced in the teaching of history, geography, music, where bourgeois Europe was always the centre of the universe.

This disassociation, divorce, or alienation from the immediate environment becomes clearer when you look at colonial language as a carrier of culture.

Since culture is a product of the history of a people which it in turn reflects, the child was now being exposed exclusively to a culture that was a product of a world external to himself. He was being made to stand outside himself to look at himself. *Catching Them Young* is the title of a book on racism, class, sex, and politics in children's literature by Bob Dixon.

'Catching them young' as an aim was even more true of a colonial child. The images of this world and his place in it implanted in a child take years to eradicate, if they ever can be.

Since culture does not just reflect the world in images but actually, through those images, conditions a child to see that world a certain way, the colonial child was made to see the world and where he stands in it as seen and defined by or reflected in the culture of the language of imposition.

And since those images are mostly passed on through orature and literature it meant the child would now only see the world as seen in the literature of his language of adoption. From the point of view of alienation, that is of seeing oneself from outside oneself as if one was another self, it does not matter that the imported literature carried the great humanist tradition of the best in Shakespeare, Goethe, Balzac, Tolstoy, Gorky, Brecht, Sholokhov, Dickens. The location of this great mirror of imagination was necessarily Europe and its history and culture and the rest of the universe was seen from that centre.

But obviously it was worse when the colonial child was exposed to images of his world as mirrored in the written languages of his coloniser. Where his own native languages were associated in his impressionable mind with low status, humiliation, corporal punishment, slow-footed intelligence and ability or downright stupidity, non-intelligibility and barbarism, this was reinforced by the world he met in the works of such geniuses of racism as a Rider Haggard or a Nicholas Monsarrat; not to mention the pronouncement of some of the giants of western intellectual and political establishment, such as Hume ('. . . The negro is naturally inferior to the whites . . .), Thomas Jefferson ('. . . The blacks . . . are inferior to the whites on the endowments of both body and mind . . .'), or Hegel with his Africa comparable to a land of childhood still enveloped in the dark mantle of the night as far as the development of self-conscious history was concerned. Hegel's statement that there was nothing harmonious with humanity to be found in the African character is representative of the racist images of Africans and Africa such a colonial child was bound to encounter in the literature of the colonial languages. The results could be disastrous.

(1986)

Tony Harrison
(ENGLAND, 1937-)

On Not Being Milton

for Sergio Vieira & Armando Guebuza (Frelimo)

Read and committed to the flames, I call
these sixteen lines that go back to my roots
my *Cahier d'un retour au pays natal*,
my growing black enough to fit my boots.

5   The stutter of the scold out of the branks
of condescension, class and counter-class
thickens with glottals to a lumpen mass
of Ludding morphemes closing up their ranks.
Each swung cast-iron Enoch of Leeds stress
10 clangs a forged music on the frames of Art,
the looms of owned language smashed apart!

Three cheers for mute ingloriousness!

Articulation is the tongue-tied's fighting.
In the silence round all poetry we quote
15   Tidd the Cato Street conspirator who wrote:

Sir, I Ham a very Bad Hand at Righting.
(1981)

Note: An 'Enoch' is an iron sledge-hammer used by the Luddites to smash the frames which were also
made by the same Enoch Taylor of Marsden. The cry was: 'Enoch made them, Enoch shall break them!'

Lola Lemire Tostevin

(CANADA, 1937–)

From 'sophie

listening to Lady Day you forget about lyrics hear
the mystery of voice trace in time a space between
the lines one note above one note below the melody
flowers beyond measure too marvelous for words give
5   me more and more and then some

on a postcard photograph on my desk gardenias
stick out from the side of her head like antennas
no sound must have gone past her

this morning I placed a bunch of gardenias by my
10   typewriter looking for the same intoxicating scent
that must have hovered about her scent of jasmine
jazz that mines the slow unfurling of delicate petals
beating time into unknown space

listening to Billie you forget about words sweet
15   strains don't explain you know what it means

beyond my window a bird is tracing against the sky
the mystery of flight as near as words I move closer
to you
(1988)

Jack Hodgins
(CANADA, 1938–)

The Lepers' Squint

Today, while Mary Brennan may be waiting for him on that tiny island high in the mountain lake called Gougane Barra, Philip Desmond is holed up in the back room of this house at Bantry Bay, trying to write his novel. A perfect stack of white paper, three black nylon-tipped pens, and a battered portable typewriter are set out before him on the wooden table. He knows the first paragraph already, has already set it down, and trusts that the rest of the story will run off the end of it like a fishing line pulled by a salmon. But it is cold, it is so cold in this house, even now in August, that he presses both hands down between his thighs to warm them up. It is so cold in this room that he finds it almost impossible to sit still, so damp that he has put on the same clothes he would wear if he were walking out along the edge of that lagoon, in the spitting rain and the wind. Through the small water-specked panes of the window he can see his children playing on the lumpy slabs of rock at the shore, beyond the bobbing branches of the fuchsia hedge. Three children; three red quilted jackets; three faces flushed up by the steady force of the cold wind; they drag tangled clots of stinking seaweed up the slope and, crouching, watch a family of swans explore the edges of a small weedy island not far out in the lagoon.

A high clear voice in his head all the while insists on singing to him of some girl so fair that the ferns uncurl to look at her. The voice of an old man in a mountain pub, singing without accompaniment, stretched and stiff as a rooster singing to the ceiling and to the crowd at the bar and to the neighbours who sit around him. *The ferns uncurled to look at her, so very fair was she, with her hair as bright as the seaweed that floats in from the sea.* But here at Ballylickey the seaweed is brown as mud and smells so strong your eyes water.

Mrs. O'Sullivan is in the next room, Desmond knows, in her own room, listening. If he coughs she will hear. If he sings. She will know exactly the moment he sets down his next word on that top sheet of paper. Mrs. O'Sullivan is the owner of this house, which Desmond rented from home through the Borde Failte people before he discovered that she would live in it with them, in the centre of the house, in her two rooms, and silently listen to the life of his family going on around her. She is a tall dry-skinned old woman with grey finger-waves caged in blue hair-net, whose thick fingers dig into the sides of her face in an agony of desire to sympathize with everything that is said to her. "Oh I know I know I know," she groans. Last night when Desmond's wife mentioned how tired she was after the long drive down from Dublin, her fingers plucked at her face, her dull eyes rolled up to search for help along the ceiling: "Oh I know I know I know." There is no end to her sympathy, there is nothing she doesn't already know. But she will be quiet as a mouse, she promised, they won't know she is here.

"Maybe she's a writer," Desmond's wife whispered to him, later in bed. "Maybe she's making notes on us. Maybe she's writing a book called *North Americans I Have Eavesdropped On.*"

"I can't live with someone listening to me breathe," Desmond said. "And I can't write with someone sitting waiting."

"Adjust," his wife said, and flicked at his nose. She who could adjust to anything, or absorb it.

On this first day of his novel Desmond has been abandoned by his wife, Carrie, who early this morning drove the car in to Cork. There are still, apparently, a few Seamus Murphy statues she hasn't seen, or touched. "Keep half an eye on the kids," she said before she left. Then she came back and kissed him and whispered, "Though if you get busy it won't matter. I'm sure Mrs. O'Sullivan won't miss anything." To be fair, to be really fair, he knows that his annoyance is unjustified. He didn't tell her he intended to work today, the first day in this house. She probably thinks that after travelling for six weeks through the country he'll rest a few more days before beginning; she may even believe that he is glad to be rid of her for the day, after all those weeks of unavoidable closeness. She certainly knows that with Mrs. O'Sullivan in the house no emergency will be overlooked, no crisis ignored.

Desmond, now that his hands have warmed a little, lifts one of the pens to write, though silently as possible, as if what he is about to do is a secret perversion from which the ears of Mrs. O'Sullivan must be protected. But he cannot, now, put down any new words. Because if the novel, which has been roaring around in his head all summer and much longer, looking for a chance to get out, should not recognize in the opening words the crack through which it is to spring forth, transformed into a string of words like a whirring fishline, then he will be left with all that paper to stare at, and an unmoving pen, and he is not ready to face that. Of course he knows the story, has seen it all in his mind a hundred times as if someone else had gone to the trouble of writing it and producing it as a movie just for him. But he has never been one for plunging into things, oceans or stories, and prefers to work his way in gently. That opening paragraph, though, is only a paragraph after all and has no magic, only a few black lifeless lines at the top of the paper. So he writes his title again, and under it his name: Barclay Philip Desmond. Then he writes the opening paragraph a second time, and again under that, and again, hoping that the pen will go on by itself to write the next words and surprise him. But it does not happen, not now. Instead, he discovers he is seeing two other words which are not there at all, as if perhaps they are embedded, somehow, just beneath the surface of the paper.

Mary Brennan.

Desmond knows he must keep the name from becoming anything more than that, from becoming a face too, or the pale scent of fear. He writes his paragraph again, over and over until he has filled up three or four pages. Then, crumpling the papers in his hand, he wonders if this will be one of those stories that remain forever in their authors' heads, driving them mad, refusing to suffer conversion into words.

It's the cold, he thinks. Blame it on the bloody weather. His children outside on the rocky slope have pulled the hoods of their jackets up over their heads. Leaves torn from the beech tree lie soaked and heavy on the grass. At the far side of the lagoon the family of swans is following the choppy retreating tide out through the gap to the open bay; perhaps they know of a calmer inlet somewhere. The white stone house with red window frames in its nest of bushes across the water has blurred behind the rain, and looks more than ever like the romantic pictures he has seen on postcards. A thin line of smoke rises from the yellowish house with the gate sign *Carrigdhoun*.

But it is easier than writing, far easier, to allow the persistent daydreams in, and memory. That old rooster-stiff man, standing in the cleared-away centre of the bar in Ballyvourney to pump his song out to the ceiling, his hands clasping and unclasping at his sides as if they are responsible for squeezing those words into life. The ferns uncurled to see her, he sings, so very fair was she. Neighbours clap rhythm, or stamp their feet. Men six-deep at the bar-counter continue to shout at each other about sheep, and the weather. With hair as bright as the seaweed that floats in from the sea.

" 'Tis an island of singers sure!" someone yells in Desmond's ear. "An island of saints and paupers and bloody singers!"

But Desmond thinks of Mary Brennan's hot apple-smelling breath against his face: "Islands do not exist until you have loved on them." The words are a Caribbean poet's, she explains, and not her own. But the sentiment is adaptable. The ferns may not uncurl to see the dark brown beauty of her eyes, but Desmond has seen men turn at her flash of hair, the reddish-brown of gleaming kelp. Turn, and smile to themselves. This day while he sits behind the wooden table, hunched over his pile of paper, he knows that she is waiting for him on a tiny hermitage island in a mountain lake not far away, beneath the branches of the crowded trees. Islands, she had told him, do not exist until you've loved on them.

Yesterday, driving south from Dublin across the Tipperary farmland, they stopped again at the Rock of Cashel so that Carrie could prowl a second time through that big roofless cathedral high up on the sudden limestone knoll and run her hands over the strange broken form of St. Patrick's Cross. The kings of Munster lived there once, she told him, and later turned it over to the church. St. Patrick himself came to baptize the king there, and accidentally pierced the poor man's foot with the point of his heavy staff.

"There's all of history here, huddled together," she said, and catalogued it for him. "A tenth-century round tower, a twelfth-century chapel, a thirteenth-century cathedral, a fourteenth-century tower, a fifteenth-century castle, and . . ." she rolled her eyes, "a twentieth-century tourist shop."

But it was the cross itself that drew her. Originally a cross within a frame, it was only the central figure of a man now, with one arm of the cross and a thin upright stem that held that arm in place. Rather like a tall narrow pitcher. There was a guide this second time, and a tour, and she pouted when he insisted they stick to the crowd and hear the official truths instead of making guesses or relying on the brief explanations on the backs of postcards. She threw him a black scowl when the guide explained the superstition about the cross: that if you can touch hand to hand around it you'll never have another toothache as long as you live. Ridiculous, she muttered; she'd spent an hour the last time looking at that thing, marvelling at the beautiful piece of sculpture nature or time or perhaps vandals had accidentally made of it, running her hands over the figures on the coronation stone at its base and up the narrow stem that supported the remaining arm of the cross.

He was more curious, though, about the round swell of land which could be seen out across the flat Tipperary farms, a perfect green hill crowned with a circle of leafy trees. The guide told him that after one of the crusades a number of people returned to Ireland with a skin disease which was mistaken for leprosy and were confined to that hill, inside that circle, and forbidden to leave it. They were brought across to Mass here on Sundays, she said, before leading him back inside the cathedral to show a small gap in the stones far up one grey wall of the empty Choir. "The poor lepers, a miserable lot altogether as you can imagine, were crowded into a little room behind that wall," she said, "and were forced to see and hear through that single narrow slit of a window. It's called the Lepers' Squint, for obvious reasons."

Afterwards, when the crowd of nuns and priests and yellow-slickered tourists had broken up to walk amongst the graves and the Celtic crosses or to climb the stone steps to the round tower, Desmond would like to have spoken to one of the priests, perhaps the short red-faced one, to say, "What do you make of all this?" or "Is it true what she told us about that fat archbishop with all his wives and children?" But he was intimidated by the black suit, that collar, and by the way the priest seemed always to be surrounded by nuns who giggled like schoolgirls at the silly jokes he told, full of words Desmond couldn't understand. He would go home without ever speaking to a single member of the one aristocracy this country still permitted itself.

But while he stood tempted in the sharp wind that howled across the high hump of rock the guide came over the grass to him. " 'Tis certain that you're not American as I thought at first," she said, "for you speak too soft for that. Would you be from England then?"

"No," he said. And without thinking: "We're from Vancouver Island."

"Yes?" she said, her eyes blank. "And where would that be now?"

"A long way from here," he said. "An island, too, like this one, with its own brand of ruins."

"There's a tiny island off our coast," he said, "where they used to send the lepers once, but the last of them died a few years ago. It's a bare and empty place they say now, except for the wind. There are even people who believe that ghosts inhabit it."

But then there were people, too, who said he was crazy to take the children to this uneasy country. It's smaller than you think, they said. You'll hear the bombs from above the border when you get there. What if war breaks out? What if the IRA decides that foreign hostages might help their cause? What about that bomb in the Dublin department store?

Choose another country, they said. A warmer safer one. Choose an island where you can lie in the sun and be waited on by smiling blacks. Why pick Ireland?

Jealousy, he'd told them. Everyone else he knew seemed to have inherited an "old country," an accent, a religion, a set of customs, from parents. His family fled the potato famine in 1849 and had had five generations in which to fade out into Canadians. "I don't know what I've inherited from them," he said, "but whatever it is has gone too deep to be visible."

They'd spent the summer travelling; he would spend the fall and winter writing.

His search for family roots, however, had ended down a narrow hedged-in lane: a half-tumbled stone cabin, stony fields, a view of misty hills, and distant neighbours who turned their damp hay with a two-tined fork and knew nothing at all of the cabin's past.

"Fled the famine did they?" the old woman said. " 'Twas many a man did that and was never heard from since."

The summer was intended as a literary pilgrimage too, and much of it was a disappointment. Yeats's castle tower near Coole had been turned into a tourist trap as artificial as a wax museum, with cassette recorders to listen to as you walk through from room to room, and a souvenir shop to sell you books and postcards; Oliver Goldsmith's village was not only deserted, it had disappeared, the site of the little schoolhouse nothing more than a potato patch and the parsonage just half a vine-covered wall; the James Joyce museum only made him feel guilty that he'd never been able to finish *Ulysses*, though there'd been a little excitement that day when a group of women's libbers crashed the male nude-bathing beach just behind the tower.

A man in Dublin told him there weren't any live writers in this country. "You'll find more of our novelists and poets in America than you'll find here," he said. "You're wasting your time on that."

With a sense almost of relief, as though delivered from a responsibility (dead writers, though disappointing, do not confront you with flesh, as living writers could, or with demands), he took the news along with a handful of hot dogs to Carrie and the kids, who had got out of the car to admire a statue. Watching her eat that onion and pork sausage "hot dog" he realized that she had become invisible to him, or nearly invisible. He hadn't even noticed until now that she'd changed her hair, that she was pinning it back; probably because of the wind. In the weeks of travel, in constant too-close confinement, she had all but disappeared, had faded out of his notice the way his own limbs must have done, oh, thirty years ago.

If someone had asked, "What does your wife look like?" he would have forgotten to mention short. He might have said dainty but that was no longer entirely true; sitting like that she appeared to have rounded out, like a copper Oriental idol: dark and squat and yet fine, perhaps elegant. He could not have forgotten her loud, almost masculine laugh of course, but he had long ago ceased to notice the quality of her speaking voice. Carrie, his Carrie, was busy having her own separate holiday, almost untouched by his, though they wore each other like old comfortable unnoticed and unchanged clothes.

"A movie would be nice," he said. "If we could find a babysitter."

But she shook her head. "We can see movies at home. And besides, by the evenings I'm tired out from all we've done, I'd never be able to keep my eyes open."

After Cashel, on their way to the Bantry house, they stopped a while in the city of Cork. And here, he discovered, here after all the disappointments, was a dead literary hero the tourist board hadn't yet got ahold of. He forgot again that she even existed as he tracked down the settings of the stories he loved: butcher shops and smelly quays and dark crowded pubs and parks.

The first house, the little house where the famous writer was born, had been torn down by a sports club which had put a high steel fence around the property, but a neighbour took him across the road and through a building to the back balcony to show him the Good Shepherd Convent where the writer's mother had grown up, and where she returned often with the little boy to visit the nuns. "If he were still alive," Desmond said, "if he still lived here, I suppose I would be scared to come, I'd be afraid to speak to him." The little man, the neighbour, took off his glasses to shine them on a white handkerchief. "Ah, he was a shy man himself. He was back here a few years before he died, with a big crew of American fillum people, and he was a friendly man, friendly enough. But you could see he was a shy man too, yes. 'Tis the shy ones sometimes that take to the book writing."

Carrie wasn't interested in finding the second house. She had never read the man's books, she never read anything at all except art histories and museum catalogues. She said she would go to the park, where there were statues, if he'd let her off there. She said if the kids didn't get out of the car soon to run off some of their energy they would drive her crazy, or kill each other. You could hardly expect children to be interested in old dead writers they'd never heard of, she said. It was no fun for them.

He knew as well as she did that if they were not soon released from the backseat prison they would do each other damage. "I'll go alone," he said.

"But don't be long. We've got a good ways to do yet if we're going to make it to that house today."

So he went in search of the second house, the house the writer had lived in for most of his childhood and youth and had mentioned in dozens of his stories. He found it high up the sloping streets on the north side of the river. Two rows of identical homes, cement-grey, faced each other across a bare sloping square of dirt, each row like a set of steps down the slope, each home just a gate in a cement waist-high wall, a door, a window. Somewhere in this square was where the barefoot grandmother had lived, and where the lady lived whose daughter refused to sleep lying down because people died that way, and where the toothless woman lived who between her sessions in the insane asylum loved animals and people with a saintly passion.

The house he was after was half-way up the left-hand slope and barely distinguishable from the others, except that there was a woman in the tiny front yard, opening the gate to come out.

"There's no one home," she said when she saw his intentions. "They weren't expecting me this time, and presumably, they weren't expecting you either."

"Then it is the right house?" Desmond said. Stupidly, he thought. Right house for what?

But she seemed to understand. "Oh yes. It's the right house. Some day the city will get around to putting a plaque on the wall but for the time being I prefer it the way it is. My name, by the way," she added, "is Mary Brennan. I don't live here but I stop by often enough. The old man, you see, was one of my teachers years ago."

She might have been an official guide, she said it all so smoothly. Almost whispering. And there was barely a trace of the musical tipped-up accent of the southern counties in her voice. Perhaps Dublin, or educated. Her name meant nothing to him at first, coming like that without warning. "There would be little point in your going inside anyway, even if they were home," she said. "There's a lovely young couple living there now but they've redone the whole thing over into a perfectly charming but very modern apartment. There's nothing at all to remind you of him. I stop by for reasons I don't begin to understand, respect perhaps, or inspiration, but certainly not to find anything of him here."

In a careless, uneven way, she was pretty. Even beautiful. She wore clothes—a yellow skirt, a sweater—as if they'd been pulled on as she'd hurried out the door. Her coat was draped over her arm, for the momentary blessing of sun. But she was tall enough to get away with the sloppiness and had brown eyes which were calm, calming. And hands that tended to behave as if they were helping deliver her words to him, stirring up the pale scent of her perfume. He would guess she was thirty, she was a little younger than he was.

"Desmond," he said. "Uh, Philip Desmond."

She squinted at him, as if she had her doubts. Then she nodded, consenting. "You're an American," she said. "And probably a writer. But I must warn you. I've been to your part of the world and you just can't do for it what he did for this. It isn't the same. You don't have the history, the sense that everything that happens is happening on top of layers of things which have already happened. Now I saw you drive up in a motor car and I arrived on a bus so if you're going back down to the city centre I'll thank you for a ride."

Mary Brennan, of course. Why hadn't he known? There were two of her books in the trunk of his car. Paperbacks. Desmond felt his throat closing. Before he'd known who she was he hadn't let him say a word, and now that she seemed to be waiting to hear what he had to offer, he was speechless. His mind was a blank. All he could think of was *Mary Brennan* and wish that she'd turned out to be only a colourful eccentric old lady, something he could handle. He was comfortable with young women only until they turned out to be better than he was at something important to him. Then his throat closed. His mind pulled down the shades and hid.

All Desmond could think to say, driving down the hill towards the River Lee, was: "A man in Dublin told me there was no literature happening in this country." He could have bitten off his tongue. This woman *was* what was happening. A country that had someone like her needed no one else.

She would not accept that, she said, not even from a man in Dublin. And she insisted that he drive her out to the limestone castle restaurant at the mouth of the river so she could buy him a drink there and convince him Dublin was wrong. Inside the castle, though, while they watched the white ferry to Swansea slide out past their window, she discovered she would rather talk about her divorce, a messy thing which had been a strain on everyone concerned and had convinced her if she needed convincing that marriage was an absurd arrangement. She touched Desmond, twice, with one hand, for emphasis.

Oh, she was a charming woman, there was no question. She could be famous for those eyes alone, which never missed a detail in that room (a setting she would use, perhaps, in her next novel of Irish infidelity and rebellion?) and at the same time somehow returned to him often enough and long enough to keep him frozen, afraid to sneak his own glances at the items she was cataloguing for herself. "Some day," she said, "they will have converted all our history into restaurants and bars like this one, just as I will have converted it all to fiction. Then what will we have?"

And when, finally, he said he must go, he really must go, the park was pretty but didn't have all that much in it for kids to do, she said, "Listen, if you want to find out what is happening here, if you really do love that old man's work, then join us tomorrow. There'll be more than a dozen of us, some of the most exciting talent in the country, all meeting up at Gougane Barra . . . you know the place, the lake in the mountains where this river rises . . . it was a spot he loved."

"Tomorrow," he said. "We'll have moved in by then, to the house we've rented for the winter."

"There's a park there now," she said. "And of course the tiny hermitage island. It will begin as a picnic but who knows how it will end." The hand, a white hand with unpainted nails, touched him again.

"Yes," he said. "Yes. We've been there. There's a tiny church on the island, he wrote a story about it, the burial of a priest. And it's only an hour or so from the house, I'd guess. Maybe. Maybe I will."

"Oh you must," she said, and leaned forward. "You knew, of course, that they call it Deep-Valleyed Desmond in the songs." She drew back, biting on a smile.

But when he'd driven her back to the downtown area, to wide St. Patrick's Street, she discovered she was not quite ready yet to let him go. "Walk with me," she said, "for just a while," and found him a parking spot in front of the Munster Arcade where dummies dressed as monks and Vikings and Celtic warriors glowered at him from behind the glass.

"This place exists," she said, "because he made it real for me. He and others, in their stories. I could never write about a place where I was the first, it would panic me. I couldn't be sure it really existed or if I were inventing it."

She led him down past the statue of sober Father Matthew and the parked double-decker buses to the bridge across the Lee. A wind, coming down the river, brought a smell like an open sewer with it. He put his head down and tried to hurry across.

"If I were a North American, like you," she said, "I'd have to move away or become a shop girl. I couldn't write."

He was tempted to say something about plastering over someone else's old buildings, but thought better of it. He hadn't even read her books yet, he knew them only by reputation, he had no right to comment. He stopped, instead, to lean over the stone wall and look at the river. It was like sticking his head into a septic tank. The water was dark, nearly black, and low. Along the edges rats moved over humps of dark shiny muck and half-buried cans and bottles. Holes in the stone wall dumped a steady stream of new sewage into the river. The stories, as far as he could remember, had never mentioned this. These quays were romantic places where young people met and teased each other, or churchgoers gathered to gossip after Mass, or old people strolled. None of them, apparently, had noses.

Wind in the row of trees. Leaves rustling. Desmond looked at her hands. The perfect slim white fingers lay motionless along her skirt, then moved suddenly up to her throat, to touch the neck of her sweater. Then the nearer one moved again, and touched his arm. Those eyes, busy recording the street, paused to look at him; she smiled. Cataloguing me too? he thought. Recording me for future reference? But she didn't know a thing about him.

"I've moved here to work on a book," he said.

Her gaze rested for a moment on the front of his jacket, then flickered away. "Not about *here*," she said. "You're not writing about *this* place?" She looked as if she would protect it from him, if necessary, or whisk it away.

"I have my own place," he said. "I don't need to borrow his."

She stopped, to buy them each an apple from an old black-shawled woman who sat up against the wall by her table of fruit. Ancient, gypsy-faced, with huge earrings hanging from those heavy lobes. Black Spanish eyes. Mary Brennan flashed a smile, counted out some silver pieces, and picked over the apples for two that were red and clear. The hands that offered change were thick and wrinkled, with crescents of black beneath the nails. They disappeared again beneath the shawl. Desmond felt a momentary twinge about biting into the apple; vague memories of parental warnings. You never know whose hands have touched it, they said, in a voice to make you shudder in horror at the possibilities and scrub at the skin of fruit until it was bruised and raw.

Mary Brennan, apparently, had not been subjected to the same warnings. She bit hugely. "Here," she said, at the bridge, "here is where I'm most aware of him. All his favourite streets converge here, from up the hill. Sunday's Well, over there where his wealthy people lived. And of course Blarney Lane. If you had the time we could walk up there, I could show you. Where his first house was, and the pub he dragged his father home from."

"I've seen it," Desmond said, and started across the bridge. She would spoil it all for him if he let her.

But she won him again on the way back down the other side with her talk of castles and churches. Did he know, she asked, the reason there was no roof on the cathedral at Cashel? Did he know why Blackrock Castle where they'd been a half-hour before was a different style altogether than most of the castles of Ireland? Did he know the origin of the word "blarney"?

No he did not, but he knew that his wife would be furious if he didn't hurry back to the park. They passed the noise of voices haggling over second-hand clothes and old books at the Coal Market, they passed the opera house, a tiny yellow book store. She could walk, he saw, the way so many women had forgotten how to walk after high-heeled shoes went out, with long legs and long strides, with some spring in her steps as if there were pleasure in it.

"Now you'll not forget," she said at his car, in his window. "Tomorrow, in Deep-Valleyed Desmond where the Lee rises." There was the scent of apple on her breath. Islands, she leaned in to say, do not exist until you've loved on them.

But today, while Mary Brennan waits on that tiny island for him, Philip Desmond is holed up in the back room of this house at Bantry Bay, trying to write his novel. His wife has taken the car to Cork. When she returns, he doesn't know what he will do. Perhaps he'll get into the car and drive up the snaking road past the crumbling O'Sullivan castle into the mountains, and throw himself into the middle of that crowd of writers as if he belongs there. Maybe he will make them think that he is important, that back home he is noticed in the way that Mary Brennan is noticed here, that his work matters. And perhaps late at night, when everyone is drunk, he will lead Mary Brennan out onto the hermitage island to visit the oratory, to speak in whispers of the stories which had happened there, and to lie on the grass beneath the trees, by the quiet edge of the lake. It is not, Desmond knows, too unthinkable. At a distance.

The piece of paper in front of him is still blank. Mrs. O'Sullivan will advertise the laziness of writers, who only pretend they are working when they are actually dreaming. Or sleeping. She will likely be able to tell exactly how many words he has written, though if he at the end of this day complains of how tired he is, she will undoubtedly go into her practised agony. He wonders if she too, from her window, has noticed that the tide had gone out, that the lagoon is empty of everything except brown shiny mud and seaweed, and that the nostril-burning smell of it is penetrating even to the inside of the house, even in here where the window hasn't been opened, likely, in years. He wonders, too, if she minds that the children, who have tired of their sea-edge exploring, are building a castle of pebbles and fuchsia branches in the middle of her back lawn. The youngest, Michael, dances like an Indian around it; maybe he has to go to the bathroom and can't remember where it is. While his father, who could tell him, who could take him there, sits and stares at a piece of paper.

For a moment Desmond wonders how the medieval masses in the cathedral at Cashel must have appeared to the lepers crowded behind that narrow hole. Of course he has never seen a Mass of any kind himself, but still he can imagine the glimpses of fine robes, the bright colours, the voices of a choir singing those high eerie Latin songs, the voice of a chanting priest, the faces of a few worshippers. It was a lean world from behind that stone wall, through that narrow hole. Like looking through the eye of a needle. The Mass, as close as they were permitted to get to the world, would be only timidly glimpsed past other pressed straining heads. For of course Desmond imagines himself far at the back of the crowd.

("Yes?" the guide said. "And where would that be now?"

"A long way from here," he said. "An island, too, like this one, with its own brand of ruins. You've never heard of it though it's nearly the size of Ireland?"

"I have, yes. And it's a long way you've come from home."

"There's a tiny island just off our coast where they used to send the lepers, but the last of them died there a few years ago. It's a bare and empty place they say now, except for the wind. There are even people who believe that ghosts inhabit it.")

What does the world look like to a leper, squinting through that narrow hole? What does it feel like to be confined to the interior of a circle of trees, at the top of a hill, from which everything else can be seen but not approached? Desmond likes to think that he would prefer the life of that famous fat archbishop, celebrating Mass in the cathedral and thinking of his hundred children.

Somewhere in the house a telephone rings. Desmond hasn't been here long enough to notice where the telephone is, whether it is in her part of the house or theirs. But he hears, beyond the wall, the sudden rustling of clothes, the snap of bones, the sound of feet walking across the carpet. Why should Mrs. O'Sullivan have a phone? There are so few telephones in this country that they are all listed in the one book. But her footsteps return, and he hears behind him the turning of his door handle, the squeal of a hinge. Then her voice whispering: "Mr. Desmond? Is it a bad time to interrupt?"

"Is it my wife?"

No it is not. And of course Desmond knows who it is. Before he left the castle-restaurant she asked for his address, for Mrs. O'Sullivan's name, for the name of this village.

"I'm sorry, Mrs. O'Sullivan," he said. "Tell her, tell them I'm working, they'll understand. Tell them I don't want to be disturbed, not just now anyway."

He doesn't turn to see how high her eyebrows lift. He can imagine. Working, she's thinking. If that's working. But when she has closed the door something in him relaxes a little—or at least suspends its tension for a while—and he writes the paragraph again at the top of the page and then adds new words after it until he discovers he has completed a second. It is not very good; he decides when he reads it over that it is not very good at all, but at least it is something. A beginning. Perhaps the dam has been broken.

But there is a commotion, suddenly, in the front yard. A car horn beeping. The children run up the slope past the house. He can hear Carrie's voice calling them. There is a flurry of excited voices and then one of the children is at the door, calling, "Daddy, Daddy, come and see what Mommy has!"

What Mommy has, he discovers soon enough, is something that seems to be taking up the whole back seat, a grey lumpy bulk. And she, standing at the open door, is beaming at him. "Come help me get this thing out!" she says. There is colour in her face, excitement. She has made another one of her finds.

It is, naturally, a piece of sculpture. There is no way Desmond can tell what it is supposed to be and he has given up trying to understand such things long ago. He pulls the figure out, staggers across to the front door, and puts it down in the hall.

"I met the artist who did it," she says. "He was in the little shop delivering something. We talked, it seemed, for hours. This is inspired by the St. Patrick's Cross, he told me, but he abstracted it even more to represent the way art has taken the place of religion in the modern world."

"Whatever it represents," Desmond says, "we'll never get it home."

Nothing, to Carrie, is a problem. "We'll enjoy it here, in this house. Then before we leave we'll crate it up and ship it home." She walks around the sculpture, delighted with it, delighted with herself.

"I could have talked to him for hours," she says, "we got along beautifully. But I remembered you asked me to have the car home early." She kisses him, pushes a finger on his nose. "See how obedient I am?"

"I said that?"

"Yes," she says. "Right after breakfast. Some other place you said you wanted to go prowling around in by yourself. I rushed home down all that long winding bloody road for you. On the wrong side, I'll never get used to it. Watching for radar traps, for heaven's sake. Do you think the gardai have radar traps here?"

But Desmond is watching Mrs. O'Sullivan, who has come out into the hall to stare at the piece of sculpture. Why does he have this urge to show her his two paragraphs? Desmond doesn't even show Carrie anything until it is finished. Why, he wonders, should he feel just because she sits there listening through the wall that she's also waiting for him to produce something? She probably doesn't even read. Still, he wants to say, "Look. Read this, isn't it good? And I wrote it in your house, only today."

Mrs. O'Sullivan's hand is knotting at her throat. The sculpture has drawn a frown, a heavy sulk. " 'Tis a queer lot of objects they've been making for the tourists, and none of them what you could put a name to."

"But oh," Carrie says, "he must be nearly the best in the country! Surely. And this is no tourist souvenir. I got it from an art shop in Cork."

Mrs. O'Sullivan's hand opens and closes, creeps closer to her mouth. "Oh," she says. "Cork." As if a lot has been explained. "You can expect anything at all from a city. Anything at all. There was people here staying in this house, 'twas last year yes, came back from Cork as pleased as the Pope with an old box of turf they had bought. They wanted to smell it burning in my fire if you don't mind. What you spend your money on is your own business, I told them, but I left the bogs behind years ago, thank you, and heat my house with electricity. Keep the turf in your car so."

Carrie is plainly insulted. Words struggle at her lips. But she dismisses them, apparently, and chooses diversion. "I'll make a pot of tea. Would you like a cup with us, Mrs. O'Sullivan? The long drive's made me thirsty."

And Mrs. O'Sullivan, whose role is apparently varied and will shift for any occasion, lets her fingers pluck at her face. "Oh I know I know I know!" Her long brown-stockinged legs move slowly across the patterned carpet. "And Mr. Desmond, too, after his work. I was tempted to take him a cup but he shouldn't be disturbed I know."

"Work?" Carrie says. "Working at what?"

"I started the novel," Desmond says.

"You have? Then that's something we should celebrate. Before you go off wherever it is you think you're going."

"It's only a page," Desmond says. "And it's not very good at all, but it's a start. It's better than the blank paper."

Like some children, he thinks, he's learned to make a virtue out of anything. Even a page of scribble. When he'd be glad to give a thousand pages of scribble for the gift of honesty. Or change. Or even blindness of a sort. What good is vision after all if it refuses to ignore the dark?

Because hasn't he heard, somewhere, that artists—painters—deliberately create frames for themselves to look through, to sharpen their vision by cutting off all the details which have no importance to their work?

He follows the women into the kitchen, where cups already clatter onto saucers. "Maybe after tea," he says, "I'll get a bit more done."

Pretending, perhaps, that the rest of the world sits waiting, like Mrs. O'Sullivan, for the words he will produce. Because his tongue, his voice, has made the decision for him. Desmond knows that he may only sit in front of that paper for the rest of that day, that he may only play with his pen—frustrated—until enough time has gone by to justify his coming out of the room. To read one of the books he's bought. To talk with Carrie about her shopping in Cork, about her sculptor. To play with the children perhaps, or take them for a walk along the road to look for donkeys, for ruins. Desmond knows that the evening may be passed in front of the television set, where they will see American movies with Irish commercials, and will later try to guess what *an nuacht* is telling them about the day's events, and that he will try very hard not to think of Mary Brennan or of the dozen Irish writers at Gougane Barra or of the tiny hermitage island which the famous writer loved. Deep-Valleyed Desmond. He knows that he could be there with them, through this day and this night, celebrating something he'd come here to find; but he acknowledges, too, the other. That words, too, were invented perhaps to do the things that stones can do. And he has come here, after all, to build his walls.

(1981)

Les Murray
(AUSTRALIA, 1938–)

Louvres

In the banana zone, in the poinciana tropics
reality is stacked on handsbreadth shelving,
open and shut, it is ruled across with lines
as in a gleaming gritty exercise book.

5   The world is seen through a cranked or levered
weatherboarding of explosive glass
angled floor-to-ceiling. Horizons which metre
the dazzling outdoors into green-edged couplets.

In the louvred latitudes
10 children fly to sleep in triplanes, and
cool nights are eerie with retracting flaps.

Their houses stand aloft among bougainvillea,
covered bridges that lead down a shining hall
from love to mystery to breakfast,
15   from babyhood to moving-out day

and visitors shimmer up in columnar gauges
to touch lives lived behind gauze
in a lantern of inventory,
slick vector geometries glossing the months of rain.

20   There, nudity is dizzily cubist, and directions
have to include: stage left, add an inch of breeze
or: enter a glistening tendril.

Every building of jinked and slatted ledges
is at times a squadron of inside-out
25   helicopters, humming with rotor fans.

For drinkers under cyclonic pressure, such
a house can be a bridge of scythes—
groundlings scuffing by stop only for dénouements.

But everyone comes out on platforms of command
30   to survey cloudy flame-trees, the plain of streets, the future:
only then descending to the level of affairs

and if these things are done in the green season
what to do in the crystalline dry? Well
below in the struts of laundry is the four-wheel drive

35   vehicle in which to make an expedition
to the bush, or as we now say the Land,
the three quarters of our continent
set aside for mystic poetry.

                                        (1994)

The Assimilation of Background

Driving on that wide jute-coloured country
we came at last to the station,
its homestead with lawn and steel awnings
like a fortress against the sun.
5   And when we knocked, no people answered;
only a black dog came politely
and accompanied us round the verandahs
as we peered into rooms, and called brightly
Anyone home? The billiard room,
10   shadowed dining room, gauze-tabled kitchen
give no answer. Cricket bats, ancient

steamer trunks, the chugging coolroom engine
disregarded us. Only the dog's very patient
claws ticked with us out of the gloom
15 to the grounds' muffling dust, to the machine shed
black with oil and bolts, with the welder
mantis-like on its cylinder of clocks
and then to the stallion's enclosure.
The great bay horse came up to the wire,
20 gold flares shifting on his muscles, and stood
as one ungelded in a thousand
of his race, but imprisoned for his sex,
a gene-transmitting engine, looking at us
gravely as a spirit, out between
25 his brain's potent programmes. Then a heifer,
Durham-roan, but with Brahman hump and rings
around her eyes, came and stood among us
and a dressy goat in sable and brushed fawn
ogled us for offerings beyond
30 the news all had swiftly gathered from us
in silence, and could, it seemed, accept.
We had been received, and no one grew impatient
but only the dog, host-like, walked with us
back to our car. The lawn-watering sprays
35 ticked over, and over. And we saw
that out on that bare, crusted country
background and foreground had merged;
nothing that existed there was background.

(1994)

Tom Raworth

(ENGLAND, 1938–)

Mirror Mirror on the Wheel

what is my frame?
dry hot handkerchief
pressed to my eyes

unreal
5   i am examining
my love for this child

who looks so like me
i am inside
his movements

10   now he drops my keys
     and stares
     at the tapedeck

     "all your sea-sick sailors
     they are rowing home"
15   we hear

     time, i love you
     you are the way
     i see the same anew
                    (1972)

Margaret Atwood

(CANADA, 1939–)

It is Dangerous to Read Newspapers

     While I was building neat
     castles in the sandbox,
     the hasty pits were
     falling with bulldozed corpses

5   and as I walked to the school
     washed and combed, my feet
     stepping on the cracks in the cement
     detonated red bombs.

     Now I am grownup
10   and literate, and I sit in my chair
     as quietly as a fuse

     and the jungles are flaming, the under-
     brush is charged with soldiers,
     the names on the difficult
15   maps go up in smoke.

     I am the cause, I am a stockpile of chemical
     toys, my body
     is a deadly gadget,
     I reach out in love, my hands are guns,
20   my good intentions are completely lethal.

     Even my
     passive eyes transmute
     everything I look at to the pocked
     black and white of a war photo,
25   how can I stop myself

It is dangerous to read newspapers.

Each time I hit a key
on my electric typewriter,
speaking of peaceful trees

30   another village explodes.

(1968)

Hesitations Outside the Door

1

I'm telling the wrong lies,
they are not even useful.

The right lies would at least
be keys, they would open the door.

5   The door is closed; the chairs,
the tables, the steel bowl, myself

shaping bread in the kitchen, wait
outside it.

2

That was a lie also,
10   I could go in if I wanted to.

Whose house is this
we both live in
but neither of us owns

How can I be expected
15   to find my way around

I could go in if I wanted to,
that's not the point, I don't have time,

I should be doing something
other than you.

3

20   What do you want from me
you who walk towards me over the long floor

your arms outstretched, your heart
luminous through the ribs

around your head a crown
25   of shining blood

This is your castle, this is your metal door,
these are your stairs, your

bones, you twist all possible
dimensions into your own

4
30 Alternate version: you advance
through the grey streets of this house,

the walls crumble, the dishes
thaw, vines grow
on the softening refrigerator

35 I say, leave me
alone, this is my winter,

I will stay here if I choose

You will not listen
to resistances, you cover me

40 with flags, a dark red
season, you delete from me
all other colours

5
Don't let me do this to you,
you are not those other people,
45 you are yourself

Take off the signatures, the false
bodies, this love
which does not fit you

This is not a house, there are no doors,
50 get out while it is
open, while you still can

6
If we make stories for each other
about what is in the room
we will never have to go in.

55 You say: my other wives
are in there, they are all
beautiful and happy, they love me, why
disturb them

I say: it is only
60   a cupboard, my collection
of envelopes, my painted
eggs, my rings

In your pockets the thin women
hang on their hooks, dismembered

65   Around my neck I wear
the head of the beloved, pressed
in the metal retina like a picked flower.

                    7
Should we go into it
together / If I go into it
70   with you I will never come out

If I wait outside I can salvage
this house or what is left
of it, I can keep
my candles, my dead uncles
75   my restrictions

but you will go
alone, either
way is loss
Tell me what it is for

80   In the room we will find nothing
In the room we will find each other
                                        (1971)

Great Unexpectations

In 1960 I was nineteen years old. I was in third-year college in Toronto, Ontario, which was
not then known as People City or The Paris of the Northeast; but as Hogtown, which was not
an inaccurate description. I had never eaten an avocado or been on an airplane or encountered a croissant or been south of Vermont. Panty hose had not yet hit the market; neither
had the Pill. We were still doing garter belts and repression. Abortion was not a word you said
out loud, and lesbians might as well have been mythological hybrids, like Sphinxes; in any case
I was quite certain I had never met one. I wanted to be—no, worse—was determined to be,
was convinced I was—a writer. I was scared to death.

I was scared to death for a couple of reasons. For one thing, I was Canadian, and the
prospects for being a Canadian and a writer, both at the same time, in 1960, were dim. The only
writers I had encountered in high school had been dead and English, and in university we
barely studied American writers, much less Canadian ones. Canadian writers, it was assumed—
by my professors, my contemporaries, and myself—were a freak of nature, like duck-billed
platypuses. Logically they ought not to exist, and when they did so anyway, they were just
pathetic imitations of the real thing. This estimate was borne out by statistics: for those few who

managed, despite the reluctance of publishers, to struggle into print (five novels in English in 1960), two hundred copies of a book of poetry was considered average to good, and a thousand made a novel a Canadian best seller. I would have to emigrate, I concluded gloomily. I faced a future of scrubbing restaurant floors in England—where we colonials could go, then, much more easily than we could to the United States—writing masterpieces in a freezing cold garret at night, and getting T.B., like Keats. Such was my operatic view of my own future.

But it was more complicated than that, because, in addition to being a Canadian, I was also a woman. In some ways this was an advantage. Being a male writer in Canada branded you a sissy, but writing was not quite so unthinkable for a woman, ranking as it did with flower painting and making roses out of wood. As one friend of my mother's put it, trying to take a cheerful view of my eccentricity, "Well that's nice dear, because you can do it at home, can't you?" She was right, as it turned out, but at that moment she aroused nothing but loathing in my adolescent soul. Home, hell. It was garret or nothing. What did she think I was, inauthentic? However, most people were so appalled by my determination to be a writer that no one even thought of saying I couldn't because I was a girl. That sort of thing was not said to me until later, by male writers, by which time it was too late.

Strangely, no one was pushing early marriage, not in my case. Canada, being a cultural backwater, had not been swept by the wave of Freudianism that had washed over the United States in the fifties—Canadian women were not yet expected to be fecund and passive in order to fulfill themselves—and there were still some bluestockings around in the educational system, women who warned us not to get silly about boys too soon and throw away our chances. What my elders had in mind for me was more along academic lines. Something, that is to say, with a salary.

But, since gender is prior to nationality, the advantages of being a Canadian woman writer were canceled out by the disadvantages of being a woman writer. I'd read the biographies, which were not encouraging. Jane Austen never married Mr. Darcy. Emily Brontë died young, Charlotte in childbirth. George Eliot never had children and was ostracized for living with a married man. Emily Dickinson flitted; Christina Rossetti looked at life through the wormholes in a shroud. Some had managed to combine writing with what I considered to be a normal life—Mrs. Gaskell, Harriet Beecher Stowe—but everyone knew they were second rate. My choices were between excellence and doom on the one hand, and mediocrity and cosiness on the other. I gritted my teeth, set my face to the wind, gave up double dating, and wore horn-rims and a scowl so I would not be mistaken for a puffball.

It was in this frame of mind that I read Robert Graves's *The White Goddess,* which further terrified me. Graves did not dismiss women. In fact he placed them right at the centre of his poetic theory; but they were to be inspirations rather than creators, and a funny sort of inspiration at that. They were to be incarnations of the White Goddess herself, alternately loving and destructive, and men who got involved with them ran the risk of disembowelment or worse. A woman just might—might, mind you—have a chance of becoming a decent poet, but only if she too took on the attributes of the White Goddess and spent her time seducing men and then doing them in. All this sounded a little strenuous, and appeared to rule out domestic bliss. It wasn't my idea of how men and women should get on together—raking up leaves in the backyard, like my mom and dad—but who was I to contradict the experts? There was no one else in view giving me any advice on how to be a writer, though female. Graves was it.

That would be my life, then. To the garret and the T.B. I added the elements of enigma and solitude. I would dress in black. I would learn to smoke cigarettes, although they gave me headaches and made me cough, and drink something romantic and unusually bad for you, such as absinthe. I would live by myself, in a suitably painted attic (black) and have lovers whom I would discard in appropriate ways, though I drew the line at bloodshed. (I was, after all, a nice Canadian girl.) I would never have children. This last bothered me a lot, as before this I had always intended to have some, and it seemed unfair, but White Goddesses did not have time for children, being too taken up with cannibalistic sex, and Art came first. I would never, never own an automatic washer-dryer. Sartre, Samuel Beckett, Kafka, and Ionesco, I was sure, did not have major appliances, and these were the writers I most admired. I had no concrete ideas about how the laundry would get done, but it would only be my own laundry, I though mournfully—no fuzzy sleepers, no tiny T-shirts—and such details could be worked out later.

I tried out the garrets, which were less glamorous than expected; so was England, and so were the cigarettes, which lasted a mere six months. There wasn't any absinthe to be had, so I tried bad wine, which made me sick. It began to occur to me that maybe Robert Graves didn't have the last word on women writers, and anyway I wanted to be a novelist as well as a poet, so perhaps that would let me off the homicide. Even though Sylvia Plath and Anne Sexton had been setting new, high standards in self-destructiveness for female poets, and people had begun asking me not whether but when I was going to commit suicide (the only authentic woman poet is a dead woman poet?), I was wondering whether it was really all that necessary for a woman writer to be doomed, any more than it was necessary for a male writer to be a drunk. Wasn't all of this just some sort of postromantic collective delusion? If Shakespeare could have kids and avoid suicide, then so could I, dammit. When Betty Friedan and Simone de Beauvoir came my way, like shorebirds heralding land, I read them with much interest. They got a lot right, for me, but there was one thing they got wrong. They were assuring me that I didn't have to get married and have children. But what I wanted was someone to tell me I could.

And so I did. The marriage and the children came in two lots—the marriage with one, child with another—but they did come. This is the part that will sound smug, I suppose, but I also suppose it's not that much smugger than my black-sweatered, garter-belted, black-stockinged, existential pronouncements at the age of nineteen. I now live a life that is pretty close to the leaves-in-the-backyard model I thought would have been out of bounds forever. Instead of rotting my brains with absinthe, I bake (dare I admit it?) chocolate chip cookies, and I find that doing the laundry with the aid of my washer-dryer is one of the more relaxing parts of my week. I worry about things like remembering Parents' Day at my daughter's school and running out of cat food, though I can only afford these emotional luxuries with the aid of some business assistants and a large man who likes kids and cats and food, and has an ego so solid it isn't threatened by mine. This state of affairs was not achieved without struggle, some of it internal—did an addiction to knitting brand me as an inauthentic writer?—but it was reached. The White Goddess still turns up in my life, but mainly as a fantasy projection on the part of certain male book reviewers, who seem to like the idea of my teeth sinking into some cringing male neck. I think of this as fifties nostalgia.

As for writing, yes. You *can* do it at home.

(1987)

Seamus Heaney

(ULSTER/IRELAND, 1939–)

Personal Helicon

For Michael Longley

As a child, they could not keep me from wells
And old pumps with buckets and windlasses.
I loved the dark drop, the trapped sky, the smells
Of waterweed, fungus and dank moss.

5   One, in a brickyard, with a rotted board top.
I savoured the rich crash when a bucket
Plummeted down at the end of a rope.
So deep you saw no reflection in it.

A shallow one under a dry stone ditch
10 Fructified like any aquarium.
When you dragged out long roots from the soft mulch
A white face hovered over the bottom.

Others had echoes, gave back your own call
With a clean new music in it. And one
15 Was scaresome for there, out of ferns and tall
Foxgloves, a rat slapped across my reflection.

Now, to pry into roots, to finger slime,
To stare, big-eyed Narcissus, into some spring
Is beneath all adult dignity. I rhyme
20 To see myself, to set the darkness echoing.

(1966)

The Forge

All I know is a door into the dark.
Outside, old axles and iron hoops rusting;
Inside, the hammered anvil's short-pitched ring,
The unpredictable fantail of sparks
5 Or hiss when a new shoe toughens in water.
The anvil must be somewhere in the centre,
Horned as a unicorn, at one end square,
Set there immoveable: an altar
Where he expends himself in shape and music.
10 Sometimes, leather-aproned, hairs in his nose,
He leans out on the jamb, recalls a clatter
Of hoofs where traffic is flashing in rows;
Then grunts and goes in, with a slam and flick
To beat real iron out, to work the bellows.

(1969)

The Wife's Tale

When I had spread it all on linen cloth
Under the hedge, I called them over.
The hum and gulp of the thresher ran down
And the big belt slewed to a standstill, straw
5   Hanging undelivered in the jaws.
There was such quiet that I heard their boots
Crunching the stubble twenty yards away.

He lay down and said 'Give these fellows theirs.
I'm in no hurry,' plucking grass in handfuls
10 And tossing it in the air. 'That looks well.'
(He nodded at my white cloth on the grass.)
'I declare a woman could lay out a field
Though boys like us have little call for cloths.'
He winked, then watched me as I poured a cup
15 And buttered the thick slices that he likes.
'It's threshing better than I thought, and mind
It's good clean seed. Away over there and look.'
Always this inspection has to be made
Even when I don't know what to look for.

20 But I ran my hand in the half-filled bags
Hooked to the slots. It was hard as shot,
Innumerable and cool. The bags gaped
Where the chutes ran back to the stilled drum
And forks were stuck at angles in the ground
25 As javelins might mark lost battlefields.
I moved between them back across the stubble.

They lay in the ring of their own crusts and dregs
Smoking and saying nothing. 'There's good yield,
Isn't there?'—as proud as if he were the land itself—
30 'Enough for crushing and for sowing both.'
And that was it. I'd come and he had shown me
So I belonged no further to the work.
I gathered cups and folded up the cloth
And went. But they still kept their ease
35 Spread out, unbuttoned, grateful, under the trees.

(1969)

Patrick Lane

(CANADA, 1939–)

The Children of Bogota

The first thing to understand, Manuel says,
is that they're not children. Don't start feeling
sorry for them. There are five thousand
roaming the streets of this city

5   and just because they look innocent
doesn't make them human. Any one
would kill you for the price of a meal.
Children? See those two in the gutter

behind that stall? I saw them put out
10   the eyes of a dog with thorns because
it barked at them. Tomorrow it could be you.
No one knows where they come from

but you can be sure they're not going.
In five years they'll be men and tired of killing
15   dogs. And when that happens you'll be the first
to cheer when the carabineros shoot them down.

(1975)

Clark Blaise

(U.S.A./CANADA, 1940–)

To Begin, To Begin

"Endings are elusive, middles are nowhere to be found, but worst of all is to begin, to begin, to begin."—Donald Barthelme

The most interesting thing about a story is not its climax or dénouement—both dated terms—nor even its style and characterization. It is its beginning, its first paragraph, often its first sentence. More decisions are made on the basis of the first few sentences of a story than on any other part, and it would seem to me after having read thousands of stories, and beginning hundreds of my own (completing, I should add, only about fifty), that something more than luck accounts for the occasional success of the operation. What I propose is theoretical, yet rooted in the practice of writing and of reading-as-a-writer; good stories *can* start unpromisingly, and well-begun stories can obviously degenerate, but the observation generally holds: the story seeks its beginning, the story many times *is* its beginning, amplified.

The first sentence of a story is an act of faith—or astonishing bravado. A story screams for attention, as it must, for it breaks a silence. It removes the reader from the everyday (no such imperative attaches to the novel, for which the reader makes his own preparation). It is an act of perfect rhythmic balance, the single crisp gesture, the drop of the baton that gathers a hundred disparate forces into a single note. The first paragraph is a microcosm of the whole, but in a way that only the whole can reveal. If the story begins one sentence too soon, or a sentence too late, the balance is lost, the energy diffused. It is in the first line that the story reveals its kinship to poetry. Not that the line is necessarily "beautiful," merely that it can exist utterly alone, and that its force draws a series of sentences behind it. The line doesn't have to "grab" or "hook" but it should be striking. Good examples I'll offer further on, but consider first some bad ones:

> Catelli plunged the dagger deeper in her breast, the dark blood oozed like cherry syrup. . . .

> The President's procession would pass under the window at 12:03 and Slattery would be ready. . . .

Such sentences can be wearying; they strike a note too heavily, too prematurely. They "start" where they should be ending. The advantages wrested will quickly dissipate. On the other hand, the "casual" opening can be just as damaging:

> When I saw Bob in the cafeteria he asked me to a party at his house that evening and since I wasn't doing much anyway I said sure. I wouldn't mind. Bob's kind of an ass, but his old man's loaded and there's always a lot of grass around. . . .

Or, *in medias res*:

> "Linda, toast is ready! Linda, are you awake?"

This is an attempt to wake up the story as well as the character.

Now what's wrong with these sentences? The tone is right. The action is promising. They're real, they communicate. Yet no experienced reader would go past them. The last two start too early (what the critics might call an imitative fallacy), and the real story is still imprisoned somewhere in the body.

Lesson One: as in poetry, a good first sentence of prose implies its opposite. If I describe a sunny morning in May (the buds, the wet-winged flies, the warm sun and cool breeze), I am also implying the perishing quality of a morning in May, and a good sensuous description of May sets up the possibility of a May disaster. It is the singular quality of that experience that counts. May follows from the sludge of April and leads to the drone of summer, and in a careful story the action will be mindful of May; it must be. May is unstable, treacherous, beguiling, seductive, and whatever experience follows from that first sentence will be, in essence, a story about the May-ness of human affairs.

What is it, for example, in this sentence from Hugh Hood's story "Fallings from Us, Vanishings" that hints so strongly at disappointment:

> Brandishing a cornucopia of daffodils, flowers for Gloria, in his right hand, Arthur Merlin crossed the dusky oak-panelled foyer of his apartment building and came into the welcoming sunlit avenue.

The name Merlin? The flourish of the opening clause, associations of the name Gloria? Here is a lover doomed to loneliness, yet a lover who seeks it, despite appearances. Nowhere, however, is it stated. Yet no one, I trust, would miss it.

Such openings are everywhere, at least in authors I admire:

The girl stood with her back to the bar, slightly in everyone's way. (Frank Tuohy.)

The thick ticking of the tin clock stopped. Mendel, dozing, awoke in fright. (Bernard Malamud.)

I owe the discovery of Uqbar to the conjunction of a mirror and an encyclopedia. (Jorge Luis Borges.)

For a little while when Walter Henderson was nine years old, he thought falling dead was the very zenith of romance, and so did a number of his friends. (Richard Yates.)

Our group is against the war. But the war goes on. (Donald Barthelme.)

The principal dish at dinner had been croquettes made of turnip greens. (Thomas Mann.)

The sky had been overcast since early morning; it was a still day, not hot, but tedious, as it usually is when the weather is gray and dull, when clouds have been hanging over the fields for a long time, and you wait for the rain that does not come. (Anton Chekhov.)

I wanted terribly to own a dovecot when I was a child. (Isaac Babel—and I didn't know what a dovecot was when I started reading.)

The first time I saw Brenda she asked me to hold her glasses. (Philip Roth—that is *Goodbye, Columbus* in its entirety.)

And almost any Cheever beginning. At least two or three times a day a story strikes me in the same way, and I read it through. By then I don't care if the climax and dénouement are elegantly turned—chances are they will be—I'm reading it because the first paragraph gave me confidence in the power and vision of the author.

Lesson Two: art wishes to begin, even more than end. Fashionable criticism—much of it very intelligent—has emphasized the so-called "apocalyptic impulse," the desire of fiction to bring the house down. I can understand the interest in endings—it's easier to explain why things end than how they began, for one thing. For another, the ending is a contrivance—artistic and believable, yet in many ways predictable; the beginning, however, is always a mystery. Criticism likes contrivances, and has little to say of mysteries. My own experience, as a writer and especially as a "working" reader, is closer to genesis than apocalypse, and I cherish openings more than endings. My memory of any given story is likely to be its first few lines.

Lesson Three: art wishes to begin *again*. The impulse is not only to finish, it is to capture. In the stories I admire, there is a sense of a continuum disrupted, then re-established, and both the disruption and reordering are part of the *beginning* of a story. The first paragraph tells us, in effect, that "this is how things have always been," or at least, how they have been until the arrival of the story. It may summarize, as Faulkner does in "That Evening Sun."

Monday is no different from any other weekday in Jefferson now. The streets are paved now, and the telephone and electric companies are cutting down more and more of the shade trees . . .

or it may envelop a life in a single sentence, as Bernard Malamud's often do:

Manischevitz, a tailor, in his fifty-first year suffered many reverses and indignities.

Whereupon Malamud embellishes the history, a few sentences more of indignities, aches, curses, until the fateful word that occurs in almost all stories, the simple terrifying adverb: *Then.*

Then, which means to the reader: "I am ready." The moment of change is at hand, the story shifts gear and for the first time, *plot* intrudes on poetry. In Malamud's story, a Negro angel suddenly ("then") appears in the tailor's living room, reading a newspaper:

Suddenly there appeared . . .

Then one morning . . .

Then one evening she wasn't home to greet him . . .

Or, in the chilling construction of Flannery O'Connor:

> . . . there appeared at her door three young men . . . they walked single file, the middle one bent carrying a black pig-shaped valise. . . .

A pig-shaped valise! This is the apocalypse, if the reader needs one; whatever the plot may reveal a few pages later is really redundant. The mysterious part of the story—that which is poetic yet sets it (why not?) above poetry—is over. The rest of the story will be an attempt to draw out the inferences of that earlier upheaval. What is often meant by "climax" in the conventional short story is merely the moment that the *character* realizes the true, the devastating meaning of "then." He will try to ignore it, he will try to start again (in my story "Eyes" the character thinks he can escape the voyeurs—himself, essentially—by moving to a rougher part of town); he can't of course.

Young readers, especially young readers who want to write, should forget what they're taught of "themes" and all the rest. Stories aren't written that way. Stories are delicate interplays of action and description; "character" is that force which tries to maintain balance between the two. "Action" I equate with danger, fear, apocalypse, life itself; "description" with quiescence, peace, death itself. And the purest part of a story, I think, is from its beginning to its "then." "Then" is the moment of the slightest tremor, the moment when the author is satisfied that all the forces are deployed, the unruffled surface perfectly cast, and the insertion, gross or delicate, can now take place. It is the cracking of the perfect, smug egg of possibility.

(1975)

Stephen Jay Gould
(U.S.A., 1941-)

Evolution as Fact and Theory

Kirtley Mather, who died last year at age 89, was a pillar of both science and the Christian religion in America and one of my dearest friends. The difference of half a century in our ages evaporated before our common interests. The most curious thing we shared was a battle we each fought at the same age. For Kirtley had gone to Tennessee with Clarence Darrow to testify for evolution at the Scopes trial of 1925. When I think that we are enmeshed again in the same struggle for one of the best documented, most compelling and exciting concepts in all of science, I don't know whether to laugh or cry.

According to idealized principles of scientific discourse, the arousal of dormant issues should reflect fresh data that give renewed life to abandoned notions. Those outside the current debate may therefore be excused for suspecting that creationists have come up with something new, or that evolutionists have generated some serious internal trouble. But nothing has changed; the creationists have not a single new fact or argument. Darrow and Bryan were at least more entertaining than we lesser antagonists today. The rise of creationism is politics, pure and simple; it represents one issue (and by no means the major concern) of the resurgent evangelical right. Arguments that seemed kooky just a decade ago have reentered the mainstream.

The basic attack of the creationists falls apart on two general counts before we even reach the supposed factual details of their complaints against evolution. First, they play upon a vernacular misunderstanding of the word "theory" to convey the false impression that we evolutionists are covering up the rotten core of our edifice. Second, they misuse a popular philosophy of science to argue that they are behaving scientifically in attacking evolution. Yet the same philosophy demonstrates that their own belief is not science and that "scientific creationism" is therefore meaningless and self-contradictory, a superb example of what Orwell called "newspeak."

In the American vernacular, "theory" often means "imperfect fact"—part of a hierarchy of confidence running downhill from fact to theory to hypothesis to guess. Thus the power of the creationist argument that evolution is "only" a theory, and intense debate now rages about many aspects of the theory. If evolution is less than a fact, and scientists can't even make up their minds about the theory, then what confidence can we have in it? Indeed, President Reagan echoed this argument before an evangelical group in Dallas when he said (in what I devoutly hope was campaign rhetoric): "Well, it is a theory. It's a scientific theory only, and it has in recent years been challenged in the world of science—that is, not believed in the scientific community to be as infallible as it once was."

Well, evolution *is* a theory. It is also a fact. And facts and theories are different things, not rungs in a hierarchy of increasing certainty. Facts are the world's data. Theories are structures of ideas that explain and interpret facts. Facts do not go away when scientists debate rival theories to explain them. Einstein's theory of gravitation replaced Newton's, but apples did not suspend themselves in mid-air pending the outcome. And human beings evolved from apelike ancestors whether they did so by Darwin's proposed mechanism or by some other, yet to be discovered.

Moreover, "fact" does not mean "absolute certainty." The final proofs of logic and mathematics flow deductively from stated premises and achieve certainty only because they are *not* about the empirical world. Evolutionists make no claim for perpetual truth, though creationists often do (and then attack us for a style of argument that they themselves favor). In science, "fact" can only mean "confirmed to such a degree that it would be perverse to withhold provisional assent." I suppose that apples might start to rise tomorrow, but the possibility does not merit equal time in physics classrooms.

Evolutionists have been clear about this distinction between fact and theory from the very beginning, if only because we have always acknowledged how far we are from completely understanding the mechanisms (theory) by which evolution (fact) occurred. Darwin continually emphasized the difference between his two great and separate accomplishments: establishing the fact of evolution, and proposing a theory—natural selection—to explain the mechanism of evolution. He wrote in *The Descent of Man*: "I had two distinct objects in view; firstly, to show that species had not been separately created, and secondly, that natural selection had been the chief agent of change . . . Hence if I have erred in . . . having exaggerated its [natural selection's] power . . . I have at least, as I hope, done good service in aiding to overthrow the dogma of separate creations."

Thus Darwin acknowledged the provisional nature of natural selection while affirming the fact of evolution. The fruitful theoretical debate that Darwin initiated has never ceased. From the 1940s through the 1960s, Darwin's own theory of natural selection did achieve a temporary hegemony that it never enjoyed in his lifetime. But renewed debate characterizes our decade, and, while no biologist questions the importance of natural selection, many now doubt its ubiquity. In particular, many evolutionists argue that substantial amounts of genetic change may not be subject to natural selection and may spread through populations at random. Others are challenging Darwin's linking of natural selection with gradual, imperceptible change through all intermediary degrees; they are arguing that most evolutionary events may occur far more rapidly than Darwin envisioned.

Scientists regard debates on fundamental issues of theory as a sign of intellectual health and a source of excitement. Science is—and how else can I say it?—most fun when it plays with interesting ideas, examines their implications, and recognizes that old information may be explained in surprisingly new ways. Evolutionary theory is now enjoying this uncommon vigor. Yet amidst all this turmoil no biologist has been led to doubt the fact that evolution occurred; we are debating how it happened. We are all trying to explain the same thing: the tree of evolutionary descent linking all organisms by ties of genealogy. Creationists pervert and caricature this debate by conveniently neglecting the common conviction that underlies it, and by falsely suggesting that we now doubt the very phenomenon we are struggling to understand.

Using another invalid argument, creationists claim that "the dogma of separate creations," as Darwin characterized it a century ago, is a scientific theory meriting equal time with evolution in high school biology curricula. But a prevailing viewpoint among philosophers of science belies this creationist argument. Philosopher Karl Popper has argued for decades that the primary criterion of science is the falsifiability of its theories. We can never prove absolutely, but we can falsify. A set of ideas that cannot, in principle, be falsified is not science.

The entire creationist argument involves little more than a rhetorical attempt to falsify evolution by presenting supposed contradictions among its supporters. Their brand of creationism, they claim, is "scientific" because it follows the Popperian model in trying to demolish evolution. Yet Popper's argument must apply in both directions. One does not become a scientist by the simple act of trying to falsify another scientific system; one has to present an alternative system that also meets Popper's criterion—it too must be falsifiable in principle.

"Scientific creationism" is a self-contradictory, nonsense phrase precisely because it cannot be falsified. I can envision observations and experiments that would disprove any evolutionary theory I know, but I cannot imagine what potential data could lead creationists to abandon their beliefs. Unbeatable systems are dogma, not science. Lest I seem harsh or rhetorical, I quote creationism's leading intellectual, Duane Gish, Ph.D., from his recent (1978) book *Evolution? The Fossils Say No!* "By creation we mean the bringing into being by a supernatural Creator of the basic kinds of plants and animals by the process of sudden, or fiat, creation. We do not know how the Creator created, what processes He used, for *He used processes which are not now operating anywhere in the natural universe* [Gish's italics]. This is why we refer to creation as special creation. We cannot discover by scientific investigations anything about the creative processes used by the Creator." Pray tell, Dr. Gish, in the light of your last sentence, what then is "scientific" creationism?

Our confidence that evolution occurred centers upon three general arguments. First, we have abundant, direct, observational evidence of evolution in action, from both the field and the laboratory. It ranges from countless experiments on change in nearly everything about fruit flies subjected to artificial selection in the laboratory to the famous British moths that turned black when industrial soot darkened the trees upon which they rest. (The moths gain protection from sharp-sighted bird predators by blending into the background.) Creationists do not deny these observations; how could they? Creationists have tightened their act. They now argue that God only created "basic kinds," and allowed for limited evolutionary meandering within them. Thus toy poodles and Great Danes come from the dog kind and moths can change colors, but nature cannot convert a dog to a cat or a monkey to a man.

The second and third arguments for evolution—the case for major changes—do not involve direct observation of evolution in action. They rest upon inference, but are no less secure for that reason. Major evolutionary change requires too much time for direct observation on the scale of recorded human history. All historical sciences rest upon inference, and evolution is no different from geology, cosmology, or human history in this respect. In principle, we cannot observe processes that operated in the past. We must infer them from results that still survive: living and fossil organisms for evolution, documents and artifacts for human history, strata and topography for geology.

The second argument—that the imperfection of nature reveals evolution—strikes many people as ironic, for they feel that evolution should be most elegantly displayed in the nearly perfect adaptation expressed by some organisms—the camber of a gull's wing, or butterflies that cannot be seen in ground litter because they mimic leaves so precisely. But perfection could be imposed by a wise creator or evolved by natural selection. Perfection covers the tracks of past history. And past history—the evidence of descent—is our mark of evolution.

Evolution lies exposed in the *imperfections* that record a history of descent. Why should a rat run, a bat fly, a porpoise swim, and I type this essay with structures built of the same bones unless we all inherited them from a common ancestor? An engineer, starting from scratch, could design better limbs in each case. Why should all the large native mammals of Australia be marsupials, unless they descended from a common ancestor isolated on this island continent? Marsupials are not "better," or ideally suited for Australia; many have been wiped out by placental mammals imported by man from other continents. This principle of imperfection extends to all historical sciences. When we recognize the etymology of September, October, November, and December (seventh, eighth, ninth, and tenth, from the Latin), we know that two additional items (January and February) must have been added to an original calendar of ten months.

The third argument is more direct: transitions are often found in the fossil record. Preserved transitions are not common—and should not be, according to our understanding of evolution (see next section)—but they are not entirely wanting, as creationists often claim. The lower jaw of reptiles contains several bones, that of mammals only one. The nonmammalian jawbones are reduced, step by step, in mammalian ancestors until they become tiny nubbins located at the back of the jaw. The "hammer" and "anvil" bones of the mammalian ear are descendants of these nubbins. How could such a transition be accomplished? the creationists ask. Surely a bone is either entirely in the jaw or in the ear. Yet paleontologists have discovered two transitional lineages of therapsids (the so-called mammal-like reptiles) with a double jaw joint—one composed of the old quadrate and articular bones (soon to become the hammer and anvil), the other of the squamosal and dentary bones (as in modern mammals). For that matter, what better transitional form could we desire that the oldest human, *Australopithecus afarensis*, with its apelike palate, its human upright stance, and a cranial capacity larger than any ape's of the same body size but a full 1,000 cubic centimeters below ours? If God made each of the half dozen human species discovered in ancient rocks, why did he create in an unbroken temporal sequence of progressively more modern features—increasing cranial capacity, reduced face and teeth, larger body size? Did he create to mimic evolution and test our faith thereby?

Faced with these facts of evolution and the philosophical bankruptcy of their own position, creationists rely upon distortion and innuendo to buttress their rhetorical claim. If I sound sharp or bitter, indeed I am—for I have become a major target of these practices.

I count myself among the evolutionists who argue for a jerky, or episodic, rather than a smoothly gradual, pace of change. In 1972 my colleague Niles Eldredge and I developed the theory of punctuated equilibrium [*Discovery*, October]. We argued that two outstanding facts of the fossil record—geologically "sudden" origin of new species and failure to change there-after (stasis)—reflect the predictions of evolutionary theory, not the imperfections of the fossil record. In most theories, small isolated populations are the source of new species, and the process of speciation takes thousands or tens of thousands of years. This amount of time, so long when measured against our lives, is a geological microsecond. It represents much less than 1 per cent of the average life span for a fossil invertebrate species—more than 10 million years. Large, widespread, and well established species, on the other hand, are not expected to change very much. We believe that the inertia of large populations explains the stasis of most fossil species over millions of years.

We proposed the theory of punctuated equilibrium largely to provide a different explanation for pervasive trends in the fossil record. Trends, we argued, cannot be attributed to gradual transformation within lineages, but must arise from the differential success of certain kinds of species. A trend, we argued, is more like climbing a flight of stairs (punctuations and stasis) than rolling up an inclined plane.

Since we proposed punctuated equilibria to explain trends, it is infuriating to be quoted again and again by creationists—whether through design or stupidity, I do not know—as admitting that the fossil record includes no transitional forms. Transitional forms are generally lacking at the species level, but are abundant between larger groups. The evolution from reptiles to mammals, as mentioned earlier, is well documented. Yet a pamphlet entitled "Harvard Scientists Agree Evolution Is a Hoax" states: "The facts of punctuated equilibrium which Gould and Eldredge . . . are forcing Darwinists to swallow fit the picture that Bryan insisted on, and which God has revealed to us in the Bible."

Continuing the distortion, several creationists have equated the theory of punctuated equilibrium with a caricature of the beliefs of Richard Goldschmidt, a great early geneticist. Goldschmidt argued, in a famous book published in 1940, that new groups can arise all at once through major mutations. He referred to these suddenly transformed creatures as "hopeful monsters." (I am attracted to some aspects of the non-caricatured version, but Goldschmidt's theory still has nothing to do with punctuated equilibrium.) Creationist Luther Sunderland talks of the "punctuated equilibrium hopeful monster theory" and tells his hopeful readers that "it amounts to tacit admission that anti-evolutionists are correct in asserting there is no fossil evidence supporting the theory that all life is connected to a common ancestor." Duane Gish writes, "According to Goldschmidt, and now apparently according to Gould, a reptile laid an egg from which the first bird, feathers and all, was produced." Any evolutionist who believed such nonsense would rightly be laughed off the intellectual stage; yet the only theory that could ever envision such a scenario for the evolution of birds is creationism—God acts in the egg.

I am both angry at and amused by the creationists; but mostly I am deeply sad. Sad for many reasons. Sad because so many people who respond to creationist appeals are troubled for the right reason, but venting their anger at the wrong target. It is true that scientists have often been dogmatic and elitist. It is true that we have often allowed the white-coated, advertising image to represent us—"Scientists say that Brand X cures bunions ten times faster than . . . ." We have not fought it adequately because we derive benefits from appearing as a new priest-hood. It is also true that faceless bureaucratic state power intrudes more and more into our lives and removes choices that should belong to individuals and communities. I can understand that requiring that evolution be taught in the schools might be seen as one more insult on all these grounds. But the culprit is not, and cannot be, evolution or any other fact of the natural world. Identify and fight your legitimate enemies by all means, but we are not among them.

I am sad because the practical result of this brouhaha will not be expanded coverage to include creationism (that would also make me sad), but the reduction or excision of evolution from high school curricula. Evolution is one of the half dozen "great ideas" developed by science. It speaks to the profound issues of genealogy that fascinate all of us—the "roots" phenomenon writ large. Where did we come from? Where did life arise? How did it develop? How are organisms related? It forces us to think, ponder, and wonder. Shall we deprive millions of this knowledge and once again teach biology as a set of dull and unconnected facts, without the thread that weaves diverse material into a supple unity?

But most of all I am saddened by a trend I am just beginning to discern among my colleagues. I sense that some now wish to mute the healthy debate about theory that has brought new life to evolutionary biology. It provides grist for creationist mills, they say, even if only by distortion. Perhaps we should lie low and rally round the flag of strict Darwinism, at least for the moment—a kind of old time religion on our part.

But we should borrow another metaphor and recognize that we too have to tread a straight and narrow path, surrounded by roads to perdition. For if we ever begin to suppress our search to understand nature, to quench our own intellectual excitement in a misguided effort to present a united front where it does not and should not exist, then we are truly lost.

(1983)

Gwendolyn MacEwen
(CANADA, 1941–1987)

The Discovery

do not imagine that the exploration
ends, that she has yielded all her mystery
or that the map you hold
cancels further discovery

5   I tell you her uncovering takes years,
takes centuries, and when you find her naked
look again,
admit there is something else you cannot name,
a veil, a coating just above the flesh
10 which you cannot remove by your mere wish

when you see the land naked, look again
(burn your maps, that is not what I mean),
I mean the moment when it seems most plain
is the moment when you must begin again

(1970)

Derek Mahon

(ULSTER, 1941–)

Rage for Order

Somewhere beyond the scorched gable end and the burnt-out buses
    there is a poet indulging
        his wretched rage for order—
or not as the case may be; for his
5   is a dying art,
    an eddy of semantic scruples
      in an unstructurable sea.

    He is far from his people,
and the fitful glare of his high window is as
10   nothing to our scattered glass.

His posture is grandiloquent and deprecating, like this,
    his diet ashes,
his talk of justice and his mother
    the rhetorical device
15   of an etiolated emperor—
Nero if you prefer, no mother there.

    '. . . and this in the face of love,
    death, and the wages of the poor . . .'

If he is silent, it is the silence of enforced humility;
20   if anxious to be heard, it is the anxiety
      of a last word
when the drums start; for his is a dying art.

Now watch me as I make history. Watch as I tear down
    to build up with a desperate love,
25   knowing it cannot be
    long now till I have need of his
      desperate ironies.

                 (1972)

The Banished Gods

Near the headwaters of the longest river
    There is a forest clearing,
        A dank, misty place
    Where light stands in columns
5   And birds sing with a noise like paper tearing.

Far from land, far from the trade routes,
    In an unbroken dream-time
        Of penguin and whale,
    The seas sigh to themselves
10 Reliving the days before the days of sail.

Where the wires end the moor seethes in silence,
    Scattered with scree, primroses,
        Feathers and faeces.
    It shelters the hawk and hears
15 In dreams the forlorn cries of lost species.

It is here that the banished gods are in hiding,
    Here they sit out the centuries
        In stone, water
    And the hearts of trees,
20 Lost in a reverie of their own natures—

Of zero-growth economics and seasonal change
    In a world without cars, computers
        Or chemical skies,
    Where thought is a fondling of stones
25 And wisdom a five-minute silence at moonrise.
                  (1975)

Marilyn Hacker
(U.S.A., 1942–)

Fourteen

We shopped for dresses which were always wrong:
sweatshop approximations of the lean-
lined girls' wear I studied in *Seventeen*.
The armholes pinched, the belt didn't belong,
5 the skirt drooped forward (I'd be told at school).
Our odd-lot bargains deformed the image,
but she and I loved Saturday rummage.

One day she listed outside Loehmann's. Drool
wet her chin. Stumbling, she screamed at me. Dropping
10 our parcels on the pavement, she fell in
what looked like a fit. I guessed: insulin.
The cop said, "Drunk," and called an ambulance
while she cursed me and slapped away my hands.
When I need a mother, I still go shopping.

(1985)

Daphne Marlatt

(AUSTRALIA/CANADA, 1942–)

musing with mothertongue

the beginning: language, a living body we enter at birth, sustains and contains us.   it does not stand in place of anything else, it does not replace the bodies around us.   placental, our flat land, our sea, it is both place (where we are situated) and body (that contains us), that body of language we speak, our mothertongue.   it bears us as we are born in it, into cognition.

language is first of all for us a body of sound.   leaving the water of the mother's womb with its one dominant sound, we are born into this other body whose multiple sounds bathe our ears from the moment of our arrival. we learn the sounds before we learn what they say: a child will speak baby-talk in pitch patterns that accurately imitate the sentence patterns of her mothertongue.   an adult who cannot read or write will speak his mothertongue without being able to say what a particular morpheme or even word in a phrase means.   we learn nursery rhymes without understanding what they refer to.   we repeat skipping songs significant for their rhythms.   gradually we learn how the sounds of our language are active as meaning and then we go on learning for the rest of our lives what the words are actually saying.

in poetry, which has evolved out of chant and song, in riming and tone-leading, whether they occur in prose or poetry, sound will initiate thought by a process of association.   words call each other up, evoke each other, provoke each other, nudge each other into utterance.   we know from dreams and schizophrenic speech how deeply association works in our psyches, a form of thought that is not rational but erotic because it works by attraction.   a drawing, a pulling toward, a "liking."   Germanic *lik-*, body, form; like, same.

like the atomic particles of our bodies, phonemes and syllables gravitate toward each other.   they attract each other in movements we call assonance, euphony, alliteration, rhyme.   they are drawn together and echo each other in rhythms we identify as feet—lines run on, phrases patter like speaking feet.   on a macroscopic level, words evoke each other in movements we know as puns and figures of speech (these endless similes, this continuing fascination with making one out of two, a new one, a simultitude.) meaning moves us deepest the more of the whole field it puts together, and so we get sense where it borders on nonsense ("what is the sense of it all?") as what we sense our way into.   the sentence.   ("life.")   making our multiplicity whole and even intelligible by the end-point, intelligible: logos there in the gathering hand, the reading eye.

hidden in the etymology and usage of so much of our vocabulary for verbal communication (contact, sharing) is a link with the body's physicality: matter (the import of what you say) and matter and by extension mother; language and tongue; to utter and outer (give birth again); a part of speech and a part of the body; pregnant with meaning; to mouth (speak) and the mouth with which we also eat and make love; sense (meaning) and that with which we sense the world; to relate (a story) and to relate to somebody, related (carried back) with its connection with bearing (a child); intimate and to intimate; vulva and voluble; even sentence which comes from a verb meaning to feel.

like the mother's body, language is larger than us and carries us along with it. it bears us, it births us, insofar as we bear with it. if we are poets we spend our lives discovering not just what *we* have to say but what language is saying as it carries us with it. in etymology we discover a history of verbal relations (a family tree, if you will) that has preceded us and given us the world we live in. the given, the immediately presented, as at birth—a given name a given world. we know language structures our world and in a crucial sense we cannot see what we cannot verbalize, as the work of Whorf and ethnolinguistics has pointed out to us. here we are truly contained within the body of our mothertongue. and even the physicists, chafing at these limits, say that the glimpse physics now gives us of the nature of the universe cannot be conveyed in a language based on the absolute difference between a noun and a verb. poetry has been demonstrating this for some time.

if we are women poets, writers, speakers, we also take issue with the given, hearing the discrepancy between what our patriarchally-loaded language bears (can bear) of our experience and the difference from it our experience bears out—how it misrepresents, even miscarries, and so leaves unsaid what we actually experience. can a pregnant woman be said to be "master" of the gestation process she finds herself within—is that her relationship to it? (see Julia Kristeva, *Desire in Language*, p. 238.) are women included in the statement "God appearing as man" (has God ever appeared as a woman?) can a woman ever say she is "lady of all she surveys" or could others ever say of her she "ladies it over them"?

so many terms for dominance in English are tied up with male experiencing, masculine hierarchies and differences (exclusion), patriarchal holdings with their legalities. where are the poems that celebrate the soft letting-go the flow of menstrual blood is as it leaves her body? how can the standard sentence structure of English with its linear authority, subject through verb to object, convey the wisdom of endlessly repeating and not exactly repeated cycles her body knows? or the mutuality her body shares embracing other bodies, children, friends, animals, all those she customarily holds and is held by? how can the separate nouns mother and child convey the fusion, bleeding womb-infant mouth, she experiences in those first days of feeding? what syntax can carry the turning herself inside out in love when she is both sucking mouth and hot gush on her lover's tongue?

Julia Kristeva says: "If it is true every national language has its own dream language and unconscious, then each of the sexes—a division so much more archaic and fundamental than the one into languages—would have its own unconscious wherein the biological and social program of the species would be ciphered in confrontation with language, exposed to its influence, but independent from it" (*Desire in Language*, p. 241). i link this with the call so many feminist writers in Quebec have issued for a language that returns us to the body, a woman's body and the largely unverbalized, presyntactic, postlexical field it knows. postlexical in that, as Mary Daly shows, with intelligence (that gathering hand) certain words (dandelion sparks) seed themselves back to original and originally-related meaning. this is a field where words mutually attract each other, fused by connection, enthused (inspired) into variation (puns, word play, rime at all levels) fertile in proliferation (offspring, rooting back to *al-*, seed syllable to grow, and leafing forward into *alma*, nourishing, a woman's given name, soul, inhabitant.)

inhabitant of language, not master, not even mistress, this new woman writer (Alma, say) in having is had, is held by it, what she is given to say. in giving it away is given herself, on that double edge where she has always lived, between the already spoken and the unspeakable, sense and non-sense. only now she writes it, risking nonsense, chaotic language leafings, unspeakable breaches of usage, intuitive leaps. inside language she leaps for joy, shoving out the walls of taboo and propriety, kicking syntax, discovering life in old roots.

language thus speaking (i.e., inhabited) relates us, "takes us back" to where we are, as it relates us to the world in a living body of verbal relations. articulation: seeing the connections (and the thighbone, and the hipbone, etc.). putting the living body of language together means putting the world together, the world we live in: an act of composition, an act of birthing, us, uttered and outered there in it.

(1984)

Arthur Nortje
(SOUTH AFRICA, 1942–1970)

Letter from Pretoria Central Prison

The bell wakes me at 6 in the pale spring dawn
with the familiar rumble of the guts negotiating
murky corridors that smell of bodies. My eyes
find salutary the insurgent light of distances.
5   Waterdrops rain crystal cold, my wet
face in ascent from an iron basin
greets its rifled shadow in the doorway.

They walk us to the workshop. I am eminent,
the blacksmith of the block: these active hours
10   fly like sparks in the furnace, I hammer metals
with zest letting the sweating muscles
forge a forgetfulness of worlds more magnetic.
The heart, being at rest, life peaceable,
your words filter softly through my fibres.

<table>
</table>

15   Taken care of, in no way am I unhappy,
being changed to neutral. You must decide
today, tomorrow, bear responsibility,
take gaps in pavement crowds, refine ideas.
Our food we get on time. Most evenings
20   I read books, Jane Austen
for elegance, agreeableness (Persuasion).

Trees are green beyond the wall, leaves through the mesh
are cool in sunshine
among the monastic white flowers of spring that floats
25   prematurely across the exercise yard, a square
of the cleanest stone I have ever walked on.
Sentinels smoke in their boxes, the wisps
curling lovely through the barbed wire.

Also music and cinema, yesterday double feature.
30   At 4 pm it's back to the cell, don't laugh
to hear how accustomed one becomes. You spoke
of hospital treatment—I see the smart nurses
bringing you grapefruit and tea—good
luck to the troublesome kidney.
35   Sorry there's no more space. But date your reply.

(August 1966)

Michael Wilding

(ENGLAND/AUSTRALIA, 1942–)

The Words She Types

Advertised it looked an interesting job: Writer requires intelligent typist. It sounded more interesting than routine copy-typing; and the "intelligent" held out the bait of some involvement. Amongst dreams had hung one of success as a great writer. Other dreams: but that one had hung there. So she answered.

The appointment required an old apartment block with heavy doors at the entrance, old, varnished wood, that swung to with a heavy oiled smoothness and closed off time at the street.

"What I expect is not difficult," the writer said; "accuracy, precision, neatness. And if you succeed in them, perhaps a little more, a little discretion. The initiative to correct, without constant recourse to me, slight carelessnesses of spelling, grammatical solecisms. But let us go along stage by stage and see how we find each other."

And within the heavy doors, the high-ceilinged still apartment, footfalls deadened on the soft carpet, walls sealed with wooden bookshelves carrying their store of the centuries, the windows double glazed against the sounds and temperatures of the street. And a small table for the tray of coffee or fruit juice or lemon tea to be placed, soundlessly. She missed only music, would have liked the room resonant to rich cadences against the deep polished wood and leather bindings.

She would come to her desk and at the right of the typewriter would be the sheets he had put for her. And as she retyped those sheets she would place them at the left of the typewriter and as soon as she had completed a piece she would collate the sheets and the carbons and leave them in manila folders for him to collect from the drawers at the left of the desk.

The earliest days were easy, copying from typescript. No problems, no uncertainties, no ambiguities. Occasionally he had jammed the keys or jumped a space or missed off the closing quotation mark; but often he had pencilled in the corrections himself. Later, though, perhaps as he became more sure of her, he omitted to make the corrections. And his typing became less punctilious. Words were sometimes misspelt, whether through ignorance or the exigencies of typing it was not for her to ask. He would sometimes use abbreviations, not spelling out a character's name in full but giving only the initial letter. And when he began to give her manuscript sheets to type from the abbreviations increased, the effort of writing out the obvious in longhand too much for him, unnecessary.

And she always managed. It was her pride always to manage, to transliterate from his degenerating scrawl that day by day yearned towards the undifferentiated horizontal, to expand the abbreviations, to fill out the lacunae with their "he said" or "she replied". Her intelligence at last being fulfilled she did not complain of the scrappier sheets that over time were presented to her. Her electric typewriter hummed quietly as ever, nothing retarded her rhythmic pressure on the keys.

He would write instructions in the margin of the drafts. Indications of where to fill out, where to add in, how to expand, interpret. And she would fulfil these instructions, incorporating them into the draft he had roughed out and presenting one whole and finished fabric. And when he offered sheets only of instruction, she knew his manner well enough to develop the sketched out plan as he required.

Was it a shock one morning to find blank sheets on the right of the typewriter? Yet her ready fingers took paper and carbons from their drawer and without hesitation touched the keys. Her eyes read over the characters as they appeared before her.

She read of a girl who saw advertised what looked an interesting job: Writer requires intelligent typist. It sounded more interesting than routine copy-typing: and the "intelligent" held out the bait of some involvement. Amongst dreams had hung one of success as a great writer. Other dreams: but that one had hung there. So she answered.

Without prompting her fingers touch the keys and tell the story. The girl cannot tell, as she writes this story of herself, if it is indeed of herself. Always the words she has typed have been the words he has presented, suggested, required. But are the words she types now any different from the other words she has typed? The girl cannot tell the truth of her situation, because for her to write is to give expression to his stories. Is this but another story she is typing for him, and the truth of her story irrecoverably lost? He has given her no notes from which to tell. And if it is not his story it is even more his story. For if she is telling the story of her story, it was he who established the story. The words she uses will be the words he has set up in setting up her story, even if they are coincidentally her own words.

She sees only what the keys stamp out on the blank paper before her. If it is her truth no one will know. He will collect the typescript in its manila folder from the drawer on the left, and will publish it whether the words were the words he required or were her words. Readers will read and register amusement or boredom or fascination or disdain, and her truth, if it is her truth, read as fiction will never after be available as truth, whether or not it ever was.

(1975)

Nikki Giovanni

(U.S.A., 1943–)

Kidnap Poem

ever been kidnapped
by a poet
if i were a poet
i'd kidnap you
5 put you in my phrases and meter
you to jones beach
or maybe coney island
or maybe just to my house
lyric you in lilacs
10 dash you in the rain
blend into the beach
to complement my see
play the lyre for you
ode you with my love song
15 anything to win you
wrap you in the red Black green
show you off to mama
yeah if i were a poet i'd kid
nap you

(1970)

Thomas King

(U.S.A./CANADA, 1943–)

A Coyote Columbus Story

You know, Coyote came by my place the other day. She was going to a party. She had her party hat and she had her party whistle and she had her party rattle.

I'm going to a party, she says.

Yes, I says, I can see that.

It is a party for Christopher Columbus, says Coyote. That is the one who found America. That is the one who found Indians.

Boy, that Coyote is one silly Coyote. You got to watch out for her. Some of Coyote's stories have got Coyote tails and some of Coyote's stories are covered with scraggy Coyote fur but all of Coyote's stories are bent.

Christopher Columbus didn't find America, I says. Christopher Columbus didn't find Indians, either. You got a tail on that story.

Oh no, says Coyote. I read it in a book.

Must have been a Coyote book, I says.

No, no, no, no, says Coyote. It was a history book. Big red one. All about how Christopher Columbus sailed the ocean blue looking for America and the Indians.

Sit down, I says. Have some tea. We're going to have to do this story right. We're going to have to do this story now.

It was all Old Coyote's fault, I tell Coyote, and here is how the story goes. Here is what really happened.

So.

Old Coyote loved to play ball, you know. She played ball all day and all night. She would throw the ball and she would hit the ball and she would run and catch the ball. But playing ball by herself was boring, so she sang a song and she danced a dance and she thought about playing ball and pretty soon along came some Indians. Old Coyote and the Indians became very good friends. You are sure a good friend, says those Indians. Yes, that's true, says Old Coyote.

But, you know, whenever Old Coyote and the Indians played ball, Old Coyote always won. She always won because she made up the rules. That sneaky one made up the rules and she always won because she could do that.

That's not fair, says the Indians. Friends don't do that.

That's the rules, says Old Coyote. Let's play some more. Maybe you will win the next time. But they don't.

You keep changing the rules, says those Indians.

No, no, no, no, says Old Coyote. You are mistaken. And then she changes the rules again.

So, after a while, those Indians find better things to do.

Some of them go fishing.

Some of them go shopping.

Some of them go to a movie.

Some of them go on a vacation.

Those Indians got better things to do than play ball with Old Coyote and those changing rules.

So, Old Coyote doesn't have anyone to play with.

So, she has to play by herself.

So, she gets bored.

When Old Coyote gets bored, anything can happen. Stick around. Big trouble is coming, I can tell you that.

Well. That silly one sings a song and she dances a dance and she thinks about playing ball. But she's thinking about changing those rules, too, and she doesn't watch what she is making up out of her head. So pretty soon, she makes three ships.

Hmmmm, says Old Coyote, where did those ships come from?

And pretty soon, she makes some people on those ships.

Hmmmm, says Old Coyote, where did those people come from?

And pretty soon, she makes some people on the beach with flags and funny-looking clothes and stuff.

Hooray, says Old Coyote. You are just in time for the ball game.

Hello, says one of the men in silly clothes and red hair all over his head. I am Christopher Columbus. I am sailing the ocean blue looking for China. Have you seen it?

Forget China, says Old Coyote. Let's play ball.

It must be around here somewhere, says Christopher Columbus. I have a map.

Forget the map, says Old Coyote. I'll bat first and I'll tell you the rules as we go along.

But that Christopher Columbus and his friends don't want to play ball. We got work to do, he says. We got to find China. We got to find things we can sell.

Yes, says those Columbus people, where is the gold?

Yes, they says, where is that silk cloth?

Yes, they says, where are those portable color televisions?

Yes, they says, where are those home computers?

Boy, says Old Coyote, and that one scratches her head. I must have sung that song wrong. Maybe I didn't do the right dance. Maybe I thought too hard. These people I made have no manners. They act as if they have no relations.

And she is right. Christopher Columbus and his friends start jumping up and down in their funny clothes and they shout so loud that Coyote's ears almost fall off.

Boy, what a bunch of noise, says Coyote. What bad manners. You guys got to stop jumping and shouting or my ears will fall off.

We got to find China, says Christopher Columbus. We got to become rich. We got to become famous. Do you think you can help us?

But all Old Coyote can think about is playing ball.

I'll let you bat first, says Old Coyote.

No time for games, says Christopher Columbus.

I'll let you make the rules, cries Old Coyote.

But those Columbus people don't listen. They are too busy running around, peeking under rocks, looking in caves, sailing all over the place. Looking for China. Looking for stuff they can sell.

I got a monkey, says one.

I got a parrot, says another.

I got a fish, says a third.

I got a coconut, says a fourth.

That stuff isn't worth poop, says Christopher Columbus. We can't sell those things in Spain. Look harder.

But all they find are monkeys and parrots and fish and coconuts. And when they tell Christopher Columbus, that one he squeezes his ears and he chews his nose and grinds his teeth. He grinds his teeth so hard, he gets a headache, and, then, he gets cranky.

And then he gets an idea.

Say, says Christopher Columbus. Maybe we could sell Indians.

Yes, says his friends, that's a good idea. We could sell Indians, and they throw away their monkeys and parrots and fish and coconuts.

Wait a minute, says the Indians, that is not a good idea. That is a bad idea. That is a bad idea full of bad manners.

When Old Coyote hears this bad idea, she starts to laugh. Who would buy Indians, she says, and she laughs some more. She laughs so hard, she has to hold her nose on her face with both her hands.

But while that Old Coyote is laughing, Christopher Columbus grabs a big bunch of Indian men and Indian women and Indian children and locks them up in his ships.

When Old Coyote stops laughing and looks around, she sees that some of the Indians are missing. Hey, she says, where are those Indians? Where are my friends?

I'm going to sell them in Spain, says Christopher Columbus. Somebody has to pay for this trip. Sailing over the ocean blue isn't cheap, you know.

But Old Coyote still thinks that Christopher Columbus is playing a trick. She thinks it is a joke. That is a good joke, she says, trying to make me think that you are going to sell my friends. And she starts to laugh again.

Grab some more Indians, says Christopher Columbus.

When Old Coyote sees Christopher Columbus grab some more Indians, she laughs even harder. What a good joke, she says. And she laughs some more. She does this four times and when she is done laughing, all the Indians are gone. And Christopher Columbus is gone and Christopher Columbus's friends are gone, too.

Wait a minute, says old Coyote. What happened to my friends? Where are my Indians? You got to bring them back. Who's going to play ball with me?

But Christopher Columbus didn't bring the Indians back and Old Coyote was real sorry she thought him up. She tried to take him back. But, you know, once you think things like that, you can't take them back. So you have to be careful what you think.

So. That's the end of the story.

Boy, says Coyote. That is one sad story.

Yes, I says. It's sad alright. And things don't get any better, I can tell you that.

What a very sad story, says Coyote. Poor Old Coyote didn't have anyone to play ball with. That one must have been lonely. And Coyote begins to cry.

Stop crying, I says. Old Coyote is fine. Some blue jays come along after that and they play ball with her.

Oh, good, says Coyote. But what happened to the Indians? There was nothing in that red history book about Christopher Columbus and the Indians.

Christopher Columbus sold the Indians, I says, and that one became rich and famous.

Oh, good, says Coyote. I love a happy ending. And that one blows her party whistle and that one shakes her party rattle and that one puts her party hat back on her head. I better get going, she says, I'm going to be late for the party.

Okay, I says. Just remember how that story goes. Don't go messing it up again. Have you got it straight, now?

You bet, says Coyote. But if Christopher Columbus didn't find America and he didn't find Indians, who found these things?

Those things were never lost, I says. Those things were always here. Those things are still here today.

By golly, I think you are right, says Coyote.

Don't be thinking, I says. This world has enough problems already without a bunch of Coyote thoughts with tails and scraggy fur running around bumping into each other.

Boy, that's the truth. I can tell you that.

(1993)

Michael Ondaatje

(SRI LANKA/CANADA, 1943–)

Prometheus, with Wings:

They splayed him scientifically on the rock,
so that a limping sun would blind him until noon,
and crack his lips and eyelids, white his hair,
and harden blood on bitten lips and thighs.

5   The bird would come, peck at his puckered flesh,
lick his ribs and peel the calloused skin
until the dusk grew fat and brown
and the bird left frowning.

His crackled knuckles then released their bite
10 and hanging he watched sea drown half his skin
which stinging like peroxide dulled the sense
so he could grin again.

Zeus
sitting with a bunch of grapes and gods
15 spat out the pips
and puzzled watched this man,
who with a whitened eye and hectic lust,
wooed a host of mermaids after dusk.

(1967)

King Kong Meets Wallace Stevens

Take two photographs—
Wallace Stevens and King Kong
(Is it significant that I eat bananas as I write this?)

Stevens is portly, benign, a white brush cut
5 striped tie. Businessman but
for the dark thick hands, the naked brain
the thought in him.

Kong is staggering
lost in New York streets again
10   a spawn of annoyed cars at his toes.
The mind is nowhere.
Fingers are plastic, electric under the skin.
He's at the call of Metro-Goldwyn-Mayer;

Meanwhile W. S. in his suit
15   is thinking chaos is thinking fences.
In his head—the seeds of fresh pain
his exorcising,
the bellow of locked blood.

The hands drain from his jacket,
20   pose in the murderer's shadow.

(1973)

Bearhug

Griffin calls to come and kiss him goodnight
I yell ok. Finish something I'm doing,
then something else, walk slowly round
the corner to my son's room.
5   He is standing arms outstretched
waiting for a bearhug. Grinning.

Why do I give my emotion an animal's name,
give it that dark squeeze of death?
This is the hug which collects
10   all his small bones and his warm neck against me.
The thin tough body under the pyjamas
locks to me like a magnet of blood.

How long was he standing there
like that, before I came?

(1979)

Eavan Boland

(IRELAND, 1944-)

An Irish Childhood in England: 1951

The bickering of vowels on the buses,
the clicking thumbs and the big hips of
the navy-skirted ticket collectors with
their crooked seams brought it home to me:
5 Exile. Ration-book pudding.
Bowls of dripping and the fixed smile
of the school pianist playing "Iolanthe",
"Land of Hope and Glory" and "John Peel".

I didn't know what to hold, to keep.
10 At night, filled with some malaise
of love for what I'd never known I had,
I fell asleep and let the moment pass.
The passing moment has become a night
of clipped shadows, freshly painted houses,
15 the garden eddying in dark and heat,
my children half-awake, half-asleep.

Airless, humid dark. Leaf-noise.
The stirrings of a garden before rain.
A hint of storm behind the risen moon.
20 We are what we have chosen. Did I choose to?—
in a strange city, in another country,
on nights in a North-facing bedroom,
waiting for the sleep that never did
restore me as I'd hoped to what I'd lost—

25 let the world I knew become the space
between the words that I had by heart
and all the other speech that always was
becoming the language of the country that
I came to in nineteen-fifty-one:
30 barely-gelled, a freckled six-year-old,
overdressed and sick on the plane
when all of England to an Irish child
was nothing more than what you'd lost and how:
was the teacher in the London convent who
35 when I produced "I amn't" in the classroom
turned and said—"you're not in Ireland now."

(1987)

Shirley Geok-Lin Lim

(MALAYSIA/U.S.A., 1944–)

Pantoun for Chinese Women

"At present, the phenomena of butchering, drowning and
leaving to die female infants have been very serious."
(The People's Daily, Peking, March 3rd, 1983)

They say a child with two mouths is no good.
5   In the slippery wet, a hollow space,
Smooth, gumming, echoing wide for food.
No wonder my man is not here at his place.

In the slippery wet, a hollow space,
A slit narrowly sheathed within its hood.
10 No wonder my man is not here at his place:
He is digging for the dragon jar of soot.

That slit narrowly sheathed within its hood!
His mother, squatting, coughs by the fire's blaze
While he digs for the dragon jar of soot.
15 We had saved ashes for a hundred days.

His mother, squatting, coughs by the fire's blaze.
The child kicks against me mewing like a flute.
We had saved ashes for a hundred days,
Knowing, if the time came, that we would.

20 The child kicks against me crying like a flute
Through its two weak mouths. His mother prays
Knowing when the time comes that we would,
For broken clay is never set in glaze.

Through her two weak mouths his mother prays.
25 She will not pluck the rooster nor serve its blood,
For broken clay is never set in glaze:
Women are made of river sand and wood.

She will not pluck the rooster nor serve its blood.
My husband frowns, pretending in his haste
30 Women are made of river sand and wood.
Milk soaks the bedding. I cannot bear the waste:

My husband frowns, pretending in his haste.
Oh clean the girl, dress her in ashy soot!
Milk soaks our bedding, I cannot bear the waste.
35 They say a child with two mouths is no good.

(1980)

Robert Bringhurst

(U.S.A./CANADA, 1946–)

Bone Flute Breathing

They say that a woman with steel-gray
eyes has lived for a thousand years
in these mountains. They say that the music
you almost hear in the level blue light
5   of morning and evening is music she played
in these mountains many years ago
on a flute she'd cut from the cannon bone
of a mule deer buck she'd tracked and wrestled
to the ground.
                They say that at the first few notes
10   she played, her sisters started giggling, because,
instead of listening, they were watching
the change that came over her face.
She stalked off in anger, and for years thereafter
only in darkness did anyone ever hear
15   the flute. Day after day
it lay silent on the mountain,
half hidden under a whitebark pine.
No one else was permitted to touch it,
much less to watch her while she played.

20   But a man came by one day from another
country, they say, who had never heard either
the flute or the story, and he found the flute
on the ground, under the pine tree, where it lay.
As soon as he put it to his lips, it played.
25   It breathed her music when he breathed,
and his hands began to find new
tunes between the tunes it played.

Angry once again at this intrusion,
the woman who lives in these mountains
30   complained about the stranger to her brother,
who lived on the other side of the world.
That very afternoon, her brother built
an elk's skull and antlers and a mountain cat's
intestines into a guitar, and as
35   he walked here, he taught himself to play.

Coming over the hills that way,
without a name, one stranger to another,
he challenged the stranger with the flute to a musical
duel to be judged by the woman who lives
40 in these mountains.
                            It may be the stranger, as many people say,
was simply unwary. It may be
the sun slivered his eyes that day
in such a way that he could see only
one choice. In any case, everyone
45 says that he consented to the contest.

They played night and day, and the stranger,
while he listened, watched the eyes,
and when they wandered, watched the lips
of the woman who lives in these mountains.
50 *Sister*, said the eyes: *sister of the other*
who is playing the guitar. But the lips said, *Music*
of the breath, music of the bone. And the breath
of the woman, whether she willed it to or no,
kept moving in the flute whenever the stranger
55 played. After seven nights and days,
everyone knew the stranger was the winner.

That was when the man with the guitar said,
Stranger, can you sing? Stranger, can you sing us
a song along with the music you play?
60 *Listen,* said the man with the guitar,
and I will show you what I mean.
And while the woman and the stranger watched
and listened, the man with the guitar stared
hard into the air, and his hands like water spiders
65 flickered over the guitar, and a song slid
out between his teeth and flowed
through the music he played.

The stranger in his turn stared
hard into the air and far into the eyes
70 of the woman who lives in these mountains.
And the eyes stared back, and the eyes said, *These*
are the eyes of the sister of the other, and the stranger
played and the stranger played, and no word
came. He stared long at her lips,
75 and the lips said, *Bone*. The lips said,
Wordless breath in the bone. And breathe
as he would, he could not
sing through the music he played.

So it was that the woman with the steel-gray
80 eyes, gazing into the whitebark
pine behind both of them, quietly declared
the man with the guitar to be the winner.

She reached for the flute,
but her brother stepped in front of her.
85 He picked up the flute and the guitar
and smacked them one against the other and against
the rocks until both of them shattered.

Then, taking the stranger by the throat,
he threw him flat against the ground.
90 And taking a splinter from the flute,
and moving swiftly, like a crouching
dancer, he peeled the living flesh
away from the stranger's feet and hands.
He peeled his face and hips and ribs
95 and neatly filleted each of his limbs.

One by one he extracted the stranger's
bones, and one by one he replaced them
with the splinters of the deerbone flute
and the shattered skull and antlers
100 that had been his own guitar.

He stitched the splinters into the stranger's
fingers, into his head and chest
and limbs with the mountain cat's intestines,
and set him on his feet, and propped the last splinter
105 of the bone flute upright in his hand,
and walked off, stopping to scrub
his own hands in a shrinking bank
of spring snow, never uttering a sound.

The stranger stood there motionless
110 for years—but they say that the music you almost
hear in the level blue light of morning
and evening, now, is the sound of the stranger
moving, walking back toward his own country,
one step at a time.

(1982)

Chrystos

(U.S.A., 1946-)

Soft

breasts of fire we live on the water my tongue
drinks you   Wind comes through your tender thighs
I am shaken   You moan the sun changes   Smoke whips
through the air burning on the water   You are a woman who
5   holds me   Could become warm sky here   Fish between
your legs gasp for air   We share a good meal
Cook pots full on the water one can see far into the wind
The crying sky changes my tongue whips you burning
I am a woman turning you in my arms like air
10   holding warm smoke delicious   Your need holds
secret wind   My fingers reach for your burning sky
You are the place of sweet water my hands drink
My breasts on your belly   Place where burning becomes
Time fishes for new water moaning
15   A place where each stroke could be as slow
as breathing smoke   Your belly makes circles of pleasure
on the water   Opening I gasp for life
Clear place where water & fire meet   Moan of wind in my hair
you could touch me & light a fire
20   My hands hold you a bouquet of lush
flowers on fire   Tall & stately my tongue
takes you down
to the water where we live

(1991)

Shame On!

(there are many forms of genocide and this is one)

fake shamen give me some money
I'll make you a catholic priest in a week
couple thousand I'll name you pope
of our crystal breakfast cereal circle of healers
5   Give me some money   you'll be free
Give me some money   you'll be whole
Give me some money   you'll be right
with past lives zooming by your door
Steal from anybody to make a paste-up tacked-on
10   holy cat box of nothing
I tell you I'm sincere & that excuses everything
I'm a sincere thief   a sincere rapist   a sincere killer

My heart is pure my head is fuzzy give me some money
& you'll be clear
15   Your pockets will be anyhow
Give me a dime   I'll erase your crime
Give me a dollar give me a ten give me a thousand
fastest growing business in america
is shame men   shame women
20   You could have a sweat same as you took manhattan
you could initiate people same as into the elks
with a bit of light around your head
& some "Indian" jewelry from hong kong why you're all set
Come on now take something more that doesn't belong to you
25   Come on & take that's what you know best
White takes   Red turns away
Listen I've got a whole bunch of holey underpants
you could use in a ceremony you can make up yourself
Be a born again Indian it's easy
30   You want to buy spiritual enlightenment we got plenty
& if you act today we'll throw in four free 100-watt lightbulbs
so you can have your own private halo
What did you say? You met lynn andrews in person?
That woman ought to be in a bitter herb stew
35   I'll sell you lies half-price better than hers
america is starving to death for spiritual meaning
It's the price you pay for taking everything
It's the price you pay for buying everything
It's the price you pay for loving your stuff more than life
40   Everything goes on without you
You can't hear the grass breathe
because you're too busy talking
about being an Indian holy woman two hundred years ago
You sure must stink if you didn't let go
45   The wind doesn't want to talk to you
because you're always right
even when you don't know what you're talking about
We've been polite for five hundred years
& you still don't get it
50   *Take nothing you cannot return*
Give to others   give more
Walk quietly   Do what needs to be done
Give thanks for your life
Respect all beings
55   *simple*
& it doesn't cost a penny

in Honor of Muriel Miguel & Spiderwoman Theatre   *(1991)*

Bill Manhire

(NEW ZEALAND, 1946–)

An Outline

First we disowned parents
because they always said *after*;
and friends promised to be around
but were not. Our teachers gave
5   encouragement and then prescribed
the lonely flower inside the brain.
One showed a picture
but soon would kick the bucket.

At home, away from home, but mostly
10   nowhere special, we took our own advice.
We got in the car and then just drove
along the road past cliffs and river,
and when we stopped
we slept on the parchment floor,
15   taking it for the real thing.
We wrote out the poem and slept on it.

Still, there was nothing good for us in words,
or nothing couched in formal English,
while being good itself was good for nothing,
20   and then again there was always something
coming next, though no particular direction.
The baby lay in its cot and cooed
or it lay afloat in water inside mother.
When once that baby grows, we said,

25   and put away the car. We built the house then
by the side of the road
at the end of the road beside the river.
Friends came and were welcome
though many failed to make sense
30   except in pieces, and others
had only rested quietly by mistake.
All day they took their boats

upon the water. We felt alone
perhaps, but full of promise.
35   We still possessed the poem in outline,
we had kept some image of the flower in mind.
Now, too, there were provisions, jars of preserves
against the future, photographs to remind
that nothing entered the picture
40   save cats and children; and the telephone rang

to tell of father's death or just
in other words to ask who's speaking.
We sat by the road and watched
the water tremble as it still stayed perfect.
45   We woke and slept and that is how
we kept in touch. The children woke in the night
and cried and we sang words to cure.
One crashed the car

and the others soon shot through.
50   We were young too: we thought
that every goodbye was the last goodbye
and that every last word was made to be careful.
We waved and we waved of course, and now
we find we don't stop waving: believing we see
55   our life at last, and thinking it over,
knowing how far the road goes home.

(1982)

Lorna Goodison

(JAMAICA/SCOTLAND, 1947–)

The Road of the Dread

That dey road no pave
like any other black-face road
it no have no definite color
and it fence two side
5   with live barbwire.

And no look fi no milepost
fi measure you walking
and no tek no stone as
dead or familiar

10 for sometime you pass a ting
   you know as . . . call it stone again
   and is a snake ready fi squeeze yu
   kill yu
   or is a dead man tek him
15 possessions tease yu.
   Then the place dem yu feel
   is resting place because time
   before that yu welcome like rain,
   go dey again?
20 bad dawg, bad face tun fi drive yu underground
   wey yu no have no light fi walk
   and yu find sey that many yu meet who sey
   them understand
   is only from dem mout dem talk.
25 One good ting though, that same treatment
   mek yu walk untold distance
   for to continue yu have fe walk far
   away from the wicked.

   Pan dis same road ya sista
30 sometime yu drink yu salt sweat fi water
   for yu sure sey at least dat no pisen,
   and bread? yu picture it and chew it accordingly
   and some time yu surprise fi know hour dat full
   man belly.

35 Some day no have no definite color
   no beginning and no ending, it just name day
   or night as how you feel fi call it.

   Den why I tread it brother?
   well mek I tell yu bout the day dem
40 when the father send some little bird
   that swallow flute fi trill me
   and when him instruct the sun fi smile pan me first.

   And the sky calm like sea when it sleep
   and a breeze like a laugh follow mi.
45 Or the man find a stream that pure like baby mind
   and the water ease down yu throat
   and quiet yu inside.

And better still when yu meet another traveler
who have flour and yu have water and man and man
50   make bread together.
And dem time dey the road run straight and sure
like a young horse that cant tire
and yu catch a glimpse of the end
through the water in yu eye
55   I wont tell yu what I spy
but is fi dat alone I tread this road.

                                        (1993)

Nanny

1   My womb was sealed
with molten wax
of killer bees
for nothing should enter
5   nothing should leave
the state of perpetual siege
the condition of the warrior.

From then my whole body would quicken
at the birth of every one of my people's children.
10   I was schooled in the green-giving ways
of the roots and vines
made accomplice to the healing acts
of Chainey root, fever grass & vervain.

My breasts flattened
15   settled unmoving against my chest
my movements ran equal
to the rhythms of the forest.

I could sense and sift
the footfall of men
20   from the animals
and smell danger
death's odor
in the wind's shift.

When my eyes rendered
25   light from the dark
my battle song opened
into a solitaire's moan
I became most knowing
and forever alone.

30   And when my training was over
they circled my waist with pumpkin seeds
and dried okra, a traveler's jigida,
and sold me to the traders
all my weapons within me.

35   I was sent, tell that to history.

When your sorrow obscures the skies
other women like me will rise.

(1986)

Medbh McGuckian

(NORTHERN IRELAND, 1950-)

The Hollywood Bed

We narrow into the house, the room, the bed,
Where sleep begins its shunting. You adopt
Your mask, your intellectual cradling of the head,
Neat as notepaper in your creaseless
5   Envelope of clothes, while I lie crosswise,
Imperial as a favoured only child,
Calmed by sagas of how we lay like spoons
In a drawer, till you blew open
My tightened bud, my fully-buttoned housecoat,
10   Like some Columbus mastering
The saw-toothed waves, the rows of letter 'm's'.

Now the headboard is disturbed
By your uncomfortable skew, your hands
Like stubborn adverbs visiting your face,
15   Or your shoulder, in your piquancy of dreams,
The outline that if you were gone,
Would find me in your place.

(1982)

A Dream in Three Colours

I am velvet stroked the wrong way:
The interval between my poems is like
The light between seasons, or the darkness
A mountain is filled with.

5   The point when I sleep is not known
By me, and words cannot carry me
Over it—it is heard only like a kiss
That flows and is not torn out.

Every hour the voices of nouns
10 Wind me up from their scattered rooms,
Where they sit for years, unable to meet,
Like pearls that have lost their clasp,

Or boards snapped by sea-water
That slither towards a shore.
15 Far more raw than the spring night
Which shook you out of its sleeve,

Your first winter sheds for you
Its strongest blue, its deepest white,
Its reddest silk lapel you can let go
20 Or hold, whichever you love best.

(1982)

Guy Vanderhaeghe
(CANADA, 1951–)

Cages

Here it is, 1967, the Big Birthday. Centennial Year they call it. The whole country is giving itself a pat on the back. Holy shit, boys, we made it.

I made it too for seventeen years, a spotless life, as they say, and for presents I get, in my senior year of high school, my graduating year for chrissakes, a six-month suspended sentence for obstructing a police officer, and my very own personal social worker.

The thing is I don't *need* this social worker woman. She can't tell me anything I haven't already figured out for myself. Take last Wednesday, Miss Krawchuk, who looks like the old widow chicken on the Bugs Bunny Show, the one who's hot to trot for Foghorn Leghorn, says to me: "You know, Billy, your father loves you just as much as he does Gene. He doesn't have a favourite."

Now I can get bullshit at the poolroom any time I want it—and without having to keep an appointment. Maybe Pop *loves* me as much as he does Gene, but Gene is still his favourite kid. Everybody has a favourite kid. I knew that much already when I was only eight and Gene was nine. I figured it out right after Gene almost blinded me.

Picture this. There the two of us were in the basement. It was Christmas holidays and the old man had kicked us downstairs to huck darts at this board he'd give us for a present. Somehow, I must've had horseshoes up my ass, I'd beat Gene six games straight. And was he pissed off! He never loses to me at nothing ever. And me being in such a real unique situation, I was giving him the needle-rooney.

"What's that now?" I said. "Is that six or seven what I won?"

"Luck," Gene said, and he sounded like somebody was slowly strangling him. "Luck. Luck. Luck." He could hardly get it out.

And that's when I put the capper on it. I tossed a bull's-eye. "Read 'er and weep," I told him. That's what the old man says whenever he goes out at rummy. It's his needle-rooney. "Read 'er and weep."

That did it. The straw what broke the frigging camel's back. All l saw was his arm blur when he let fly at me. I didn't even have time to *think* about ducking. Bingo. Dead centre in the forehead, right in the middle of the old noggin he drills me with a dart. And there it stuck. Until it loosened a bit. Then it sagged down real slow between my eyes, hung for a second, slid off of my nose, and dropped at my feet. I hollered bloody blue murder, you better believe it.

For once, Pop didn't show that little bastard any mercy. He took after him from room to room whaling him with this extension cord across the ass, the back of the legs, the shoulders. Really hard. Gene, naturally, was screaming and blubbering and carrying on like it was a goddamn axe murder or something. He'd try to get under a bed, or behind a dresser or something, and get stuck halfway. Then old Gene would really catch it. He didn't know whether to plough forward, back up, shit, or go blind. And all the time the old man was lacing him left and right and saying in this sad, tired voice: "You're the oldest. Don't you know no better? You could of took his eye out, you crazy little bugger."

But that was only justice. He wasn't all that mad at Gene. Me he was mad at. If that makes any sense. Although I have to admit he didn't lay a hand on me. But yell? Christ, can that man yell. Especially at me. Somehow I'm the one that drives him squirrelly.

"Don't you *never, never* tease him again!" he bellowed and his neck started to swell. When the old man gets mad you can see it, honest. "You know he can't keep a hold of himself. One day you'll drive him so goddamn goofy with that yap of yours he'll do something terrible! Something he'll regret for the rest of his life. And it'll all be your fault!" The old man had to stop there and slow down or a vein would've exploded in his brain, or his arsehole popped inside out, or something. "So smarten, up," he said, a little quieter, finally, "or you'll be the death of me and all my loved ones."

So there you are. I never pretended the world was fair, and I never bitched because it wasn't. But I do resent the hell out of being forced to listen to some dried-up old broad who gets paid by the government to tell me it is. Fuck her. She never lived in the Simpson household with my old man waiting around for Gene to do that *terrible* thing. It spoils the atmosphere. Makes a person edgy, you know?

Of course, Gene has done a fair number of *bad things* while everybody was waiting around for him to do the one great big *terrible thing*; and he's done them in a fair number of places. That's because the old man is a miner, and for a while there he was always telling some foreman to go piss up a rope. So we moved around a lot. That's why the Simpson household has a real history. But Gene's is the best of all. In Elliot Lake he failed grade three; in Bombertown he got picked up for shoplifting; in Flin Flon he broke some snotty kid's nose and got sent home from school. And every grade he goes higher, it gets a little worse. Last year, when we were both in grade eleven, I'm sure the old man was positive Gene was finally going to pull off the *terrible thing* he's been worrying about as long as I can remember.

It's crazy. Lots of times when I think about it, I figure I don't get on with the old man because I treat him nice. That I try too hard to make him like me. I'm not the way Gene is, I respect Pop. He slogs it out, shift after shift, on a shitty job he hates. Really hates. In fact, he told me once he would have liked to been a farmer. Which only goes to show you how crazy going down that hole day after day makes you. Since we moved to Saskatchewan I've seen lots of farmers, and if you ask me, being one doesn't have much to recommend it.

But getting back to that business of being nice to Dad. Last year I started waiting up for him to come home from the afternoon shift. The one that runs from four p.m. in the afternoon until midnight. It wasn't half bad. Most nights I'd fall asleep on the chesterfield with the TV playing after Mom went to bed. Though lots of times I'd do my best to make it past the national news to wait for Earl Cameron and his collection of screwballs. Those guys kill me. They're always yapping off because somebody or something rattled their chain. Most of those characters with all the answers couldn't pour piss out of a rubber boot if they read the instructions printed on the sole. They remind me of Gene; he's got all the answers too. But still, quite a few of them are what you'd call witty. Which Gene is in his own way too.

But most times, as I say, I'd doze off. Let me give you a sample evening. About twelve-thirty the lights of his half-ton would come shooting into the living-room, bouncing off the walls, scooting along the ceiling when he wheeled into the driveway like a madman. It was the lights flashing in my eyes that woke me up most nights, and if that didn't do it there was always his grand entrance. When the old man comes into the house, from the sound of it you'd think he never heard of door knobs. I swear sometimes I'm sure he's taking a battering-ram to the back door. Then he thunks his lunch bucket on the kitchen counter and bowls his hard hat into the landing. This is because he always comes home from work mad. Never once in his life has a shift ever gone right for that man. Never. They could pack his pockets with diamonds and send him home two hours early and he'd still bitch. So every night was pretty much the same. He had a mad on. Like in my sample night.

He flicked on the living-room light and tramped over to his orange recliner with the bottle of Boh. "If you want to ruin your eyes, do it on school-books, not on watching TV in the goddamn dark. It's up to somebody in this outfit to make something of themselves."

"I was sleeping."

"You ought to sleep in bed." *Keerash*! He weighs two hundred and forty-four pounds and he never sits down in a chair. He falls into it. "Who's that? Gary Cooper?" he asked. He figures any movie star on the late show taller than Mickey Rooney is Cooper. He doesn't half believe you when you tell him they aren't.

"Cary Grant."

"What?"

"Cary Grant. Not Gary Cooper. Cary Grant."

"Oh." There he sat in his recliner, big meaty shoulders sagging, belly propped up on his belt buckle like a pregnant pup's. Eyes red and sore, hair all mussed up, the top of his beer bottle peeking out of his fist like a little brown nipple. He has cuts all over those hands of his, barked knuckles and raspberries that never heal because the salt in the potash ore keeps them open, eats right down to the bone sometimes.

"How'd it go tonight?"

"Usual shit. We had a breakdown." He paused. "Where's your brother? In bed?"

"Out."

"Out? Out? *Out*? What kind of goddamn answer is that? Out where?"

I shrugged.

"Has he got his homework done?" That's the kind of question I get asked. *Has your brother got his homework done*?

"How the hell would I know?"

"I don't know why you don't help him with his school-work," the old man said, peeved as usual.

"You mean do it for him."

"Did I say that? Huh? I said help him. Didn't I say that?" he griped, getting his shit in a knot.

He thinks it's that easy. Just screw the top of old Gene and pour it in. No problem. Like an oil change.

"He's got to be around to help," I said.

That reminded him. He jumped out of the chair and gawked up and down the deserted street. "It's almost one o'clock. On a school night. I'll kick his ass." He sat down and watched the screen for a while and sucked on his barley sandwich.

Finally, he made a stab at acting civilized. "So how's baseball going?"

"What?"

"Baseball. For chrissakes clean out your ears. How's it going?"

"I quit last year. Remember?"

"Oh yeah." He didn't say nothing at first. Then he said:

"You shouldn't have. You wasn't a bad catcher."

"The worst. No bat and no arm—just a flipper. They stole me blind."

"But you had the head," said the old man. And the way he said it made him sound like he was pissed at me for mean-mouthing myself. That surprised me. I felt kind of good about that. "You had the head," he repeated, shaking his own. "I never told you but Al came up to me at work and said you were smart back there behind the plate. He said he wished Gene had your head."

I can't say that surprised me. Gene is one of those cases of a million-dollar body carrying around a ten-cent head. He's a natural. Flop out his glove and, smack, the ball sticks. He's like Mickey Mantle. You know those stop-action photos where they caught Mickey with his eyes glommed onto the bat, watching the ball jump off the lumber? That's Gene. And he runs like a Negro, steals bases like Maury Wills for chrissake.

But stupid and conceited? You wouldn't believe the half of it. Give him the sign to bunt to move a runner and he acts as if you're asking him to bare his ass in public. Not him. He's a big shot. He swings for the fence. Nothing less. And old Gene is always in the game, if you know what I mean? I don't know what happens when he gets on base, maybe he starts thinking of the hair pie in the stands admiring him or something, but he always dozes off at the wheel. Once he even started to comb his hair at first base. Here it is, a 3 and 2 count with two men out, and my brother forgets to run on the pitch because he's combing his hair. I could have died. Really I could have. The guy is such an embarrassment sometimes.

"He can have my head," I said to Pop. "If I get his girls."

That made the old man wince. He's sure that Gene is going to knock up one of those seat-covers he takes out and make him a premature grandpa.

"You pay attention to school. There's plenty of time later for girls." And up he jumped again and stuck his nose against the window looking for Gene again. Mom has to wash the picture window once a week; he spots it all up with nose grease looking for Gene.

"I don't know why your mother lets him out of the house," he said. "Doesn't she have any control over that boy?"

That's what he does, blames everybody but himself. Oh hell, maybe nobody's to blame. Maybe Gene is just Gene, and there's nothing to be done about it.

"I don't know what she's supposed to do. You couldn't keep him in if you parked a tank in the driveway and strung barbed wire around the lot."

Of course that was the wrong thing to say. I usually say it.

"Go to bed!" he yelled at me. "You're no better than your brother. I don't see you in bed neither. What'd I do, raise alley cats or kids? Why can't you two keep hours like human beings!"

And then the door banged and we knew the happy wanderer was home. Gene makes almost as much noise as the old man does when he comes in. It's beneath his dignity to sneak in like me.

Dad hoisted himself out of the chair and steamed off for the kitchen. He can move pretty quick for a big guy when he wants to. Me, I was in hot pursuit. I don't like to miss much.

Old Gene was hammered, and grinning from ass-hole to ear-lobes. The boy's got a great smile. Even when he grins at old ladies my mother's age you can tell they like it.

"Come here and blow in my face," said my father.

"Go on with you," said Gene. All of a sudden the smile was gone and he was irritated. He pushed past Pop, took the milk out of the fridge and started to drink out of the container.

"Use a glass."

Gene burped. He's a slob.

"You stink of beer," said the old man. "Who buys beer for a kid your age?"

"I ain't drunk," said Gene.

"Not much. Your eyes look like two piss-holes in the snow."

"Sure, sure," said Gene. He lounged, he swivelled over to me and lifted my Players out of my shirt pocket. "I'll pay you back tomorrow," he said, taking out a smoke. I heard that one before.

"I don't want to lose my temper," said Dad, being patient with him as usual, "so don't push your luck, sunshine." The two of them eyeballed it, hard. Finally Gene backed down, looked away and fiddled with his matches. "I don't ride that son of a bitch of a cage up and down for my health. I do it for you two," Dad said. "But I swear to God, Gene, if you blow this year of school there'll be a pair of new work boots for you on the back step, come July 1. Both of you know my rules. Go to school, work, or pack up. I'm not having bums put their feet under my table."

"I ain't scared of work," said Gene. "Anyways, school's a pain in the ass."

"Well, you climb in the cage at midnight with three hours of sleep and see if *that* ain't a pain in the ass. Out there nobody says, please do this, please do that. It ain't school out there, it's life."

"Ah, I wouldn't go to the mine. The mine sucks."

"Just what the hell do you think you'd do?"

"He'd open up shop as a brain surgeon," I said. Of course, Gene took a slap at me and grabbed at my shirt. He's a tough guy. He wasn't really mad, but he likes to prevent uppityness.

"You go to bed!" the old man hollered. "You ain't helping matters!"

So off I went. I could hear them wrangling away even after I closed my door. You'd wonder how my mother does it, but she sleeps through it all. I think she's just so goddamn tired of the three of us she's gone permanently deaf to the sound of our voices. She just don't hear us any more.

The last thing I heard before I dropped off was Pop saying: "I've rode that cage all my life, and take it from me, there wasn't a day I didn't wish I'd gone to school and could sit in an office in a clean white shirt." Sometimes he can't remember what he wants to be, a farmer or a pencil-pusher.

The cage. He's always going on about the cage. It's what the men at the mine call the elevator car they ride down the shaft. They call it that because it's all heavy reinforced-steel mesh. The old man has this cage on the brain. Ever since we were little kids he's been threatening us with it. *Make something of yourself,* he'd warn us, *or you'll end up like your old man, a monkey in the cage! Or: What's this, Gene? Failed arithmetic? Just remember, dunces don't end up in the corner. Hell no, they end up in the cage! Look at me!* My old man really hates that cage and the mine. He figures it's the worst thing you can threaten anybody with.

I was in the cage, once. A few years ago, when I was fourteen, the company decided they'd open the mine up for tours. It was likely the brainstorm of some public relations tit sitting in head office in Chicago. In my book it was kind of like taking people into the slaughterhouse to prove you're kind to the cows. Anyway, Pop offered to take us on one of his days off. As usual, he was about four years behind schedule. When we were maybe eleven we might have been nuts about the idea, but just then it didn't thrill us too badly. Gene, who is about as sub-tle as a bag of hammers, said flat out he wasn't interested. I could see right away the old man was hurt by that. It isn't often he plays the buddy to his boys, and he probably had the idea he could whiz us about the machines and stuff. Impress the hell out of us. So it was up to me to slobber and grin like some kind of half-wit over the idea, to perk him up, see? Everybody suffers when the old man gets into one of his moods.

Of course, like always when I get sucked into this good-turn business, I shaft myself. I'd sort of forgotten how much I don't like tight places and being closed in. When we were younger, Gene used to make me go berserk by holding me under the covers, or stuffing a pil-low in my face, or locking me in the garage whenever he got the chance. The jerk.

To start with, they packed us in the cage with twelve other people, which didn't help mat-ters any. Right away my chest got tight and I felt like I couldn't breathe. Then the old cables started groaning and grinding and this fine red dust like chili powder sprinkled down through the mesh and dusted our hard hats with the word GUEST stencilled on them. It was rust. Kind of makes you think.

"Here we go," said Pop.

We went. It was like all of a sudden the floor fell away from under my boots. That cage just dropped in the shaft like a stone down a well. It rattled and creaked and banged. The bare light bulb in the roof started to flicker, and all the faces around me started to dance and shake up and down in the dark. A wind twisted up my pant-legs and I could hear the cables squeak and squeal. It made me think of big fat fucking rats.

"She needs new brake shoes," said this guy beside me and he laughed. He couldn't fool me. He was scared shitless too, in his own way.

"It's not the fall that kills you," his neighbour replied. "It's the sudden stop." There's a cou-ple of horses' patoots in every crowd.

We seemed to drop forever. Everybody got quieter and quieter. They even stopped shuf-fling and coughing. Down. Down. Down. Then the cage started to slow, I felt a pressure build in my knees and my crotch and my ears. The wire box started to shiver and clatter and shake. *Bang!* We stopped. The cage bobbed a little up and down like a yo-yo on the end of a string. Not much though, just enough to make you queasy.

"Last stop, Hooterville!" said the guide, who thought he was funny, and threw back the door. Straight ahead I could see a low-roofed big open space with tunnels running from it into the ore. Every once in a while I could see the light from a miner's helmet jump around in the blackness of one of those tunnels like a firefly flitting in the night.

First thing I thought was: *What if I get lost? What if I lose the group? There's miles and miles and miles of tunnel under here.* I caught a whiff of the air. It didn't smell like air up top. It smelled used. You could taste the salt. *I'm suffocating*, I thought. *I can't breathe this shit.*

I hadn't much liked the cage but this was worse. When I was in the shaft I knew there was a patch of sky over my head with a few stars in it and clouds and stuff. But all of a sudden I realized how deep we were. How we were sort of like worms crawling in the guts of some dead animal. Over us were billions, no, trillions, of tons of rock and dirt and mud pressing down. I could imagine it caving in and falling on me, crushing my chest, squeezing the air out slowly, dust fine as flour trickling into my eyes and nostrils, or mud plugging my mouth so I couldn't even scream. And then just lying there in the dark, my legs and arms pinned so I couldn't even twitch them. For a long time maybe. Crazy, lunatic stuff was what I started to think right on the spot.

My old man gave me a nudge to get out. We were the last.

"No," I said quickly and hooked my fingers in the mesh.

"We get out here," said the old man. He hadn't caught on yet.

"No, I can't," I whispered. He must have read the look on my face then. I think he knew he couldn't have pried me off that mesh with a gooseneck and winch.

Fred, the cage operator, lifted his eyebrows at Pop. "What's up, Jack?"

"The kid's sick," said Pop. "We'll take her up. He don't feel right." My old man was awful embarrassed.

Fred said, "I wondered when it'd happen. Taking kids and women down the hole."

"Shut your own goddamn hole," said the old man. "He's got the flu. He was up all last night."

Fred looked what you'd call sceptical.

"Last time I take you any place nice," the old man said under his breath.

The last day of school has always got to be some big deal. By nine o'clock all the dipsticks are roaring their cars up and down main street with their goofy broads hanging out their windows yelling, and trying to impress on one another how drunk they are.

Dad sent me to look for Gene because he didn't come home for supper at six. I found him in the poolroom playing dollar-a-hand poker pool.

"Hey, little brother," he waved to me from across the smoky poolroom, "come on here and I'll let you hold my cards!" I went over. He grinned to the goofs he was playing with. "You watch out now, boys," he said, "my little brother always brings me luck. Not that I need it," he explained to me, winking.

Yeah, I always brought him luck. *I* kept track of the game. *I* figured out what order to take the balls down. *I* reminded him not to put somebody else out and to play the next guy safe instead of slamming off some cornball shot. When *I* did all that Gene won—because I brought him luck. Yeah.

Gene handed me his cards. "You wouldn't believe these two," he said to me out of the corner of his mouth, "genuine plough jockeys. These boys couldn't find their ass in the dark with both hands. I'm fifteen dollars to the good."

I admit they didn't look too swift. The biggest one, who was *big*, was wearing an out-of-town team jacket, a Massey-Ferguson cap, and shit-kicker wellingtons. He was maybe twenty-one, but his skin hadn't cleared up yet by no means. His pan looked like all-dressed pizza, heavy on the cheese. His friend was a dinky little guy with his hair designed into a duck's ass. The kind of guy who hates the Beatles. About two feet of a dirty comb was sticking out of his ass pocket.

Gene broke the rack and the nine went down. His shot.

"Dad's looking for you. He wants to know if you passed," I said.

"You could've told him."

"Well, I didn't."

"Lemme see the cards." I showed him. He had a pair of treys, a six, a seven, and a lady. Right away he stopped to pocket the three. I got a teacher who always talks about thought processes. Gene doesn't have them.

"Look at the table," I said. "Six first and you can come around up her." I pointed.

"No coaching," said Pizza Face. I could see this one was a poor loser.

Gene shifted his stance and potted the six.

"What now?" he asked.

"The queen, and don't forget to put pants on her." I paused. "Pop figured you were going to make it. He really did, Gene."

"So tough titty. I didn't. Who the hell cares? He had your suck card to slobber over, didn't he?" He drilled the lady in the side pocket. No backspin. He'd hooked himself on the three. "Fuck."

"The old man is on graveyard shift. You better go home and face the music before he goes to work. It'll be worse in the morning when he needs sleep," I warned him.

"Screw him."

I could see Gene eyeballing the four. He didn't have any four in his hand, so I called him over and showed him his cards. "You can't shoot the four. It's not in your hand."

"Just watch me." He winked. "I've been doing it all night. It's all pitch and no catch with these prizes." Gene strolled back to the table and coolly stroked down the four. He had shape for the three which slid in the top pocket like shit through a goose. He cashed in on the seven. "That's it, boys," he said. "That's all she wrote."

I was real nervous. I tried to bury the hand in the deck but the guy with the runny face stopped me. He was getting tired of losing, I guess. Gene doesn't even cheat smart. You got to let them win once in a while.

"Gimme them cards," he said. He started counting the cards off against the balls, flipping down the boards on the felt. "Three." He nodded. "Six, seven, queen. I guess you got them all," he said slowly, with a look on his face like he was pissing ground glass.

That's when Duck Ass chirped up. "Hey, Marvin," he said, "that guy shot the four. He shot the four."

"Nah," said Gene.

Marvin studied on this for a second, walked over to the table and pulled the four ball out of the pocket. Just like little Jack Horner lifting the plum out of the pie. "Yeah," he said. "You shot the four."

"Jeez," said Gene, "I guess I did. Honest mistake. Look, here's a dollar for each of you." He took two bills out of his shirt pocket. "You got to pay for your mistakes is what I was always taught."

"I bet you he's been cheating all along," said Duck Ass.

"My brother don't cheat," I said.

"I want all my money back," said Marvin. Quite loud. Loud enough that some heads turned and a couple of tables stopped playing. There was what you would call a big peanut gallery, it being the beginning of vacation and the place full of junior high kids and stags.

"You can kiss my ass, bozo," said Gene. "Like my brother here said, I never cheated nobody in my life."

"You give us our money back," threatened Marvin, "or I'll pull your head off, you skinny little prick."

Guys were starting to drift towards us, curious. The manager, Fat Bert, was easing his guts out from behind the cash register.

"Give them their money, Gene," I said, "and let's get out of here."

"No."

Well, that was that. You can't change his mind. I took a look at old Marvin. As I said before, Marvin was *big*. But what was worse was that he had this real determined look people who aren't too bright get when they finally dib on to the fact they've been hosed and somebody has been laughing up his sleeve at them. They don't like it too hot, believe me.

"Step outside, shit-head," said Marvin.

"Fight," somebody said encouragingly. A real clump of ringsiders was starting to gather. "Fight." Bert came hustling up, bumping his way through the kids with his bay window. "Outside, you guys. I don't want nothing broke in here. Get out or I'll call the cops."

Believe me, was I tense. Real tense. I know Gene pretty well and I was sure that he had looked at old Marvin's muscles trying to bust out everywhere. Any second I figured he was going to even the odds by pasting old Marv in the puss with his pool cue, or at least sucker-punching him.

But Gene is full of surprises. All of a sudden he turned peacemaker. He laid down his pool cue (which I didn't figure was too wise) and said: "You want to fight over this?" He held up the four ball. "Over this? An honest mistake?"

"Sure I do," said Marvin. "You're fucking right I do, cheater."

"Cheater, cheater," said Duck Ass. I was looking him over real good because I figured if something started in there I'd get him to tangle with.

Gene shrugged and even kind of sighed, like the hero does in the movies when he has been forced into a corner and has to do something that is against his better nature. He tossed up the four ball once, looked at it, and then reached behind him and shoved it back into the pocket. "All right," he said, slouching a little and jamming his hands into his jacket pockets. "Let's go, sport."

That started the stampede. "Fight! Fight!" The younger kids, the ones thirteen and fourteen, were really excited; the mob kind of swept Marvin and Gene out the door, across the street and into the OK Economy parking lot where most beefs get settled. There's lots of dancing-room there. A nice big ring.

Marvin settled in real quick. He tugged the brim of his Massey-Ferguson special a couple of times, got his dukes up and started to hop around like he'd stepped right out of the pages of *Ring* magazine. He looked pretty stupid, especially when Gene just looked at him, and kept his hands rammed in his jacket pockets. Marvin kind of clomped from foot to foot for a bit and he said: "Get 'em up."

"You get first punch," said Gene.

"What?" said Marv. He was so surprised his yap fell open.

"If I hit you first," said Gene, "you'll charge me with assault. I know your kind."

Marvin stopped clomping. I suspect it took too much co-ordination for him to clomp and think at the same time. "Oh no," he said, "I ain't falling for that. If I hit *you* first, you'll charge *me* with assault." No flies on Marvin. "*You* get the first punch."

"Fight. Come on, fight," said some ass-hole, real disgusted with all the talk and no action.

"Oh no," said Gene. "I ain't hitting *you* first."

Marvin brought his hands down. "Come on, come on, let fly."

"You're sure?" asked Gene.

"Give her your best shot," said Marvin. "You couldn't hurt a fly, you scrawny shit. Quit stalling. Get this show on the road."

Gene uncorked on him. It looked like a real pansy punch. His right arm whipped out of his jacket pocket, stiff at the elbow like a girl's when she slaps. It didn't look like it had nothing behind it, sort of like Gene had smacked him kind of contemptuous in the mouth with the flat of his hand. That's how it looked. It *sounded* like he'd hit him in the mouth with a ball-peen hammer. Honest to God, you could hear the teeth crunch when they broke.

Big Marvin dropped on his knees like he'd been shot in the back of the neck. His hands flew up to his face and the blood just ran through his fingers and into his cuffs. It looked blue under the parking-lot lights. There was an awful lot of it.

"Get up, you dick licker," said Gene.

Marvin pushed off his knees with a crazy kind of grunt that might have been a sob. I couldn't tell. He came up under Gene's arms, swept him off his feet and dangled him in the air, crushing his ribs in a bear hug.

"*Waauugh!*" said Gene. I started looking around right smartly for something to hit the galoot with before he popped my brother like a pimple.

But then Gene lifted his fist high above Marvin's head and brought it down on his skull, hard as he could. It made a sound like he was banging coconuts together. Marvin sagged a little at the knees and staggered. *Chunk! Chunk!* Gene hit him two more times and Marvin toppled over backwards. My brother landed on top of him and right away started pasting him left and right. Everybody was screaming encouragement. There was no invitation to the dick licker to get up this time. Gene was still clobbering him when I saw the cherry popping on the cop car two blocks away. I dragged him off Marvin.

"Cops," I said, yanking at his sleeve. Gene was trying to get one last kick at Marvin. "Come on, fucker," he was yelling. "Fight now!"

"Jesus," I said, looking at Gene's jacket and shirt, "you stupid bugger, you're all over blood." It was smeared all over him. Marvin tried to get up. He only made it to his hands and knees. There he stayed, drooling blood and saliva on the asphalt. The crowd started to edge away as the cop car bounced up over the curb and gave a long, low whine out of its siren.

I took off my windbreaker and gave it to Gene. He pulled off his jacket and threw it down. "Get the fuck out of here," I said. "Beat it."

"I took the wheels off his little red wagon," said Gene. "It don't pull so good now." His hands were shaking and so was his voice. He hadn't had half enough yet. "I remember that other guy," he said. "Where's his friend?"

I gave him a shove. "Get going." Gene slid into the crowd that was slipping quickly away. Then I remembered his hockey jacket. It was wet with blood. It also had flashes with his name and number on it. It wouldn't take no Sherlock Holmes cop to figure out who'd beat on Marvin. I picked it up and hugged it to my belly. Right away I felt something hard in the pocket. Hard and round. I started to walk away. I heard a car door slam. I knew what was in that pocket. The controversial four ball old Gene had palmed when he pretended to put it back. He likes to win.

I must have been walking too fast or with a guilty hunch to my shoulders, because I heard the cop call, "Hey you, the kid with the hair." Me, I'm kind of a hippy for this place, I guess. Lots of people mention my hair.

I ran. I scooted round the corner of the supermarket and let that pool ball fly as hard as I could, way down the alley. I never rifled a shot like that in my life. If coach Al had seen me trigger that baby he'd have strapped me into a belly pad himself. Of course, a jacket don't fly for shit. The bull came storming around the corner just as I give it the heave-ho. I was kind of caught with shit on my face, if you know what I mean?

Now a guy with half a brain could have talked his way out of that without too much trouble. Even a cop understands how somebody would try to help his brother. They don't hold it too much against you. And I couldn't really protect Gene. That geek Marvin would have flapped his trap if I hadn't. And it wasn't as if I hadn't done old Gene *some* good. After all, they never found out about that pool ball. The judge would have pinned Gene's ears back for him if he'd known he was going around thwacking people with a hunk of shatter-proof plastic. So Gene came out smelling like a rose, same suspended sentence as me, and a reputation for having hands of stone.

But at a time like that you get the nuttiest ideas ever. I watched them load Marvin in a squad car to drive him to the hospital while I sat in the back seat of another. And I thought to myself: *I'll play along with this. Let the old man come down to the cop shop over me for once. Me he takes for granted. Let him worry about Billy for a change. It wouldn't hurt him.*

So I never said one word about not being the guy who bopped Marvin. It was kind of fun in a crazy way, making like a hard case. At the station I was real rude and lippy. Particularly to a sergeant who was a grade A dink if I ever saw one. It was only when they took my shoelaces and belt that I started to get nervous.

"Ain't you going to call my old man?" I asked.

The ass-hole sergeant gave me a real smile. "In the morning," he said. "All in good time."

"In the morning?" And then I said like a dope: "Where am I going to sleep?"

"Show young Mr. Simpson where he's going to sleep," said the sergeant. He smiled again. It looked like a ripple on a slop pail. The constable who he was ordering around like he was his own personal slave took me down into the basement of the station. Down there it smelled of stale piss and old puke. I kind of gagged. I got a weak stomach.

Boy, was I nervous. I saw where he was taking me. There were four cells. They weren't even made out of bars, just metal strips riveted into a cross hatch you couldn't stick your hand through. They were all empty.

"Your choice," said the corporal. He was real humorous too, like his boss.

"You don't have to put me in one of them, sir," I said. "I won't run away."

"That's what all the criminals say." He opened the door. "Entrez-vous."

I was getting my old crazy feeling really bad. Really bad. I felt kind of dizzy. "I got this thing," I said, "about being locked up. It's torture."

"Get in."

"No—please," I said. "I'll sit upstairs. I won't bother anybody."

"You think you've got a choice? You don't have a choice. Move your ass."

I was getting ready to cry. I could feel it. I was going to bawl in front of a cop. "I didn't do it," I said. "I never beat him up. Swear to Jesus I didn't."

"I'm counting three," he said, "and then I'm applying the boots to your backside."

It all came out. Just like that. *It was my fucking ass-hole brother, Gene!* I screamed. The only thing I could think of was, if they put me in there I'll be off my head by morning. I really will. *I didn't do nothing! I never do nothing! You can't put me in there for him!*

They called my old man. I guess I gave a real convincing performance. Not that I'm proud of it. I actually got sick on the spot from nerves. I just couldn't hold it down.

Pop had to sign for me and promise to bring Gene down in the morning. It was about twelve-thirty when everything got cleared up. He'd missed his shift and his ride in the cage.

When we got in the car he didn't start it. We just sat there with the windows rolled down. It was a beautiful night and there were lots of stars swimming in the sky. This town is small enough that street-lights and neon don't interfere with the stars. It's the only thing I like about this place. There's plenty of sky and lots of air to breathe.

"Your brother wasn't enough," he said. "You I trusted."

"I only tried to help him."

"You goddamn snitch." He needed somebody to take it out on, so he belted me. Right on the snout with the back of his hand. It started to bleed. I didn't try to stop it. I just let it drip on those goddamn furry seat-covers that he thinks are the cat's ass. "They were going to put me in this place, this cage, for him, for that useless shit!" I yelled. I'd started to cry. "No more, Pop. He failed! He failed on top of it all! So is he going to work? You got the boots ready on the back step? Huh? Is he going down in the fucking cage?"

"Neither one of you is going down in the cage. Not him, not you," he said.

"Nah, I didn't think so," I said, finally wiping at my face with the back of my hand. "I didn't think so."

"I don't have to answer to you," he said. "You just can't get inside his head. You were always the smart one. I didn't have to worry about you. You always knew what to do. But Gene . . ."

He pressed his forehead against the steering-wheel, hard. "Billy, I see him doing all sorts of stuff. Stuff you can't imagine. I see it until it makes me sick." He looked at me. His face was yellow under the street-light, yellow like a lemon. "I try so hard with him. But he's got no sense. He just does things. He could have killed that other boy. He wouldn't even think of that, you know." All of a sudden the old man's face got all crumpled and creased like paper when you ball it up. "What's going to happen to him?" he said, louder than he had to. "What's going to happen to Eugene?" It was sad. It really was.

I can never stay mad at my old man. Maybe because we're so much alike, even though he can't see it for looking the other way. Our minds work alike. I'm a chip off the old block. Don't ever doubt it.

"Nothing."

"Billy," he said, "you mean it?"

I knew what he was thinking. "Yes," I said, "I'll do my best."

(1982)

Rohinton Mistry
(INDIA/CANADA, 1952–)

Swimming Lessons

The old man's wheelchair is audible today as he creaks by in the hallway: on some days it's just a smooth whirr. Maybe the way he slumps in it, or the way his weight rests has something to do with it. Down to the lobby he goes, and sits there most of time, talking to people on their way out or in. That's where he first spoke to me a few days ago. I was waiting for the elevator, back from Eaton's with my new pair of swimming trunks.

"Hullo," he said. I nodded, smiled.

"Beautiful summer day we've got."

"Yes," I said, "it's lovely outside."

He shifted the wheelchair to face me squarely. "How old do you think I am?"

I looked at him blankly, and he said, "Go on, take a guess."

I understood the game; he seemed about seventy-five although the hair was still black, so I said, "Sixty-five?" He made a sound between a chuckle and a wheeze: "I'll be seventy-seven next month." Close enough.

I've heard him ask that question several times since, and everyone plays by the rules. Their faked guesses range from sixty to seventy. They pick a lower number when he's more depressed than usual. He reminds me of Grandpa as he sits on the sofa in the lobby, staring out vacantly at the parking lot. Only difference is, he sits with the stillness of stroke victims, while Grandpa's Parkinson's disease would bounce his thighs and legs and arms all over the place. When he could no longer hold the *Bombay Samachar* steady enough to read, Grandpa took to sitting on the veranda and staring emptily at the traffic passing outside Firozsha Baag. Or waving to anyone who went by the compound: Rustomji, Nariman Hansotia in his 1932 Mercedes-Benz, the fat ayah Jaakaylee with her shopping-bag, the *kuchrawalli* with her basket and long bamboo broom.

The Portuguese woman across the hall has told me a little about the old man. She is the communicator for the apartment building. To gather and disseminate information, she takes the liberty of unabashedly throwing open her door when newsworthy events transpire. Not for Portuguese Woman the furtive peerings from thin cracks or spyholes. She reminds me of a character in a movie, *Barefoot In The Park* I think it was, who left empty beer cans by the landing for anyone passing to stumble and give her the signal. But PW does not need beer cans. The gutang-khutang of the elevator opening and closing is enough.

The old man's daughter looks after him. He was living alone till his stroke, which coincided with his youngest daughter's divorce in Vancouver. She returned to him and they moved into this low-rise in Don Mills. PW says the daughter talks to no one in the building but takes good care of her father.

Mummy used to take good care of Grandpa, too, till things became complicated and he was moved to the Parsi General Hospital. Parkinsonism and osteoporosis laid him low. The doctor explained that Grandpa's hip did not break because he fell, but he fell because the hip, gradually growing brittle, snapped on that fatal day. That's what osteoporosis does, hollows out the bones and turns effect into cause. It has an unusually high incidence in the Parsi community, he said, but did not say why. Just one of those mysterious things. We are the chosen people where osteoporosis is concerned. And divorce. The Parsi community has the highest divorce rate in India. It also claims to be the most westernized community in India. Which is the result of the other? Confusion again, of cause and effect.

The hip was put in traction. Single-handed, Mummy struggled valiantly with bedpans and dressing for bedsores which soon appeared like grim spectres on his back. *Mamaiji*, bent double with her weak back, could give no assistance. My help would be enlisted to roll him over on his side while Mummy changed the dressing. But after three months, the doctor pronounced a patch upon Grandpa's lungs, and the male ward of Parsi General swallowed him up. There was no money for a private nursing home. I went to see him once, at Mummy's insistence. She used to say that the blessings of an old person were the most valuable and potent of all, they would last my whole life long. The ward had rows and rows of beds; the din was enormous, the smells nauseating, and it was just as well that Grandpa passed most of his time in a less than conscious state.

But I should have gone to see him more often. Whenever Grandpa went out, while he still could in the days before parkinsonism, he would bring back pink and white sugar-coated almonds for Percy and me. Every time I remember Grandpa, I remember that; and then I think: I should have gone to see him more often. That's what I also thought when our telephone-owning neighbour, esteemed by all for that reason, sent his son to tell us the hospital had phoned that Grandpa died an hour ago.

The postman rang the doorbell the way he always did, long and continuous; Mother went to open it, wanting to give him a piece of her mind but thought better of it, she did not want to risk the vengeance of postmen, it was so easy for them to destroy letters; workers nowadays thought no end of themselves, strutting around like peacocks, ever since all this Shiv Sena agitation about Maharashtra for Maharashtrians, threatening strikes and Bombay bundh *all the time, with no respect for the public; bus drivers and conductors were the worst, behaving as if they owned the buses and were doing favours to commuters, pulling the bell before you were in the bus, the driver purposely braking and moving with big jerks to make the standees lose their balance, the conductor so rude if you did not have the right change.*

But when she saw the airmail envelope with a Canadian stamp her face lit up, she said wait to the postman, and went in for a fifty paisa piece, a little baksheesh *for you, she told him, then shut the door and kissed the envelope, went in running, saying my son has written, my son has sent a letter, and Father looked up from the newspaper and said, don't get too excited, first read it, you know what kind of letters he writes, a few lines of empty words, I'm fine, hope you are all right, your loving son—that kind of writing I don't call letter-writing.*

Then Mother opened the envelope and took out one small page and began to read silently, and the joy brought to her face by the letter's arrival began to ebb; Father saw it happening and knew he was right, he said read aloud, let me also hear what our son is writing this time, so Mother read: My dear Mummy and Daddy, Last winter was terrible, we had record-breaking low temperatures all through February and March, and the first official day of spring was colder than the first official day of winter had been, but it's getting warmer now. Looks like it will be a nice warm summer. You asked about my new apartment. It's small, but not bad at all. This is just a quick note to let you know I'm fine, so you won't worry about me. Hope everything is okay at home.

After Mother put it back in the envelope, Father said everything about his life is locked in silence and secrecy. I still don't understand why he bothered to visit us last year if he had nothing to say; every letter of his has been a quick note so we won't worry—what does he think we worry about, his health, in that country everyone eats well whether they work or not, he should be worrying about us with all the black market and rationing, has he forgotten already how he used to go to the ration-shop and wait in line every week; and what kind of apartment description is that, not bad at all; and if it is a Canadian weather report I need from him, I can go with Nariman Hansotia from A Block to the Cawasji Framji Memorial Library and read all about it, there they get newspapers from all over the world.

The sun is hot today. Two women are sunbathing on the stretch of patchy lawn at the periphery of the parking lot. I can seem them clearly from my kitchen. They're wearing bikinis and I'd love to take a closer look. But I have no binoculars. Nor do I have a car to saunter out to and pretend to look under the hood. They're both luscious and gleaming. From time to time they smear lotion over their skin, on the bellies, on the inside of the thighs, on the shoulders. Then one of them gets the other to undo the string of her top and spread some there. She lies on her stomach with the straps undone. I wait. I pray that the heat and haze make her forget, when it's time to turn over, that the straps are undone.

But the sun is not hot enough to work this magic for me. When it's time to come in, she flips over, deftly holding up the cups, and reties the top. They arise, pick up towels, lotions and magazines, and return to the building.

This is my chance to see them closer. I race down the stairs to the lobby. The old man says hullo. "Down again?"

"My mailbox," I mumble.

"It's Saturday," he chortles. For some reason he finds it extremely funny. My eye is on the door leading in from the parking lot.

Through the glass panel I see them approaching. I hurry to the elevator and wait. In the dimly lit lobby I can see their eyes are having trouble adjusting after the bright sun. They don't seem as attractive as they did from the kitchen window. The elevator arrives and I hold it open, inviting them in with what I think is a gallant flourish. Under the fluorescent glare in the elevator I see their wrinkled skin, aging hands, sagging bottoms, varicose veins. The lustrous trick of sun and lotion and distance has ended.

I step out and they continue to the third floor. I have Monday night to look forward to, my first swimming lesson. The high school behind the apartment building is offering among its usual assortment of macramé and ceramics and pottery classes, a class for non-swimming adults.

The woman at the registration desk is quite friendly. She even gives the opening to satisfy the compulsion I have about explaining my non-swimming status.

"Are you from India?" she asks. I nod. "I hope you don't mind my asking, but I was curious because an Indian couple, husband and wife, also registered a few minutes ago. Is swimming not encouraged in India?"

"On the contrary," I say. "Most Indians swim like fish. I'm an exception to the rule. My house was five minutes walking distance from Chaupatty beach in Bombay. It's one of the most beautiful beaches in Bombay, or was, before the filth took over. Anyway, even though we lived so close to it, I never learned to swim. It's just one of those things."

"Well," says the woman, "that happens sometimes. Take me, for instance, I never learned to ride a bicycle. It was the mounting that used to scare me, I was afraid of falling." People have lined up behind me. "It's been very nice talking to you," she says, "hope you enjoy the course."

The art of swimming had been trapped between the devil and the deep blue sea. The devil was money, always scarce, and kept the private swimming clubs out of reach; the deep blue sea of Chaupatty beach was grey and murky with garbage, too filthy to swim in. Every so often we would muster our courage and Mummy would take me there to try to teach me. But a few minutes of paddling was all we could endure. Sooner or later something would float up against our legs or thighs or waists, depending on how deep we'd gone in, and we'd be revulsed and stride out to the sand.

Water imagery in my life is recurring. Chaupatty beach, now the high-school swimming pool. The universal symbol of life and regeneration did nothing but frustrate me. Perhaps the swimming pool will overturn that failure.

When images and symbols abound in this manner, sprawling or rolling across the page without guile or artifice, one is prone to say, how obvious, how skilless; symbols, after all, should be still and gentle as dewdrops, tiny, yet shining with a world of meaning. But what happens when, on the page of life itself, one encounters the ever-moving, all-engirdling sprawl of the filthy sea? Dewdrops and oceans both have their rightful places; Nariman Hansotia certainly knew that when he told his stories to the boys of Firozsha Baag.

The sea of Chaupatty was fated to endure the finales of life's everyday functions. It seemed that the dirtier it became, the more crowds it attracted: street urchins and beggars and beachcombers, looking through the junk that washed up. (Or was it the crowds that made it dirtier?—another instance of cause and effect blurring and evading identification.)

Too many religious festivals also used the sea as repository for their finales. Its use should have been rationed, like rice and kerosene. On Ganesh Chaturthi, clay idols of the god Ganesh, adorned with garlands and all manner of finery, were carried in processions to the accompaniment of drums and a variety of wind instruments. The music got more frenzied the closer the processions got to Chaupatty and to the moment of immersion.

Then there was Coconut Day, which was never as popular as Ganesh Chaturthi. From a bystander's viewpoint, coconuts chucked into the sea do not provide as much of a spectacle. We used the sea, too, to deposit the leftovers from Parsi religious ceremonies, things such as flowers, or the ashes of the sacred sandalwood fire, which just could not be dumped with the regular garbage but had to be entrusted to the care of Avan Yazad, the guardian of the sea. And things which were of no use but which no one had the heart to destroy were also given Avan Yazad. Such as old photographs.

After Grandpa died, some of his things were flung out to sea. It was high tide; we always checked the newspaper when going to perform these disposals; an ebb would mean a long walk in squelchy sand before finding water. Most of the things were probably washed up on shore. But we tried to throw them as far out as possible, then waited a few minutes; if they did not float back right away we would pretend they were in the permanent safekeeping of Avan Yazad, which was a comforting thought. I can't remember everything we sent out to sea, but his brush and comb were in the parcel, his *kusti*, and some Kemadrin pills, which he used to take to keep the parkinsonism under control.

Our paddling sessions stopped for lack of enthusiasm on my part. Mummy wasn't too keen either, because of the filth. But my main concern was the little guttersnipes, like naked fish with little buoyant penises, taunting me with their skills, swimming underwater and emerging unexpectedly all around me, or pretending to masturbate—I think they were too young to achieve ejaculation. It was embarrassing. When I look back, I'm surprised that Mummy and I kept going as long as we did.

I examine the swimming-trunks I bought last week. Surf King, says the label, Made in Canada—Fabriqué Au Canada. I've been learning bits and pieces of French from bilingual labels at the supermarket too. These trunks are extremely sleek and streamlined hipsters, the distance from waistband to pouch tip the barest minimum. I wonder how everything will stay in place, not that I'm boastful about my endowments. I try them on, and feel that the tip of my member lingers perilously close to the exit. Too close, in fact, to conceal the exigencies of my swimming lesson fantasy: a gorgeous woman in the class for non-swimmers, at whose sight I will be instantly aroused, and she spying the shape of my desire, will look me straight in the eye with her intentions; she will come home with me, to taste the pleasures of my delectable Asian brown body whose strangeness has intrigued her and unleashed uncontrollable surges of passion inside her throughout the duration of the swimming lesson.

I drop the Eaton's bag and wrapper in the garbage can. The swimming-trunks cost fifteen dollars, same as the fee for the ten weekly lessons. The garbage bag is almost full. I tie it up and take it outside. There is a medicinal smell in the hallway; the old man must have just returned to his apartment.

PW opens her door and says, "Two ladies from the third floor were lying in the sun this morning. In bikinis."

"That's nice," I say, and walk to the incinerator chute. She reminds me of Najamai in Firozsha Baag, except that Najamai employed a bit more subtlety while going about her life's chosen work.

PW withdraws and shuts her door.

Mother had to reply because Father said he did not want to write to his son till his son had something sensible to write to him, his questions had been ignored long enough, and if he wanted to keep his life a secret, fine, he would get no letters from his father.

But after Mother started the letter he went and looked over her shoulder, telling her what to ask him, because if they kept on writing the same questions, maybe he would understand how interested they were in knowing about things over there; Father said go on, ask him what his work is at the insurance company, tell him to take some courses at night school, that's how everyone moves ahead over there, tell him not to be discouraged if his job is just clerical right now, hard work will get him ahead, remind him he is a Zoroastrian: manashni, gavashni, kunashni, better write the translation also: good thoughts, good words, good deeds—he must have forgotten what it means, and tell him to say prayers and do kusti *at least twice a day.*

Writing it all down sadly, Mother did not believe he wore his sudra *and* kusti *anymore, she would be very surprised if he remembered any of the prayers; when she had asked him if he needed new* sudras *he said not to take any trouble because the Zoroastrian Society of Ontario imported them from Bombay for their members, and this sounded like a story he was making up, but she was leaving it in the hands of God, ten thousand miles away there was nothing she could do but write a letter and hope for the best.*

Then she sealed it, and Father wrote the address on it as usual because his writing was much neater than hers, handwriting was important in the address and she did not want the

postman in Canada to make any mistake; she took it to the post office herself, it was impossi-
ble to trust anyone to mail it ever since the postage rates went up because people just tore off
the stamps for their own use and threw away the letter, the only safe way was to hand it over
the counter and make the clerk cancel the stamps before your own eyes.

Berthe, the building superintendent, is yelling at her son in the parking lot. He tinkers away with his van. This happens every fine-weathered Sunday. It must the be van that Berthe dislikes because I've seen mother and son together in other quite amicable situations.

Berthe is a big Yugoslavian with high cheekbones. Her nationality was disclosed to me by PW. Berthe speaks a very rough-hewn English, I've overheard her in the lobby scolding tenants for late rents and leaving dirty lint screens in the dryers. It's exciting to listen to her, her words fall like rocks and boulders, and one can never tell where or how the next few will drop. But her Slavic yells at her son are a different matter, the words fly swift and true, well-aimed missiles that never miss. Finally, the son slams down the hood in disgust, wipes his hands on a rag, accompanies mother Berthe inside.

Berthe's husband has a job in a factory. But he loses several days of work every month when he succumbs to the booze, a word Berthe uses often in her Slavic tirades on those days, the only one I can understand, as it clunks down heavily out of the tight-flying formation of Yugoslavian sentences. He lolls around in the lobby, submitting passively to his wife's tongue-lashings. The bags under his bloodshot eyes, his stringy moustache, stubbled chin, dirty hair are so vulnerable to the poison-laden barbs (poison works the same way in any language) emanating from deep within the powerful watermelon bosom. No one's presence can embarrass or dignify her into silence.

No one except the old man who arrives now. "Good morning," he says, and Berthe turns, stops yelling, and smiles. Her husband rises, positions the wheelchair at the favourite angle. The lobby will be peaceful as long as the old man is there.

It was hopeless. My first swimming lesson. The water terrified me. When did that happen, I wonder, I used to love splashing at Chaupatty, carried about by the waves. And this was only a swimming pool. Where did all that terror come from? I'm trying to remember.

Armed with my Surf King I enter the high school and go to the pool area. A sheet with instructions for the new class is pinned to the bulletin board. All students must shower and then assemble at eight by the shallow end. As I enter the showers three young boys, probably from a previous class, emerge. One of them holds his nose. The second begins to hum, under his breath: Paki Paki, smell like curry. The third says to the first two: pretty soon all the water's going to taste of curry. They leave.

It's a mixed class, but the gorgeous woman of my fantasy is missing. I have to settle for another, in a pink one-piece suit, with brown hair and a bit of a stomach. She must be about thirty-five. Plain-looking.

The instructor is called Ron. He gives us a pep talk, sensing some nervousness in the group. We're finally all in the water, in the shallow end. He demonstrates floating on the back, then asks for a volunteer. The pink one-piece suit wades forward. He supports her, tells her to lean back and let her head drop in the water.

She does very well. And as we all regard her floating body, I see what was not visible outside the pool: her bush, curly bits of it, straying out at the pink Spandex V. Tongues of water lapping against her delta, as if caressing it teasingly, make the brown hair come alive in a most tantalizing manner. The crests and troughs of little waves, set off by the movement of our bodies in a circle around her, dutifully irrigate her, the curls alternately wave free inside the crest, then adhere to her wet thighs, beached by the inevitable trough. I could watch this forever, and I wish the floating demonstration would never end.

Next we are shown how to grasp the rail and paddle, face down in the water. Between practising floating and paddling, the hour is almost gone. I have been trying to observe the pink one-piece suit, getting glimpses of her straying pubic hair from various angles. Finally, Ron wants a volunteer for the last demonstration, and I go forward. To my horror he leads the class to the deep end. Fifteen feet of water. It is so blue, and I can see the bottom. He picks up a metal hoop attached to a long wooden stick. He wants me to grasp the hoop, jump in the water, and paddle, while he guides me by the stick. Perfectly safe, he tells me. A demonstration of how paddling propels the body.

It's too late to back out; besides, I'm so terrified I couldn't find the words to do so even if I wanted to. Everything he says I do as if in a trance. I don't remember the moment of jumping. The next thing I know is, I'm swallowing water and floundering, hanging on to the hoop for dear life. Ron draws me to the rails and helps me out. The class applauds.

We disperse and one thought is on my mind: what if I'd lost my grip? Fifteen feet of water under me. I shudder and take deep breaths. This is it. I'm not coming next week. This instructor is an irresponsible person. Or he does not value the lives of non-white immigrants. I remember the three teenagers. Maybe the swimming pool is the hangout of some racial group, bent on eliminating all non-white swimmers, to keep their waters pure and their white sisters unogled.

The elevator takes me upstairs. Then gutang-khutang. PW opens her door as I turn the corridor of medicinal smells. "Berthe was screaming loudly at her husband tonight," she tells me.

"Good for her," I say, and she frowns indignantly at me.

The old man is in the lobby. He's wearing thick wool gloves. He wants to know how the swimming was, must have seen me leaving with my towel yesterday. Not bad, I say.

"I used to swim a lot. Very good for the circulation." He wheezes. "My feet are cold all the time. Cold as ice. Hands too."

Summer is winding down, so I say stupidly, "Yes, it's not so warm any more."

The thought of the next swimming lesson sickens me. But as I comb through the memories of that terrifying Monday, I come upon the straying curls of brown pubic hair. Inexorably drawn by them, I decide to go.

It's a mistake, of course. This time I'm scared even to venture in the shallow end. When everyone has entered the water and I'm the only one outside, I feel a little foolish and slide in.

Instructor Ron says we should start by reviewing the floating technique. I'm in no hurry. I watch the pink one-piece pull the swim-suit down around her cheeks and flip back to achieve perfect flotation. And then reap disappointment. The pink Spandex triangle is perfectly streamlined today, nothing strays, not a trace of fuzz, not one filament, not even a sign of post-depilation irritation. Like the airbrushed parts of glamour magazine models. The barrenness of her impeccably packaged apex is a betrayal. Now she is shorn like the other women in the class. Why did she have to do it?

The weight of this disappointment makes the water less manageable, more lung-penetrating. With trepidation, I float and paddle my way through the remainder of the hour, jerking my head out every two seconds and breathing deeply, to continually shore up a supply of precious, precious air without, at the same time, seeming too anxious and losing my dignity.

I don't attend the remaining classes. After I've missed three, Ron the instructor telephones. I tell him I've had the flu and am still feeling poorly, but I'll try to be there the following week.

He does not call again. My Surf King is relegated to an unused drawer. Total losses: one fantasy plus thirty dollars. And no watery rebirth. The swimming pool, like Chaupatty beach, has produced a stillbirth. But there is a difference. Water means regeneration only if it is pure and cleansing. Chaupatty was filthy, the pool was not. Failure to swim through filth must mean something other than failure of rebirth—failure of symbolic death? Does that equal success of symbolic life? death of a symbolic failure? death of a symbol? What is the equation?

The postman did not bring a letter but a parcel, he was smiling because he knew that every time something came from Canada his baksheesh was guaranteed, and this time because it was a parcel Mother gave him a whole rupee, she was quite excited, there were so many stickers on it besides the stamps, one for Small Parcel, another Printed Papers, a red sticker saying Insured; she showed it to Father, and opened it, then put both hands on her cheeks, not able to speak because the surprise and happiness was so great, tears came to her eyes and she could not stop smiling, till Father became impatient to know and finally got up and came to the table.

When he saw it he was surprised and happy too, he began to grin, then hugged Mother saying our son is a writer, and we didn't even know it, he never told us a thing, here we are thinking he is still clerking away at the insurance company, and he has written a book of stories, all these years in school and college he kept his talent hidden, making us think he was just like one of the boys in the Baag, shouting and playing the fool in the compound, and now what a surprise; then Father opened the book and began reading it, heading back to the easy chair, and Mother so excited, still holding his arm, walked with him, saying it was not fair him reading it first, she wanted to read it too, and they agreed that he would read the first story, then give it to her so she could also read it, and they would take turns in that manner.

Mother removed the staples from the padded envelope in which he had mailed the book, and threw them away, then straightened the folded edges of the envelope and put it away safely with the other envelopes and letters she had collected since he left.

The leaves are beginning to fall. The only ones I can identify are maple. The days are dwindling like the leaves. I've started a habit of taking long walks every evening. The old man is in the lobby when I leave, he waves as I go by. By the time I'm back, the lobby is usually empty.

Today I was woken up by a grating sound outside that made my flesh crawl. I went to the window and saw Berthe raking the leaves in the parking lot. Not in the expanse of patchy lawn on the periphery, but in the parking lot proper. She was raking the black tarred surface. I went back to bed and dragged a pillow over my head, not releasing it till noon.

When I return from my walk in the evening, PW, summoned by the elevator's gutang-khutang, says, "Berthe filled six big black garbage bags with leaves today."

"Six bags!" I say. "Wow!"

Since the weather turned cold, Berthe's son does not tinker with his van on Sundays under my window. I'm able to sleep late.

Around eleven, there's a commotion outside. I reach out and switch on the clock radio. It's a sunny day, the window curtains are bright. I get up, curious, and see a black Olds Ninety-Eight in the parking lot, by the entrance to the building. The old man is in his wheelchair, bundled up, with a scarf wound several times round his neck as though to immobilize it, like a surgical collar. His daughter and another man, the car-owner, are helping him from the wheelchair into the front seat, encouraging him with words like: that's it, easy does it, attaboy. From the open door of the lobby, Berthe is shouting encouragement too, but hers is confined to one word: yah, repeated at different levels of pitch and volume, with variations on vowel-length. The stranger could be the old man's son, he has the same jet black hair and piercing eyes.

Maybe the old man is not well, it's an emergency. But I quickly scrap that thought—this isn't Bombay, an ambulance would have arrived. They're probably taking him out for a ride. If he is his son, where has he been all this time, I wonder.

The old man finally settles in the front seat, the wheelchair goes in the trunk, and they're off. The one I think is the son looks up and catches me at the window before I can move away, so I wave, and he waves back.

In the afternoon I take down a load of clothes to the laundry room. Both machines have completed their cycles, the clothes inside are waiting to be transferred to dryers. Should I remove them and place them on top of the dryer, or wait? I decide to wait. After a few minutes, two women arrive, they are in bathrobes, and smoking. It takes me a while to realize that these are the two disappointments who were sunbathing in bikinis last summer.

"You didn't have to wait, you could have removed the clothes and carried on, dear," says one. She has a Scottish accent. It's one of the few I've learned to identify. Like maple leaves.

"Well," I say, "some people might not like strangers touching their clothes."

"You're not a stranger, dear," she says, "you live in this building, we've seen you before."

"Besides, your hands are clean," the other one pipes in. "You can touch my things any time you like."

Horny old cow. I wonder what they've got on under their bathrobes. Not much, I find, as they bend over to place their clothes in the dryers.

"See you soon," they say, and exit, leaving me behind in an erotic wake of smoke and perfume and deep images of cleavages. I start the washers and depart, and when I come back later, the dryers are empty.

PW tells me, "The old man's son took him out for a drive today. He has a big beautiful black car."

I see my chance, and shoot back: "Olds Ninety-Eight."

"What?"

"The car," I explain, "it's an Oldsmobile Ninety-Eight."

She does not like this at all, my giving her information. She is visibly nettled, and retreats with a sour face.

Mother and Father read the first five stories, and she was very sad after reading some of them, she said he must be so unhappy there, all his stories are about Bombay, he remembers every little thing about his childhood, he is thinking about it all the time even though he is ten thousand miles away, my poor son, I think he misses his home and us and everything he left behind, because if he likes it over there why would he not write stories about that, there must be so many new ideas that his new life could give him.

But Father did not agree with this, he said it did not mean that he was unhappy, all writers worked in the same way, they used their memories and experiences and made stories out of them, changing some things, adding some, imagining some, all writers were very good at remembering details of their lives.

Mother said, how can you be sure that he is remembering because he is a writer, or whether he started to write because he is unhappy and thinks of his past, and wants to save it all by making stories of it; and Father said that is not a sensible question, anyway, it is now my turn to read the next story.

The first snow has fallen, and the air is crisp. It's not very deep, about two inches, just right to go for a walk in. I've been told that immigrants from hot countries always enjoy the snow the first year, maybe for a couple of years more, then inevitably the dread sets in, and the approach of winter gets them fretting and moping. On the other hand, if it hadn't been for my conversation with the woman at the swimming registration desk, they might now be saying that India is a nation of non-swimmers.

Berthe is outside, shovelling the snow off the walkway in the parking lot. She has a heavy, wide pusher which she wields expertly.

The old radiators in the apartment alarm me incessantly. They continue to broadcast a series of variations on death throes, and go from hot to cold and cold to hot at will, there's no controlling their temperature. I speak to Berthe about it in the lobby. The old man is there too, his chin seems to have sunk deeper into his chest, and his face is a yellowish grey.

"Nothing, not to worry about anything," says Berthe, dropping rough-hewn chunks of language around me. "Radiator no work, you tell me. You feel cold, you come to me, I keep you warm," and she opens her arms wide, laughing. I step back, and she advances, her breasts preceding her like the gallant prows of two ice-breakers. She looks at the old man to see if he is appreciating the act: "You no feel scared, I keep you safe and warm."

But the old man is staring outside, at the flakes of falling snow. What thoughts is he thinking as he watches them? Of childhood days, perhaps, and snowmen with hats and pipes, and snowball fights, and white Christmases, and Christmas trees? What will I think of, old in this country, when I sit and watch the snow come down? For me, it is already too late for snowmen and snowball fights, and all I will have is thoughts about childhood thoughts and dreams, built around snowscapes and winter-wonderlands on the Christmas cards so popular in Bombay; my snowmen and snowball fights and Christmas trees are in the pages of Enid Blyton's books, dispersed amidst the adventures of the Famous Five, and the Five Find-Outers, and the Secret Seven. My snowflakes are even less forgettable than the old man's, for they never melt.

It finally happened. The heat went. Not the usual intermittent coming and going, but out completely. Stone cold. The radiators are like ice. And so is everything else. There's no hot water. Naturally. It's the hot water that goes through the rads and heats them. Or is it the other way around? Is there no hot water because the rads have stopped circulating it? I don't care, I'm too cold to sort out the cause and effect relationship. Maybe there is no connection at all.

I dress quickly, put on my winter jacket, and go down to the lobby. The elevator is not working because the power is out, so I take the stairs. Several people are gathered, and Berthe has announced that she has telephoned the office, they are sending a man. I go back up the stairs. It's only one floor, the elevator is just a bad habit. Back in Firozsha Baag they were broken most of the time. The stairway enters the corridor outside the old man's apartment, and I think of his cold feet and hands. Poor man, it must be horrible for him without heat.

As I walk down the long hallway, I feel there's something different but can't pin it down. I look at the carpet, the ceiling, the wallpaper, it all seems the same. Maybe it's the freezing cold that imparts a feeling of difference.

PW opens her door. "The old man had another stroke yesterday. They took him to the hospital."

The medicinal smell. That's it. It's not in the hallway any more.

In the stories that he'd read so far Father said that all the Parsi families were poor or middle-class, but that was okay; nor did he mind that the seeds for the stories were picked from the sufferings of their own lives; but there should also have been something positive about Parsis, there was so much to be proud of: the great Tatas and their contribution to the steel industry, or Sir Dinshaw Petit in the textile industry who made Bombay the Manchester of the East, or Dadabhai Naoroji in the freedom movement, where he was the first to use the word swaraj, *and the first to be elected to the British Parliament where he carried on his campaign; he should have found some way to bring some of these wonderful facts into his stories, what would people reading these stories think, those who did not know about Parsis—that the whole community was full of cranky, bigoted people; and in reality it was the richest, most advanced and philanthropic community in India, and he did not need to tell his own son that Parsis had a reputation for being generous and family-oriented. And he could have written something also about the historic background, how Parsis came to India from Persia because of Islamic persecution in the seventh century, and were the descendants of Cyrus the Great and the magnificent Persian Empire. He could have made a story of all this, couldn't he?*

Mother said what she liked best was his remembering everything so well, how beautifully he wrote about it all, even the sad things, and though he changed some of it, and used his imagination, there was truth in it.

My hope is, Father said, that there will be some story based on his Canadian experience, that way we will know something about our son's life there, if not through his letters then in his stories; so far they are all about Parsis and Bombay, and the one with a little bit about Toronto, where a man perches on top of the toilet, is shameful and disgusting, although it is funny at times and did make me laugh, I have to admit, but where does he get such an imagination from, what is the point of such a fantasy; and Mother said that she would also enjoy some stories about Toronto and the people there; it puzzles me, she said, why he writes nothing about it, especially since you say that writers use their own experience to make stories out of.

Then Father said this is true, but he is probably not using his Toronto experience because it is too early; what do you mean, too early, asked Mother and Father explained it takes a writer about ten years time after an experience before he is able to use it in his writing, it takes that long to be absorbed internally and understood, thought out and thought about, over and over again, he haunts it and it haunts him if it is valuable enough, till the writer is comfortable with it to be able to use it as he wants; but this is only one theory I read somewhere, it may or may not be true.

That means, said Mother, that his childhood in Bombay and our home here is the most valuable thing in his life just now, because he able to remember it all to write about it, and you were so bitterly saying he is forgetting where he came from; and that may be true, said Father, but that is not what the theory means, according to the theory he is writing of these things because they are far enough in the past for him to deal with objectively, he is able to achieve what critics call artistic distance, without emotions interfering; and what do you mean emotions, said Mother, you are saying he does not feel anything for his characters, how can he write so beautifully about so many sad things without any feelings in his heart?

But before Father could explain more, about beauty and emotion and inspiration and imagination, Mother took the book and said it was her turn now and too much theory she did not want to listen to, it was confusing and did not make as much sense as reading the stories, she would read them her way and Father could read them his.

My books on the windowsill have been damaged. Ice has been forming on the inside ledge, which I did not notice, and melting when the sun shines in. I spread them in a corner of the living-room to dry out.

The winter drags on. Berthe wields her snow pusher as expertly as ever, but there are signs of weariness in her performance. Neither husband nor son is ever seen outside with a shovel. Or anywhere else, for that matter. It occurs to me that the son's van is missing, too.

The medicinal smell is in the hall again, I sniff happily and look forward to seeing the old man in the lobby. I go downstairs and peer in the mailbox, see the blue and magenta of an Indian aerogramme with Don Mills, Ontario, Canada in Father's flawless hand through the slot.

I pocket the letter and enter the main lobby. The old man is there, but not in his usual place. His is not looking out through the glass door. His wheelchair is facing a bare wall where the wallpaper is torn in places. As though he is not interested in the outside world any more, having finished with all that, and now it's time to see inside. What does he see inside, I wonder? I go up to him and say hullo. He says hullo without raising his sunken chin. After a few seconds his grey countenance faces me. "How old do you think I am?" His eyes are dull and glazed; he is looking even further inside than I first presumed.

"Well, let's see, you're probably close to sixty-four."

"I'll be seventy-eight next August." But he does not chuckle or wheeze. Instead, he continues softly, "I wish my feet did not feel so cold all the time. And my hands." He lets his chin fall again.

In the elevator I start opening the aerogramme, a tricky business because a crooked tear means lost words. Absorbed in this while emerging, I don't notice PW occupying the centre of the hallway, arms folded across her chest: "They had a big fight. Both of them have left."

I don't immediately understand her agitation. "What . . . who?"

"Berthe. Husband and son both left her. Now she is alone."

Her tone and stance suggest that we should not be standing here talking but do something to bring Berthe's family back. "That's very sad," I say, and go in. I picture father and son in the van, driving away, driving across the snow-covered country, in the dead of winter, away from wife and mother; away to where? how far will they go? Not son's van nor father's booze can take them far enough. And the further they go, the more they'll remember, they can take it from me.

All the stories were read by Father and Mother, and they were sorry when the book was finished, they felt they had come to know their son better now, yet there was much more to know, they wished there were many more stories; and this is what they mean, said Father, when they say that the whole story can never be told, the whole truth can never be known; what do you mean, they say, asked Mother, who they, and Father said writers, poets, philosophers. I don't care what they say, said Mother, my son will write as much or as little as he wants to, and if I can read it I will be happy.

The last story they liked the best of all because it had the most in it about Canada, and now they felt they knew at least a little bit, even if it was a very little bit, about his day-to-day life in his apartment; and Father said if he continues to write about such things he will become popular because I am sure they are interested there in reading about life through the eyes of an immigrant, it provides a different viewpoint; the only danger is if he changes and becomes so much like them that he will write like one of them and lose the important difference.

The bathroom needs cleaning. I open a new can of Ajax and scour the tub. Sloshing with mug from bucket was standard bathing procedure in the bathrooms of Firozsha Baag, so my preference now is always for a shower. I've never used the tub as yet; besides, it would be too much like Chaupatty or the swimming pool, wallowing in my own dirt. Still, it must be cleaned.

When I've finished, I prepare for a shower. But the clean gleaming tub and the nearness of the vernal equinox give me the urge to do something different today. I find the drain plug in the bathroom cabinet, and run the bath.

I've spoken so often to the old man, but I don't know his name. I should have asked him the last time I saw him, when his wheelchair was facing the bare wall because he had seen all there was to see outside and it was time to see what was inside. Well, tomorrow. Or better yet, I can look it up in the directory in the lobby. Why didn't I think of that before? It will only have an initial and a last name, but then I can surprise him with: hullo Mr Wilson, or whatever it is.

The bath is full. Water imagery is recurring in my life: Chaupatty beach, swimming pool, bathtub. I step in and immerse myself up to the neck. It feels good. The hot water loses its opacity when the chlorine, or whatever it is, has cleared. My hair is still dry. I close my eyes, hold my breath, and dunk my head. Fighting the panic, I stay under and count to thirty. I come out, clear my lungs and breathe deeply.

I do it again. This time I open my eyes under water, and stare blindly without seeing, it takes all my will to keep the lids from closing. Then I am slowly able to discern the underwater objects. The drain plug looks different, slightly distorted; there is hair trapped between the hole and the plug, it waves and dances with the movement of the water. I come up, refresh my lungs, examine quickly the overwater world of the washroom, and go in again. I do it several times, over and over. The world outside the water I have seen a lot of, it is now time to see what is inside.

The spring session for adult non-swimmers will begin in a few days at the high school. I must not forget the registration date.

The dwindled days of winter are now all but forgotten; they have grown and attained a respectable span. I resume my evening walks, it's spring, and a vigorous thaw is on. The snowbanks are melting, the sound of water on its gushing, gurgling journey to the drains is beautiful. I plan to buy a book of trees, so I can identify more than the maple as they begin to bloom.

When I return to the building, I wipe my feet energetically on the mat because some people are entering behind me, and I want to set a good example. Then I go to the board with its little plastic letters and numbers. The old man's apartment is the one on the corner by the stairway, that makes it number 201. I run down the list, come to 201, but there are no little white plastic letters beside it. Just the empty black rectangle with holes where the letters would be squeezed in. That's strange. Well, I can introduce myself to him, then ask his name.

However, the lobby is empty. I take the elevator, exit at the second floor, wait for the gutang-khutang. It does not come: the door closes noiselessly, smoothly. Berthe has been at work, or has made sure someone else has. PW's cue has been lubricated out of existence.

But she must have the ears of a cockroach. She is waiting for me. I whistle my way down the corridor. She fixes me with an accusing look. She waits till I stop whistling, then says: "You know the old man died last night."

I cease groping for my key. She turns to go and I take a step towards her, my hand still in my trouser pocket. "Did you know his name?" I ask, but she leaves without answering.

Then Mother said, the part I like best in the last story is about Grandpa, where he wonders if Grandpa's spirit is really watching him and blessing him, because you know I really told him that, I told him helping an old suffering person who is near death is the most blessed thing to do, because that person will ever after watch over you from heaven, I told him this when he was disgusted with Grandpa's urine-bottle and would not touch it, would not hand it to him even when I was not at home.

Are you sure, said Father, that you really told him this, or you believe you told him because you like the sound of it, you said yourself the other day that he changes and adds and alters things in the stories but he writes it all so beautifully that it seems true, so how can you be sure; this sounds like another theory, said Mother, but I don't care, he says I told him and I believe now I told him, so even if I did not tell him then it does not matter now.

Don't you see, said Father, that you are confusing fiction with facts, fiction does not create facts, fiction can come from facts, it can grow out of facts by compounding, transposing, augmenting, diminishing, or altering them in any way; but you must not confuse cause and effect, you must not confuse what really happened with what the story says happened, you must not loose your grasp on reality, that way madness lies.

Then Mother stopped listening because, as she told Father so often, she was not very fond of theories, and she took out her writing pad and started a letter to her son; Father looked over her shoulder, telling her to say how proud they were of him and were waiting for his next book, he also said, leave a little space for me at the end, I want to write a few lines when I put the address on the envelope.

(1987)

Rita Dove
(U.S.A., 1952–)

The Great Palaces of Versailles

Nothing nastier than a white person!
She mutters as she irons alterations
in the backroom of Charlotte's Dress Shoppe.
The steam rising from a cranberry wool
5   comes alive with perspiration
and stale Evening of Paris.
Swamp she born from, swamp
she swallow, swamp she got to sink again.

The iron shoves gently
10   into a gusset, waits until
the puckers bloom away. Beyond
the curtain, the white girls are all
wearing shoulder pads to make their faces
delicate. That laugh would be Autumn,
15   tossing her hair in imitation of Bacall.

Beulah had read in the library
how French ladies at court would tuck
their fans in a sleeve
and walk in the gardens for air. Swaying
20   among lilies, lifting shy layers of silk,
they dropped excrement as daintily
as handkerchieves. Against all rules

she had saved the lining from a botched coat
to face last year's gray skirt. She knows
25   whenever she lifts a knee
she flashes crimson. That seems legitimate;
but in the book she had read
how the *cavaliere* amused themselves
wearing powder and perfume and spraying
30   yellow borders knee-high on the stucco
of the *Orangerie*.

A hanger clatters
in the front of the shoppe.
Beulah remembers how
35   even Autumn could lean into a settee
with her ankles crossed, sighing
I need a man who'll protect me
while smoking her cigarette down to the very end.
                                        (1986)

The Event

Ever since they'd left the Tennessee ridge
with nothing to boast of
but good looks and a mandolin,

the two Negroes leaning
5   on the rail of a riverboat
were inseparable: Lem plucked

to Thomas' silver falsetto.
But the night was hot and they were drunk.
They spat where the wheel

10   churned mud and moonlight,
they called to the tarantulas
down among the bananas

to come out and dance.
You're so fine and mighty; let's see
15   *what you can do*, said Thomas, pointing

to a tree-capped island.
Lem stripped, spoke easy: *Them's chestnuts,*
I believe. Dove

quick as a gasp. Thomas, dry
20   on deck, saw the green crown shake
as the island slipped

under, dissolved
in the thickening stream.
At his feet

25   A stinking circle of rags,
the half-shell mandolin.
Where the wheel turned the water

gently shirred.
                                        (1986)

Daniel David Moses

(CANADA, 1952–)

Grandmother of the Glacier

The icefield she had in her head started
sliding the instant she died. *Was murdered*
would be more precise—would also explain
how her corpse became this high and open

5   ravine. But who's got the wit to split words
when that ice is coming at us? The world
can't ever again be that room we sat
in a circle in—the mainland rain hard

on a window as we listened to her
10   trying to explain about words. *Winter,*
she grinned. *That's the constant thought behind all
our words. In Canada we never can*

forget the edge on the wind. But the edge
on a knife cut in, cutting off more than
15   her words. So now it's hard to remember
how that edge and this cold thought grinding down

out of her head ever seemed separate.
Now they're a mouth that bites off and chews and
it's getting so close that breath flakes like snow.
20   So we go mute too—that mouth edge so red

that words drop from our own lips like stones. None
is as finished as those of hers that fell
into our hands. But the stars now are shards
of ice—they too are cutting in. There's no

25   time for her method—to split and polish
words against our own skin. Is that how hers
got so coarse she could embrace and contain
not only the stars but the rest of this freeze?

Her body's been swallowed. Ours may be next.
30   But even though we throw them in, her words
keep surfacing. May ours too be heard from
again—edging some terminal moraine.

(1990)

Dionne Brand

(TRINIDAD/CANADA, 1953–)

At the Lisbon Plate

The sky in the autumn is full of telephone and telegraph wires; it is not like sitting in the Portuguese bar on Kensington in the summer, outside—the beer smell, the forgetful waiter. I wonder what happened to Rosa. She was about forty and wore a tight black dress, her face appliquéed with something I could barely identify as life. Her false mole, the one she wore beside her mouth, shifted everyday and faded by evening. She had a look that was familiar to me. Possibly she had lived in Angola or Mozambique and was accustomed to Black women, so she looked at me kindly, colonially.

"Do you have fish, Rosa?" I would ask.

"Oh yes, good Portuguese fish."

"From the lake or from the sea."

"Ah the sea, of course."

This would be our conversation every time I would come to the bar, her "of course" informing me of her status in our relationship.

My life was on the upswing, and whenever that happened I went to the bar on Kensington. That was usual in the summertime. After twenty years and half my life in this city I still have to wait for the summertime to get into a good mood. My body refuses to appreciate dull, gray days. Truthfully, let me not fool you, my life was neither up nor down, which for me is an upswing and I don't take chances, I celebrate what little there is. Which is why I come to this bar. This is my refuge, as it is. I believe in contradictions.

So Rosa ran from Angola and Mozambique. Well, well! By the looks of it she'd come down a peg or two. At the Lisbon Plate, Rosa seems quite ordinary, quite different from the woman who entertained in the European drawing rooms in Luanda and Lorenços Marques. Then, she gave orders to Black women, whom she called 'as pretinhas.' Then, she minced over to the little consul from Lisbon and the general, whose family was from Oporto and whom she made promise to give her a little gun for her protection when the trouble started.

I figured anyone who left Angola was on the other side, on the run. Rosa did have a kind enough look, personally. The wholesale merchant she was married to or his general manager, whom she slept with from time to time, had to leave. So, Rosa left too. This does not absolve Rosa however. I'm sure that she acquired her plumpness like a bed bug, sucking a little blood here, a little there.

As I've said, my life was on the upswing. Most other times it was a bitch. But I had spent two successive days with no major setbacks. Nobody called me about money, nobody hurt my feelings, and I didn't wake up feeling shaky in the stomach about how this world was going. And, I had twenty clear bucks to come to the bar. This is my refuge. It is where I can be invisible or, if not invisible, at least drunk. Drinking makes me introspective, if not suicidal. In these moments I have often looked at myself from the third floor window of the furniture store across from the bar. Rheumy-eyed, I have seen a woman sitting there, whom I recognize as myself. A Black woman, legs apart, chin resting in the palm of her hand, amusement and revulsion travelling across her face in uneasy companionship; the years have taken a bit of the tightness out of my skin but the expression has not changed, searching and uneasy, haunted like a plantation house. Surrounded by the likes of Rosa and her compadres. A woman in enemy territory.

It has struck me more than once that a little more than a century ago I may have been Rosa's slave and not more than twenty-five years ago, her maid, whom she maimed, playing with the little gun that she got from the general from Oporto. My present existence is mere chance, luck, syzygy.

Rosa's brother, Joao the priest, was now living in New Jersey. He used to live in Toronto, but before that he lived in Angola. One day, in a village there, during the liberation war, two whites were kidnapped and the others, including Rosa's brother, the priest, went into the village and gunned down a lot of people—women, children to death, everything. He told this story to Maria de Conseçao, my friend, and she told me. People think that saying that women and children were killed makes the crime more disgusting. I was sorry that Maria de Conseçao told me, because whenever I think about it I see Joao the priest confiding this crime as if he relished it, rather than repented it. I think Maria de Conseçao told me the story just to get rid of it. It's the kind of story which occurs to you when you're doing something pleasant and it's the kind of story you can't get rid of. I've kept it.

I am not a cynical woman under ordinary circumstances, but if you sit here long enough anyone can see how what appears to be ordinary, isn't.

For, on the other hand, I look like a woman I met many years ago. As old as dirt, she sat at a roadside waiting her time, an ivory pipe stuck in her withered lips and naked as she was born. That woman had stories, more lucid than mine and more frightening for that.

The day I met her, her bones were black powder and her fingers crept along my arm causing me to shiver. She was a dangerous woman. I knew it the moment I saw her and I should have left her sitting there, the old grave-digger. But no. Me, I had to go and look. I had to follow that sack of dust into places I had no right being. Me, I had to look where she pointed. She wanted to show me her condiments and her books. I thought nothing of it. Why not humour an old woman, I said in my mind. They were old as ashes. All tied up and knotted in a piece of cloth and, when she opened it up, you would not believe the rattling and the odour, all musty and sweet. A bone here and a fingernail there. They looked like they'd been sitting in mud for centuries, like her. When it came to the books, it was before they had pages and the writing was with stones, which the old thing threw on the ground and read to me. I never laughed so much as I laughed at her jokes, not to mention her stories which made me cry so much I swore I'd turn to salt water myself. It was one of her stories which led me here, in search of something I will recognize, once I see it.

But back to things that we can understand, because I want to forget that harridan in the road and her unpleasantness.

Today I am waiting for Elaine, as usual. She likes to make entrances of the type that white girls make in movies. The truth is she's always getting away from something or someone. She is always promising too much and escaping. Which is why we get along. I never believe a promise and I, myself, am in constant flight.

Elaine is a mysterious one. Two days ago she told me to meet her here at one o'clock. I've been sitting here ever since. I know that she'll turn up a new woman. She'll say that she's moving to Tanzania to find her roots. She'll have her head tied in a wrap and she'll have gold bracelets running up her arms. She'll be learning Swahili, she'll show me new words like 'jambo' and she'll be annoyed if I don't agree to go with her. Elaine wants to be a queen in ancient Mali or Songhai. A rich woman with gold and land.

The bar has a limited view of Kensington market. Across the street from it there's a parkette, in the centre of which there is a statue of Cristobal Colon. Columbus, the carpetbagger.

It's most appropriate that they should put his stoney arse right where I can see it. I know bitterness doesn't become me, but that son of a bitch will get his soon enough too. The smell from the market doesn't bother me. I've been here before, me and the old lady. We know the price of things. Which is why I feel safe in telling stories here. They will be sure to find me. For fish you must have bait; for some people you must have blood. Spread the truth around enough, and you must dig up a few liars.

In the summertime, I come to the bar practically every day. After my first beer I'm willing to talk to anyone. I'm willing to reveal myself entirely. Which is a dirty habit since it has made me quite a few enemies. Try not to acquire it. The knots in my head loosen up and I may start telling stories about my family.

I keep getting mixed up with old ladies; for instance, I have an old aunt, she used to be beautiful. Not in the real sense, but in that sense that you had to be, some years ago. Hair slicked back to bring out the Spanish and hide the African. You could not resemble your mother or your father. This would only prove your guilt. This aunt went mad in later years. I think that it must have been from so much self-denial or, given the way that it turned out . . .

Anyway, when I was a child we used to go to their house. It was made of stone and there was a garden around it. A thick green black garden. A forest. My aunt worked in the garden every day, pruning and digging. There was deep red hibiscus to the far right wall. The soil was black and loose and damp and piled around the roots of roses and xoras and anthuriums and orchids. In the daylight, the garden was black and bright; in the night, it was shadowy and dark. Only my aunt was allowed to step into the garden. At the edges, shading the forest-garden were great calabash mango trees. Their massive trunks and roots gave refuge from my aunt when she climbed into a rage after merely looking at us all day. She would run after us screaming, "beasts! worthless beasts!" Her rage having not subsided, she would grab us and scrub us, as if to take the black out of our skins. Her results would never please her. Out we would come five still bright-black little girls, blackness intent on our skins. She would punish us by having us stand utterly still, dressed in stiffly starched dresses.

Elaine never reveals herself and she is the most frustrating storyteller. She handles a story as if stories were scarce. "Well," she says, as she sits down at the table. Then she pauses, far too long a pause, through which I say, in my mind, "I'm going to last out this pause." Then quickly getting upset, I say, "For god's sake, tell me." Then I have to drag it out of her, in the middle of which I say, "Forget it, I don't want to hear," then she drops what she thinks is the sinker and I nonchalantly say, "Is that it?" to which she swears that never again would she tell me a story. The truth is that Elaine picks up on great stories, but the way she tells them makes people suffer. I, on the other hand, am quite plain. Particularly when I'm in my waters. Drink, I mean. I've noticed that I'm prepared to risk anything. But truthfully, what makes a good story if not for the indiscretions we reveal, the admissions of being human. In this way, I will tell you some of my life; though I must admit that some of it is fiction, not much mind you, but what is lie, I do not live through with any less tragedy. Anyway, these are not state secrets, people live the way that they have to and handle what they can. But don't expect any of the old woman's tales. There are things that you know and things that you tell. Well, soon and very soon, as they say.

Listen, I can drink half a bottle of whisky and refuse to fall down. It's from looking at Rosa that I get drunk and it's from looking at Rosa that I refuse to fall down. I was a woman with a face like a baby before I met Rosa, a face waiting to hold impressions.

I saw the little minx toddle over to the statue of Columbus, the piss-face in the parkette, and kiss his feet. Everyone has their rituals, I see. And then, before her mirror, deciding which side to put the mole on. Her face as dry as a powder. Perfuming herself in her bedroom in Lorençes

Marques, licking the oil off that greasy merchant of hers. Even though the weather must have been bad for her, she stuck it out until they were driven away. It's that face that Rosa used cursing those "sons of bitches in the bush," when the trouble started. "When the trouble started" indeed. These European sons of bitches always say "when the trouble started" when *their* life in the colonies begins to get miserable.

I never think of murder. I find it too intimate and there's a smell in the autumn that I do not like. I can always tell. The first breath of the fall. It distracts me from everyone. I will turn down the most lucrative dinner invitation to go around like a bloodhound smelling the fall. Making sure and making excuses, suggesting and insinuating that the summer is not over. But of course, as soon as I get a whiff of that smell I know. It's the autumn. Then the winter comes in, as green and fresh as spring and I know that I have to wait another ten months for the old woman's prophecy to come true. That hag by the road doesn't know what she gave me and what an effort I must make to see it through. On top of that, I have to carry around her juju belt full of perfidious mixtures and insolent smells and her secrets. Her secrets. My god, you don't know what a soft pain in the chest they give me. I grow as withered as the old hag with their moaning. She's ground them up like seasoning and she's told me to wear them close to my skin, like a poultice. I thought nothing of it at first. A little perfume, I said, a little luxury. I now notice that I cannot take the juju off. I lift up my camisole and have a look. It's hardly me there anymore. There's a hole like a cave with an echo.

The old hag hates the winter too; says it dries her skin out. God knows she's no more than dust, but vain as hell. She migrates like a soucouyant in the winter, goes back to the tropics, says she must mine the Sargasso for bones and suicides. I must say, I envy the old bagsnatcher. Though she's promised me her memories, her maps and her flight plans, when it's over. Until then, I wait and keep watch here, frozen like a lizard in Blue Mountain, while she suns her quaily self in some old slave port.

At this bar, as I have my first beer and wait for the African princess, Elaine, I discover substantive philosophical arguments concerning murder. The beauty is, I have a lot of time. I have watched myself here, waiting. A woman so old her skin turned to water, her eyes blazing like a dead candle. I'm starting to resemble that bag of dust, the longer I live.

Now they have a man waiting on tables at the bar. I suppose the pay must be better. Elaine says he resembles Rosa except for her beauty mole and her breasts. It doesn't matter how Rosa looks in her disguises, I am doomed to follow her like a bloodhound after a thief. He is quite forgetful. Twenty minutes ago I asked him for another beer and up to now he hasn't brought it. Elaine's the one who got me into beer drinking anyway. In the old days—before the great mother old soul in the road and before I sussed out Rosa and her paramour—Elaine and I used to roam the streets together, looking. The old bone digger must have spotted my vacant look then. Elaine, on the other hand, had very definite ideas. Even then Elaine was looking for a rich African to help her make her triumphal return to the motherland.

Still, a rumour went around that Elaine and I were lovers. It wouldn't have bothered either of us if it were true at the time or if it wasn't said in such a malicious way. But it was because of how we acted. Simply, we didn't defer to the men around and we didn't sleep with them, or else when we did we weren't their slaves for ever or even for a while. So both factions, those we slept with and those we didn't, started the rumour that we were lovers. Actually, Elaine and I laughed at the rumours. We liked to think of ourselves as free spirits and realists. We never attempted to dispel the rumours; it would have taken far too much of commitment to do that. It would be a full time job of subjecting yourself to any prick on two legs. And anyway, if the nastiest thing that they could say about you is that you loved another woman, well . . .

Elaine and I would take the last bus home, bags full of unopened beer, or pay a taxi, after I had persuaded her that the man she was looking at was too disgusting to sleep with, just for a ride home. Elaine takes the practical to the absurd sometimes.

We've been to other bars. Elaine looked for the bars, she scouted all the hangouts. She determined the ambience, the crowd, and then she asked me to meet her there. There's no accounting for her taste. I'd get to the appointed bar and it would be the grungiest, with the most oily food, the most vulgar horrible men and a juke box with music selected especially to insult women. This was during Elaine's nationalist phase. Everything was culture, rootsy. The truth is, I only followed Elaine to see if I could shake the old woman's stories or, alternately, if I could find the something for her and get her off my back. It's not that I don't like the old schemer. At first I didn't mind her, but then she started to invade me like a spirit. So I started to drink. You get drunk enough and you think you can forget, but you get even greater visions. At the beginning of any evening the old woman's stories are a blip on the horizon; thirteen ounces into a bottle of scotch or four pints of beer later the stories are as lurid as a butcher's block.

I had the fever for two days and dreamt that the stove had caught afire. My big sister was just standing there as I tried furiously to douse the fire which kept getting bigger and bigger. Finally, my sister dragged the stove from the wall and with a knowledgeable air, put the fire out. When I woke up, I heard that the stock exchange in Santiago had been blown up by a bomb in a suitcase and that some group called the communist fighting cell had declared war on NATO by destroying troop supply lines in Belgium. Just as I was thinking of Patrice Lumumba. For you Patrice! From this I surmised that my dreams have effects. Though, they seem somewhat unruly. They escape me. They have fires in them and they destine at an unknown and precipitous pace.

I followed Elaine through her phases, though there were some that she hid from me. Now we come to this bar, where we cannot understand the language most of the time. Here Elaine plans the possibilities of living grandly and, if not, famously. As for me, I tolerate her dreams because when Elaine found this bar I knew it was my greatest opportunity. All of the signs were there. The expatriates from the colonial wars, the money changers and the skin dealers, the whip handlers, the coffle makers and the boatswains. Their faces leathery from the African sun and the tropical winter. They were swilling beer like day had no end. Rosa was in her glory, being pawed and pinched. Of course, they didn't notice me in my new shape. Heavens, I didn't notice me. It scared the hell out of me when the juju surged to my head and I was a thin smoke over the Lisbon Plate. What a night! They said things that shocked even me, things worse than Joao, the priest. The old-timers boasted about how many piezas de indias they could pack into a ship for a bauble or a gun. The young soldiers talked about the joys of filling a black with bullets and stuffing a black cunt with dynamite. Then they gathered around Columbus, the whoremaster, and sang a few old songs. The old woman and I watched the night's revelry with sadness, the caves in our chest rattling the echo of unkindness, but I noticed the old woman smiling as she counted them, pointing and circling with her hand, over and over again, mumbling "jingay, jingay where you dey, where you dey, where you dey, spirit nah go away." Before you know it, I was mumbling along with her too, "jingay, jingay, where you dey. . . . " We stayed with them all night, counting and mumbling. Now, all I have to do is choose the clay and the spot and it's done. The old woman loves fanfare and flourish, so it will have to be spectacular. If Elaine knew what a find this bar was, she'd charge me money.

Elaine never cared for Rosa one way or the other, which is where Elaine and I are different. Some people would have no effect on her whatsoever. This way she remained friends with everyone. Me, I hate you or I love you. Always getting into fights, always adding enemies to my lists. Which is why I'll never get any place, as they say. But Elaine will. Elaine, sadly, is a drunk without vision. I, unfortunately, am a drunk with ideas. Which is probably why the old woman chose me to be her steed.

I pride myself with keeping my ear to the ground. I read the news and I listen to the radio every day, even if it is the same news. I look for nuances, changes in the patter. It came to me the other night, when listening to the news. One Polish priest had been killed and the press was going wild. At the same time, I don't know how many African labourers got killed and, besides that, fell to their deaths from third floor police detention rooms in Johannesburg; and all that the scribes talked about was how moderate the Broderbond is. We should be grateful I suppose.

It occurred to me that death, its frequency, causes, sequence and application to written history, favours, even anticipates, certain latitudes. The number of mourners, their enthusiasms, their entertainments, their widows' weeds, all mapped by a cartographer well schooled in pre-Galileo geography. I'm waxing. Don't stop me. I couldn't tell you the things I know.

Meanwhile back at the bar, still waiting for Elaine to surface, there have been several interesting developments. Speaking of politics. First, I hear that the entire bourgeoisie of Bolivia is dead. It was on the radio not more than half an hour ago. The deaths are not significant in and of themselves. What is interesting is that only a few days ago, when I heard that president Suazo was kidnapped in La Paz and that there was possibly a coup, I said in my mind, that the entire bourgeoisie should perish. It was the Bolivian army who killed Ernesto Che Guevara, you see. They put his body in the newspapers with their smiles. Now, I hear the news that the entire bourgeoisie of Bolivia is dead. Of course, from this I learned that as I become more and more of a spirit, I have more and more possibilities. First Santiago and Belgium and now Bolivia.

Second, and most, most important, the big white boy has arrived here. He's ordered a beer from Rosa's brother. I would know those eyes anywhere. The last time I saw them, I was lying in the hold of a great ship leaving Conakry for the new world. It was just a glimpse, but I remember as if it were yesterday. I am a woman with a lot of time and I have waited, like shrimp wait for tide, I have waited, like dirt waits for worms. That hell-hole stank of my own flesh before I left it, its walls mottled with my spittle and waste. For days I lived with my body rotting and the glare of those eyes keeping me alive, as I begged to die and follow my carcass. This is the story the old road woman told me. Days and days and night and nights, dreaming death like a loved one; but those hellish eyes kept me alive and dreadfully human until reaching a port in the new world. His pitiless hands placed me on a block of wood like a yoke, when my carcass could not stand any more for the worms had eaten my soul. Running, running a long journey over hot bush, I found a cliff one day at the top of an island and jumped— jumped into the jagged blue water of an ocean, swimming, swimming to Conakry.

Elaine has also arrived and disappeared again, she's always disappearing into the bar to make phone calls. I never get an explanation of these phone calls mainly because I simply continue with my story. But I have the feeling, as the afternoon progresses into evening, and as different moods cross Elaine's face after every phone call, that some crisis is being made, fought and resolved. I have a feeling that Elaine needs my stories as a curtain for her equally spyish dramas.

The big white boy was sitting with his dog. I did not see his face at first, but I recognized him as you would recognize your hands. His hair was cut with one patch down the middle. He was wearing black and moaning as he sat there smoking weed. Like Rosa, he had fallen on his luck. I heard him say this.

"I don't have nobody, no friends, I ain't got no love, no nothing, just my dog."

He was blond. At least, that was the colour of his hair presently. I felt for him the compassion of a warship, the maudlin sentiment of a boot stepping on a face. He said this to Rosa, who gave him an unsympathetic look as she picked her teeth. I'm not fooled by their lack of affection for each other. They are like an alligator and a parasite. I felt like rushing to his throat, but something held me back. The old woman's burning hand. I've seen him and Rosa whispering behind my back. What would a punk ku klux klansman and a washed-up ex-colonial siren have in common. Except me and the old lady. I suppose they're wondering who I am. Wonder away you carrion! I wonder if they recognize me as quickly as I, them. I saw them do their ablutions on the foot of the statue in the parkette. How lovingly they fondled his bloody hands. They have their rituals, but I've lived longer than they.

Listen, I neglected to say that my old aunt of the forest has gone mad. She told my sister, and indeed the whole town of Monas Bay, that on Easter Sunday of 1979, this year, jesus christ had descended from the heavens and entered her bedroom and had been there ever since. She had had a vision. After days of fasting and kneeling on the mourning ground, she had entered a desert where nothing grew. No water and inedible shrubs. The sun's heat gave the air a glassiness upon looking into the distance. Then she saw christ. He was withered and young as a boy of twenty. Christ and my aunt conversed for many days and planned to marry three years from the time of their meeting. They would have a son who would grow to be the new christ. My aunt related this incident to any one who would listen and cursed into hell and damnation anyone who did not believe. Few, needless to say, didn't. Anyone with a vision was helpful in bad times and people said that at least she had the guts to have a vision, which was not like the politicians in those parts.

Even my aunt's garden had descended into sand and tough shrub. It had become like the desert of her vision. She no longer made any attempt to grow plants, she said that armageddon was at hand anyway. Her bedroom, she turned into a shrine on the very day of her meeting with christ. On the wall hung bits of cardboard with glossy photographs of her fiancé cut out of the *Plain Truth*, and candles burnt endlessly in the four corners of the shrine. Sundry chaplets of jumbie beads, plastic and ivory manoeuvred themselves on the windows and bedposts. My aunt knows that some people think that she is mad; so, in the style of her affianced, she prays for their salvation. If she is mad. . . . Which is a debate that I will never personally enter, having seen far too much in my short life and knowing that if you live in places with temporary electricity and plenty of hard work, jesus christ (if not god) is extant. Not to mention that, the last time that I saw her, she stood at what was once the gate to the forest garden and was now dead wire, wearing a washed-out flowered dress and her last remaining tooth, even though she was only a woman of fifty, and told me that the land taxes for the forest and the stone house was paid up or would be as soon as she went to town. This, to me, attested to her sanity. Come hell or high water, as they say, though these might be the obvious causes of her madness, if she were mad, they were certainly legal. Anyway, if she is mad, her vision is clearly not the cause of it. Rather it has made her quite sane. At any rate she no longer uses face powder.

This trick that I learned in Bolivia and the dream in Santiago has set me to thinking. She, the old poui stick, is not the only one who can have plans. The dear old lady only gave me seven red hot peppers and told me to write their names seven times on seven scraps of paper. Then put the seven pieces of paper into the seven red hot peppers and throw them into seven latrines. This, she said, would do for them. This and sprinkling guinea pepper in front of their door every morning. Then, she said, I should wait for the rest. The old hag is smart, but she never anticipated the times or perhaps that's what she means.

Elaine thinks I'm taking things too far, of course. But, I cannot stand this endless waiting. I've practically turned into a spirit with all this dreadfulness around the Lisbon Plate. I want to get back to my life and forget this old woman and her glamorous ideas. So, what must be done, must be done. Elaine's on her way to Zaire, at any moment anyway. I think she's landed Mobutu Sese Seku.

For now I've taken to hiding things from her. She doesn't care about anything. Each time I mention it she says, "Oh for god's sake, forget them." As if it's that easy. You tell me! When there's a quaily skinned battle-axe riding on your shoulder and whispering in your ear. Well fine, if Elaine can have her secret telephone calls, and I don't think that I mentioned her disappearances, I can have my secret fires too. She can't say that I didn't try to warn her.

Wait! Well, I'll be damned! They're coming in like flies, old one. I eavesdrop on conversations here. I listen for plots, hints. You never know what these people are up for. This way, I amuse myself and scout for my opportunity. Listen,

"Camus' *Outsider* can be interpreted as the ultimate alienation!"

Ha! Did you hear that? Now, literature! Jesus. That's the one who looks like a professor, all scruffy and sensitive. If the truth be known several hundred years ago he made up the phrase "Dark Ages," then he attached himself to an expedition around the Bight of Benin from which, as the cruder of his sea company packed human cargo into the hold of their ship, he rifled the gold statues and masks and he then created a "museum of primitive art" to store them. Since his true love was phrase-making he made up "museum of primitive art," elaborating his former success "Dark Ages." Never trust white men who look sensitive. They're the worst kind of phonies. They want the best of both worlds. Compared to him, the big white boy looks like a saint.

Anyway, alienation, my ass! Camus! Camus wrote a novel about a European, un pied noir, killing an Arab on a beach outside Algiers. He works it so that the sun gets into the European's eyes (they have their rituals) and the heat and his emotionlessness to his mother's dying and all this. But killing an Arab, pumping successive bullets into an Arab is not and never has been an alienating experience for a European. It was not unusual. It need not symbolize any alienation from one's being or anything like that. It was customary in Algeria, so how come all this high shit about Camus. Didn't it ever strike you that Meursault was a European and the Arab on the beach was an Arab? And the Arab was an Arab, but this European was Meursault.

You want to hear a story? Let me tell you a real story. I have no art for phraseology, I'll warn you.

Ahmed. Ahmed. Ahmed. Ahmed came to the beach with Ousmane to get away. The town, stiffly hot, drove him from the bicycle factory, making an excuse to his boss. Headache, my little brother has a headache three days now. He needs the salt air. The grimy hands of the boss closed around a dry cigar in the tin can ashtray. "Ahmed, if you leave I don't pay for the week. That's it. That's it you hear." Ahmed retreating, feeling free already, sweat trickling and drying under his chin. He would go to the beach, Ousmane was waiting for him, the sand would be damp. Ousmane was at the corner, he held his flute anxiously looking up and down the narrow street. His face lit up as he saw Ahmed. "You got away, good Ahmed," running beside Ahmed's bicycle. Ousmane climbed onto the handle bars. Ahmed pedalled in the hot silence toward the beach. Nearing the sea, their legs and arms eased from the tension of the town. Ousmane's bare feet leapt from the makeshift seat at the same time that Ahmed braked. They headed for their favourite rock wheeling and lifting the bicycle through the sand, hot and stinging. Already he felt tranquil as the thin wind shaking the flowers. He dropped the bicycle, raced Ousmane to the water, crushing softly underfoot the vine and silky mangrove. Ahmed and Ousmane fell into the sea fully clothed, he washing away the sticky oil of the bicycle shop, Ousmane drowning his headache. Then they lay beside the rock, talking and falling asleep.

Ousmane awakening, felt hungry; his dungarees, still damp, felt steamy on his legs. Shading his eyes from the sun which had narrowed the shadow of the rock, his headache came back. He stood up, lifted his flute and played a tune he'd made over and over again as if to tame the ache in his head. After a while he wandered down the beach, looking for a food-seller.

Ahmed, Ahmed. Ahmed awoke, feeling Ousmane's absence at the same moment that he heard an explosion close to his ear. Ahmed felt his eyes taking an eternity to open into the glassy haze of the afternoon. A blurred white form wobbling in the heat's haze. Sound exploded on the other side of Ahmed. He barely raised his body, shielding his eyes as he made out the white form of a European. Far out in the ocean a steamer was passing. The sand around Ahmed pulsated with the heat and the loud ringing in his ears. Ousmane! Run!

Ahmed's vision pinpointed the white's face, the tooth-pick between the white's teeth and lip moving. The gun transfixed his arms. Beneath a veil of brine and tears, his eyes were blinded; they watched the steamer's latitude longingly. "Born slackers!" Ahmed's chest sprang back, tendrilled. "Born liars!" A pump of blood exploded in his left side. "Born criminals!" Sheets of flame poured down his ribs. "Born . . . !" Ahmed!

That is what happened! And as for Camus. Murderer.

This is it baby. The old woman has given the go-ahead. Now that they're all gathered—Rosa, the big white boy, the professor, the money-changers and the skin dealers, the whip handlers, the coffle makers and the boatswains, the old timers and the young soldiers. I'm going to kill them. I'll tell them I have something to sell. That'll get them going; it always has. Then we'll strangle them. It'll be a night for the old woman to remember. That'll make up for it. Then that'll be the end of it.

We chained them around the statue of Cristobal Colon, the prick head. The old woman and I slashed his face to ribbons then we chewed on the stones and spit them into the eyes of the gathering. When that was over and they were all jumping and screaming, the old woman drew out her most potent juju and sprayed them all with oceans of blood which, she said, she had carried for centuries.

"En't is blood all you like?!" she whispered in their ears maliciously.

Then we sang "jingay . . ." and made them call out everything that they had done over and over again, as they choked on the oceans of blood from the old hag's juju. Then we marinated them in hot peppers, like the old woman wanted. What an everlasting sweet night we had. The old woman was so happy, she laughed until her belly burst.

When Elaine returned from her continuous phone call, I convinced her to stuff the bodies in her trunk to Zaire. It wasn't easy, as she almost could not see me and kept saying how much my face had changed. I promised her the Queendom and riches of Songhai. She bought it. The old lady has promised me her big big juju, so this is where the African princess and I must part. I'm off to see my new love and companion, the old hag of a banyan tree.

Endnote: "Ahmed's death" is intended to echo and counterpoint the corresponding scene in *L'Étranger* and therefore echoes the language of the Penguin edition, English language translation.

(1988)

Joan MacLeod

(CANADA, 1954–)

Jewel

The original version of Jewel *was performed at The Banff Centre, February, 1985. This version, revised and expanded substantially, premiered at Tarragon Theatre in Toronto, April, 1987.*

MARJORIE   *Joan MacLeod*

Directed by Andy McKim.
Set and costume design by Linda Muir.
Lighting design by Heather Sherman.
Stage manager—Beth Bruck.

The Setting

The play is set in the Peace River on Valentine's Day, 1985, in Marjorie's mobile home.

Characters

Marjorie Clifford is 30 years old.

The Running Time

The play runs approximately one hour with no intermission.

Prologue

MARJORIE is standing in her nightgown beside a full bucket of fresh milk. She speaks directly to the audience.

MARJORIE   Valentine's through the ages. You are six years old and folding up this gigantic piece of white tissue paper until it's the size of your hand then attacking it with these dull little scissors, chopping the corners off, driving a hole right through the middle. But when you unfold it—pure magic: triangles and diamonds pinwheeling out from the centre, a thousand crescent moons. So you cut out this heart and paste it onto red cardboard. Print his name very carefully, then your own name, right along side. It's so special you can barely stand it. Only when you get to school you discover that every girl in your class has done the very same thing. And the most popular boy in the world just stuffs all those valentines into his desk without saying a word. By the end of the afternoon you realize that some of those hearts have turned into paper airplanes, some into spitballs. Valentine's through the ages. Alright.

You are thirteen and at the Claresholme Teen Stomp and everything is dumb: the red punch, the heart-shaped plates, Claresholme, the records that are all old and country. But the dumbest thing ever is Lucy who you're down here visiting.

Lucy is fifteen and what your mother calls mature meaning she has big tits, smokes and is also stupid. She visited you last month and was afraid to get on an escalator. But it gets worse. Because right now, Lucy is dancing with some wonderful boy and she's danced ten thousand times since she got here. You haven't been asked once. You also don't care a damn but there goes Lucy again, right up to the boys lining the rear wall of the gym. She tells them to go dance with her cousin Marjorie. That's you. And it's like all your nerves have gone electric and the air too. Nobody moves. They're just lined up like some kind of firing squad, a big string of monkeys and now all you can look at is their boots and the dumb floor. Lucy says please and that you're an orphan, which isn't true, but you still just die. No matter how many times you tell dumb-ass Lucy she still wants to hear about orphanages and that.

Then you notice it—black cowboy boots two feet in front of you. And someone you're afraid to look at is asking you to dance. Okay. It's a slow song. You decide to kill yourself but there you are now. You can do it. Damp hands bumping together. His neck is red as a brick. He speaks. "Where you from?" And you're still afraid to look at him but by some miracle you manage it, "Calgary."

Then two perfect minutes, moving ever-so-small, one side to another. You just want to take a peek. His eyes are flat and brown as a frozen puddle and staring straight at your cousin Lucy. Suddenly he looks clean into you and tells you he wouldn't live in Calgary if it was the last place on earth. And it feels so stupid and mean. "That's fine," you tell him. That's just great. Then you explain how the Beatles love Calgary and that they're moving there next month.

Everything changes. He is looking at you special. Some of the others are too. Questions come from everywhere. "When? What would they do that for? Have you met them?" And for the first time, you, are right at the centre of a very perfect world. Invented, but still perfect. Valentine's through the ages. You are thirteen years old and dizzy with love.

Two years later, you're at a sleepover. Nine other girls there in flannel nighties. You've all arrived with an inch of liquor, stolen from your folks' rye and scotch and gin bottles.

You mix this up with a twenty-sixer of Tahiti Treat and sit cross-legged in a circle, passing the bottle around. Everytime you take a sip, you tell a truth—how you went to second with so and so. Who it is you're really in love with this week. It's all marvelous. It's all made up. You're half-sick with pink liquor and trying to French inhale Peter Jackson cigarettes. You light a candle and listen to Joni Mitchell sing *Both Sides Now* eleven times in a row. You're delirious with sadness. You phone up a dozen boys, say something absolutely filthy then hang up the phone. This liquor in your gut. This tingling in your legs. You are fifteen years old and sick with love.

Valentine's through the ages marches on. You've been going to the university and are all grown up. You have a boyfriend—this range management student who comes from the Arctic Circle. Well nearly. Range management: the choreography (*beat*) of cows. You met in February but now it's August. You're camping near his folks' place in northern Alberta. You're out of your territory. (*beat*) And you love it. Because there is something about him and this place that's like coming home after a long, long journey. And it's true in a way, coming home.

The inside of your blue nylon tent sweats in the morning sun. Through this gauzy half-moon of a window mosquitoes crash around; two little kids collect beer bottles in a potato sack, eat O'Henry bars at six a.m.

The cattle arranger, with his sleeping bag zipped up with yours, is enjoying the sleep of the dead. You are enjoying this chance to examine his face: high cheekbones, lashes like a woman's, black hair sticking out in a million directions. Out of your territory. And last night, at six minutes to midnight, he asked you to stay out of your territory forever. Marriage. "Marry me, Marjorie." There's this land he's wanting to buy and no money for cattle yet but the oil patch is right around the corner. He's got his welder's papers. The money will flow. Maybe five winters of working out then full-time farming or ranching or whatever. He talks about buying a milk cow and (*picking up bucket*) you nearly pass out with the romance of it. One of his hands is against his heart as if he were taking a pledge. And the other one is meandering up your nightgown. Valentine's through the ages.

A country song starts, up softly on radio.

Six years later now. You're still crazy with love.

Scene One

> *Lighting change signifies that MARJORIE is now in her trailer. She turns up the radio and carries her bucket into the kitchen area. While singing along to the radio she pours milk into two large glass jars and places them in the fridge. She removes another milk jar from the fridge and skims the cream off the top. She listens to Message Time. She drinks beer.*

MARJORIE   Christ I'm thirsty. Thirsty for everything except milk. Your dad made this beer. I mean it doesn't taste terrible but it sort of leaves fur on your teeth. No one can really make good beer, they all just think they can, and are dying for you to drink this flat stuff that's clear as mud. Oh well, Harry. You know what they say to do with failed beer? Drink it.

RADIO   And that's it for Country Countdown tonight. Happy Valentine's. And you better snuggle up to the one you love because, according to Environment Canada, it's a chilly thirty-three below in Fort St. John tonight and it looks like it's going to dip down even lower.

MARJORIE   You hear that Harry? Cozy up.

RADIO	And now Message Time. The link between you and your loved ones. A community service brought to you by CKNL North Country.
MARJORIE	You'll have to stay quiet for a minute. Think you can manage that?
RADIO	To Connie Brown: Happy Valentine's. Wish I could be there with love from Stanley. To Cynthia, Ruthie and Jason; home on Saturday, love from your daddy, Jason Senior. To Beatrice George; call Credit Union immediately, very important.
MARJORIE	Poor Beatrice. They're broke.
RADIO	To Billy Gustafson; your cattle are out and in Chevron property south of Fish Creek. Remove at once. To Marjorie Clifford;
MARJORIE	Yes sir.
RADIO	Your order is in at Buckerfields'. Will be delivered on the 17th.
MARJORIE	Well it's about time.
RADIO	To Rebecca Cochrane; not coming home as planned, will call on Saturday, Aubrey Cochrane. To Sally Harper; Happy Valentines. You are my one and only, love Frank.
	MARJORIE turns off radio.
MARJORIE	You know Harry? I was listening to Message Time. When was it? Christmas Eve, years ago. You were working for Esso out on Cotcho Lake. I'd just come up from school and missed you by half a day. I mean that first year of being married we must've spent all of ten minutes together. So me and Deb are drinking egg nog and listening to the messages. They're gushy as hell. "To Ruth in Dawson who I met in the bar last night. I love you more than life itself." That sort of thing. Even Debbie got something half-way romantic from Walter. And I'm sitting there waiting then getting worried that maybe you forgot. Then realizing you'd never do that and getting very excited and it comes. "To Marjorie Clifford. Merry Christmas. The calf will be needing her worm shot on the twenty-seventh." Period.

Was I pissed off Harry? I threw my egg nog at the radio. And then I start to stand up for you. Defend your good name. Telling Debbie how you're really very romantic but in a private sort of way. Which was true enough I suppose.

The sound of a dog barking is heard outside.

But Jesus. Worm shot.

No! You've been outside for all of two seconds. Go chase a weasel. That dog, Harry. Remember going down to Beaverlodge to buy him? Staying in that very lousy motel called Shady Glenn or Palm Grove—some Prairie name like that. And the guy with the litter's explaining that this dog's part wolf. I mean there's no person north of Edmonton that doesn't own a dog part wolf. It can be purebred Chihuahua and people round here would still say "Careful. That dog's got wolf in it." So we buy this thing that looks like a guinea pig and, in a fit of inspiration, we name him (*beat*) Wolf.

And on the way home, he's sitting on the floor of the truck, quivering for a hundred miles. He hasn't changed. I mean he's big now. In fact he's fat. His only goal in life seems to be figuring out a way of never going outside. I think Wolf would rather live with my folks in the city, eat canned dog food, and lie around all day on their wall-to-wall.

I meant to explain why I never came home last night. No Harry. I was not out fooling around. I was at Debbie's. She put the kids to bed and we made this massive supper. Walter had just gone back to the bush and I guess the guy that picked him up had this bag of shrimp, fresh from the coast that morning. So we shucked them or whatever the hell it is you do with shrimp. And we made this white wine sauce. Then drank what was left over which was about a gallon each. Deb's doing fine. I mean her and Walter are in debt over this new tractor like you wouldn't believe but they're making out. Where was I? Deb's last night—right.

So we're just sitting there talking and getting very drunk and there's this knock at the door. It's not even eight-thirty but feels around midnight and I'm thinking, shit—it's your dad. Then it dawns on me that Munroe's never knocked on a door in his life. He just comes in and yells, "I'm here! Where's the coffee?"

Well. Guess who? Guess who wears sensible shoes and overcoats and, more than likely, have a good case of pimples on the go? It's the Mormons.

Come all the way from the state of Utah to bring us the word of God. I don't get up off the couch. That is to say I'm incapable of getting off the couch. And I'm thinking—this is great. We actually live in a place that needs missionaries. I mean I know they do their business in the cities too but I'm pretending the North is like darkest Africa and that Deb and me have rings through our noses and these big, black breasts hanging out front, like torpedos, like National Geographic. And the younger one, he's all of eighteen or something. He asks me if I've been saved and I tell him, "UNGOWA!"

These two are very embarrassed. They pack up their stuff, give us some pamphlets, head out into forty below in this little Japanese car. We laugh about it for a while longer then end up feeling bad. I mean it's like being drafted, it's something they have to do.

I stayed over night. Which is something I do quite often when Walter's off in the bush. We sleep in the same bed and hug and that but it's not gay or anything. It's just very nice when you're on your own to have other people close by. And we understand one another quite well. Debbie and me.

The sound of a dog barking is heard outside.

No! Go make some friends. That dog. Wolf must've had something very horrible happen to him when he was real young. Old Wolf and me, eh? Or maybe before we got hold of him that guy beat him, or his mother tried to eat him. Yeah, that suits Wolf. He's just hanging around with all his brothers and sisters, trying to have a good time and his mother tries to eat him.

Remember when we tried to take him hunting for lynx? Wolf is obsessed with thoughts of his own death and refuses to leave the truck. Your wife, who is me, is also obsessed with death but is equally obsessed with making this marriage work. Lucky for you, the shits for me. How's your beer there, Harry? You're looking a little pale around the edges tonight.

Wanna dance? C'mon dance with me. (*Turning on radio and dancing to fiddle waltz.*)

It's Valentine's night at the Ranch Cabaret. We're dancing to a band called Hot Lightning. Dancing tight and slow. Your shirt smelling like cedar and diesel. Smoke.

We've been ice fishing all day. The sky just getting heavy with snow when we leave for town, the dark coming in. By the time we get there, these big flakes. Everything pretty as Christmas cards.

Your folks are there. Your mother waltzing bolt upright and scared, shy at being in town. Your eyes in her face—that wonderful jade. Munroe leading her, proud and near drunk. His arm around me at the table for the first time. Telling how when you were little you stole his truck and sunk it in the lake. All of us proud and near drunk. This mirror ball's sprinkling light all round the room and across your face. We've just gone into life-time debt for buying the land and this trailer. I believe we are perfectly happy. That is to say, I, am perfectly happy.

RADIO   And that's our request waltz for this evening and goes out to Mr. and Mrs. R. Johnson. And now more easy listening on CKNL, your north country station.

She turns off the radio.

MARJORIE   And on the way home in the pick-up, all four of us squeezed inside, your dad says —"Look at them cheeks of Marjorie's, all glowy and red. I like that in a woman. Looks freshly slapped." And I think, great, I've married into a family of insane people. But I figured it out pretty quick—this father and son. When you went down, Munroe was the only one that didn't mind my staying quiet, that could keep comfortable with it.

They're still looking out for me, Harry. They're both doing fine. (*pause*) That was nice. You are some dancer. In fact you're wearing me out.

Today I was at the Co-op in town, buying groceries and that. This kid is pushing the buggy. I think he's one of Beatrice's boys but then it's hard to keep track. And this other kid who's working there yells from across the parking lot, "Hey Mitchell! What's got four legs, is three hundred feet tall and goes down on Newfoundland?" And this kid Mitchell looks real embarrassed. You can just tell he's praying his buddy over there will shut up. Because old Mitchell knows who I am. I mean I am one hell of a famous widow Harry. We're talking *Time* magazine. Reporters all the way from Texas braving forty below and gravel roads just to get a picture of me and Wolf. And this kid yells it again, "Mitch? What's a thousand feet tall, has four legs and goes down on Newfoundland?" And I end up apologizing! Saying I've always been one to make jokes about anything and everything. This idiot, he yells it out (*beat*) "The Ocean Ranger!" (*beat*) Old Mitch practically has a heart attack right on the spot. By the time he's got the truck loaded it looks like he's decided to be a priest.

You know I always thought it was a ridiculous name—the Ocean Ranger. Like a speedboat full of Girl Guides. And when you first got the job I just panicked because I didn't know how to imagine you there. That's important Harry. It's important to women who have husbands who work out to know how to imagine them in a place. I mean all I had to do was drive into town or walk to your dad's to see a rig on the ground, to set you somewhere. And usually you were just up around Nelson and I knew that if I went squirrelly I could jump in the truck and find you. But Newfoundland! That is practically four thousand miles away. Right from the start it felt wrong. I mean we're supposed to be farmers and there you are out on this floating thing in the middle of some ocean. The Atlantic Ocean.

And when I got the call that you'd gone down, all I could think was that you were drifting, that you might sink for a minute, then get caught up in kelp or some current, and set off again, that you'd never settle. You'd never arrive on something solid again. And I thought about that Harry, non-stop. Thought about that for fourteen months without a break.

Then I'm living with my folks, and my mother, she signs me up for some god-awful thing called a grieving workshop. All this group stuff going on that just makes me mental. I mean this is a very private business if you ask me. Everyone wanting me to come to terms with this. Those sort of expressions are another thing that makes me crazy. They're just pieces of air. And all I'm really wanting is for everyone just to leave me alone. Some church ran this thing and they're tossing scripture around like a volley ball. I mean as if that's going to fill my bed or help me make payments.

Okay, we got our money since then. But I mean this isn't some cheque that just showed up in the mail one day. This is after two years of drawn out bull shit with lawyers and Louisiana accents. Every time you open the paper or a magazine or letter, more stuff about the Ocean Ranger. What I want, through the whole inquiry, is to narrow it down to one man. But we couldn't even narrow it down to one company. But it's still what I keep wanting, just pare it all down. Leave me one man, up there on the top floor, behind some marble top desk.

I want him to say "Yup, I'm your boy, it was my fault. My fault about the design flaws, the lack of survival suits, my fault about the evacuation procedure and that the lifeboats would've gone down in a lake. I'm your boy. Not that I meant any of it but I sure as hell did screw things up. You think safety is top priority but it gets lost somewhere along the way. You get tested like that and completely fail the test. I screwed up. Big time."

I don't want to cause this man any harm. But I would like to place him aboard a drilling platform, after midnight in February, over a hundred miles from the coast of Newfoundland. An alarm calls this man from sleep and onto a deck that is pitch black and tipped over fifteen degrees and all covered in ice. The wind is screaming. Salt water and snow pelt his face. Everybody is running around and nobody knows what to do. He is in his pajamas and being lowered in a life raft with twenty other men, into a sea of fifty foot waves.

Then I would reach down and lift that man up from this terrible place just like the hand of God come to save him. Remove him from all that terror and certain death. I place him somewhere warm and dry. Relief here and family. Take his shivering hand inside my own and turn his hand over and over and over. Until he sees it. Palm up and attached and staring straight at him. His hand is the hand of God and he could have gathered them all up. Saved eighty-four men from the North Atlantic. He chose not to.

And I don't care who owns you mister. I don't care if you're ODECO or Mobil Oil, a fed or provincial. My sadness, my husband's death—it was handmade by someone.

You know at first, right after, I thought my insides were made out of paper. Very white paper. I would even walk carefully because I thought something might rip inside. Where am I? Right. We were talking about the grieving workshop. I go off in a corner with a Bible just so they won't bug me. And I actually found something that made sense: the book of Genesis, page one, "Let the waters teem with living creatures and let the birds fly above the earth within the vault of Heaven. And so it was, God created great whales."

Well. I hold onto those lines like a goddamn life jacket. I start pretending you are this very fine whale with the sun on your back and just having the life of Riley in general.

You see, Harry. What I loved about that is I'm thinking you have no heart and no memory. I mean I know that whales have warm blood and a heart and that but it's not the sort that makes you barge through everything like some open nerve. And I thought, that's the ticket. No heart and no memory. I thought that was about the best way to live that anyone had ever come up with.

Very crazy stuff. Well old friend. (*looking at ring*) You don't have a heart and you don't have a memory anymore. I suppose that part's the truth. But I do.

Even this summer. I'd just moved back here and everyone was so worried that I'd go crazy again. And sure enough, that's when I started having these little night-time chats of ours. But it wasn't like now.

I'd tell you about the kid driving grain truck, the one helping out with harvest. I'd bring him out these sandwiches at noon. Because of the heat, he would take off his shirt and this line of sweat would sort of weep down his belly. We lean against the wheel of the truck for shade and drink ice water out of a thermos, passing it back and forth.

And I told you I took him to the granary. The air is very cool in there. We take off all our clothes without looking at one another. He folds up his jeans and makes a pillow, like for under my head. The floor boards and loose seed cut into the backs of my legs. Everything smells very clean and very dry. Like gravel. And I mean this kid is really inside. And he's moving above me and on me and all around me. And it's like there are these thousands of minnows that have just been sleeping under my skin forever and all at once they rush for the surface. And it's . . . it's (*beat*) bravery. And I think, fuck you, Harry! Dying and leaving me is about the most gutless thing anyone could ever do.

All those stories about that kid driving grain truck? I made everyone of them up. Just wanting to make you jealous. Just trying to make you mad. Trying every trick in the book to get some kind of response. I mean he was barely seventeen or something. That's called the Angry Phase, Harry. I think I'm starting to come out of it though.

I'll tell you a story that's true. There is a guy teaching school here that I've gone out with a few times. Some dinners in town. Last week we went to a play in Dawson Creek. He's a very nice man. Sort of shy. Or maybe it's lack of character. No. There's something quite good there.

He comes from Vancouver which is kind of an excuse but you know what he reminds me of? Me. When I first got here. All set to live on roots and berries, grow our own vegetables and animals and furniture. Seeing your folks' place for the first time I remember thinking—this is great—big old log house, smoke in the chimney. Your mum's real warm to me and she's making bread or canning moose or something equally terrific. But Munroe. It's afternoon and he's watching television. He doesn't even look up when we're introduced. Rude old bugger, I think but hating it just as much that he's watching TV instead of trimming wicks or milking some creature. We leave and on the way to the truck I can hear him yelling at his grandson, "Don't lick that cat. You'll get leukemia."

His name is Gordon, Harry. This school teacher guy. Gord. I don't like his name one bit. Monday night I was over at his place for the first time. It's all cleaned up which it probably is anyway but I still like it, this making me feel special. He's cooked jackfish, wrapped up in some kind of leaves. Baked apples.

His place is all cedar and just half-done because he bought from Wilson who went bankrupt like you said he would. Gordon is determined with me. Serious as a machine.

The smell of wood makes me crazy. First winter with you in that cabin? Because we're just married I don't care a damn at first that we've built this little box to live in with wood that's green as lettuce. And that you stick to the wall everytime you touch it. That there's no power or water and nearly no windows. That making coffee means half a day's work. But then I begin to notice everything; nothing is smooth, it's dark all the time, my clothes are alive with sawdust and the walls are alive with sap. So it starts. Small at first but eventually this enormous longing, desperate and ashamed. I want to live in a trailer. I need to live in a mobile home.

Gordon asked me to stay overnight. But I didn't. Or maybe I'm telling you lies again. Maybe I got him drunk on rye and coke; sex crazed widow flattens new-comer. You know I don't think I ever lied to you once the whole time we were together. But now, Jesus. I did this when I was little too, make up stuff to put in my diary.

But this, Harry, is the goods on Gordon. This is a story that's true. I didn't stay overnight but I did go to bed with him. I'm just telling you, not asking permission. It was alright. The best part being those very pure times when thinking stops. Just touch, react. But the flipside is thinking at a million miles an hour. How it is still your body that I know better than my own. How being held by living arms, hands, brings home what a body must be like lifeless. All the women wanted the bodies found, all the families of the victims. I never thought it'd be like that. You'd think lost would be better than dead. A strand of hope, invisible, thin. But it makes you crazy, never knowing a hundred percent. It was way harder in the long run.

I am glad of meeting Gordon. Gord. I'm not saying you two would've hit it off in a huge way but I do like him, Harry. It's quite wonderful to have that small leap in the gut again when I know he's coming over, that kind of thing.

Wolf thinks of him as a minor God. Just lies at his feet with his paws up in the air like he's waiting to be sacrificed or trying to communicate tele-pathically that's he's trapped in a trailer with a maniac.

Wolf and me went for a walk on Sunday down to the lake. You know what he's doing? Sniffing around and making circles. Peeing on every-thing in sight and acting like a general lunatic. I'm explaining to him that it's February for God's sake and all the bears are asleep and to quit being so damn antsy. Then it dawns on me—he's still looking for your scent. I mean it's been three years but Wolf's still after your scent. And of course everything is froze solid and you can't smell a thing but whatever. Wolf is thinking you're around every corner, maybe skidding out birch for the woodpile or ice fishing or I don't know what dogs think.

So we get to the shore and there's these three kids from the reserve skating out on the lake. Boys, maybe seven years old. Needless to say, Wolf is scared of them. He stands on the shore rocking back and forth, quivering like a race horse. These kids are banging around a soccer ball with these big plastic baseball bats. Wolf is dying to get out there. He wants to run and bark and fool around with those kids and just be a regular dog. But he can't do it. He just stays there and yelps, does a few circles around me. And for once I don't give him shit. I just pat his head and let him be. Poor old Wolf. Just wanting to be a regular dog. Everyone else wanting him to be that way too. But Wolf's got a few things figured out. He knows his limits. Feels real good about those pats on the head.

So we just sat there for a long time, watching those kids skate and the sun going down. I love that time of day in winter. Used to be I hated the night coming but it's alright now. I mean it's not out-and-out terror anymore. Not all the time at least.

Just a few more things, Harry. Then I'm going to bed. They finally got me going to another widows' group at the Elks twice a month. In Newfoundland, they've got a group just for Ranger families and it's supposed to be great. But this bunch, I don't know. There's a couple of new ones there who are in a very bad way and it is good to talk things out with them . . . support your sisters, that kind of stuff. But there's this one woman there, she's from town, works at the Bay, around your mum's age. And she says that widowhood, it's like checking into a motel for one night. One night that lasts the rest of your life. I mean let's face it. The Elks is about the most depressing way to spend an evening that's ever been invented.

Then this lady says that nothing feels like home anymore. It's like we're all just waiting to get to another place. And I thought—right. Not that I think I'm going to another place. It's just that it feels like that . . . the waiting.

You know how when you stay in a motel everything looks different— the bed, the pattern on the carpet? Even some dumb old TV show that you've watched every night of your life seems nearly exotic when you're in a motel. Very new.

Or those summers in Calgary before I met you. I had this really terrible job in an insurance office. Really punching the clock. Working in this little room without any windows. But every Friday at ten o'clock I'd have to go to the Treasury Branch. And I'd step out onto Centre Street and the world looked different: the bus stop right out front, even the way people walked. Everything transformed and clear and spooky, all at the same time.

So maybe that lady had a point, but she hasn't figured out the whole thing completely. I mean the world certainly does feel like a motel just in that everything looks so different. But you know Harry? Part of me likes that. It makes a walk with Wolf or just making dinner nearly miraculous.

I know. When we went to visit my folks and on the way down we stayed in Edmonton in that rather swanky place. We fooled around, practically overdosed on Cable TV. And we got room service for breakfast, opened the curtains up really wide and there's this apartment across the way. We watched all these people run around and get ready for work. The window's acting like a magnifying glass, everyone looks bigger than life. Even the air is defined and lively, just sparkling with light.

Okay. Sometimes I do feel like I'm just visiting here or stuck on the shore like old Wolf, not really able to get involved in anything. And very, very scared of going out on the ice again.

But I'll tell you something. I am beginning to feel again and part of me just loves staying in a motel. So maybe it's because I'm so much younger than most of them at the Elks but I'm not just waiting, not anymore. Not held down by that sadness. I mean I know it's part of me but it can't run the show forever. (*looking at ring*) What do you think of that? My perfect jewel.

And what that lady from the Bay doesn't know or anybody else is that you got through to me. Valentine's through the ages. 1982.

You are about to slam, face first, into such a storm. But not yet. Maybe it's still quiet out there, just for a moment. I hope so. Wolf and me have been down at the barn, checking on things. I mean the animals would have to be doing something absolutely bizarre for us to see anything wrong but whatever. It's just before noon. I come in the kitchen, the radio's on. And there it is. First one out of the gate, a Valentine's message, short and sweet and probably sent the day before but meant to be mine now. I carry it around inside, hold onto it all day. It sends me to bed warm. Loud and clear. You love me. You got through.

Then late that night another message, hand delivered by an embarrassed RCMP. The rig has been evacuated. The constable offers to wait with me. They will call again in an hour on his car radio. I apologize for not having a phone, for all his trouble. I make tea. Wolf has gone wild. He can't believe his good luck. All this activity in the middle of the night.

Evacuated. What does it mean? Bombed out villages, buildings. Living in an air raid shelter. Living. He has left the rig and is in a life boat. There is a bad storm, a fifty foot sea.

How high? Like a grain elevator, fir tree. No. Too tall. I know. Me and Lucy are at Uncle Ray's, spitting down from the loft to where the cowshit is, "You kids get the hell down from there. You want to fall fifty feet and land on your heads?" That's when I know. Anything that big and made out of water is a deadly thing. But don't think it or it will be true and my fault. My legs are weak as bread. I grab hold of the counter and the kitchen floor moves like a raft underneath me. And there you are, clear as ice for a single moment. In a little boat, wearing that awful parka from Sears.

The horn on the police car blats out of nowhere. Twice. Wolf and the police go to get the message on the radio phone. And I know it again but don't believe it for a second. Not on your life. I should go to Munroe's

Joan MacLeod **411**

because your mother believes in God and I don't. I didn't mean it. The RCMP catches me down on my knees on the cold linoleum. He shakes his head. This is very hard for him, trying to tell me that my husband is dead.

But he doesn't tell me that. He says the rig has gone down and two of the lifeboats but the third boat is still out there. That means you. I know it.

But then this cop tells me they said not to have much hope. And I slap him across the back of the head.

I should have listened to him. It would've made the next few days a lot easier. All that waiting and glued to the radio. I should go to Newfoundland but I'm afraid of flying now, of moving, of leaving the ground. Then the names of the dead are just read over the radio, in Munroe's kitchen. Confirmed. At the service, someone from your company is there telling me how sad this has made him. What I don't realize at the time is he can't apologize because it might make them liable. If you'd worked for Mobil itself, they wouldn't even have tried to make contact after the accident. Just hear it on the news with everyone else.

It doesn't start for a week or so because I suppose I'm in shock but I relive your death for a long, long time. You're in the lifeboat that nearly made it. That's what all the widows think. We think alike. I can't go through that stuff anymore.

Nearly midnight, Harry. Valentine's through the ages is coming to a close. Remember how I told you that first message sent me to bed warm? It's still there. A little bit.

MARJORIE removes the ring from her finger and leaves it on the table.

But wearing this forever. I don't know. I don't think it's such a great idea anymore. Does that make sense? I hope so. It does for me and I guess that's the important part.

It always felt so mean that it had to be Valentine's Day, that it was the last day you were alive. But I'm not so sure anymore.

This is what I'm sure of. You loved me. You got through.

The End

(1987)

Sujata Bhatt
(INDIA, 1956–)

What Does One Write When the World Starts to Disappear?

for Eleanor and Bob

If only the earth
would rise up
        and turn itself
into a woman—
5   the way she did long ago
in Vedic times
at the foothills of the Himalayas.
It would be so easy.
There
10 she would stand
complaining to Shiva:
'My head's been hurting all day—'
        she would groan,
'and my stomach burns
15 with all their swords and guns
their missiles, satellites, microphones, radios. . .
I can't go on like this.
It's about time you did something.'
Then Shiva would frown, this time
20 there's a seven-headed cobra in his hair.
It rears up, all seven hoods flared—
a huge, angry claw.
Shiva would frown
and the seven-headed cobra
25 hisses in the right direction
paralysing all the armies
into a definite peace.
It would be so easy.

What does one do
30 when the world starts to disappear?
Where does one go?
What does one take along?
And who will read our books
tomorrow? Who will listen
35 to our music, tune the sitars
        and the violins?
I mean, what species?

I too, have a recurring dream
of the morning after.
40 I see the earth strewn
with gas masks and plastic—
body bags
bones rattling
in the wind.
45 Perhaps a few lizards
have managed to survive,
a few snakes . . .
I see them crawling out
from the rocks
50 that sheltered them.
I dream
a lizard tail's
rippling dance
through the eye-hole
55 of a gas mask.
A snake's forked tongue
flicks out, flicks in,
flicks out again, investigating
the nature of plastic.

(1991)

Lucy Ng
(CANADA, 1966–)

From "The Sullen Shapes of Poems"

Father, in the autumn of your life you embarked
on a 28-day 22-city tour of China. I remember
the names—Beijing, Suzhou, Guilin—the sounds
and shapes delightful to your tongue as you
5 repeated them to us around the dinner table.
Sometimes dreaming or reading, I think I know
what you must have felt when you climbed that
Great Wall or wandered through those magnificent
rooms, finger-deep in dust. Did you feel the
10 pain of recognition—thirty years gone—as
you chanced upon this, the undiscovered country,
its imprint in your heart?

The reddish dust of Beijing seeps through our
clothes, chafes at our skin—North American
15 bred, the disdainful tour guide notes.

Chinese cafe, grocery, laundry—skipping rope
rhymes—you want something different for me.
Poet? you say. What's that? You recall Li Po
drunk under the white moon, chasing her cold
5   reflection in the river. His body skimming and
sinking, the blue and white robes twisting
brushstroke of calligraphy on water.

You gave me these: a river, a boat,
a bridge. The sullen shapes of poems.

(1991)

Traditions

Geoffrey Chaucer

(c. 1343–1400)

From "The General Prologue" to *The Canterbury Tales*

    Whan that Aprille with his shoures soote
The droghte of Marche hath percéd to the roote,
And bathed every veyne in swich licour,
Of which vertu engendred is the flour;
5 Whan Zephirus eek with his swete breeth
Inspiréd hath in every holt and heeth
The tendre croppes, and the yonge sonne
Hath in the Ram his halfe cours y-ronne,
And smale fowles maken melodye,
10 That slepen al the night with open yë,
(So priketh hem nature in hir corages),
Than longen folk to goon on pilgrimages,
And palmers for to seken straunge strondes,
To ferne halwes, couthe in sondry londes,
15 And specially, from every shires ende
Of Engelond, to Caunterbury they wende,
The holy blisful martir for to seke,
That hem hath holpen, whan that they were seeke.
    Bifel that, in that sesoun on a day,
20 In Southwerk at the Tabard as I lay
Redy to wenden on my pilgrimage
To Caunterbury with ful devout corage,
At night was come in-to that hostelrye
Wel nyne and twenty in a companye,
25 Of sondry folk, by aventure y-falle
In felawshipe, and pilgrims were they alle,
That toward Caunterbury wolden ryde;
The chambres and the stables weren wyde,
And wel we weren esed atte beste.
30 And shortly, whan the sonne was to reste,
So hadde I spoken with hem everichon,
That I was of hir felawshipe anon,
And made forward erly for to ryse,
To take our wey, ther as I yow devyse.
35 But natheles, whyl I have tyme and space,
Ere that I ferther in this tale pace,
Me thinketh it acordaunt to resoun,
To telle yow al the condicioun
Of ech of hem, so as it semed me,
40 And whiche they weren, and of what degree,

And eek in what array that they were inne;
And at a knight than wol I first biginne.
    A KNIGHT ther was, and that a worthy man,
That fro the tyme that he first bigan
45 To ryden out, he loved chivalrye,
Trouthe and honour, fredom and curteisye.
Ful worthy was he in his lordes werre,
And therto hadde he riden, no man ferre,
As wel in cristendom as hethenesse,
50 And ever honoured for his worthinesse.
At Alisaundre he was, when it was wonne;
Ful ofte tyme he hadde the bord bigonne
Aboven alle naciouns in Pruce.
In Lettow hadde he reysed and in Ruce,
55 No cristen man so ofte of his degree.
In Gernade at the sege eek hadde he be
Of Algezir, and riden in Belmarye.
At Lyeys was he, and at Satalye,
Whan they were wonne; and in the Grete See
60 At many a noble aryve hadde he be.
At mortal batailles hadde he been fiftene,
And foughten for our feith at Tramissene
In listes thryes, and ay slayn his foo.
This ilke worthy knight hadde been also
65 Sometyme with the lord of Palatye,
Ageyn another hethen in Turkye.
And everemore he hadde a sovereyn prys,
And though that he were worthy, he was wys,
And of his port as meek as is a mayde.
70 He nevere yet no vileinye ne sayde
In al his lyf, un-to no maner wight.
He was a verray parfit gentil knight.
But for to tellen yow of his array,
His hors were goode, but he was nat gay.
75 Of fustian he weréd a gipoun
Al bismoteréd with his habergeoun,
For he was late y-come from his viage,
And wente for to doon his pilgrimage.
    With him there was his sone, a yong SQUYER,
80 A lovyere, and a lusty bacheler,
With lokkes crulle, as they were leyd in presse.
Of twenty yeer of age he was, I gesse.
Of his stature he was of evene lengthe,
And wonderly deliver, and of greet strengthe.
85 And he had been somtyme in chivachye,
In Flaundres, in Artoys, and Picardye,
And born him wel, as of so litel space,
In hope to stonden in his lady grace.

Embrouded was he, as it were a mede
90 Al ful of fresshe floures, whyte and rede.
Singinge he was, or floytinge, al the day;
He was as fressh as is the month of May.
Short was his goune, with sleves longe and wyde.
Wel coude he sitte on hors, and faire ryde.
95 He coude songes make and wel endyte,
Juste and eek daunce, and wel purtreye and wryte.
So hote he lovede, that by nightertale
He sleep namore than doth a nightingale.
Curteys he was, lowly, and servisable,
100 And carf biforn his fader at the table.

(c. 1390)

Popular Ballads

Edward

"Why dois your brand sae drap wi bluid,
        Edward, Edward,
Why dois your brand sae drap wi bluid,
    And why sae sad gang yee O?"
5 "O I hae killed my hauke sae guid,
        Mither, Mither,
O I hae killed my hauke sae guid,
    And I had nae mair bot hee O."

"Your haukis bluid was nevir sae reid,
10   Edward, Edward,
Your haukis bluid was nevir sae reid,
    My deir son I tell thee O."
"O I hae killed my reid-roan steid,
        Mither, Mither,
15 O I hae killed my reid-roan steid,
    That erst was sae fair and frie O."

"Your steid was auld, and ye hae gat mair,
        Edward, Edward,
Your steid was auld, and ye hae gat mair,
20   Sum other dule ye drie O."
"O I hae killed my fadir deir,
        Mither, Mither,
O I hae killed my fadir deir,
    Alas, and wae is mee O!"

25 "And whatten penance wul ye drie for that,
       Edward, Edward?
And whatten penance wul ye drie for that?
       My deir son, now tell me O."
"Ile set my feit in yonder boat,
30   Mither, Mither,
Ile set my feit in yonder boat,
       And Ile fare ovir the sea O."

"And what wul ye doe wi your towirs and your ha,
       Edward, Edward?
35 And what wul ye doe wi your towirs and your ha,
       That were sae fair to see O?"
"Ile let thame stand tul they doun fa,
       Mither, Mither,
Ile let thame stand tul they doun fa,
40   For here nevir mair maun I bee O."

"And what wul ye leive to your bairns and your wife,
       Edward, Edward?
And what wul ye leive to your bairns and your wife,
       Whan ye gang ovir the sea O?"
45 "The warldis room, late them beg thrae life,
       Mither, Mither,
The warldis room, late them beg thrae life,
       For them nevir mair wul I see O."

"And what wul ye leive to your ain mither deir,
50   Edward, Edward?
And what wul ye leive to your ain mither deir?
       My deir son, now tell me O."
"The curse of hell frae me sall ye beir,
       Mither, Mither,
55 The curse of hell frae me sail ye beir,
       Sic counseils ye gave to me O."

Sir Patrick Spence

The king sits in Dunferline toune,
    Drinking the blude-reid wine:
'O quhar will I get a guid sailor,
    To sail this schip of mine?'

5 Up and spak an eldern knicht,
    Sat at the king's richt knee
'Sir Patrick Spence is the best sailor,
    That sails upon the see.'

The king has written a braid letter,
10   And signed it wi’ his hand;
And sent it to Sir Patrick Spence,
Was walking on the sand.

The first line that Sir Patrick red,
        A loud lauch lauched he:
15 The next line that Sir Patrick red,
        The teir blinded his e’e.

‘O quha is this has don this deid,
        This ill deid don to me;
To send me out this time o’ the yeir,
20   To sail upon the see?

Mak haste, mak haste, my mirry men all,
        Our guid schip sails the morne.’
‘O say na sae, my master deir,
        For I feir a deadlie storme.

25 Late, late yestreen I saw the new moone
        Wi’ the auld moone in hir arme;
And I feir, I feir, my deir master,
        That we will come to harme.’

O our Scots nobles wer richt laith
30   To weet their cork-heil’d schoone;
Bot lang owre a’ the play wer played,
        Thair hats they swam aboone.

O lang, lang may thair ladies sit
        Wi’ thair fans into their hand,
35 Or eir they se Sir Patrick Spence
        Com sailing to the land.

O lang, lang may the ladies stand
        Wi’ thair gold kems in their hair,
Waiting for thair ain deir lords,
40   For they’ll se thame na mair.

Half owre, haf owre to Aberdour,
        It’s fiftie fadom deip:
And thair lies guid Sir Patrick Spence,
        Wi’ the Scots lords at his feit.

Edmund Spenser

(1552–1599)

From *Amoretti*

75

One day I wrote her name upon the strand,
    but came the waves and washed it away:
    agayne I wrote it with a second hand,
    but came the tyde, and made my paynes his pray.
5 Vayne man, sayd she, that doest in vaine assay,
    a mortall thing so to immortalize,
    for I my selve shall lyke to this decay,
    and eek my name bee wyped out lykewize.
Not so, (quod I) let baser things devize
10   to dy in dust, but you shall live by fame:
    my verse your vertues rare shall eternize,
    and in the hevens wryte your glorious name.
Where whenas death shall all the world subdew,
    our love shall live, and later life renew.

79

Men call you fayre, and you doe credit it,
    For that your selfe ye dayly such doe see:
    but the trew fayre, that is the gentle wit,
    and vertuous mind, is much more praysd of me.
5 For all the rest, how ever fayre it be,
    shall turne to nought and loose that glorious hew:
    but onely that is permanent and free
    from frayle corruption, that doth flesh ensew.
That is true beautie: that doth argue you
10   to be divine and borne of heavenly seed:
    deriv'd from that fayre Spirit, from whom al true
    and perfect beauty did at first proceed.
He onely fayre, and what he fayre hath made,
    all other fayre lyke flowres untymely fade.

81

Fayre is my love, when her fayre golden heares,
    with the loose wynd ye waving chance to marke:
    fayre when the rose in her red cheekes appeares,
    or in her eyes the fyre of love does sparke.
5 Fayre when her brest lyke a rich laden barke,
    with pretious merchandize she forth doth lay:
    fayre when that cloud of pryde, which oft doth dark
    her goodly light with smiles she drives away.

But fayrest she, when so she doth display
10   the gate with pearles and rubyes richly dight:
     throgh which her words so wise do make their way
     to beare the message of her gentle spright.
The rest be works of natures wonderment,
     but this the worke of harts astonishment.

                         (1595)

Sir Philip Sidney
(1554–1586)

From *Astrophel and Stella*

Sonnet 1
Loving in truth, and fain in verse my love to show,
That she, dear she, might take some pleasure of my pain,
Pleasure might cause her read, reading might make her know,
Knowledge might pity win, and pity grace obtain,
5   I sought fit words to paint the blackest face of woe;
Studying inventions fine, her wits to entertain,
Oft turning others' leaves to see if thence would flow
Some fresh and fruitful showers upon my sunburned brain.
But words came halting forth, wanting invention's stay;
10 Invention, nature's child, fled stepdame Study's blows,
And others' feet still seemed but strangers in my way.
Thus, great with child to speak, and helpless in my throes,
Biting my truant pen, beating myself for spite,
"Fool," said my muse to me, "look in thy heart and write."

                         (1582)

Psalm 8   *Domine, Dominus*

O Lord that rul'st our mortall lyne,
     How through the world thy name doth shine:
     That hast of thine unmatched glory
     Upon the heav'ns engrav'n the story.

5   From sucklings hath thy honor sprong,
     Thy force hath flow'd from babies tongue,
     Whereby thou stopp'st thine en'mies prating
     Bent to revenge and ever-hating.

When I upon the heav'ns do look,
10   Which all from thee their essence took;
        When Moon and Starrs, my thoughts beholdeth,
        Whose life no life but of thee holdeth:

        Then thinck I: Ah, what is this man
        Whom that greate God remember can?
15   And what the race, of him descended,
        It should be ought of God attended?

        For though in lesse than Angells state
        Thou planted hast this earthly mate;
        Yet hast thou made ev'n hym an owner
20   Of glorious crown, and crowning honor.

        Thou placest hym upon all landes
        To rule the workes of thine own handes:
        And so thou hast all things ordained,
        That ev'n his feete, have on them raigned.

25 Thou under his dominion plac't
        Both sheepe and oxen wholy hast;
        And all the beastes for ever breeding,
        Which in the fertill fieldes be feeding.

        The Bird, free-burgesse of the Aire;
30   The Fish, of sea the native heire;
        And what things els of waters traceth
        The unworn pathes, his rule embraceth.
                O Lord, that rul'st our mortall lyne,
                How through the world thi name doth shine!
                            (c. 1584)

Sir Francis Bacon

(1561–1626)

Of Studies

Studies serve for delight, for ornament, and for ability. Their chief use for delight is in privateness and retiring; for ornament, is in discourse; and for ability, is in the judgement and disposition of business. For expert men can execute, and perhaps judge of particulars, one by one; but the general counsels, and the plots and marshalling of affairs, come best from those that are learned. To spend too much time in studies is sloth; to use them too much for ornament is affectation; to make judgement wholly by their rules is the humour of a scholar. They perfect nature, and are perfected by experience; for natural abilities are like natural plants, that need proyning by study; and studies themselves do give forth directions too much at large, except they be bounded in by experience. Crafty men contemn studies; simple men admire them; and wise men use them: for they teach not their own use; but that is a wisdom without them and above them, won by observation. Read not to contradict and confute; nor to believe and take for granted; nor to find talk and discourse; but to weigh and consider. Some books are to be tasted, others to be swallowed, and some few to be chewed and digested: that is, some books are to be read only in parts; others to be read, but not curiously; and some few to be read wholly, and with diligence and attention. Some books also may be read by deputy, and extracts made of them by others; but that would be only in the less important arguments, and the meaner sort of books; else distilled books are like common distilled waters, flashy things. Reading maketh a full man; conference a ready man; and writing an exact man. And therefore, if a man write little, he had need have a great memory; if he confer little, he had need have a present wit; and if he read little, he had need have much cunning, to seem to know that he doth not. Histories make men wise; poets witty; the mathematics subtile; natural philosophy deep; moral grave; logic and rhetoric able to contend. *Abeunt studia in mores*. Nay, there is no stond or impediment in the wit, but may be wrought out by fit studies: like as diseases of the body may have appropriate exercises. Bowling is good for the stone and reins; shooting for the lungs and breast; gentle walking for the stomach; riding for the head; and the like. So if a man's wit be wandering, let him study the mathematics; for in demonstrations, if his wit be called away never so little, he must begin again: if his wit be not apt to distinguish or find differences, let him study the schoolmen; for they are *cymini sectores*: if he be not apt to beat over matters, and to call one thing to prove and illustrate another, let him study the lawyers' cases: so every defect of the mind may have a special receipt.

(1597–1625)

William Shakespeare

(1564–1616)

From *The Sonnets*

18

Shall I compare thee to a summer's day?
Thou art more lovely and more temperate:
Rough winds do shake the darling buds of May,
And summer's lease hath all too short a date:
5   Sometime too hot the eye of heaven shines,
And often is his gold complexion dimmed;
And every fair from fair sometimes declines,
By chance or nature's changing course untrimmed:
But thy eternal summer shall not fade
10   Nor lose possession of that fair thou ow'st,
Nor shall Death brag thou wand'rest in his shade,
When in eternal lines to time thou grow'st.
     So long as men can breathe or eyes can see,
     So long lives this, and this gives life to thee.

55

Not marble, nor the gilded monuments
Of princes, shall outlive this pow'rful rhyme;
But you shall shine more bright in these contents
Than unswept stone, besmeared with sluttish time.
5 When wasteful war shall statues overturn,
And broils root out the work of masonry,
Nor Mars his sword nor war's quick fire shall burn
The living record of your memory.
'Gainst death and all-oblivious enmity
10 Shall you pace forth; your praise shall still find room
Even in the eyes of all posterity
That wear this world out to the ending doom.
    So, till the judgment that yourself arise,
    You live in this, and dwell in lovers' eyes.

73

That time of year thou mayst in me behold
When yellow leaves, or none, or few, do hang
Upon those boughs which shake against the cold,
Bare ruined choirs where late the sweet birds sang.
5 In me thou see'st the twilight of such day
As after sunset fadeth in the west,
Which by and by black night doth take away,
Death's second self that seals up all in rest.
In me thou see'st the glowing of such fire
10 That on the ashes of his youth doth lie,
As the deathbed whereon it must expire,
Consumed with that which it was nourished by.
    This thou perceiv'st, which makes thy love more strong
    To love that well which thou must leave ere long.

116

Let me not to the marriage of true minds
Admit impediments. Love is not love
Which alters when it alteration finds,
Or bends with the remover to remove.
5 O no! it is an ever-fixèd mark
That looks on tempests and is never shaken;
It is the star to every wand'ring bark,
Whose worth's unknown, although his height be taken.
Love's not Time's fool, though rosy lips and cheeks
10 Within his bending sickle's compass come.
Love alters not with his brief hours and weeks,
But bears it out even to the edge of doom.
    If this be error, and upon me proved,
    I never writ, nor no man ever loved.

130

My mistress' eyes are nothing like the sun;
Coral is far more red than her lips' red;
If snow be white, why then her breasts are dun;
If hairs be wires, black wires grow on her head.
5 I have seen roses damasked, red and white,
But no such roses see I in her cheeks;
And in some perfumes is there more delight
Than in the breath that from my mistress reeks.
I love to hear her speak, yet well I know
10 That music hath a far more pleasing sound;
I grant I never saw a goddess go;
My mistress, when she walks, treads on the ground.
    And yet, by heaven, I think my love as rare
    As any she belied with false compare.

(c. 1593–1600)

From *As You Like It*

(II. vii. 139–66)

                    All the world's a stage,
140 And all the men and women merely players.
They have their exits and their entrances,
And one man in his time plays many parts,
His acts being seven ages. At first the infant,
Mewling and puking in the nurse's arms.
145 Then, the whining school-boy with his satchel
And shining morning face, creeping like snail
Unwillingly to school. And then the lover,
Sighing like furnace, with a woeful ballad
Made to his mistress' eyebrow. Then, a soldier,
150 Full of strange oaths, and bearded like the pard,
Jealous in honour, sudden, and quick in quarrel,
Seeking the bubble reputation
Even in the cannon's mouth. And then, the justice,
In fair round belly, with good capon lin'd,
155 With eyes severe, and beard of formal cut,
Full of wise saws, and modern instances,
And so he plays his part. The sixth age shifts
Into the lean and slipper'd pantaloon,
With spectacles on nose, and pouch on side,
160 His youthful hose well sav'd, a world too wide
For his shrunk shank, and his big manly voice,
Turning again toward childish treble, pipes
And whistles in his sound. Last scene of all,
That ends this strange eventful history,
165 Is second childishness and mere oblivion,
Sans teeth, sans eyes, sans taste, sans everything.

(1599)

Psalm 8: Several Early Versions

John Wycliffe and His Followers—Two Versions

Lord, oure Lord; hou myche merueilous is thi name in al the erthe. For rerid vp is thi grete doing, ouer heuenes. Of the mouth of vnspekende childer and soukende thou performedist preising, for thin enemys; that thou destroȝe the enemy and the veniere. For I shal see thin heuenes, the werkis of thi fingris; the mone and the sterris, that thou hast foundid. What is a man, that myndeful thou art of hym; or the son of man, for thou visitist hym? Thou lassedest hym a litil lasse fro aungelis; with glorie and worshipe thou crounedest hym, and settist hym ouer the werkis of thin hondys. Alle thingus thou leidist vnder his feet, shep and oxen alle; ferthermor and the bestis of the feeld; the foulis of heuene, and the fishis of the se; that thurȝ gon the sties of the se. Lord, oure Lord; hou myche merueilous is thi name in al erthe.

✿ ✿ ✿ ✿ ✿

Lord, *thou art* oure Lord; thi name is ful wonderful in al erthe. For thi greet doyng is reisid, aboue heuenes. Of the mouth of ȝonge children, not spekynge and soukynge mylk, thou madist perfitli heriyng, for thin enemyes; that thou destrie the enemy and avengere. For Y schal se thin heuenes, the werkis of thi fyngris; the moone and sterris, whiche thou hast foundid. What is a man, that thou art myndeful of hym; ethir the sone of a virgyn, for thou visitist hym? Thou hast maad hym a litil lesse than aungels; thou hast corouned hym with glorie and onour, and hast ordeyned hym aboue the werkis of thin hondis. Thou hast maad suget alle thingis vndur hise feet; alle scheep and oxis, ferthermore and the beestis of the feeld; the briddis of the eir, and the fischis of the see; that passen bi the pathis of the see. Lord, *thou art* oure Lord; thi name is wondurful in al erthe.

(late 14th century)

Miles Coverdale

O LORDE oure governoure: how wonderfull is thy name in all the worlde; how excellent is thy glory above the heavens! Out of the mouth of the very babes & sucklinges thou hast ordened prayse, because of thine enemies, that thou mightest destroye the enemie and the avenger. For I considre thy heavens, even the worke off thy fyngers: the Moone and the starres which thou hast made. Oh what is man, that thou art so myndfull of him; ether the sonne of man that thou visitest him; After thou haddest for a season made him lower then the angels, thou crownedest him with honor & glory. Thou hast set him above the workes off thy hondes: then hast put all thinges in subieccion under his fete. All shepe and oxen, yee and the beastes of the felde. The foules of the ayre: the fysh of the see, and what so walketh thorow the wayes of the see. O LORDE oure governoure, how wonderfull is thy name in all the worlde.

(1535)

The Geneva Bible

1   O Lord our Lord, how excellent is thy Name in all the worlde! which hast set thy glorie above the heavens.

2   Out of the mouth of babes and suckelings hast thou ordeined strength, because of thine enemies, that thou mightest stil the enemie and the avenger.

3   When I beholde thine heavens, even the workes of thy fingers, the moone and the starres which thou hast ordeined,

4   What is man, say I, that thou art mindful of him? and the sonne of man, that thou visitest him?

5   For thou hast made him a little lower then God, and crowned him with glorie and worship.

6   Thou hast made him to have dominion in the workes of thine hands: thou hast put all things under his fete:

7   All shepe and oxen: yea, and the beastes of the field:

8   The foules of the aire, and the fish of the sea, & that which passeth through the paths of the seas.

9   O Lord our Lord, how excellent is thy Name in all the worlde!

(1560)

The Bishops' Bible

1   O God our Lorde, howe excellent is thy name in all the earth; for that thou has set thy glory above the heavens.

2   Out of the mouth of very babes and sucklinges thou hast layde the foundation of thy strength for thyne adversaries sake: that thou mightest styll the enemie and the avenger.

3   For I will consider thy heavens, even the workes of thy fingers: the moone and the starres whiche thou hast ordayned.

4   What is man that thou art myndfull of him; and the sonne of man that thou visitest hym;

5   Thou hast made hym somthyng inferiour to angels: thou hast crowned him with glory and worship.

6   Thou makest hym to have dominion of the workes of thy handes: and thou hast put all thinges [in subiection] under his feete,

7   All sheepe and oxen, & also the beastes of the fielde: the foules of the ayre, and the fishe of the sea, and whatsoever swymmeth in the seas.

8   O God our Lorde: howe excellent great is thy name in all the earth.

(1586)

The Douay Version

1   Unto the end, for the presses: a psalm for David.

2   O LORD our Lord, how admirable is thy name in the whole earth! For thy magnificence is elevated above the heavens.

3   Out of the mouth of infants and of sucklings thou hast perfected praise, because of thy enemies, that thou mayst destroy the enemy and the avenger.

4   For I will behold thy heavens, the works of thy fingers: the moon and the stars which thou hast founded.

5   What is man that thou art mindful of him? or the son of man that thou visitest him?

6   Thou hast made him a little less than the Angels, thou hast crowned him with glory and honour:

7   and hast set him over the works of thy hands.

8   Thou hast subjected all things under his feet, all sheep and oxen: moreover the beasts also of the fields.

9   The birds of the air, and the fishes of the sea, that pass through the paths of the sea.

10   O Lord our Lord, how admirable is thy name in all the earth!

(1609)

The Authorized (King James) Version

O LORD our Lord,
How excellent is thy name in all the earth!
Who hast set thy glory above the heavens.
Out of the mouth of babes and sucklings hast thou ordained strength,
5 Because of the thine enemies,
That thou mightest still the enemie and the avenger.
When I consider thy heavens, the worke of thy fingers,
The moone and the starres which thou hast ordained;
What is man, that thou art mindfull of him?
10 And the sonne of man, that thou visitest him?
For thou hast made him a little lower then the Angels;
And hast crowned him with glory and honour.
Thou madest him to have dominion over the workes of thy hands;
Thou hast put all things under his feete.
15 All sheepe and oxen,
Yea and the beasts of the field.
The foule of the aire, and the fish of the sea,
And whatsoever passeth through the paths of the seas.
O LORD our Lord,
20 How excellent is thy name in all the earth!

(1611)

From *The Whole Booke of Psalmes*

Collected into English meeter, by Thomas Sternhold, John Hopkins, and others

O God our Lord, how wonderfull
    are thy works every where,
Whose fame surmounts in dignity,
    above the heavens cleere!

5   Even by the mouthes of sucking babes
    thou wilt confound thy foes:
For in those babes thy might is seene,
    thy graces they disclose.

And when I see the heavens hye,
10   the works of thine owne hand:
The sun the moone, and eke the stars,
    in order as they stand: then

What thing is man (Lord) thinke I
    that thou dost him remember?
15   Or what is mans posterity,
    that thou dost him consider?

For thou hast made him little lesse,
    then Angels in degree.
And thou hast crowned him also,
20   with glory and dignity.

Thou hast prefer'd him to be Lord,
    of all thy works of wonder:
And at his feet hast set all things,
    that he should keepe them under.

25   As sheepe & neat, and al beasts else,
    that in the field doe feed:
Foules of the ayre, fish in the sea,
    and all that therein breed.

Therefore must I say once againe,
30   O God thou art our Lord,
How famous and how wonderfull,
    are thy works through the world.

                    (1633)

The Bay Psalm Book

1 O Lord our God in all the earth
    how's thy name wondrous great!
  who hast thy glorious majesty
    above the heavens set.
2 out of the mouth of sucking babes
    thy strength thou didst ordeine,
  that thou mightst still the enemy,
    and them that thee disdaine.
3 when I thy fingers work, thy Heav'ns,
    the moone and starres consider
4 which thou hast set. What's wretched man
    that thou dost him remember?
  or what's the Son of man, that thus
    him visited thou hast?
5 For next to Angells, thou hast him
    a litle lower plac't
  and hast with glory crowned him,
    and comely majesty:
6 And on thy works hast given him,
    lordly authority.
7 All hast thou put under his feet;
    all sheep and oxen, yea
8 and beasts of field. Foules of the ayre,
    and fishes of the sea,
  and all that passe through paths of seas.
9 O Jehovah our Lord,
  how wondrously-magnificent
    is thy name through the world?

(1640)

From The Bible–The Authorized (King James) Version

From *Genesis*

CHAPTER 1

IN the beginning God created the heaven and the earth.

2 And the earth was without form, and void; and darkness *was* upon the face of the deep. And the Spirit of God moved upon the face of the waters.

 3 And God said, Let there be light: and there was light.

4 And God saw the light, that *it was* good: and God divided the light from the darkness.

5 And God called the light Day, and the darkness he called Night. And the evening and the morning were the first day.

6 And God said, Let there be a firmament in the midst of the waters, and let it divide the waters from the waters.

7 And God made the firmament, and divided the waters which *were* under the firmament from the waters which *were* above the firmament: and it was so.

8 And God called the firmament Heaven. And the evening and the morning were the second day.

9 And God said, Let the waters under the heaven be gathered together unto one place, and let the dry *land* appear: and it was so.

10 And God called the dry *land* Earth; and the gathering together of the waters called he Seas: and God saw that *it was* good.

11 And God said, Let the earth bring forth grass, the herb yielding seed, *and* the fruit tree yielding fruit after his kind, whose seed *is* in itself, upon the earth: and it was so.

12 And the earth brought forth grass, *and* herb yielding seed after his kind, and the tree yielding fruit, whose seed *was* in itself, after his kind: and God saw that *it was* good.

13 And the evening and the morning were the third day.

14 And God said, Let there be lights in the firmament of the heaven to divide the day from the night; and let them be for signs, and for seasons, and for days, and years:

15 And let them be for lights in the firmament of the heaven to give light upon the earth: and it was so.

16 And God made two great lights; the greater light to rule the day, and the lesser light to rule the night: *he made* the stars also.

17 And God set them in the firmament of the heaven to give light upon the earth,

18 And to rule over the day and over the night, and to divide the light from the darkness: and God saw that *it was* good.

19 And the evening and the morning were the fourth day.

20 And God said, Let the waters bring forth abundantly the moving creature that hath life, and fowl *that* may fly above the earth in the open firmament of heaven.

21 And God created great whales, and every living creature that moveth, which the waters brought forth abundantly, after their kind, and every winged fowl after his kind: and God saw that *it was* good.

22 And God blessed them, saying, Be fruitful, and multiply, and fill the waters in the seas, and let fowl multiply in the earth.

23 And the evening and the morning were the fifth day.

24 And God said, Let the earth bring forth the living creature after his kind, cattle, and creeping thing, and beast of the earth after his kind: and it was so.

25 And God made the beast of the earth after his kind, and cattle after their kind, and every thing that creepeth upon the earth after his kind: and God saw that *it was* good.

26 And God said, Let us make man in our image, after our likeness: and let them have dominion over the fish of the sea, and over the fowl of the air, and over the cattle, and over all the earth, and over every creeping thing that creepeth upon the earth.

27 So God created man in his *own* image, in the image of God created he him; male and female created he them.

28 And God blessed them, and God said unto them, Be fruitful, and multiply, and replenish the earth, and subdue it: and have dominion over the fish of the sea, and over the fowl of the air, and over every living thing that moveth upon the earth.

29 And God said, Behold, I have given you every herb bearing seed, which *is* upon the face of all the earth, and every tree, in the which *is* the fruit of a tree yielding seed; to you it shall be for meat.

30 And to every beast of the earth, and to every fowl of the air, and to every thing that creepeth upon the earth, wherein *there is* life, *I have given* every green herb for meat: and it was so.

31 And God saw every thing that he had made, and, behold, *it was* very good. And the evening and the morning were the sixth day.

CHAPTER 2

T HUS the heavens and the earth were finished, and all the host of them.

2 And on the seventh day God ended his work which he had made; and he rested on the seventh day from all his work which he had made.

3 And God blessed the seventh day, and sanctified it: because that in it he had rested from all his work which God created and made.

4 These *are* the generations of the heavens and of the earth when they were created, in the day that the LORD God made the earth and the heavens,

5 And every plant of the field before it was in the earth, and every herb of the field before it grew: for the LORD God had not caused it to rain upon the earth, and *there was* not a man to till the ground.

6 But there went up a mist from the earth, and watered the whole face of the ground.

7 And the LORD God formed man *of* the dust of the ground, and breathed into his nostrils the breath of life; and man became a living soul.

8 And the LORD God planted a garden eastward in Eden; and there he put the man whom he had formed.

9 And out of the ground made the LORD God to grow every tree that is pleasant to the sight, and good for food; the tree of life also in the midst of the garden, and the tree of knowledge of good and evil.

10 And a river went out of Eden to water the garden; and from thence it was parted, and became into four heads.

11 The name of the first *is* Pison; that *is* it which compasseth the whole land of Havilah, where *there is* gold;

12 And the gold of that land *is* good; there *is* bdellium and the onyx stone.

13 And the name of the second river *is* Gihon: the same *is* it that compasseth the whole land of Ethiopia.

14 And the name of the third river *is* Hiddekel: that *is* it which goeth toward the east of Assyria. And the fourth river *is* Euphrates.

15 And the LORD God took the man, and put him into the garden of Eden to dress it and to keep it.

16 And the LORD God commanded the man, saying, Of every tree of the garden thou mayest freely eat:

17 But of the tree of the knowledge of good and evil, thou shalt not eat of it: for in the day that thou eatest thereof thou shalt surely die.

18 And the LORD God said, *It is* not good that the man should be alone; I will make him an help meet for him.

19 And out of the ground the LORD God formed every beast of the field, and every fowl of the air; and brought *them* unto Adam to see what he would call them: and whatsoever Adam called every living creature, that *was* the name thereof.

20 And Adam gave names to all cattle, and to the fowl of the air, and to every beast of the field; but for Adam there was not found an help meet for him.

21 And the LORD God caused a deep sleep to fall upon Adam, and he slept: and he took one of his ribs, and closed up the flesh instead thereof;

22 And the rib, which the LORD God had taken from man, made he a woman, and brought her unto the man.

23 And Adam said, This *is* now bone of my bones, and flesh of my flesh: she shall be called Woman, because she was taken out of Man.

24 Therefore shall a man leave his father and his mother, and shall cleave unto his wife: and they shall be one flesh.

25 And they were both naked, the man and his wife, and were not ashamed.

CHAPTER 3

NOW the serpent was more subtil than any beast of the field which the LORD God had made. And he said unto the woman, Yea, hath God said, Ye shall not eat of every tree of the garden?

2 And the woman said unto the serpent, We may eat of the fruit of the trees of the garden:

3 But of the fruit of the tree which *is* in the midst of the garden, God hath said, Ye shall not eat of it, neither shall ye touch it, lest ye die.

4 And the serpent said unto the woman, Ye shall not surely die:

5 For God doth know that in the day ye eat thereof, then your eyes shall be opened, and ye shall be as gods, knowing good and evil.

6 And when the woman saw that the tree *was* good for food, and that it *was* pleasant to the eyes, and a tree to be desired to make *one* wise, she took of the fruit thereof, and did eat, and gave also unto her husband with her; and he did eat.

7 And the eyes of them both were opened, and they knew that they *were* naked; and they sewed fig leaves together, and made themselves aprons.

8 And they heard the voice of the LORD God walking in the garden in the cool of the day: and Adam and his wife hid themselves from the presence of the LORD God amongst the trees of the garden.

9 And the LORD God called unto Adam, and said unto him, Where *art* thou?

10 And he said, I heard thy voice in the garden, and I was afraid, because I *was* naked; and I hid myself.

11 And he said, Who told thee that thou *wast* naked? Hast thou eaten of the tree, whereof I commanded thee that thou shouldest not eat?

12 And the man said, The woman whom thou gavest *to be* with me, she gave me of the tree, and I did eat.

13 And the LORD God said unto the woman, What *is* this *that* thou hast done? And the woman said, The serpent beguiled me, and I did eat.

14 And the LORD God said unto the serpent, Because thou hast done this, thou art cursed above all cattle, and above every beast of the field; upon thy belly shalt thou go, and dust shalt thou eat all the days of thy life:

15 And I will put enmity between thee and the woman, and between thy seed and her seed; it shall bruise thy head, and thou shalt bruise his heel.

16 Unto the woman he said, I will greatly multiply thy sorrow and thy conception; in sorrow thou shalt bring forth children; and thy desire *shall be* to thy husband, and he shall rule over thee.

17 And unto Adam he said, Because thou hast hearkened unto the voice of thy wife, and hast eaten of the tree, of which I commanded thee, saying, Thou shalt not eat of it: cursed *is* the ground for thy sake; in sorrow shalt thou eat of it all the days of thy life;

18 Thorns also and thistles shall it bring forth to thee; and thou shalt eat the herb of the field;

19 In the sweat of thy face shalt thou eat bread, till thou return unto the ground; for out of it wast thou taken; for dust thou *art*, and unto dust shalt thou return.

20 And Adam called his wife's name Eve; because she was the mother of all living.

21 Unto Adam also and to his wife did the LORD God make coats of skins, and clothed them.

22 And the LORD God said, Behold, the man is become as one of us, to know good and evil: and now, lest he put forth his hand, and take also of the tree of life, and eat, and live for ever:

23 Therefore the LORD God sent him forth from the garden of Eden, to till the ground from whence he was taken.

24 So he drove out the man; and he placed at the east of the garden of Eden Cherubims, and a flaming sword which turned every way, to keep the way of the tree of life.

CHAPTER 4

AND Adam knew Eve his wife; and she conceived, and bare Cain, and said, I have gotten a man from the LORD.

2 And she again bare his brother Abel. And Abel was a keeper of sheep, but Cain was a tiller of the ground.

3 And in process of time it came to pass, that Cain brought of the fruit of the ground an offering unto the LORD.

4 And Abel, he also brought of the firstlings of his flock and of the fat thereof. And the LORD had respect unto Abel and to his offering:

5 But unto Cain and to his offering he had not respect. And Cain was very wroth, and his countenance fell.

6 And the LORD said unto Cain, Why art thou wroth? and why is thy countenance fallen?

7 If thou doest well, shalt thou not be accepted? and if thou doest not well, sin lieth at the door. And unto thee *shall be* his desire, and thou shalt rule over him.

8 And Cain talked with Abel his brother: and it came to pass, when they were in the field, that Cain rose up against Abel his brother, and slew him.

9 And the LORD said unto Cain, Where *is* Abel thy brother? And he said, I know not: *Am* I my brother's keeper?

10 And he said, What hast thou done? the voice of thy brother's blood crieth unto me from the ground.

11 And now *art* thou cursed from the earth, which hath opened her mouth to receive thy brother's blood from thy hand;

12 When thou tillest the ground, it shall not henceforth yield unto thee her strength; a fugitive and a vagabond shalt thou be in the earth.

13 And Cain said unto the LORD, My punishment is greater than I can bear.

14 Behold, thou hast driven me out this day from the face of the earth; and from thy face shall I be hid; and I shall be a fugitive and a vagabond in the earth; and it shall come to pass, *that* every one that findeth me shall slay me.

15 And the LORD said unto him, Therefore whosoever slayeth Cain, vengeance shall be taken on him sevenfold. And the LORD set a mark upon Cain, lest any finding him should kill him.

16 And Cain went out from the presence of the LORD, and dwelt in the land of Nod, on the east of Eden.

☆ ☆ ☆ ☆ ☆

CHAPTER 6

AND it came to pass, when men began to multiply on the face of the earth, and daughters were born unto them,

2 That the sons of God saw the daughters of men that they *were* fair; and they took them wives of all which they chose.

3 And the LORD said, My spirit shall not always strive with man, for that he also *is* flesh: yet his days shall be an hundred and twenty years.

4 There were giants in the earth in those days; and also after that, when the sons of God came in unto the daughters of men, and they bare *children* to them, the same *became* mighty men which *were* of old, men of renown.

5 And God saw that the wickedness of man *was* great in the earth, and *that* every imagination of the thoughts of his heart *was* only evil continually.

6 And it repented the LORD that he had made man on the earth, and it grieved him at his heart.

7 And the LORD said, I will destroy man whom I have created from the face of the earth; both man, and beast, and the creeping thing, and the fowls of the air; for it repenteth me that I have made them.

8 But Noah found grace in the eyes of the LORD.

9 These *are* the generations of Noah: Noah was a just man *and* perfect in his generations, and Noah walked with God.

10 And Noah begat three sons, Shem, Ham, and Japheth.

11 The earth also was corrupt before God, and the earth was filled with violence.

12 And God looked upon the earth, and, behold, it was corrupt; for all flesh had corrupted his way upon the earth.

13 And God said unto Noah, The end of all flesh is come before me; for the earth is filled with violence through them; and, behold, I will destroy them with the earth.

14 Make thee an ark of gopher wood; rooms shalt thou make in the ark, and shalt pitch it within and without with pitch.

15 And this *is the fashion* which thou shalt make it *of*: The length of the ark *shall be* three hundred cubits, the breadth of it fifty cubits, and the height of it thirty cubits.

16 A window shalt thou make to the ark, and in a cubit shalt thou finish it above; and the door of the ark shalt thou set in the side thereof; *with* lower, second, and third *stories* shalt thou make it.

17 And, behold, I, even I, do bring a flood of waters upon the earth, to destroy all flesh, wherein *is* the breath of life, from under heaven; *and* every thing that *is* in the earth shall die.

18 But with thee will I establish my covenant; and thou shalt come into the ark, thou, and thy sons, and thy wife, and thy sons' wives with thee.

19 And of every living thing of all flesh, two of every *sort* shalt thou bring into the ark, to keep *them* alive with thee; they shall be male and female.

20 Of fowls after their kind, and of cattle after their kind, of every creeping thing of the earth after his kind, two of every *sort* shall come unto thee, to keep *them* alive.

21 And take thou unto thee of all food that is eaten, and thou shalt gather *it* to thee; and it shall be for food for thee, and for them.

22 Thus did Noah; according to all that God commanded him, so did he.

CHAPTER 7

AND the LORD said unto Noah, Come thou and all thy house into the ark; for thee have I seen righteous before me in this generation.

2 Of every clean beast thou shalt take to thee by sevens, the male and his female: and of beasts that *are* not clean by two, the male and his female.

3 Of fowls also of the air by sevens, the male and the female; to keep seed alive upon the face of all the earth.

4 For yet seven days, and I will cause it to rain upon the earth forty days and forty nights; and every living substance that I have made will I destroy from off the face of the earth.

5 And Noah did according unto all that the LORD commanded him.

6 And Noah was six hundred years old when the flood of waters was upon the earth.

7 And Noah went in, and his sons, and his wife, and his sons' wives with him, into the ark, because of the waters of the flood.

8 Of clean beasts, and of beasts that *are* not clean, and of fowls, and of every thing that creepeth upon the earth,

9 There went in two and two unto Noah into the ark, the male and the female, as God had commanded Noah.

10 And it came to pass after seven days, that the waters of the flood were upon the earth.

11 In the six hundredth year of Noah's life, in the second month, the seventeenth day of the month, the same day were all the fountains of the great deep broken up, and the windows of heaven were opened.

12 And the rain was upon the earth forty days and forty nights.

13 In the selfsame day entered Noah, and Shem, and Ham, and Japheth, the sons of Noah, and Noah's wife, and the three wives of his sons with them, into the ark;

14 They, and every beast after his kind, and all the cattle after their kind, and every creeping thing that creepeth upon the earth after his kind, and every fowl after his kind, every bird of every sort.

15 And they went in unto Noah into the ark, two and two of all flesh, wherein *is* the breath of life.

16 And they that went in, went in male and female of all flesh, as God had commanded him: and the LORD shut him in.

17 And the flood was forty days upon the earth; and the waters increased, and bare up the ark, and it was lift up above the earth.

18 And the waters prevailed, and were increased greatly upon the earth; and the ark went upon the face of the waters.

19 And the waters prevailed exceedingly upon the earth; and all the high hills, that *were* under the whole heaven, were covered.

20 Fifteen cubits upward did the waters prevail; and the mountains were covered.

21 And all flesh died that moved upon the earth, both of fowl, and of cattle, and of beast, and of every creeping thing that creepeth upon the earth, and every man:

22 All in whose nostrils *was* the breath of life, of all that *was* in the dry *land*, died.

23 And every living substance was destroyed which was upon the face of the ground, both man, and cattle, and the creeping things, and the fowl of the heaven; and they were destroyed from the earth: and Noah only remained *alive*, and they that *were* with him in the ark.

24 And the waters prevailed upon the earth an hundred and fifty days.

CHAPTER 8

AND God remembered Noah, and every living thing, and all the cattle that *was* with him in the ark: and God made a wind to pass over the earth, and the waters assuaged;

2 The fountains also of the deep and the windows of heaven were stopped, and the rain from heaven was restrained;

3 And the waters returned from off the earth continually: and after the end of the hundred and fifty days the waters were abated.

4 And the ark rested in the seventh month, on the seventeenth day of the month, upon the mountains of Ararat.

5 And the waters decreased continually until the tenth month: in the tenth *month*, on the first *day* of the month, were the tops of the mountains seen.

6 And it came to pass at the end of forty days, that Noah opened the window of the ark which he had made:

7 And he sent forth a raven, which went forth to and fro, until the waters were dried up from off the earth.

8 Also he sent forth a dove from him, to see if the waters were abated from off the face of the ground;

9 But the dove found no rest for the sole of her foot, and she returned unto him into the ark, for the waters *were* on the face of the whole earth: then he put forth his hand, and took her, and pulled her in unto him into the ark.

10 And he stayed yet other seven days; and again he sent forth the dove out of the ark;

11 And the dove came in to him in the evening; and, lo, in her mouth *was* an olive leaf pluckt off: so Noah knew that the waters were abated from off the earth.

12 And he stayed yet other seven days; and sent forth the dove; which returned not again unto him any more.

13 And it came to pass in the six hundredth and first year, in the first *month*, the first *day* of the month, the waters were dried up from off the earth: and Noah removed the covering of the ark, and looked, and, behold, the face of the ground was dry.

Psalm 23

THE LORD *is* my shepherd; I shall not want.

2 He maketh me to lie down in green pastures: he leadeth me beside the still waters.

3 He restoreth my soul: he leadeth me in the paths of righteousness for his name's sake.

4 Yea, though I walk through the valley of the shadow of death, I will fear no evil: for thou *art* with me; thy rod and thy staff they comfort me.

5 Thou preparest a table before me in the presence of mine enemies: thou anointest my head with oil; my cup runneth over.

6 Surely goodness and mercy shall follow me all the days of my life; and I will dwell in the house of the LORD for ever.

Luke 10:23–37 (The Parable of the Good Samaritan)

23 And he turned him unto *his* disciples, and said privately, Blessed *are* the eyes which see the things that ye see:

24 For I tell you, that many prophets and kings have desired to see those things which ye see, and have not seen *them*; and to hear those things which ye hear, and have not heard *them*.

25 And, behold, a certain lawyer stood up, and tempted him, saying, Master, what shall I do to inherit eternal life?

26 He said unto him, What is written in the law? how readest thou?

27 And he answering said, Thou shalt love the Lord thy God with all thy heart, and with all thy soul, and with all thy strength, and with all thy mind; and thy neighbour as thyself.

28 And he said unto him, Thou hast answered right: this do, and thou shalt live.

29 But he, willing to justify himself, said unto Jesus, And who is my neighbour?

30 And Jesus answering said, A certain *man* went down from Jerusalem to Jericho, and fell among thieves, which stripped him of his raiment, and wounded *him*, and departed, leaving *him* half dead.

31 And by chance there came down a certain priest that way; and when he saw him, he passed by on the other side.

32 And likewise a Levite, when he was at the place, came and looked *on him*, and passed by on the other side.

33 But a certain Samaritan, as he journeyed, came where he was: and when he saw him, he had compassion *on him*,

34 And went to *him*, and bound up his wounds, pouring in oil and wine, and set him on his own beast, and brought him to an inn, and took care of him.

35 And on the morrow when he departed, he took out two pence, and gave *them* to the host, and said unto him, Take care of him; and whatsoever thou spendest more, when I come again, I will repay thee.

36 Which now of these three, thinkest thou, was neighbour unto him that fell among the thieves?

37 And he said, He that shewed mercy on him. Then said Jesus unto him, Go, and do thou likewise.

(1611)

John Donne

(1572–1631)

Meditation 17

Nunc lento sonitu dicunt, morieris

Now, this bell tolling softly for another, says to me, Thou must die.

Perchance he for whom this bell tolls may be so ill as that he knows not it tolls for him; and perchance I may think myself so much better than I am as that they who are about me and see my state may have caused it to toll for me, and I know not that. The church is catholic, universal, so are all her actions: all that she does belongs to all. When she baptizes a child, that action concerns me; for that child is thereby connected to that body which is my head too and ingrafted into that body whereof I am a member. And when she buries a man, that action concerns me. All mankind is of one author, and is one volume; when one man dies, one chapter is not torn out of the book, but translated into a better language; and every chapter must be so translated. God employs several translators; some pieces are translated by age, some by sickness, some by war, some by justice; but God's hand is in every translation, and his hand shall bind up all our scattered leaves again for that library where every book shall lie open to one another. As therefore the bell that rings to a sermon calls not upon the preacher only but upon the congregation to come, so this bell calls us all; but how much more me who am brought so near the door by this sickness! There was a contention as far as a suit—in which piety and dignity, religion and estimation, were mingled—which of the religious orders should ring to prayers first in the morning; and it was determined that they should ring first that rose earliest. If we understand aright the dignity of this bell that tolls for our evening prayer, we would be glad to make it ours by rising early, in that application, that it might be ours as well as his, whose indeed it is. The bell doth toll for him that thinks it doth; and though it intermit again, yet from that minute that that occasion wrought upon him he is united to God. Who casts not up his eye to the sun when it rises? but who takes off his eye from a comet when that breaks out? Who bends not his ear to any bell which upon any occasion rings? but who can remove it from that bell which is passing a piece of himself out of this world? No man is an island entire of itself; every man is a piece of the continent, a part of the main. If a clod be washed away by the sea, Europe is the less, as well as if a promontory were, as well as if a manor of thy friend's or of thine own were. Any man's death diminishes me, because I am involved in mankind, and therefore never send to know for whom the bell tolls; it tolls for thee. Neither can we call this a begging of misery or a borrowing of misery, as though we were not miserable enough of ourselves but must fetch in more from the next house, in taking upon us the misery of our neighbors. Truly it were an excusable covetousness if we did, for affliction is a treasure, and scarce any man hath enough of it. No man hath affliction enough that is not matured and ripened by it and made fit for God by that affliction. If a man carry treasure in bullion or in a wedge of gold and have none coined into current money, his treasure will not defray him as he travels. Tribulation is treasure in the nature of it, but it is not current money in the use of it, except we get nearer and nearer our home, heaven, by it. Another man may be sick too, and sick to death, and this affliction may lie in his bowels as gold in a mine and be of no use to him; but this bell that tells me of his affliction digs out and applies that gold to me, if by this consideration of another's danger I take mine own into contemplation and so secure myself by making my recourse to my God, who is our only security.

(1623)

From *Holy Sonnets*

10

Death, be not proud, though some have callèd thee
Mighty and dreadful, for thou art not so;
For those whom thou think'st thou dost overthrow
Die not, poor Death, nor yet canst thou kill me.
5 From rest and sleep, which but thy pictures be,
Much pleasure; then from thee much more must flow;
And soonest our best men with thee do go,
Rest of their bones and souls' delivery.
Thou'rt slave to fate, chance, kings, and desperate men,
10 And dost with poison, war, and sickness dwell;
And poppy or charms can make us sleep as well
And better than thy stroke. Why swell'st thou then?
One short sleep past, we wake eternally,
And Death shall be no more: Death, thou shalt die.

(1633)

14

Batter my heart, three person'd God; for, you
As yet but knocke, breathe, shine, and seeke to mend;
That I may rise, and stand, o'erthrow mee, and bend
Your force, to breake, blowe, burn and make me new.
5   I, like an usurpt towne, to another due,
Labour to admit you, but Oh, to no end,
Reason your viceroy in mee, mee should defend,
But is captiv'd, and proves weake or untrue.
Yet dearely I love you, and would be loved faine,
10   But am betroth'd unto your enemie:
Divorce mee, untie, or breake that knot againe,
Take mee to you, imprison mee, for I
Except you enthrall mee, never shall be free,
Nor ever chast, except you ravish mee.

(1633)

A Valediction: Forbidding Mourning

As virtuous men pass mildly away,
    And whisper to their souls to go,
Whilst some of their sad friends do say
    The breath goes now, and some say, No;

5   So let us melt, and make no noise,
    No tear-floods, nor sigh-tempests move,
'Twere profanation of our joys
    To tell the laity our love.

Moving of th' earth brings harms and fears,
10   Men reckon what it did and meant;
But trepidation of the spheres,
    Though greater far, is innocent.

Dull sublunary lovers' love
    (Whose soul is sense) cannot admit
15   Absence, because it doth remove
    Those things which elemented it.

But we by a love so much refined
That our selves know not what it is,
Inter-assuréd of the mind,
20   Care less, eyes, lips, and hands to miss.

Our two souls therefore, which are one,
    Though I must go, endure not yet
A breach, but an expansion,
    Like gold to airy thinness beat.

25 If they be two, they are two so
   As stiff twin compasses are two;
   Thy soul, the fixed foot, makes no show
   To move, but doth, if th' other do.

   And though it in the centre sit,
30   Yet when the other far doth roam,
   It leans and harkens after it,
       And grows erect, as that comes home.

   Such wilt thou be to me, who must
       Like th' other foot, obliquely run;
35 Thy firmness makes my circle just,
       And makes me end where I begun.

                                      (1633)

Ben Jonson
(1573-1637)

On My First Daughter

   Here lies, to each her parents' ruth,
   Mary, the daughter of their youth;
   Yet all heaven's gifts being heaven's due,
   It makes the father less to rue.
5 At six months' end she parted hence
   With safety of her innocence;
   Whose soul heaven's queen, whose name she bears,
   In comfort of her mother's tears,
   Hath placed amongst her virgin-train:
10 Where, while that severed doth remain,
   This grave partakes the fleshly birth;
   Which cover lightly, gentle earth!

                                      (1616)

On My First Son

   Farewell, thou child of my right hand, and joy;
   My sin was too much hope of thee, loved boy:
   Seven years thou'wert lent to me, and I thee pay,
   Exacted by thy fate, on the just day.
5 O could I lose all father now! for why
   Will man lament the state he should envy,
   To have so soon 'scaped world's and flesh's rage,

And, if no other misery, yet age?
Rest in soft peace, and asked, say, "Here doth lie
10 Ben Jonson his best piece of poetry."
For whose sake henceforth all his vows be such
As what he loves may never like too much.

(1616)

Robert Herrick

(1591–1674)

Upon a Child That Died

Here she lies, a pretty bud,
Lately made of flesh and blood,
Who as soon fell fast asleep
As her little eyes did peep.
5 Give her strewings, but not stir
The earth that lightly covers her.

(1648)

George Herbert

(1593–1633)

The Altar

A broken ALTAR, Lord, thy servant reares,
Made of a heart, and cemented with teares:
Whose parts are as thy hand did frame;
No workmans tool hath touch'd the same.
5   A HEART alone
          Is such a stone,
          As nothing but
          Thy pow'r doth cut.
          Wherefore each part
10   Of my hard heart
          Meets in this frame,
          To praise thy Name:
That, if I chance to hold my peace,
These stones to praise thee may not cease.
15 O let thy blessed SACRIFICE be mine,
And sanctifie this ALTAR to be thine.

(1633)

Edmund Waller

(1606–1687)

Go, Lovely Rose

    Go, lovely rose—
Tell her that wastes her time and me
    That now she knows,
When I resemble her to thee,
5   How sweet and fair she seems to be.

    Tell her that's young,
And shuns to have her graces spied,
    That hadst thou sprung
In deserts where no men abide,
10   Thou must have uncommended died.

    Small is the worth
Of beauty from the light retired:
    Bid her come forth,
Suffer herself to be desired,
15   And not blush so to be admired.

    Then die—that she
The common fate of all things rare
    May read in thee:
How small a part of time they share
20   That are so wondrous sweet and fair.
              (1645)

John Milton

(1608–1674)

From *Areopagitica*

I deny not, but that it is of greatest concernment in the Church and Commonwealth, to have a vigilant eye how books demean themselves as well as men; and thereafter to confine, imprison, and do sharpest justice on them as malefactors. For books are not absolutely dead things, but do contain a potency of life in them to be as active as that soul was whose progeny they are; nay, they do preserve as in a vial the purest efficacy and extraction of that living intellect that bred them. I know they are as lively, and as vigorously productive, as those fabulous dragon's teeth; and being sown up and down, may chance to spring up armed men. And yet, on the other hand, unless wariness be used, as good almost kill a man as kill a good book. Who kills a man kills a reasonable creature, God's image; but he who destroys a good book, kills reason itself, kills the image of God, as it were in the eye. Many a man lives a burden to the earth; but a good book is the precious life-blood of a master-spirit, embalmed and treasured up on purpose to a life beyond life. 'Tis true, no age can restore a life, whereof perhaps there is no great loss; and revolutions of ages do not oft recover the loss of a rejected truth, for the want of which whole nations fare the worse.

We should be wary therefore what persecution we raise against the living labours of public men, how we spill that seasoned life of man, preserved and stored up in books; since we see a kind of homicide may be thus committed, sometimes a martyrdom, and if it extend to the whole impression, a kind of massacre; whereof the execution ends not in the slaying of an elemental life, but strikes at that ethereal and fifth essence, the breath of reason itself, slays an immortality rather than a life.

(1644)

On His Blindness

When I consider how my light is spent,
Ere half my days, in this dark world and wide,
And that one talent which is death to hide
Lodged with me useless, though my soul more bent
5   To serve therewith my Maker, and present
My true account, lest he returning chide;
"Doth God exact day-labour, light denied?"
I fondly ask; But Patience, to prevent
That murmur, soon replies: "God doth not need
10 Either man's work or his own gifts; who best
Bear his mild yoke, they serve him best. His state
Is kingly: thousands at his bidding speed
And post o'er land and ocean without rest.
They also serve who only stand and wait."

(c. 1652)

Psalm VIII

Aug. 14, 1653.

O Jehovah, our Lord, how wondrous great
    And glorious is thy name through all the earth!
So as above the Heavens thy praise to set
    Out of the tender mouths of latest birth,

5   Out of the mouths of babes and sucklings thou
    Hast founded strength because of all thy foes,
To stint th'enemy, and slack th'avenger's brow
    That bends his rage thy providence to oppose.

Then I behold thy Heavens, thy Fingers' art,
10   The Moon and Stars which thou so bright hast set.
In the pure firmament, then saith my heart,
        O what is man that thou rememb'rest yet,

And think'st upon him? or of man begot
        That him thou visit'st and of him art found?
15 Scarce be less than Gods, thou mad'st his lot,
        With honour and with state thou hast him crown'd.

O'er the works of thy hand thou mad'st him Lord,
        Thou hast put all under his lordly feet,
All Flocks, and Herds, by thy commanding word,
20   All beasts that in the field or forest meet:

Fowl of the Heavens, and Fish that through the wet
        Sea-paths in shoals do slide, and know no dearth.
O Jehovah, our Lord, how wondrous great
        And glorious is thy name through all the earth!

(1653)

On the Late Massacre in Piemont

Avenge, O Lord, thy slaughter'd Saints, whose bones
        Lie scatter'd on the Alpine mountains cold,
        Ev'n them who kept thy truth so pure of old
        When all our Fathers worship't Stocks and Stones,
5   Forget not: in thy book record their groans
        Who were thy Sheep and in their ancient Fold
        Slain by the bloody *Piemontese* that roll'd
        Mother with Infant down the Rocks. Their moans
The Vales redoubl'd to the Hills, and they
10   To Heav'n. Their martyr'd blood and ashes sow
        O'er all th'*Italian* fields where still doth sway
The triple Tyrant: that from these may grow
        A hunderd-fold, who having learnt thy way
        Early may fly the *Babylonian* woe.

(1655)

From *Paradise Lost*

Book I

Lines 242–270

"Is this the region, this the soil, the clime,"
Said then the lost Archangel, "this the seat
That we must change for heav'n, this mournful gloom
245 For that celestial light? Be it so, since he
Who now is sovran can dispose and bid
What shall be right: fardest from him is best,
Whom reason hath equaled, force hath made supreme
Above his equals. Farewell, happy fields,
250 Where joy for ever dwells! Hail, horrors, hail,
Infernal world, and thou, profoundest hell,
Receive thy new possessor: one who brings
A mind not to be changed by place or time.
The mind is its own place, and in itself
255 Can make a heav'n of hell, a hell of heav'n.
What matter where, if I be still the same,
And what I should be, all but less than he
Whom thunder hath made greater? Here at least
We shall be free; th' Almighty hath not built
260 Here for his envy, will not drive us hence:
Here we may reign secure, and in my choice
To reign is worth ambition, though in hell:
Better to reign in hell than serve in heav'n.
But wherefore let we then our faithful friends,
265 Th' associates and copartners of our loss,
Lie thus astonished on th' oblivious pool,
And call them not to share with us their part
In this unhappy mansion, or once more
With rallied arms to try what may be yet
270 Regained in heav'n, or what more lost in hell?"

Book IV

Lines 32–113

"O thou that with surpassing glory crowned
Look'st from thy sole dominion like the god
Of this new world; at whose sight all the stars
35 Hide their diminished heads; to thee I call,
But with no friendly voice, and add thy name,
O sun, to tell thee how I hate thy beams
That bring to my remembrance from what state
I fell, how glorious once above thy sphere;
40 Till pride and worse ambition threw me down
Warring in heav'n against heav'n's matchless King.

Ah wherefore? He deserved no such return
From me, whom he created what I was
In that bright eminence, and with his good
45 Upbraided none; nor was his service hard.
What could be less than to afford him praise,
The easiest recompense, and pay him thanks,
How due! Yet all his good proved ill in me,
And wrought but malice; lifted up so high
50 I 'sdained subjection, and thought one step higher
Would set me highest, and in a moment quit
The debt immense of endless gratitude,
So burthensome still paying, still to owe;
Forgetful what from him I still received,
55 And understood not that a grateful mind
By owing owes not, but still pays, at once
Indebted and discharged; what burden then?
O had his powerful destiny ordained
Me some inferior angel, I had stood
60 Then happy; no unbounded hope had raised
Ambition. Yet why not? Some other Power
As great might have aspired, and me though mean
Drawn to his part; but other Powers as great
Fell not, but stand unshaken, from within
65 Or from without, to all temptations armed.
Hadst thou the same free will and power to stand?
Thou hadst. Whom hast thou then or what to accuse,
But Heav'n's free love dealt equally to all?
Be then his love accurst, since love or hate,
70 To me alike, it deals eternal woe.
Nay cursed be thou, since against his thy will
Chose freely what it now so justly rues.
Me miserable! which way shall I fly
Infinite wrath, and infinite despair?
75 Which way I fly is hell; myself am hell;
And in the lowest deep a lower deep
Still threat'ning to devour me opens wide,
To which the hell I suffer seems a heav'n.
O then at last relent: is there no place
80 Left for repentance, none for pardon left?
None left but by submission; and that word
Disdain forbids me, and my dread of shame
Among the Spirits beneath, whom I seduced
With other promises and other vaunts
85 Than to submit, boasting I could subdue
Th' Omnipotent. Ay me, they little know
How dearly I abide that boast so vain,
Under what torments inwardly I groan;
While they adore me on the throne of hell,

90   With diadem and scepter high advanced,
     The lower still I fall, only supreme
     In misery; such joy ambition finds.
     But say I could repent and could obtain
     By act of grace my former state; how soon
95   Would highth recall high thoughts, how soon unsay
     What feigned submission swore: ease would recant
     Vows made in pain, as violent and void.
     For never can true reconcilement grow
     Where wounds of deadly hate have pierced so deep;
100 Which would but lead me to a worse relapse
     And heavier fall: so should I purchase dear
     Short intermission bought with double smart.
     This knows my Punisher; therefore as far
     From granting he, as I from begging peace.
105 All hope excluded thus, behold instead
     Of us outcast, exiled, his new delight,
     Mankind created, and for him this world.
     So farewell hope, and with hope farewell fear,
     Farewell remorse! All good to me is lost;
110 Evil, be thou my good; by thee at least
     Divided empire with heav'n's King I hold
     By thee, and more than half perhaps will reign;
     As man ere long, and this new world shall know."

                                      (1667)

Richard Lovelace

(1618–1657)

To Lucasta, Going to the Wars

     Tell me not, Sweet, I am unkind,
          That from the nunnery
     Of thy chaste breast and quiet mind
          To war and arms I fly.

5   True, a new mistress now I chase,
          The first foe in the field;
     And with a stronger faith embrace
          A sword, a horse, a shield.

     Yet this inconstancy is such
10   As thou too shalt adore;
     I could not love thee, Dear, so much,
          Loved I not Honour more.

                         (1649)

Andrew Marvell

(1621–1678)

Bermudas

Where the remote *Bermudas* ride
In th' Oceans bosome unespy'd,
From a small Boat, that row'd along,
The listning Winds receiv'd this Song.
5   What should we do but sing his Praise
That led us through the watry Maze,
Unto an Isle so long unknown,
And yet far kinder than our own?
Where he the huge Sea-Monsters wracks,
10   That lift the Deep upon their Backs.
He lands us on a grassy Stage;
Safe from the Storms, and Prelat's rage.
He gave us this eternal Spring,
Which here enamells every thing;
15   And sends the Fowl's to us in care,
On daily Visits through the Air.
He hangs in shades the Orange bright,
Like golden Lamps in a green Night.
And does in the Pomgranates close,
20   Jewels more rich than *Ormus* shows.
He makes the Figs our mouths to meet;
And throws the Melons at our feet.
But Apples plants of such a price,
No Tree could ever bear them twice.
25   With Cedars, chosen by his hand,
From *Lebanon*, he stores the Land.
And makes the hollow Seas, that roar,
Proclaime the Ambergris on shoar.
He cast (of which we rather boast)
30   The Gospels Pearl upon our Coast.
And in these Rocks for us did frame
A Temple, where to sound his Name.
Oh let our Voice his Praise exalt,
Till it arrive at Heavens Vault:
35   Which thence (perhaps) rebounding, may
Eccho beyond the *Mexique Bay*.
Thus sung they, in the *English* boat,
An holy and a chearful Note,
And all the way, to guide their Chime,
40   With falling Oars they kept the time.

(1681)

The Garden

I

How vainly men themselves amaze
To win the Palm, the Oke, or Bayes;
And their uncessant Labours see
Crown'd from some single Herb or Tree.
5 Whose short and narrow verged Shade
Does prudently their Toyles upbraid;
While all Flow'rs and all Trees do close
To weave the Garlands of repose.

II

Fair quiet, have I found thee here,
10 And Innocence thy Sister dear!
Mistaken long, I sought you then
In busie Companies of Men.
Your sacred Plants, if here below,
Only among the Plants will grow.
15 Society is all but rude,
To this delicious Solitude.

III

No white nor red was ever seen
So am'rous as this lovely green.
Fond Lovers, cruel as their Flame,
20 Cut in these Trees their Mistress name.
Little, Alas, they know, or heed,
How far these Beauties Hers exceed!
Fair Trees! where s'eer your barkes I wound,
No Name shall but your own be found.

IV

25 When we have run our Passions heat,
Love hither makes his best retreat.
The *Gods*, that mortal Beauty chase,
Still in a Tree did end their race.
Apollo hunted *Daphne* so,
30 Only that She might Laurel grow.
And *Pan* did after *Syrinx* speed,
Not as a Nymph, but for a Reed.

V

What wond'rous Life in this I lead!
Ripe Apples drop about my head;
35 The Luscious Clusters of the Vine
Upon my Mouth do crush their Wine;
The Nectaren, and curious Peach,
Into my hands themselves do reach;
Stumbling on Melons, as I pass,
40 Insnar'd with Flow'rs, I fall on Grass.

Mean while the Mind, from pleasure less,
Withdraws into its happiness:
The Mind, that Ocean where each kind
Does streight its own resemblance find;
45 Yet it creates, transcending these,
Far other Worlds, and other Seas;
Annihilating all that's made
To a green Thought in a green Shade.

VII

Here at the Fountains sliding foot,
50 Or at some Fruit-trees mossy root,
Casting the Bodies Vest aside,
My Soul into the boughs does glide:
There like a Bird it sits, and sings,
Then whets, and combs its silver Wings;
55 And, till prepar'd for longer flight,
Waves in its Plumes the various Light.

VIII

Such was that happy Garden-state,
While Man there walk'd without a Mate:
After a Place so pure, and sweet,
60 What other Help could yet be meet!
But 'twas beyond a Mortal's share
To wander solitary there:
Two Paradises 'twere in one
To live in Paradise alone.

IX

65 How well the skilful Gardner drew
Of flow'rs and herbes this Dial new;
Where from above the milder Sun
Does through a fragrant Zodiack run;
And, as it works, th' industrious Bee
70 Computes its time as well as we.
How could such sweet and wholsome Hours
Be reckon'd but with herbs and flow'rs!

(1681)

John Bunyan
(1628–1688)

From *The Pilgrim's Progress*

From This World to That Which is to Come, Delivered Under the Similitude of a Dream

As I walked through the wilderness of this world, I lighted on a certain place where was a Den,[1] and I laid me down in that place to sleep: and as I slept I dreamed a dream. I dreamed, and behold I saw a man clothed with rags, standing in a certain place, with his face from his own house, a book in his hand, and a great burden upon his back. I looked, and saw him open the book and read therein; and as he read, he wept and trembled; and not being able longer to contain, he brake out with a lamentable cry, saying, "What shall I do?"

In this plight, therefore, he went home and refrained himself as long as he could, that his wife and children should not perceive his distress; but he could not be silent long, because that his trouble increased. Wherefore at length he brake his mind to his wife and children; and thus he began to talk to them. O my dear wife, said he, and you the children of my bowels, I, your dear friend, am in myself undone by reason of a burden that lieth hard upon me; moreover, I am for certain informed that this our city will be burned with fire from heaven, in which fearful overthrow both myself, with thee my wife, and you my sweet babes, shall miserably come to ruin, except (the which yet I see not) some way of escape can be found, whereby we may be delivered. At this his relations were sore amazed; not for that they believed that what he said to them was true, but because they thought that some frenzy distemper had got into his head; therefore, it drawing towards night, and they hoping that sleep might settle his brains, with all haste they got him to bed. But the night was as troublesome to him as the day; wherefore, instead of sleeping, he spent it in sighs and tears. So, when the morning was come, they would know how he did. He told them, Worse and worse: he also set to talking to them again: but they began to be hardened. They also thought to drive away his distemper by harsh and surly carriages to him; sometimes they would deride, sometimes they would chide, and sometimes they would quite neglect him. Wherefore he began to retire himself to his chamber, to pray and pity them, and also to condole his own misery; he would also walk solitarily in the fields, sometimes reading, and sometimes praying: and thus for some days he spent his time.

Now I saw, upon a time when he was walking in the fields, that he was (as he was wont) reading in his book, and greatly distressed in his mind; and as he read, he burst out, as he had done before, crying, "What shall I do to be saved?"

I saw also that he looked this way and that way, as if he would run; yet he stood still, because (as I perceived) he could not tell which way to go. I looked then, and saw a man named Evangelist coming to him, who asked, Wherefore dost thou cry?

He answered, Sir, I perceive by the book in my hand that I am condemned to die, and after that to come to judgment, and I find that I am not willing to do the first, nor able to do the second.

---

[1] The Jail.

Then said Evangelist, Why not willing to die, since this life is attended with so many evils? The man answered, Because I fear that this burden that is upon my back will sink me lower than the grave, and I shall fall into Tophet. And, sir, if I be not fit to go to prison, I am not fit to go to judgment, and from thence to execution; and the thoughts of these things make me cry.

Then said Evangelist, If this be thy condition, why standest thou still? He answered, Because I know not whither to go. Then he gave him a parchment roll, and there was written within, "Fly from the wrath to come."

The man therefore read it, and looking upon Evangelist very carefully, said, Whither must I fly? Then said Evangelist, pointing with his finger over a very wide field, Do you see yonder wicket-gate? The man said, No. Then said the other, Do you see yonder shining light? He said, I think I do. Then said Evangelist, Keep that light in your eye, and go up directly thereto: so shalt thou see the gate;[2] at which when thou knockest it shall be told thee what thou shalt do. So I saw in my dream that the man began to run. Now, he had not run far from his own door, but his wife and children perceiving it, began to cry after him to return; but the man put his fingers in his ears, and ran on, crying, Life! life! eternal life! So he looked not behind him, but fled towards the middle of the plain.

The neighbours also came out to see him run; and as he ran, some mocked, others threatened, and some cried after him to return; and, among those that did so, there were two that resolved to fetch him back by force. The name of the one was Obstinate, and the name of the other Pliable. Now by this time the man was got a good distance from them; but, however, they were resolved to pursue him, which they did, and in a little time they overtook him. Then said the man, Neighbours, wherefore are ye come? They said, To persuade you to go back with us. But he said, That can by no means be; you dwell, said he, in the City of Destruction, the place also where I was born: I see it to be so; and dying there, sooner or later, you will sink lower than the grave, into a place that burns with fire and brimstone: be content, good neighbours, and go along with me.

OBST. What! said Obstinate, and leave our friends and our comforts behind us?

CHR. Yes, said Christian (for that was his name), because that all which you shall forsake is not worthy to be compared with a little of that which I am seeking to enjoy; and if you will go along with me, and hold it, you shall fare as I myself; for there where I go is enough and to spare. Come away, and prove my words.

OBST. What are the things you seek, since you leave all the world to find them?

CHR. I seek "an inheritance incorruptible, undefiled, and that fadeth not away," and it is laid up in heaven, and safe there, to be bestowed, at the time appointed, on them that diligently seek it. Read it so, if you will, in my book.

OBST. Tush! said Obstinate, away with your book. Will you go back with us or no?

CHR. No, not I, said the other, because I have laid my hand to the plough.

OBST. Come then, neighbour Pliable, let us turn again and go home without him; there is a company of these crazed-headed coxcombs, that, when they take a fancy by the end, are wiser in their own eyes "than seven men that can render a reason."

PLI. Then said Pliable, Don't revile; if what the good Christian says is true, the things he looks after are better than ours: my heart inclines to go with my neighbour.

OBST. What! more fools still! Be ruled by me, and go back; who knows whither such a brain-sick fellow will lead you? Go back, go back, and be wise.

---

[2] Christ, and the way to him cannot be found without the Word.

CHR. Nay, but do thou come with thy neighbour, Pliable; there are such things to be had which I spoke of, and many more glories besides. If you believe me not, read here in this book; and for the truth of what is expressed therein, behold all is confirmed by the blood of Him that made it.

PLI. Well, neighbour Obstinate, said Pliable, I begin to come to a point; I intend to go along with this good man, and to cast in my lot with him; but, my good companion, do you know the way to this desired place?

CHR. I am directed by a man whose name is Evangelist, to speed me to a little gate that is before us, where we shall receive instructions about the way.

PLI. Come then, good neighbour, let us be going. Then they went both together.

OBST. And I will go back to my place, said Obstinate; I will be no companion of such misled, fantastical fellows.

Now I saw in my dream that, when Obstinate was gone back, Christian and Pliable went talking over the plain; and thus they began their discourse.

CHR. Come, neighbour Pliable, how do you do? I am glad you are persuaded to go along with me. Had even Obstinate himself but felt what I have felt of the powers and terrors of what is yet unseen, he would not thus lightly have given us the back.

PLI. Come, neighbour Christian, since there are none but us two here, tell me now further what the things are, and how to be enjoyed, whither we are going.

CHR. I can better conceive of them with my mind, than speak of them with my tongue; but yet, since you are desirous to know, I will read of them in my book.

PLI. And do you think that the words of your book are certainly true?

CHR. Yes, verily; for it was made by Him that cannot lie.

PLI. Well said; what things are they?

CHR. There is an endless kingdom to be inhabited, and everlasting life to be given us, that we may inhabit that kingdom for ever.

PLI. Well said; and what else?

CHR. There are crowns of glory to be given us, and garments that will make us shine like the sun in the firmament of heaven!

PLI. This is very pleasant; and what else?

CHR. There shall be no more crying nor sorrow; for He that is owner of the place will wipe all tears from our eyes.

PLI. And what company shall we have there?

CHR. There we shall be with seraphims and cherubims, creatures that will dazzle your eyes to look on them. There also you shall meet with thousands and ten thousands that have gone before us to that place; none of them are hurtful, but loving and holy; every one walking in the sight of God, and standing in his presence with acceptance for ever. In a word, there we shall see the elders with their golden crowns; there we shall see the holy virgins with their golden harps; there we shall see men that by the world were cut in pieces, burnt in flames, eaten of beasts, drowned in the seas, for the love that they bare to the Lord of the place, all well, and clothed with immortality as with a garment.

PLI. The hearing of this is enough to ravish one's heart. But are these things to be enjoyed? How shall we get to be sharers thereof?

CHR. The Lord, the Governor of the country, hath recorded that in this book; the substance of which is: If we be truly willing to have it, he will bestow it upon us freely.

PLI. Well, my good companion, glad am I to hear of these things; come on, let us mend our pace.

CHR. I cannot go so fast as I would, by reason of this burden that is on my back.

Now I saw in my dream that just as they had ended this talk they drew near to a very miry slough that was in the midst of the plain; and they, being heedless, did both fall suddenly into the bog. The name of the slough was Despond. Here, therefore, they wallowed for a time, being grievously bedaubed with the dirt; and Christian, because of the burden that was on his back, began to sink in the mire.

PLI. Then said Pliable, Ah, neighbour Christian, where are you now?

CHR. Truly, said Christian, I do not know.

PLI. At that Pliable began to be offended, and angrily said to his fellow, Is this the happiness you have told me all this while of? If we have such ill speed at our first setting out, what may we expect 'twixt this and our journey's end? May I get out again with my life, you shall possess the brave country alone for me. And with that he gave a desperate struggle or two, and got out of the mire on that side of the slough which was next to his own house: so away he went, and Christian saw him no more.

Wherefore Christian was left to tumble in the Slough of Despond alone: but still he endeavoured to struggle to that side of the slough that was still further from his own house, and next to the wicket-gate; the which he did, but could not get out, because of the burden that was upon his back: but I beheld in my dream that a man came to him, whose name was Help, and asked him, What he did there?

CHR. Sir, said Christian, I was bid go this way by a man called Evangelist, who directed me also to yonder gate, that I might escape the wrath to come; and as I was going thither I fell in here.

HELP. But why did not you look for the steps?

CHR. Fear followed me so hard that I fled the next way and fell in.

HELP. Then said he, Give me thy hand: so he gave him his hand, and he drew him out, and set him upon sound ground, and bid him go on his way.

(1678)

Charles Perrault

(FRANCE, 1628–1703)

The Blue Beard

There was once upon a time a man who had several fine houses both in town and country, a good deal of silver and gold plate, embroider'd furniture, and coaches gilt all over with gold. But this same man had the misfortune to have a *Blue Beard*, which made him so frightfully ugly that all the women and girls ran away from him.

One of his neighbours, a lady of quality, had two daughters who were perfect beauties. He desired of her one of them in marriage, leaving to her the choice of which of them she would bestow upon him. They would neither of them have him, and sent him backwards and forwards from one another, being resolved never to marry a man that had a *Blue Beard*. That which moreover gave them the greater disgust and aversion, was that he had already been marry'd to several wives, and no body ever knew what were become of them.

The *Blue Beard*, to engage their affection, took them with my lady their mother, and three or four other ladies of their acquaintance, and some young people of the neighbourhood, to one of his country seats, where they staid full eight days. There was nothing now to be seen but parties of pleasure, hunting of all kinds, fishing, dancing, feasts and collations. No body went to bed, they past the night in rallying and playing upon one another: In short, every thing so well succeeded, that the youngest daughter began to think, that the master of the house had not a *Beard* so very *Blue*, and that he was a very civil gentleman.

As soon as they returned home the marriage was concluded. About a month afterwards the *Blue Beard* told his wife, that he was obliged to take a journey into a distant country for six weeks at least, about an affair of very great consequence, desiring her to divert herself in his absence, if she pleased, and make good cheer wherever she was: Here said he, are the keys of the two great rooms that hold my best and richest furniture; these are of my silver and gold plate, which is not to be made use of every day; these open my strong boxes, which hold my gold and silver money; these my casket of jewels; and this is the master-key that opens all my apartments: But for this little one here, it is the key of the closet at the end of the great gallery on the ground floor. Open them all, go into all and every one except that little closet, which I forbid you, and forbid you in such a manner, that if you happen to open it, there is nothing but what you may expect from my just anger and resentment. She promised to observe every thing he order'd her, who, after having embraced her, got into his coach and proceeded on his journey.

Her neighbours and good friends did not stay to be sent for by the new married lady, so great was their impatience to see all the rich furniture of her house, not daring to come while the husband was there, because of his *Blue Beard* which frighten'd them. They ran through all the rooms, closets, wardrobes, which were all so rich and fine that they seemed to surpass one another. After that, they went up into the two great rooms where were the best and richest furniture; they could not sufficiently admire the number and beauty of the tapestry, beds, couches, cabinets, stands, tables and looking-glasses, in which you might see yourself from head to foot; some of them were framed with glass, others with silver and silver gilt, the finest and most magnificent as ever were seen: They never ceased to extol and envy the happiness of their friend, who in the mean time no ways diverted herself in looking upon all these rich things, because of the impatience she had to go and open the closet of the ground floor. She was so much pressed by her curiosity, that without considering that it was very uncivil to leave her company, she went down a back pair of stairs, and with such an excessive haste, that she had like to have broken her neck two or three times.

Being come to the closet door, she stopt for some time, thinking upon her husband's orders, and considering what unhappiness might attend her were she disobedient; but the temptation was so strong she could not overcome it: She took then the little key and opened it in a very great trembling. But she could see nothing distinctly, because the windows were shut; after some moments she began to observe that the floor was all covered over with clotted blood, on which lay the bodies of several dead women ranged against the walls. (These were all the wives that the *Blue Beard* had married and murder'd one after another.) She thought that she should have died for fear, and the key that she pulled out of the lock fell out of her hand: After having somewhat recover'd her surprise, she took up the key, locked the door and went up stairs into her chamber to recover herself, but she could not, so much was she frightened. Having observed that the key of the closet was stain'd with blood, she tried two or three times to wipe it off, but the blood would not come out; in vain did she wash it and even rub it with soap and sand, the blood still remained, for the key was a Fairy, and she could never quite make it clean; when the blood was gone off from one side, it came again on the other.

The *Blue Beard* returned from his journey the same evening, and said he had received letters upon the road, informing him that the affair he went about was finished to his advantage. His wife did all she could to convince him she was extremely glad of his speedy return. The next morning he asked for the keys, which she returned, but with such a trembling hand, that he easily guess'd what had happen'd. What is the matter, said he, that the key of the closet is not amongst the rest? I must certainly, said she, have left it above upon the table. Do not fail, said the *Blue Beard*, of giving it to me presently: After several goings backwards and forwards she was forced to bring him the key. The *Blue Beard* having very attentively consider'd it, said to his Wife, how comes this blood upon the key? I don't know, said the poor Woman paler than death. You don't know, replied the *Blue Beard*, I know very well, you were resolv'd to go into the closet, were you not? Very well, Madam, you shall go in, and take your place amongst the ladies you saw there.

Upon this she threw herself at her husband's feet, and begged his pardon with all the signs of a true repentance, and that she would never more be disobedient. She would have melted a rock, so beautiful and sorrowful was she; but the *Blue Beard* had a heart harder than the hardest rock! You must die, Madam, said he, and that presently. Since I must die, said she, looking upon him with her eyes all bathed in tears, give me some little time to say my prayers. I give you, said the *Blue Beard*, a quarter of an hour, but not one moment more.

When she was alone, she called out to her sister, and said to her, Sister *Anne*, for that was her name, go up, I desire thee, upon the top of the tower, and see if my brothers are not coming, they promised me that they would come to day, and if thou seest them, give them a sign to make haste. Her sister *Anne* went up upon the top of the tower, and the poor afflicted lady cried out from time to time, *Anne, sister Anne, dost thou see nothing coming?* And sister *Anne* said, *I see nothing but the sun that makes a dust, and the grass that grows green.* In the mean while the *Blue Beard*, holding a great cutlass in his hand, cried out as loud as he could to his wife, Come down, presently, or I'll come up to you. One moment longer, if you please, said his wife, and immediately she cried out very softly, *Anne, sister Anne, dost thou see nothing coming?* And sister *Anne* said, *I see nothing but the sun that makes a dust, and the grass that grows green.* Come down quickly, cried the *Blue Beard*, or I'll come up to you. I am coming, answer'd his wife, and then she cried, *Anne, sister Anne, dost thou see nothing coming?* I see, replied sister *Anne*, a great dust that comes on this side here. *Are they my brothers?* Alas! no, my dear sister, I see a flock of sheep. Will you not come down? cried the *Blue Beard*. One moment longer, said his wife, and then she cried out, *Anne, sister Anne, dost thou see nothing coming?* I see, said she, two horsemen coming, but they are yet a great way off. God be praised, said she immediately after, they are my brothers. I have made them a sign as well as I can to make haste. The *Blue Beard* cried out now so loud, that he made the whole house tremble.

The poor Lady came down and threw herself at his feet all in tears with her hair about her shoulders: This signifies nothing, says the *Blue Beard*, you must die; then taking hold of her hair with one hand, and holding up the cutlass with the other, he was going to cut off her head. The poor lady turning about to him, and looking at him with dying eyes, desired him to afford her one little moment to recollect herself: No, no, said he, recommend thy self to God: for at this very instant there was such a loud knocking at the gate, that the *Blue Beard* stopt short of a sudden: They open'd the gate, and immediately enter'd two horsemen, who drawing their swords, ran directly to the *Blue Beard*. He knew them to be his wife's brothers, one a dragoon, the other a musqueteer, so that he ran away immediately to save himself: but the two brothers pursued him so close, that they overtook him before he could get to the steps of the porch, when they ran their swords through his body and left him dead.

The poor lady was almost as dead as her husband, and had not strength enough to rise and embrace her brothers. The *Blue Beard* had no heirs, and so his wife became mistress of all his estate. She made use of one part of it to marry her sister *Anne* to a young gentleman who had loved her a long while, another part to buy captains commissions for her brothers, and the rest to marry herself to a very honest gentleman, who made her forget the ill time she had pass'd with the *Blue Beard*.

(1697; English translation
by Robert Samber, 1729)

John Dryden
(1631–1700)

To the Memory of Mr. Oldham

Farewell, too little, and too lately known,
Whom I began to think and call my own:
For sure our souls were near allied, and thine
Cast in the same poetic mold with mine.
5   One common note on either lyre did strike,
And knaves and fools we both abhorred alike.
To the same goal did both our studies drive;
The last set out the soonest did arrive.
Thus Nisus fell upon the slippery place,
10   Whilst his young friend performed and won the race.
O early ripe! to thy abundant store
What could advancing age have added more?
It might (what nature never gives the young)
Have taught the numbers of thy native tongue.
15   But satire needs not those, and wit will shine
Through the harsh cadence of a rugged line:
A noble error, and but seldom made,
When poets are by too much force betrayed.
Thy generous fruits, though gathered ere their prime,
20   Still showed a quickness; and maturing time
But mellows what we write to the dull sweets of rhyme.
Once more, hail and farewell; farewell, thou young,
But ah too short, Marcellus of our tongue;
Thy brows with ivy, and with laurels bound;
25   But fate and gloomy night encompass thee around.

(1684)

Anne Finch
(1661–1720)

Adam Pos'd

Cou'd our First Father, at his toilsome Plough,
Thorns in his Path, and Labour on his Brow,
Cloath'd only in a rude, unpolish'd Skin,
Cou'd he a vain Fantastick Nymph have seen,
5 In all her Airs, in all her antick Graces,
Her various Fashions, and more various Faces;
How had it pos'd that Skill, which late assign'd
Just Appellations to Each several Kind!
A right Idea of the Sight to frame;
10 T'have guest from what New Element she came:
T'have hit the wav'ring Form, or giv'n this Thing a Name.

(1709)

Jonathan Swift
(1667–1745)

Stella's Birth-day, 1727

This Day, whate'er the Fates decree,
Shall still be kept with Joy by me:
This Day then, let us not be told,
That you are sick, and I grown old,
5 Nor think on our approaching Ills,
And talk of Spectacles and Pills;
To morrow will be Time enough
To hear such mortifying Stuff.
Yet, since from Reason may be brought
10 A better and more pleasing Thought,
Which can in spite of all Decays,
Support a few remaining Days:
From not the gravest of Divines,
Accept for once some serious Lines.
15 Although we now can form no more
Long Schemes of Life, as heretofore;
Yet you, while Time is running fast,
Can look with Joy on what is past.

Were future Happiness and Pain,
20 A mere Contrivance of the Brain,
As Atheists argue, to entice
And fit their Proselytes for Vice;
(The only Comfort they propose,
To have Companions in their Woes.)
25 Grant this the Case, yet sure 'tis hard,
That Virtue, stil'd its own Reward,
And by all Sages understood
To be the chief of human Good,
Should acting, die, nor leave behind
30 Some lasting Pleasure in the Mind,
Which by Remembrance will assuage,
Grief, Sickness, Poverty, and Age;
And strongly shoot a radiant Dart,
To shine through Life's declining Part.
35   Say, *Stella*, feel you no Content,
Reflecting on a Life well spent?
Your skilful Hand employ'd to save
Despairing Wretches from the Grave;
And then supporting with your Store,
40 Those whom you dragg'd from Death before:
(So Providence on Mortals waits,
Preserving what it first creates)
Your gen'rous Boldness to defend
An innocent and absent Friend;
45 That Courage which can make you just,
To Merit humbled in the Dust:
The Detestation you express
For Vice in all its glitt'ring Dress:
That Patience under tort'ring Pain,
50 Where stubborn Stoicks would complain.
    Must these like empty Shadows pass,
Or Forms reflected from a Glass?
    Or mere Chimæra's in the Mind,
That fly and leave no Marks behind?
55 Does not the Body thrive and grow
By Food of twenty Years ago?
And, had it not been still supply'd,
It must a thousand Times have dy'd.
Then, who with Reason can maintain,
60 That no Effects of Food remain?
And, is not Virtue in Mankind
The Nutriment that feeds the Mind?
Upheld by each good Action past,
And still continued by the last:
65 Then, who with Reason can pretend,
That all Effects of Virtue end?

Believe me *Stella*, when you show
That true Contempt for Things below,
Nor prize your Life for other Ends
70   Than merely to oblige your Friends;
Your former Actions claim their Part,
And join to fortify your Heart.
For Virtue in her daily Race,
Like *Janus*, bears a double Face;
75   Looks back with Joy where she has gone,
And therefore goes with Courage on.
She at your sickly Couch will wait,
And guide you to a better State.
      O then, whatever Heav'n intends,
80   Take Pity on your pitying Friends;
Nor let your Ills affect your Mind,
To fancy they can be unkind.
Me, surely me, you ought to spare,
Who gladly would your Suff'rings share;
85   Or give my Scrap of Life to you,
And think it far beneath your Due;
You, to whose Care so oft I owe,
That I'm alive to tell you so.

                                        (1727)

A Modest Proposal

For preventing the children of poor people in Ireland from being a burden to their parents or country, and for making them beneficial to the public.

It is a melancholy object to those who walk through this great town, or travel in the country, when they see the streets, the roads, and cabin-doors crowded with beggars of the female sex, followed by three, four, or six children, *all in rags*, and importuning every passenger for an alms. These mothers instead of being able to work for their honest livelihood, are forced to employ all their time in strolling, to beg sustenance for their helpless infants, who, as they grow up, either turn thieves for want of work, or leave their dear Native Country to fight for the Pretender in Spain, or sell themselves to the Barbadoes.

I think it is agreed by all parties, that this prodigious number of children, in the arms, or on the backs, or at the heels of their mothers, and frequently of their fathers, is in the present deplorable state of the kingdom a very great additional grievance; and therefore whoever could find out a fair, cheap and easy method of making these children sound useful members of the commonwealth would deserve so well of the public, as to have his statue set up for a preserver of the nation.

But my intention is very far from being confined to provide only for the children of professed beggars; it is of a much greater extent, and shall take in the whole number of infants at a certain age, who are born of parents in effect as little able to support them, as those who demand our charity in the streets.

As to my own part, having turned my thoughts, for many years, upon this important subject, and maturely weighed the several schemes of other projectors, I have always found them grossly mistaken in their computation. It is true a child, just dropped from its dam, may be supported by her milk for a solar year with little other nourishment, at most not above the value of two shillings, which the mother may certainly get, or the value in scraps, by her lawful occupation of begging, and it is exactly at one year old that I propose to provide for them, in such a manner, as, instead of being a charge upon their parents, or the parish, or wanting food and raiment for the rest of their lives, they shall, on the contrary, contribute to the feeding and partly to the clothing of many thousands.

There is likewise another great advantage in my scheme, that it will prevent those voluntary abortions, and that horrid practice of women murdering their bastard children, alas, too frequent among us, sacrificing the poor innocent babes, I doubt, more to avoid the expense, than the shame, which would move tears and pity in the most savage and inhuman breast.

The number of souls in this kingdom being usually reckoned one million and a half, of these I calculate there may be about two hundred thousand couple whose wives are breeders, from which number I subtract thirty thousand couples, who are able to maintain their own children, although I apprehend there cannot be so many under the present distresses of the kingdom, but this being granted, there will remain an hundred and seventy thousand breeders. I again subtract fifty thousand for those women who miscarry, or whose children die by accident, or disease within the year. There only remain an hundred and twenty thousand children of poor parents annually born: the question therefore is, how this number shall be reared, and provided for, which, as I have already said, under the present situation of affairs, is utterly impossible by all the methods hitherto proposed, for we can neither employ them in handicraft, or agriculture; we neither build houses, (I mean in the country) nor cultivate land: they can very seldom pick up a livelihood by stealing till they arrive at six years old, except where they are of towardly parts, although, I confess they learn the rudiments much earlier, during which time, they can however be properly looked upon only as *probationers*, as I have been informed by a principal gentleman in the County of Cavan, who protested to me, that he never knew above one or two instances under the age of six, even in a part of the kingdom so renowned for the quickest proficiency in that art.

I am assured by our merchants, that a boy or a girl, before twelve years old, is no saleable commodity, and even when they come to this age, they will not yield above three pounds, or three pounds and half-a-crown at most on the Exchange, which cannot turn to account either to the parents or kingdom, the charge of nutriment and rags having been at least four times that value.

I shall now therefore humbly propose my own thoughts, which I hope will not be liable to the least objection.

I have been assured by a very knowing American of my acquaintance in London, that a young healthy child well nursed is at a year old a most delicious, nourishing, and wholesome food, whether stewed, roasted, baked, or boiled, and I make no doubt that it will equally serve in a fricassee, or ragout.

I do therefore humbly offer it to public consideration, that of the hundred and twenty thousand children, already computed, twenty thousand may be reserved for breed, whereof only one fourth part to be males, which is more than we allow to sheep, black-cattle, or swine, and my reason is that these children are seldom the fruits of marriage, a circumstance not much regarded by our savages, therefore one male will be sufficient to serve four females. That the remaining hundred thousand may at a year old be offered in sale to the persons of quality, and fortune, through the kingdom, always advising the mother to let them suck plentifully in the last month, so as to render them plump, and fat for a good table. A child will make two dishes at an entertainment for friends, and when the family dines alone, the fore or hind quarter will make a reasonable dish, and seasoned with a little pepper or salt will be very good boiled on the fourth day, especially in winter.

I have reckoned upon a medium, that a child just born will weigh 12 pounds, and in a solar year if tolerably nursed increaseth to 28 pounds.

I grant this food will be somewhat dear, and therefore very proper for landlords, who, as they have already devoured most of the parents, seem to have the best title to the children.

Infants' flesh will be in season throughout the year, but more plentiful in March, and a little before and after, for we are told by a grave author, an eminent French Physician, that fish being a prolific diet, there are more children born in Roman Catholic countries about nine months after Lent, than at any other season; therefore reckoning a year after Lent, the markets will be more glutted than usual, because the number of Popish infants is at least three to one in this kingdom, and therefore it will have one other collateral advantage by lessening the number of Papists among us.

I have already computed the charge of nursing a beggar's child (in which list I reckon all cottagers, labourers, and four-fifths of the farmers) to be about two shillings *per annum*, rags included, and I believe no gentleman would repine to give ten shillings for the carcass of a good fat child, which, as I have said, will make four dishes of excellent nutritive meat, when he hath only some particular friend, or his own family to dine with him. Thus the Squire will learn to be a good landlord, and grow popular among his tenants; the mother will have eight shillings net profit, and be fit for work till she produces another child.

Those who are more thrifty (as I must confess the times require) may flay the carcass; the skin of which, artificially dressed, will make admirable gloves for ladies, and summer boots for fine gentlemen.

As to our City of Dublin, shambles may be appointed for this purpose, in the most convenient parts of it, and butchers we may be assured will not be wanting, although I rather recommend buying the children alive, and dressing them hot from the knife, as we do roasting pigs.

A very worthy person, a true lover of his country, and whose virtues I highly esteem, was lately pleased, in discoursing on this matter, to offer a refinement upon my scheme. He said, that many gentlemen of this kingdom, having of late destroyed their deer, he conceived that the want of venison might be well supplied by the bodies of young lads and maidens, not exceeding fourteen years of age, nor under twelve, so great a number of both sexes in every country being now ready to starve, for want of work and service: and these to be disposed of by their parents if alive, or otherwise by their nearest relations. But with due deference to so excellent a friend, and so deserving a patriot, I cannot be altogether in his sentiments; for as to the males, my American acquaintance assured me from frequent experience, that their flesh was generally tough and lean, like that of our schoolboys, by continual exercise, and their taste disagreeable, and to fatten them would not answer the charge. Then as to the females, it would, I think with humble submission, be a loss to the public, because they soon would become breeders themselves: and besides, it is not improbable that some scrupulous people might be apt to censure such a practice, (although indeed very unjustly) as a little bordering upon cruelty, which, I confess, hath always been with me the strongest objection against any project, however so well intended.

But in order to justify my friend, he confessed that this expedient was put into his head by the famous Psalmanazar, a native of the island Formosa, who came from thence to London, above twenty years ago, and in conversation told my friend, that in his country when any young person happened to be put to death, the executioner sold the carcass to persons of quality, as a prime dainty, and that, in his time, the body of a plump girl of fifteen, who was crucified for an attempt to poison the emperor, was sold to his Imperial Majesty's Prime Minister of State, and other great Mandarins of the Court, in joints from the gibbet, at four hundred crowns. Neither indeed can I deny, that if the same use were made of several plump young girls in this town, who, without one single groat to their fortunes, cannot stir abroad without a chair, and appear at the playhouse, and assemblies in foreign fineries, which they never will pay for, the kingdom would not be the worse.

Some persons of a desponding spirit are in great concern about that vast number of people, who are aged, diseased, or maimed, and I have been desired to employ my thoughts what course may be taken, to ease the nation of so grievous an encumbrance. But I am not in the least pain upon that matter, because it is very well known, that they are every day dying, and rotting, by cold, and famine, and filth, and vermin, as fast as can be reasonably expected. And as to the younger labourers they are now in almost as hopeful a condition. They cannot get work, and consequently pine away for want of nourishment, to a degree, that if at any time they are accidentally hired to common labour, they have not strength to perform it; and thus the country and themselves are in a fair way of being soon delivered from the evils to come.

I have too long digressed, and therefore shall return to my subject. I think the advantages by the proposal which I have made are obvious and many, as well as of the highest importance.

For first, as I have already observed, it would greatly lessen the number of Papists, with whom we are yearly over-run, being the principal breeders of the nation, as well as our most dangerous enemies, and who stay at home on purpose with a design to deliver the kingdom to the Pretender, hoping to take their advantage by the absence of so many good Protestants, who have chosen rather to leave their country, than stay at home, and pay tithes against their conscience, to an Episcopal curate.

Secondly, The poorer tenants will have something valuable of their own, which by law may be made liable to distress, and help to pay their landlord's rent, their corn and cattle being already seized, and *money a thing unknown*.

Thirdly, Whereas the maintenance of an hundred thousand children, from two years old, and upwards, cannot be computed at less than ten shillings a piece *per annum*, the nation's stock will be thereby increased fifty thousand pounds *per annum*, besides the profit of a new dish, introduced to the tables of all gentlemen of fortune in the kingdom, who have any refinement in taste, and the money will circulate among ourselves, the goods being entirely of our own growth and manufacture.

Fourthly, The constant breeders, besides the gain of eight shillings sterling *per annum*, by the sale of their children, will be rid of the charge of maintaining them after the first year.

Fifthly, This food would likewise bring great custom to taverns, where the vintners will certainly be so prudent as to procure the best receipts for dressing it to perfection, and consequently have their houses frequented by all the fine gentlemen, who justly value themselves upon their knowledge in good eating; and a skilful cook, who understands how to oblige his guests, will contrive to make it as expensive as they please.

Sixthly, This would be a great inducement to marriage, which all wise nations have either encouraged by rewards, or enforced by laws and penalties. It would increase the care and tenderness of mothers toward their children, when they were sure of a settlement for life, to the poor babes, provided in some sort by the public to their annual profit instead of expense. We should see an honest emulation among the married women, which of them could bring the fattest child to the market; men would become as fond of their wives, during the time of their pregnancy, as they are now of their mares in foal, their cows in calf, or sows when they are ready to farrow, nor offer to beat or kick them (as it is too frequent a practice) for fear of a miscarriage.

Many other advantages might be enumerated: For instance, the addition of some thousand carcasses in our exportation of barrelled beef; the propagation of swine's flesh, and improvement in the art of making good bacon, so much wanted among us by the great destruction of pigs, too frequent at our tables, which are no way comparable in taste or magnificence to a well-grown, fat yearling child, which roasted whole will make a considerable figure at a Lord Mayor's feast, or any other public entertainment. But this and many others I omit, being studious of brevity.

Supposing that one thousand families in this city, would be constant customers for infants' flesh, besides others who might have it at merry-meetings, particularly weddings and christenings, I compute that Dublin would take off annually about twenty thousand carcasses, and the rest of the kingdom (where probably they will be sold somewhat cheaper) the remaining eighty thousand.

I can think of no one objection, that will possibly be raised against this proposal, unless it should be urged that the number of people will be thereby much lessened in the kingdom. This I freely own, and was indeed one principal design in offering it to the world. I desire the reader will observe, that I calculate my remedy *for this one individual Kingdom of Ireland, and for no other that ever was, is, or, I think, ever can be upon earth*. Therefore let no man talk to me of other expedients: *Of taxing our absentees at five shillings a pound: Of using neither clothes, nor household furniture, except what is of our own growth and manufacture: Of utterly rejecting the materials and instruments that promote foreign luxury: Of curing the expensiveness of pride, vanity, idleness, and gaming in our women: Of introducing a vein of parsimony, prudence and temperance: Of learning to love our Country, wherein we differ even from* LAPLANDERS, *and the inhabitants of* TOPINAMBOO: *Of quitting our animosities and factions, nor act any longer like the Jews, who were murdering one another at the very moment their city was taken: Of being a little cautious not to sell our country and consciences for nothing: Of teaching landlords to have at least one degree of mercy toward their tenants. Lastly, of putting a spirit of honesty, industry, and skill into our shopkeepers, who, if a resolution could now be taken to buy our native goods, would immediately unite to cheat and exact upon us in the price, the measure, and the goodness, nor could ever yet be brought to make one fair proposal of just dealing, though often and earnestly invited to it.*

Therefore I repeat, let no man talk to me of these and the like expedients, till he hath at least some glimpse of hope that there will ever be some hearty and sincere attempt to put them in practice.

But as to myself, having been wearied out for many years with offering vain, idle, visionary thoughts, and at length utterly despairing of success, I fortunately fell upon this proposal, which as it is wholly new, so it hath something solid and real, of no expense and little trouble, full in our own power, and whereby we can incur no danger in *disobliging* ENGLAND. For this kind of commodity will not bear exportation, the flesh being of too tender a consistence, to admit a long continuance in salt, *although perhaps I could name a country, which would be glad to eat up our whole nation without it.*

After all I am not so violently bent upon my own opinion, as to reject any offer, proposed by wise men, which shall be found equally innocent, cheap, easy and effectual. But before something of that kind shall be advanced in contradiction to my scheme, and offering a better, I desire the author or authors will be pleased maturely to consider two points. First, as things now stand, how they will be able to find food and raiment for an hundred thousand useless mouths and backs. And secondly, there being a round million of creatures in human figure, throughout this kingdom, whose whole subsistence put into a common stock would leave them in debt two millions of pounds sterling; adding those who are beggars by profession to the bulk of farmers, cottagers, and labourers with their wives and children, who are beggars in effect; I desire those politicians who dislike my overture, and may perhaps be so bold to attempt an answer, that they will first ask the parents of these mortals, whether they would not at this day think it a great happiness to have been sold for food at a year old, in the manner I prescribe, and thereby have avoided such a perpetual scene of misfortunes, as they have since gone through, by the oppression of landlords, the impossibility of paying rent without money or trade, the want of common sustenance, with neither house nor clothes to cover them from the inclemencies of the weather, and the most inevitable prospect of entailing the like, or greater miseries upon their breed for ever.

I profess in the sincerity of my heart that I have not the least personal interest in endeavouring to promote this necessary work, having no other motive than the *public good of my country, by advancing our trade, providing for infants, relieving the poor, and giving some pleasure to the rich.* I have no children by which I can propose to get a single penny; the youngest being nine years old, and my wife past child-bearing.

(1729)

Alexander Pope

(1688–1744)

From *An Essay on Criticism*

Lines 337–383

But most by *Numbers* judge a Poet's Song,
And *smooth* or *rough*, with them is *right* or *wrong*;
In the bright *Muse* tho' thousand *Charms* conspire,
340　Her *Voice* is all these tuneful Fools admire,
Who haunt *Parnassus* but to please their Ear,
Not mend their Minds; as some to *Church* repair,
Not for the *Doctrine*, but the *Musick* there.
These *Equal Syllables* alone require,
345　Tho' oft the Ear the *open Vowels* tire,
While *Expletives* their feeble Aid *do* join,
And ten low Words oft creep in one dull Line.
While they ring round the same *unvary'd Chimes*,
With sure *Returns* of still *expected Rhymes*.
350　Where-e'er you find the *cooling Western Breeze*,
In the next Line, it *whispers thro' the Trees*;
If *Chrystal Streams with pleasing Murmurs creep*,
The Reader's threaten'd (not in vain) with *Sleep*.
Then, at the *last*, and *only* Couplet fraught
355　With some *unmeaning* Thing they call a *Thought*,
A *needless Alexandrine* ends the Song,
That like a wounded Snake, drags its slow length along.

Leave such to tune their own dull Rhimes, and know
What's *roundly smooth*, or *languishingly slow*;
360 And praise the *Easie Vigor* of a Line,
Where *Denham's* Strength, and *Waller's* Sweetness join.
True Ease in Writing comes from Art, not Chance,
As those move easiest who have learn'd to dance.
'Tis not enough no Harshness gives Offence,
365 The *Sound* must seem an *Eccho* to the *Sense*.
Soft is the Strain when *Zephyr* gently blows,
And the *smooth Stream* in *smoother Numbers* flows;
But when loud Surges lash the sounding Shore,
The *hoarse, rough Verse* shou'd like the *Torrent* roar.
370 When *Ajax* strives, some Rock's vast Weight to throw,
The Line too *labours*, and the Words move *slow*;
Not so, when swift *Camilla* scours the Plain,
Flies o'er th'unbending Corn, and skims along the Main.
Hear how *Timotheus'* vary'd Lays surprize,
375 And bid Alternate Passions fall and rise!
While, at each Change, the Son of *Lybian Jove*
Now *burns* with Glory, and then *melts* with Love;
Now his *fierce Eyes* with *sparkling Fury* glow;
Now *Sighs* steal out, and *Tears begin to flow*:
380 *Persians* and *Greeks* like *Turns of Nature* found,
And the *World's Victor* stood subdu'd by *Sound*!
The Pow'rs of Musick all our Hearts allow;
And what *Timotheus* was, is *Dryden* now.

(1709)

Samuel Johnson

(1709–1784)

Ned Drugget

(Idler No. 16)

I paid a visit yesterday to my old friend *Ned Drugget*, at his country-lodgings. *Ned* began trade with a very small fortune; he took a small house in an obscure street, and for some years dealt only in remnants. Knowing that *light gains make a heavy purse*, he was content with moderate profit; having observed or heard the effects of civility, he bowed down to the counter edge at the entrance and departure of every customer, listened, without impatience, to the objections of the ignorant, and refused, without resentment, the offers of the penurious. His only Recreation was to stand at his own door and look into the street. His dinner was sent him from a neighbouring Alehouse, and he opened and shut the shop at a certain hour with his own hands.

His reputation soon extended from one end of the street to the other, and Mr. *Drugget's* exemplary conduct was recommended by every master to his apprentice, and by every father to his son. *Ned* was not only considered as a thriving trader, but as a man of Elegance and Politeness, for he was remarkably neat in his dress, and would wear his coat threadbare without spotting it; his hat was always brushed, his shoes glossy, his wig nicely curled, and his stockings without a wrinkle. With such qualifications it was not very difficult for him to gain the heart of Miss *Comfit*, the only daughter of Mr. *Comfit* the confectioner.

Ned is one of those whose happiness marriage has encreased. His wife had the same disposition with himself, and his method of life was very little changed, except that he dismissed the lodgers from the first floor, and took the whole house into his own hands.

He had already, by his parsimony, accumulated a considerable sum, to which the fortune of his wife was now added. From this time he began to grasp at greater acquisitions, and was always ready, with money in his hand, to pick up the refuse of a Sale, or to buy the Stock of a Trader who retired from business. He soon added his parlour to his shop, and was obliged, a few months afterwards, to hire a warehouse.

He had now a Shop splendidly and copiously furnished with every thing that time had injured, or fashion had degraded, with fragments of tissues, odd yards of brocade, vast bales of faded silk, and innumerable boxes of antiquated ribbons. His shop was soon celebrated through all quarters of the town, and frequented by every form of ostentatious Poverty. Every maid, whose misfortune it was to be taller than her Lady, matched her gown at Mr. *Drugget's*; and many a maiden who had passed a winter with her aunt in *London*, dazzled the Rustics, at her return, with cheap finery which Drugget had supplied. His shop was often visited in a morning by Ladies, who left their coaches in the next street, and crept through the Alley in linnen gowns. *Drugget* knows the rank of his customers by their bashfulness, and when he finds them unwilling to be seen, invites them up stairs, or retires with them to the back window.

I rejoiced at the encreasing prosperity of my friend, and imagined that as he grew rich, he was growing happy. His mind has partaken the enlargement of his fortune. When I stepped in for the first five years, I was welcomed only with a shake of the hand; in the next period of his life, he beckoned across the way for a pot of beer; but, for six years past, he invites me to dinner; and, if he bespeaks me the day before, never fails to regale me with a fillet of veal.

His riches neither made him uncivil nor negligent: He rose at the same hour, attended with the same assiduity, and bowed with the same gentleness. But for some years he has been much inclined to talk of the fatigues of business, and the confinement of a shop, and to wish that he had been so happy as to have renewed his uncle's lease of a farm, that he might have lived without noise and hurry, in a pure air, in the artless society of honest Villagers, and the contemplation of the works of nature.

I soon discovered the cause of my friend's Philosophy. He thought himself grown rich enough to have a lodging in the country, like the mercers on *Ludgate-hill*, and was resolved to enjoy himself in the decline of life. This was a revolution not to be made suddenly. He talked three years of the pleasures of the country, but passed every night over his own shop. But at last he resolved to be happy, and hired a lodging in the Country, that he may steal some hours in the week from business; for, says he, *when a man advances in life he loves to entertain himself sometimes with his own thoughts.*

I was invited to this seat of quiet and contemplation among those whom Mr. *Drugget* considers as his most reputable friends, and desires to make the first witnesses of his elevation to the highest dignities of a Shopkeeper. I found him at *Islington*, in a room which overlooked the high road, amusing himself with looking through the window, which the clouds of dust would not suffer him to open. He embraced me, told me I was welcome into the Country, and asked me, If I did not feel myself refreshed. He then desired that dinner might be hastened, for fresh air always sharpened his appetite, and ordered me a toast and a glass of wine after my walk. He told me much of the pleasures he found in retirement, and wondered what had kept him so long out of the Country. After dinner company came in, and Mr. *Drugget* again repeated the praises of the Country, recommended the pleasures of Meditation, and told them, that he had been all the morning at the window, counting the carriages as they passed before him.

(1758)

Thomas Gray

(1716-1771)

Elegy Written in a Country Churchyard

The curfew tolls the knell of parting day,
    The lowing herd wind slowly o'er the lea,
The plowman homeward plods his weary way,
    And leaves the world to darkness and to me.

5   Now fades the glimmering landscape on the sight,
    And all the air a solemn stillness holds,
Save where the beetle wheels his droning flight,
    And drowsy tinklings lull the distant folds;

Save that from yonder ivy-mantled tower
10   The moping owl does to the moon complain
Of such, as wandering near her secret bower,
    Molest her ancient solitary reign.

Beneath those rugged elms, that yew tree's shade,
    Where heaves the turf in many a mouldering heap,
15   Each in his narrow cell forever laid,
    The rude forefathers of the hamlet sleep.

The breezy call of incense-breathing Morn,
    The swallow twittering from the straw-built shed,
The cock's shrill clarion, or the echoing horn,
20   No more shall rouse them from their lowly bed.

For them no more the blazing hearth shall burn,
    Or busy housewife ply her evening care;
No children run to lisp their sire's return,
    Or climb his knees the envied kiss to share.

25   Oft did the harvest to their sickle yield,
    Their furrow oft the stubborn glebe has broke;
How jocund did they drive their team afield!
    How bowed the woods beneath their sturdy stroke!

Let not Ambition mock their useful toil,
30   Their homely joys, and destiny obscure;
Nor Grandeur hear with a disdainful smile
        The short and simple annals of the poor.

The boast of heraldry, the pomp of power,
        And all that beauty, all that wealth, e'er gave,
35 Awaits alike the inevitable hour.
        The paths of glory lead but to the grave.

Nor you, ye proud, impute to these the fault,
        If Memory o'er their tomb no trophies raise,
Where through the long-drawn aisle and fretted vault
40   The pealing anthem swells the note of praise.

Can storied urn or animated bust
        Back to its mansion call the fleeting breath?
Can Honour's voice provoke the silent dust,
        Or Flattery soothe the dull cold ear of Death?

45 Perhaps in this neglected spot is laid
        Some heart once pregnant with celestial fire;
Hands that the rod of empire might have swayed,
        Or waked to ecstasy the living lyre.

But Knowledge to their eyes her ample page
50   Rich with the spoils of time did ne'er unroll;
Chill Penury repressed their noble rage,
        And froze the genial current of the soul.

Full many a gem of purest ray serene,
        The dark unfathomed caves of ocean bear:
55 Full many a flower is born to blush unseen,
        And waste its sweetness on the desert air.

Some village Hampden, that with dauntless breast
        The little tyrant of his fields withstood;
Some mute inglorious Milton here may rest,
60   Some Cromwell guiltless of his country's blood.

The applause of listening senates to command,
        The threats of pain and ruin to despise,
To scatter plenty o'er a smiling land,
        And read their history in a nation's eyes,

65 Their lot forbade: nor circumscribed alone
        Their growing virtues, but their crimes confined;
Forbade to wade through slaughter to a throne,
        And shut the gates of mercy on mankind,

The struggling pangs of conscious truth to hide,
70   To quench the blushes of ingenuous shame,
Or heap the shrine of Luxury and Pride
    With incense kindled at the Muse's flame.

Far from the madding crowd's ignoble strife,
    Their sober wishes never learned to stray;
75 Along the cool sequestered vale of life
    They kept the noiseless tenor of their way.

Yet even these bones from insult to protect
    Some frail memorial still erected nigh,
With uncouth rhymes and shapeless sculpture decked,
80   Implores the passing tribute of a sigh.

Their name, their years, spelt by the unlettered Muse,
    The place of fame and elegy supply:
And many a holy text around she strews,
    That teach the rustic moralist to die.

85 For who to dumb Forgetfulness a prey,
    This pleasing anxious being e'er resigned,
Left the warm precincts of the cheerful day,
    Nor cast one longing lingering look behind?

On some fond breast the parting soul relies,
90   Some pious drops the closing eye requires;
Even from the tomb the voice of Nature cries,
    Even in our ashes live their wonted fires.

For thee, who mindful of the unhonoured dead
    Dost in these lines their artless tale relate;
95 If chance, by lonely contemplation led,
    Some kindred spirit shall inquire thy fate,

Haply some hoary-headed swain may say,
    "Oft have we seen him at the peep of dawn
Brushing with hasty steps the dews away
100   To meet the sun upon the upland lawn.

"There at the foot of yonder nodding beech
    That wreathes its old fantastic roots so high,
His listless length at noontide would he stretch,
    And pore upon the brook that babbles by.

105 "Hard by yon wood, now smiling as in scorn,
    Muttering his wayward fancies he would rove,
Now drooping, woeful wan, like one forlorn,
    Or crazed with care, or crossed in hopeless love.

"One morn I missed him on the customed hill,
110   Along the heath and near his favorite tree;
Another came; nor yet beside the rill,
    Nor up the lawn, nor at the wood was he;

"The next with dirges due in sad array
    Slow through the churchway path we saw him borne.
115 Approach and read (for thou canst read) the lay,
    Graved on the stone beneath yon aged thorn."

          The Epitaph

Here rests his head upon the lap of Earth
    A youth to Fortune and to Fame unknown.
Fair Science frowned not on his humble birth,
120   *And Melancholy marked him for her own.*
Large was his bounty, and his soul sincere,
    Heaven did a recompense as largely send:
He gave to Misery all he had, a tear,
    He gained from Heaven ('twas all he wished) a friend.
125 *No farther seek his merits to disclose,*
    Or draw his frailties from their dread abode
(There they alike in trembling hope repose),
    The bosom of his Father and his God.

                                    (1751)

Anonymous

Botany Bay

Farewell to old England for ever,
Farewell to my rum culls as well,
Farewell to the well-known Old Bailey,
Where I used for to cut such a swell.

5   Chorus Singing, too-ral, li-ooral, li-addity,
              Singing, too-ral, li-ooral, li-ay.
              Singing, too-ral, li-ooral, li-addity,
              Singing, too-ral, li-ooral, li-ay.

10 There's the captain as is our commander,
There's the bo'sun and all the ship's crew,
There's the first- and the second-class passengers,
Knows what we poor convicts goes through.

'Tain't leaving old England we care about,
15 'Tain't cos we misspells wot we knows,
But because all we light-fingered gentry
Hops round with a log on our toes.

For fourteen long years I have ser-vi-ed,
And for fourteen long years and a day,
20 For meeting a bloke in the area,
And sneaking his ticker away.

Oh had I the wings of a turtle-dove,
I'd soar on my pinions so high,
Slap bang to the arms of my Polly love,
25 And in her sweet presence I'd die.

Now, all my young Dook-ies and Duch-ess-es,
Take warning from what I've to say—
Mind all is your own as you touch-es-es,
Or you'll meet us in Botany Bay.

(late 18th century)

Alexander Henry

(U.S.A./CANADA, 1739–1824)

From *Travels and Adventures in Canada and the Indian Territories*

Massacre at Fort Michilimackinac

The morning was sultry. A Chipeway came to tell me that his nation was going to play at *bag'-gat'iway*, with the Sacs or Saakies, another Indian nation, for a high wager. He invited me to witness the sport, adding that the commandant was to be there, and would bet on the side of the Chipeways. In consequence of this information, I went to the commandant, and expostulated with him a little, representing that the Indians might possibly have some sinister end in view; but, the commandant only smiled at my suspicions.

Baggatiway, called by the Canadians *le jeu de la crosse*, is played with a bat and ball. The bat is about four feet in length, curved, and terminating in a sort of racket. Two posts are planted in the ground, at a considerable distance from each other, as a mile, or more. Each party has its post, and the game consists in throwing the ball up to the post of the adversary. The ball, at the beginning, is placed in the middle of the course, and each party endeavours as well to throw the ball out of the direction of its own post, as into that of the adversary's.

I did not go myself to see the match which was now to be played without the fort, because, there being a canoe prepared to depart, on the following day, for Montréal, I employed myself in writing letters to my friends; and even when a fellow-trader, Mr. Tracy, happened to call upon me, saying that another canoe had just arrived from Détroit, and proposing that I should go with him to the beach, to inquire the news, it so happened that I still remained, to finish my letters; promising to follow Mr. Tracy, in the course of a few minutes. Mr. Tracy had not gone more than twenty paces from my door, when I heard an Indian war-cry, and a noise of general confusion.

Going instantly to my window, I saw a crowd of Indians, within the fort, furiously cutting down and scalping every Englishman they found. In particular, I witnessed the fate of Lieutenant Jemette.

I had, in the room in which I was, a fowling-piece, loaded with swan-shot. This I immediately seized, and held it for a few minutes, waiting to hear the drum beat to arms. In this dreadful interval, I saw several of my countrymen fall, and more than one struggling between the knees of an Indian, who, holding him in this manner, scalped him, while yet living.

At length, disappointed in the hope of seeing resistance made to the enemy, and sensible, of course, that no effort, of my own unassisted arm, could avail against four hundred Indians, I thought only of seeking shelter. Amid the slaughter which was raging, I observed many of the Canadian inhabitants of the fort, calmly looking on, neither opposing the Indians, nor suffering injury; and, from this circumstance, I conceived a hope of finding security in their houses.

Between the yard-door of my own house, and that of M. Langlade, my next neighbour, there was only a low fence, over which I easily climbed. At my entrance, I found the whole family at the windows, gazing at the scene of blood before them. I addressed myself immediately to M. Langlade, begging that he would put me into some place of safety, until the heat of the affair should be over; an act of charity by which he might perhaps preserve me from the general massacre; but, while I uttered my petition, M. Langlade, who had looked for a moment at me, turned again to the window, shrugging his shoulders, and intimating, that he could do nothing for me:—"*Que voudriez-vous que j'en ferais?*"

This was a moment for despair; but, the next, a Pani woman, a slave of M. Langlade's, beckoned to me to follow her. She brought me to a door, which she opened, desiring me to enter, and telling me that it led to the garret, where I must go and conceal myself. I joyfully obeyed her directions; and she, having followed me up to the garret-door, locked it after me, and with great presence of mind took away the key.

This shelter obtained, if shelter I could hope to find it, I was naturally anxious to know what might still be passing without. Through an aperture, which afforded me a view of the area of the fort, I beheld, in shapes the foulest and most terrible, the ferocious triumphs of barbarian conquerors. The dead were scalped and mangled; the dying were writhing and shrieking, under the unsatiated knife and tomahawk; and, from the bodies of some ripped open, their butchers were drinking the blood, scooped up in the hollow of joined hands, and quaffed amid shouts of rage and victory. I was shaken, not only with horror, but with fear. The sufferings which I witnessed, I seemed on the point of experiencing. No long time elapsed, before every one being destroyed, who could be found, there was a general cry, of "All is finished!" At the same instant, I heard some of the Indians enter the house in which I was.

The garret was separated from the room below, only by a layer of single boards, at once the flooring of the one and the ceiling of the other. I could therefore hear every thing that passed; and, the Indians, no sooner in, than they inquired, whether or not any Englishman were in the house? M. Langlade replied, that "He could not say—he did not know of any;"—answers in which he did not exceed the truth; for the Pani woman had not only hidden me by stealth, but kept my secret, and her own; M. Langlade was therefore, as I presume, as far from a wish to destroy me, as he was careless about saving me, when he added to these answers, that "They might examine for themselves, and would soon be satisfied, as to the object of their question." Saying this, he brought them to the garret-door.

The state of my mind will be imagined. Arrived at the door, some delay was occasioned by the absence of the key, and a few moments were thus allowed me, in which to look around for a hiding place. In one corner of the garret was a heap of those vessels of birch-bark, used in maple-sugar making, as I have recently described.

The door was unlocked, and opening, and the Indians ascending the stairs before I had completely crept into a small opening which presented itself, at one end of the heap. An instant later, four Indians entered the room, all armed with tomahawks, and all besmeared with blood, upon every part of their bodies.

The die appeared to be cast. I could scarcely breathe; but I thought that the throbbing of my heart occasioned a noise loud enough to betray me. The Indians walked in every direction about the garret, and one of them approached me so closely that at a particular moment, had he put out his hand, he must have touched me. Still, I remained undiscovered; a circumstance to which the dark colour of my clothes, and the corner in which I was must have contributed. In a word, after taking several turns in the room, during want of light, in a room which had no window, and in which they told M. Langlade how many they had killed, and how many scalps they had taken, they returned down stairs, and I, with sensations not to be expressed, heard the door, which was the barrier between me and my fate, locked for the second time.

There was a feather-bed on the floor; and, on this, exhausted as I was, by the agitation of my mind, I threw myself down and fell asleep. In this state I remained till the dusk of the evening, when I was awakened by a second opening of the door. The person, that now entered, was M. Langlade's wife, who was much surprised at finding me, but advised me not to be uneasy, observing, that the Indians had killed most of the English, but that she hoped I might myself escape.—A shower of rain having begun to fall, she had come to stop a hole in the roof. On her going away, I begged her to send me a little water, to drink; which she did.

As night was now advancing, I continued to lie on the bed, ruminating on my condition, but unable to discover a resource, from which I could hope for life. A flight, to Détroit, had no probable chance of success. The distance, from Michilimackinac, was four hundred miles; I was without provisions; and the whole length of the road lay through Indian countries, countries of an enemy in arms, where the first man whom I should meet would kill me. To stay where I was, threatened nearly the same issue. As before, fatigue of mind, and not tranquility, suspended my cares, and procured me further sleep.

(1809)

William Blake

(1757–1827)

From *Songs of Innocence*

The Little Black Boy

> My mother bore me in the southern wild,
> And I am black, but O! my soul is white;
> White as an angel is the English child:
> But I am black as if bereav'd of light.

5　My mother taught me underneath a tree,
　　And sitting down before the heat of day,
　　She took me on her lap and kissèd me,
　　And pointing to the east, began to say:

　　"Look on the rising sun: there God does live,
10　And gives his light, and gives his heat away;
　　And flowers and trees and beasts and men receive
　　Comfort in morning, joy in the noon day.

　　"And we are put on earth a little space,
　　That we may learn to bear the beams of love,
15　And these black bodies and this sun-burnt face
　　Is but a cloud, and like a shady grove.

　　"For when our souls have learn'd the heat to bear,
　　The cloud will vanish; we shall hear his voice,
　　Saying, 'Come out from the grove, my love & care,
20　And round my golden tent like lambs rejoice.'"

　　Thus did my mother say, and kissèd me;
　　And thus I say to little English boy:
　　When I from black and he from white cloud free,
　　And round the tent of God like lambs we joy,

25　I'll shade him from the heat till he can bear
　　To lean in joy upon our father's knee;
　　And then I'll stand and stroke his silver hair,
　　And be like him, and he will then love me.

                                        (1789)

The Chimney Sweeper

　　When my mother died I was very young,
　　And my father sold me while yet my tongue
　　Could scarcely cry " 'weep, 'weep, 'weep, 'weep,"
　　So your chimneys I sweep & in soot I sleep.

5　There's little Tom Dacre who cried when his head,
　　That curl'd like a lamb's back, was shav'd: so I said,
　　"Hush, Tom, never mind it, for when your head's bare
　　You know that the soot cannot spoil your white hair."

　　And so he was quiet, & that very night,
10　As Tom was a sleeping, he had such a sight,
　　That thousands of sweepers, Dick, Joe, Ned & Jack,
　　Were all of them lock'd up in coffins of black.

And by came an Angel who had a bright key,
And he open'd the coffins & set them all free;
15 Then down a green plain, leaping, laughing, they run,
And wash in a river, and shine in the Sun.

Then naked & white, all their bags left behind,
They rise upon clouds, and sport in the wind;
And the Angel told Tom, if he'd be a good boy,
20 He'd have God for his father & never want joy.

And so Tom awoke; and we rose in the dark,
And got with our bags & our brushes to work.
Tho' the morning was cold, Tom was happy & warm;
So if all do their duty they need not fear harm.

(1789)

From *Songs of Experience*

The Chimney Sweeper

A little black thing among the snow,
Crying " 'weep, 'weep," in notes of woe!
"Where are thy father & mother, say?"
"They are both gone up to the church to pray.

5 "Because I was happy upon the heath,
And smil'd among the winter's snow,
They clothed me in the clothes of death,
And taught me to sing the notes of woe.

"And because I am happy, & dance & sing,
10 They think they have done me no injury,
And are gone to praise God & his Priest & King,
Who make up a heaven of our misery."

(1794)

The Sick Rose

O Rose, thou art sick.
The invisible worm
That flies in the night
In the howling storm

5 Has found out thy bed
Of crimson joy,
And his dark secret love
Does thy life destroy.

(1794)

London

I wander thro' each charter'd street,
Near where the charter'd Thames does flow,
And mark in every face I meet
Marks of weakness, marks of woe.

5   In every cry of every Man,
In every Infant's cry of fear,
In every voice, in every ban,
The mind-forg'd manacles I hear.

How the Chimney-sweeper's cry
10   Every blackning Church appalls;
And the hapless Soldier's sigh
Runs in blood down Palace walls.

But most thro' midnight streets I hear
How the youthful Harlot's curse
15   Blasts the new-born Infant's tear,
And blights with plagues the Marriage hearse.

(1794)

Robert Burns

(1759–1796)

To a Mouse, on Turning Her Up in Her Nest with the Plough, November, 1785

Wee, sleekit, cow'rin', tim'rous beastie,
O what a panic's in thy breastie!
Thou need na start awa sae hasty,
               Wi' bickering brattle!
5   I wad be laith to rin an' chase thee
               Wi' murd'ring pattle!

I'm truly sorry man's dominion
Has broken Nature's social union,
An' justifies that ill opinion
10   Which makes thee startle
At me, thy poor earth-born companion,
               An' fellow-mortal!

I doubt na, whiles, but thou may thieve;
What then? poor beastie, thou maun live!
15 A daimen-icker in a thrave
                    'S a sma' request:
I'll get a blessin' wi' the lave,
                    And never miss 't!

Thy wee bit housie, too, in ruin!
20 Its silly wa's the win's are strewin'!
An' naething, now, to big a new ane,
                    O' foggage green!
An' bleak December's winds ensuin',
                    Baith snell an' keen!

25 Thou saw the fields laid bare and waste,
An' weary winter comin' fast,
An' cozie here, beneath the blast,
                    Thou thought to dwell,
Till crash! the cruel coulter past
30   Out-thro' thy cell.

That wee bit heap o' leaves an' stibble
Has cost thee mony a weary nibble!
Now thou's turn'd out, for a' thy trouble,
                    But house or hald,
35 To thole the winter's sleety dribble,
                    An' cranreuch cauld!

But, Mousie, thou art no thy lane,
In proving foresight may be vain:
The best laid schemes o' mice an' men
40   Gang aft a-gley,
An' lea'e us nought but grief an' pain
                    For promis'd joy.

Still thou art blest compar'd wi' me!
The present only toucheth thee:
45 But och! I backward cast my e'e
                    On prospects drear!
An' forward tho' I canna see,
                    I guess an' fear!

                                    (1785)

William Wordsworth
(1770-1850)

London, 1802

Milton! thou shouldst be living at this hour:
England hath need of thee: she is a fen
Of stagnant waters: altar, sword, and pen,
Fireside, the heroic wealth of hall and bower,
5   Have forfeited their ancient English dower
Of inward happiness. We are selfish men;
Oh! raise us up, return to us again;
And give us manners, virtue, freedom, power.
Thy soul was like a Star, and dwelt apart;
10   Thou hadst a voice whose sound was like the sea:
Pure as the naked heavens, majestic, free,
So didst thou travel on life's common way,
In cheerful godliness; and yet thy heart
The lowliest duties on herself did lay.

(1802)

The World Is Too Much with Us

The world is too much with us; late and soon,
Getting and spending, we lay waste our powers:
Little we see in Nature that is ours;
We have given our hearts away, a sordid boon!
5   This Sea that bares her bosom to the moon;
The winds that will be howling at all hours,
And are up-gathered now like sleeping flowers;
For this, for everything, we are out of tune;
It moves us not.—Great God! I'd rather be
10   A Pagan suckled in a creed outworn;
So might I, standing on this pleasant lea,
Have glimpses that would make me less forlorn;
Have sight of Proteus rising from the sea;
Or hear old Triton blow his wreathed horn.

(1807)

Samuel Taylor Coleridge
(1772–1834)

Kubla Khan

Or a Vision in a Dream. A Fragment

In Xanadu did Kubla Khan
A stately pleasure dome decree:
Where Alph, the sacred river, ran
Through caverns measureless to man
5   Down to a sunless sea.
So twice five miles of fertile ground
With walls and towers were girdled round:
And there were gardens bright with sinuous rills,
Where blossomed many an incense-bearing tree;
10   And here were forests ancient as the hills,
Enfolding sunny spots of greenery.

But oh! that deep romantic chasm which slanted
Down the green hill athwart a cedarn cover!
A savage place! as holy and enchanted
15   As e'er beneath a waning moon was haunted
By woman wailing for her demon lover!
And from this chasm, with ceaseless turmoil seething,
As if this earth in fast thick pants were breathing,
A mighty fountain momently was forced:
20   Amid whose swift half-intermitted burst
Huge fragments vaulted like rebounding hail,
Or chaffy grain beneath the thresher's flail:
And 'mid these dancing rocks at once and ever
It flung up momently the sacred river.
25   Five miles meandering with a mazy motion

Through wood and dale the sacred river ran,
Then reached the caverns measureless to man,
And sank in tumult to a lifeless ocean:
And 'mid this tumult Kubla heard from far
30   Ancestral voices prophesying war!

The shadow of the dome of pleasure
Floated midway on the waves;
Where was heard the mingled measure
From the fountain and the caves.
35   It was a miracle of rare device,
A sunny pleasure dome with caves of ice!

A damsel with a dulcimer
In a vision once I saw:
It was an Abyssinian maid,
40 And on her dulcimer she played,
Singing of Mount Abora.
Could I revive within me
Her symphony and song,
To such a deep delight 'twould win me,
45 That with music loud and long,
I would build that dome in air,
That sunny dome! those caves of ice!
And all who heard should see them there,
And all should cry, Beware! Beware!
50 His flashing eyes, his floating hair!
Weave a circle round him thrice,
And close your eyes with holy dread,
For he on honey-dew hath fed,
And drunk the milk of Paradise.

(1798)

Metrical Feet

Lesson for a Boy

Tróchĕe tríps frŏm lóng tŏ shórt;
From long to long in solemn sort
Slów Spóndée stálks; stróng fóot! yet ill able
Évĕr tŏ cóme ŭp with Dáctўl trĭsýllăblĕ.
5 Iámbĭcs márch frŏm shórt tŏ lóng:—
Wĭth ă léap ănd ă bóund thĕ swĭft Ánăpæsts thróng;
One syllable long, with one short at each side,
Ămphíbrăchўs hástes wĭth ă státelў stríde:—
Fírst ănd lást bĕíng lóng, míddlĕ shórt, Ámphĭmácer
10 Stríkes hĭs thúndérĭng hóofs líke ă próud hígh-brĕd Rácer.
If Derwent be innocent, steady, and wise,
And delight in the things of earth, water, and skies;
Tender warmth at his heart, with these metres to show it,
With sound sense in his brains, may make Derwent a poet,—
15 May crown him with fame, and must win him the love
Of his father on earth and his Father above.
My dear, dear child!
Could you stand upon Skiddaw, you would not from its whole ridge
See a man who so loves you as your fond S. T. Coleridge.

(1806)

Percy Bysshe Shelley

(1792–1822)

Ozymandias

I met a traveller from an antique land
Who said: Two vast and trunkless legs of stone
Stand in the desert . . . Near them, on the sand,
Half sunk, a shattered visage lies, whose frown,
5   And wrinkled lip, and sneer of cold command,
Tell that its sculptor well those passions read
Which yet survive, (stamped on these lifeless things,)
The hand that mocked them and the heart that fed:
And on the pedestal these words appear:
10   'My name is Ozymandias, king of kings:
Look on my works, ye Mighty, and despair!'
Nothing beside remains. Round the decay
Of that colossal wreck, boundless and bare
The lone and level sands stretch far away.

(1818)

John Keats

(1795–1821)

Ode to a Nightingale

1

My heart aches, and a drowsy numbness pains
   My sense, as though of hemlock I had drunk,
Or emptied some dull opiate to the drains
   One minute past, and Lethe-wards had sunk:
5   'Tis not through envy of thy happy lot,
    But being too happy in thine happiness,—
      That thou, light-winged Dryad of the trees,
      In some melodious plot
   Of beechen green, and shadows numberless,
10   Singest of summer in full-throated ease.

O, for a draught of vintage! that hath been
  Cool'd a long age in the deep-delved earth,
Tasting of Flora and the country green,
  Dance, and Provençal song, and sunburnt mirth!
15 O for a beaker full of the warm South,
    Full of the true, the blushful Hippocrene,
      With beaded bubbles winking at the brim,
        And purple-stained mouth;
  That I might drink, and leave the world unseen,
20   And with thee fade away into the forest dim:

3

Fade far away, dissolve, and quite forget
  What thou among the leaves hast never known,
The weariness, the fever, and the fret
  Here, where men sit and hear each other groan;
25 Where palsy shakes a few, sad, last gray hairs,
    Where youth grows pale, and spectre-thin, and dies;
      Where but to think is to be full of sorrow
        And leaden-eyed despairs,
  Where Beauty cannot keep her lustrous eyes,
30   Or new Love pine at them beyond to-morrow.

4

Away! away! for I will fly to thee,
  Not charioted by Bacchus and his pards,
But on the viewless wings of Poesy,
  Though the dull brain perplexes and retards:
35 Already with thee! tender is the night,
    And haply the Queen-Moon is on her throne,
      Cluster'd around by all her starry Fays;
        But here there is no light,
  Save what from heaven is with the breezes blown
40   Through verdurous glooms and winding mossy ways.

5

I cannot see what flowers are at my feet,
  Nor what soft incense hangs upon the boughs,
But, in embalmed darkness, guess each sweet
  Wherewith the seasonable month endows
45 The grass, the thicket, and the fruit-tree wild;
    White hawthorn, and the pastoral eglantine;
      Fast fading violets cover'd up in leaves;
        And mid-May's eldest child,
  The coming musk-rose, full of dewy wine,
50   The murmurous haunt of flies on summer eves.

6

Darkling I listen; and, for many a time
  I have been half in love with easeful Death,
Call'd him soft names in many a mused rhyme,
  To take into the air my quiet breath;
55 Now more than ever seems it rich to die,
    To cease upon the midnight with no pain,
      While thou art pouring forth thy soul abroad
        In such an ecstasy!
    Still wouldst thou sing, and I have ears in vain—
60   To thy high requiem become a sod.

7

Thou wast not born for death, immortal Bird!
  No hungry generations tread thee down;
The voice I hear this passing night was heard
  In ancient days by emperor and clown:
65 Perhaps the self-same song that found a path
    Through the sad heart of Ruth, when, sick for home
      She stood in tears amid the alien corn;
        The same that oft-times hath
    Charm'd magic casements, opening on the foam
70   Of perilous seas, in faery lands forlorn.

8

Forlorn! the very word is like a bell
  To toll me back from thee to my sole self!
Adieu! the fancy cannot cheat so well
  As she is fam'd to do, deceiving elf.
75 Adieu! adieu! thy plaintive anthem fades
    Past the near meadows, over the still stream,
      Up the hill-side; and now 'tis buried deep
        In the next valley-glades:
    Was it a vision, or a waking dream?
80   Fled is that music:—Do I wake or sleep?

(1819)

To Autumn

1

Season of mists and mellow fruitfulness,
   Close bosom-friend of the maturing sun;
Conspiring with him how to load and bless
   With fruit the vines that round the thatch-eves run;
5   To bend with apples the moss'd cottage-trees,
     And fill all fruit with ripeness to the core;
       To swell the gourd, and plump the hazel shells
     With a sweet kernel; to set budding more,
And still more, later flowers for the bees,
10 Until they think warm days will never cease,
       For summer has o'er-brimm'd their clammy cells.

2

Who hath not seen thee oft amid thy store?
   Sometimes whoever seeks abroad may find
Thee sitting careless on a granary floor,
15   Thy hair soft-lifted by the winnowing wind;
Or on a half-reap'd furrow sound asleep,
   Drows'd with the fume of poppies, while thy hook
     Spares the next swath and all its twined flowers:
And sometimes like a gleaner thou dost keep
20   Steady thy laden head across a brook;
   Or by a cyder-press, with patient look,
     Thou watchest the last oozings hours by hours.

3

Where are the songs of spring? Ay, where are they?
   Think not of them, thou hast thy music too,—
25 While barred clouds bloom the soft-dying day,
   And touch the stubble-plains with rosy hue;
Then in a wailful choir the small gnats mourn
   Among the river sallows, borne aloft
     Or sinking as the light wind lives or dies;
30 And full-grown lambs loud bleat from hilly bourn;
   Hedge-crickets sing; and now with treble soft
   The red-breast whistles from a garden-croft;
     And gathering swallows twitter in the skies.

(1819)

Edgar Allan Poe
(U.S.A., 1809–1849)

To Helen

Helen, thy beauty is to me
   Like those Nicèan barks of yore,
That gently, o'er a perfumed sea,
   The weary, way-worn wanderer bore
5   To his own native shore.

On desperate seas long wont to roam,
   Thy hyacinth hair, thy classic face,
Thy Naiad airs have brought me home
   To the glory that was Greece,
10 And the grandeur that was Rome.

Lo! in yon brilliant window-niche
   How statue-like I see thee stand,
   The agate lamp within thy hand!
Ah, Psyche, from the regions which
15   Are Holy Land!

                  (1823)

Sonnet—To Science

Science! true daughter of Old Time thou art!
    Who alterest all things with thy peering eyes.
Why preyest thou thus upon the poet's heart,
    Vulture, whose wings are dull realities?
5   How should he love thee? or how deem thee wise?
    Who wouldst not leave him in his wandering
To seek for treasure in the jeweled skies,
    Albeit he soared with an undaunted wing?
Hast thou not dragged Diana from her car?
10   And driven the Hamadryad from the wood
To seek a shelter in some happier star?
    Hast thou not torn the Naiad from her flood,
The Elfin from the green grass, and from me
The summer dream beneath the tamarind tree?

                  (1829)

The Cask of Amontillado

The thousand injuries of Fortunato I had borne as I best could, but when he ventured upon insult, I vowed revenge. You, who so well know the nature of my soul, will not suppose, however, that I gave utterance to a threat. *At length* I would be avenged; this was a point definitively settled—but the very definitiveness with which it was resolved, precluded the idea of risk. I must not only punish, but punish with impunity. A wrong is unredressed when retribution overtakes its redresser. It is equally unredressed when the avenger fails to make himself felt as such to him who has done the wrong.

It must be understood that neither by word nor deed had I given Fortunato cause to doubt my good will. I continued as was my wont, to smile in his face, and he did not perceive that my smile *now* was at the thought of his immolation.

He had a weak point—this Fortunato—although in other regards he was a man to be respected and even feared. He prided himself on his connoisseurship in wine. Few Italians have the true virtuoso spirit. For the most part their enthusiasm is adapted to suit the time and opportunity—to practice imposture upon the British and Austrian *millionaires*. In painting and gemmary Fortunato, like his country men, was a quack—but in the matter of old wines he was sincere. In this respect I did not differ from him materially: I was skilful in the Italian vintages myself, and bought largely whenever I could.

It was about dusk, one evening during the supreme madness of the carnival season, that I encountered my friend. He accosted me with excessive warmth, for he had been drinking much. The man wore motley. He had on a tight-fitting parti-striped dress, and his head was surmounted by the conical cap and bells. I was so pleased to see him, that I thought I should never have done wringing his hand.

I said to him: "My dear Fortunato, you are luckily met. How remarkably well you are looking to-day! But I have received a pipe of what passes for Amontillado, and I have my doubts."

"How?" said he "Amontillado? A pipe? Impossible! And in the middle of the carnival!"

"I have my doubts," I replied; "and I was silly enough to pay the full Amontillado price without consulting you in the matter. You were not to be found, and I was fearful of losing a bargain."

"Amontillado!"

"I have my doubts."

"Amontillado!"

"And I must satisfy them."

"Amontillado!"

"As you are engaged, I am on my way to Luchesi. If any one has a critical turn, it is he. He will tell me—"

"Luchesi cannot tell Amontillado from Sherry."

"And yet some fools will have it that his taste is a match for your own."

"Come, let us go."

"Whither?"

"To your vaults."

"My friend, no; I will not impose upon your good nature. I perceive you have an engagement. Luchesi—"

"I have no engagement—come."

"My friend, no. It is not the engagement, but the severe cold with which I perceive you are afflicted. The vaults are insufferably damp. They are encrusted with nitre."

"Let us go, nevertheless. The cold is merely nothing. Amontillado! You have been imposed upon. And as for Luchesi, he cannot distinguish Sherry from Amontillado."

Thus speaking, Fortunato possessed himself of my arm. Putting on a mask of black silk, and drawing a *roquelaire* closely about my person, I suffered him to hurry me to my palazzo.

There were no attendants at home; they had absconded to make merry in honor of the time. I had told them that I should not return until the morning, and had given them explicit orders not to stir from the house. These orders were sufficient, I well knew, to insure their immediate disappearance, one and all, as soon as my back was turned.

I took from their sconces two flambeaux, and giving one to Fortunato, bowed him through several suites of rooms to the archway that led into the vaults. I passed down a long and winding staircase, requesting him to be cautious as he followed. We came at length to the foot of the descent, and stood together on the damp ground of the catacombs of the Montresors.

The gait of my friend was unsteady, and the bells upon his cap jingled as he strode.

"The pipe?" said he.

"It is farther on," said I; "but observe the white webwork which gleams from these cavern walls."

He turned toward me, and looked into my eyes with two filmy orbs that distilled the rheum of intoxication.

"Nitre?" he asked, at length.

"Nitre," I replied. "How long have you had that cough?"

"Ugh! ugh! ugh!—ugh! ugh! ugh!—ugh! ugh! ugh!—ugh! ugh! ugh!—ugh! ugh! ugh!"

My poor friend found it impossible to reply for many minutes.

"It is nothing," he said, at last.

"Come," I said, with decision, "we will go back; your health is precious. You are rich, respected, admired, beloved; you are happy, as once I was. You are a man to be missed. For me it is no matter. We will go back; you will be ill, and I cannot be responsible. Besides, there is Luchesi—"

"Enough," he said; "the cough is a mere nothing; it will not kill me. I shall not die of a cough."

"True—true," I replied; "and, indeed, I had no intention of alarming you unnecessarily; but you should use all proper caution. A draught of this Medoc will defend us from the damps."

Here I knocked off the neck of a bottle which I drew from a long row of its fellows that lay upon the mould.

"Drink," I said, presenting him the wine.

He raised it to his lips with a leer. He paused and nodded to me familiarly, while his bells jingled.

"I drink," he said, "to the buried that repose around us."

"And I to your long life."

He again took my arm, and we proceeded.

"These vaults," he said, "are extensive."

"The Montresors," I replied, "were a great and numerous family."

"I forget your arms."

"A huge human foot d'or, in a field azure; the foot crushes a serpent rampant whose fangs are imbedded in the heel."

"And the motto?"

"Nemo me impune lacessit."

"Good!" he said.

The wine sparkled in his eyes and the bells jingled. My own fancy grew warm with the Medoc. We had passed through walls of piled bones, with casks and puncheons intermingling, into the inmost recesses of the catacombs. I paused again, and this time I made bold to seize Fortunato by an arm above the elbow.

"The nitre!" I said; "see, it increases. It hangs like moss upon the vaults. We are below the river's bed. The drops of moisture trickle among the bones. Come, we will go back ere it is too late. Your cough—"

"It is nothing," he said; "let us go on. But first, another draught of the Medoc."

I broke and reached him a flagon of De Grave. He emptied it at a breath. His eyes flashed with a fierce light. He laughed and threw the bottle upward with a gesticulation I did not understand.

I looked at him in surprise. He repeated the movement—a grotesque one.

"You do not comprehend?" he said.

"Not I," I replied.

"Then you are not of the brotherhood."

"How?"

"You are not of the masons."

"Yes, yes," I said; "yes, yes."

"You? Impossible! A mason?"

"A mason," I replied.

"A sign," he said.

"It is this," I answered, producing a trowel from beneath the folds of my *roquelaire.*

"You jest," he exclaimed, recoiling a few paces. "But let us proceed to the Amontillado."

"Be it so," I said, replacing the tool beneath the cloak, and again offering him my arm. He leaned upon it heavily. We continued our route in search of the Amontillado. We passed through a range of low arches, descended, passed on, and descending again, arrived at a deep crypt, in which the foulness of the air caused our flambeaux rather to glow than flame.

At the most remote end of the crypt there appeared another less spacious. Its walls had been lined with human remains, piled to the vault overhead, in the fashion of the great catacombs of Paris. Three sides of this interior crypt were still ornamented in this manner. From the fourth the bones had been thrown down, and lay promiscuously upon the earth, forming at one point a mound of some size. Within the wall thus exposed by the displacing of the bones, we perceived a still interior recess, in depth about four feet, in width three, in height six or seven. It seemed to have been constructed for no especial use within itself, but formed merely the interval between two of the colossal supports of the roof of the catacombs, and was backed by one of their circumscribing walls of solid granite.

It was in vain that Fortunato, uplifting his dull torch, endeavored to pry into the depth of the recess. Its termination the feeble light did not enable us to see.

"Proceed," I said; "herein is the Amontillado. As for Luchesi—"

"He is an ignoramus," interrupted my friend, as he stepped unsteadily forward, while I followed immediately at his heels. In an instant he had reached the extremity of the niche, and finding his progress arrested by the rock, stood stupidly bewildered. A moment more and I had fettered him to the granite. In its surface were two iron staples, distant from each other about two feet, horizontally. From one of these depended a short chain, from the other a padlock. Throwing the links about his waist, it was but the work of a few seconds to secure it. He was too much astounded to resist. Withdrawing the key I stepped back from the recess.

"Pass your hand," I said, "over the wall; you cannot help feeling the nitre. Indeed it is *very* damp. Once more let me *implore* you to return. No? Then I must positively leave you. But I must first render you all the little attentions in my power."

"The Amontillado!" ejaculated my friend, not yet recovered from his astonishment.

"True," I replied; "the Amontillado."

As I said these words I busied myself among the pile of bones of which I have before spoken. Throwing them aside, I soon uncovered a quantity of building stone and mortar. With these materials and with the aid of my trowel, I began vigorously to wall up the entrance of the niche.

I had scarcely laid the first tier of the masonry when I discovered that the intoxication of Fortunato had in a great measure worn off. The earliest indication I had of this was a low moaning cry from the depth of the recess. It was *not* the cry of a drunken man. There was then a long and obstinate silence. I laid the second tier, and the third, and the fourth; and then I heard the furious vibrations of the chain. The noise lasted for several minutes, during which, that I might hearken to it with the more satisfaction, I ceased my labors and sat down upon the bones. When at last the clanking subsided, I resumed the trowel, and finished without interruption the fifth, the sixth, and the seventh tier. The wall was now nearly upon a level with my breast. I again paused, and holding the flambeaux over the masonwork, threw a few feeble rays upon the figure within.

A succession of loud and shrill screams, bursting suddenly from the throat of the chained form, seemed to thrust me violently back. For a brief moment I hesitated—I trembled. Unsheathing my rapier, I began to grope with it about the recess; but the thought of an instant reassured me. I placed my hand upon the solid fabric of the catacombs, and felt satisfied. I reapproached the wall. I replied to the yells of him who clamored. I re-echoed—I aided—I surpassed them in volume and in strength. I did this, and the clamorer grew still.

It was now midnight, and my task was drawing to a close. I had completed the eighth, the ninth, and the tenth tier. I had finished a portion of the last and the eleventh; there remained but a single stone to be fitted and plastered in. I struggled with its weight; I placed it partially in its destined position. But now there came from out the niche a low laugh that erected the hairs upon my head. It was succeeded by a sad voice, which I had difficulty in recognizing as that of the noble Fortunato. The voice said—

"Ha! ha! ha!—he! he!—a very good joke indeed—an excellent jest. We will have many a rich laugh about it at the palazzo—he! he! he!—over our wine—he! he! he!"

"The Amontillado!" I said.

"He! he! he!—he! he! he!—yes, the Amontillado. But is it not getting late? Will not they be awaiting us at the palazzo, the Lady Fortunato and the rest? Let us be gone."

"Yes," I said, "let us be gone."

"For the love of God, Montresor!"

"Yes," I said, "for the love of God!"

But to these words I hearkened in vain for a reply. I grew impatient. I called aloud;

"Fortunato!"

No answer. I called again;

"Fortunato!"

No answer still. I thrust a torch through the remaining aperture and let it fall within. There came forth in return only a jingling of the bells. My heart grew sick—on account of the dampness of the catacombs. I hastened to make an end of my labor. I forced the last stone into its position; I plastered it up. Against the new masonry I re-erected the old rampart of bones. For the half of a century no mortal has disturbed them. *In pace requiescat!*

(1846)

Alfred, Lord Tennyson
(1809–1892)

Ulysses

It little profits that an idle king,
By this still hearth, among these barren crags,
Matched with an aged wife, I mete and dole
Unequal laws unto a savage race,
5   That hoard, and sleep, and feed, and know not me.
I cannot rest from travel; I will drink
Life to the lees. All times I have enjoyed
Greatly, have suffered greatly, both with those
That loved me, and alone; on shore, and when
10   Through scudding drifts the rainy Hyades
Vexed the dim sea: I am become a name;
For always roaming with a hungry heart
Much have I seen and known—cities of men
And manners, climates, councils, governments,
15   Myself not least, but honoured of them all;
And drunk delight of battle with my peers,
Far on the ringing plains of windy Troy.
I am a part of all that I have met;
Yet all experience is an arch wherethrough
20   Gleams that untraveled world whose margin fades
For ever and for ever when I move.
How dull it is to pause, to make an end,
To rust unburnished, not to shine in use!
As though to breathe were life! Life piled on life
25   Were all too little, and of one to me
Little remains; but every hour is saved
From that eternal silence, something more,
A bringer of new things; and vile it were
For some three suns to store and hoard myself,
30   And this gray spirit yearning in desire
To follow knowledge like a sinking star,
Beyond the utmost bound of human thought.

This is my son, mine own Telemachus,
To whom I leave the scepter and the isle—
35 Well-loved of me, discerning to fulfil
This labour, by slow prudence to make mild
A rugged people, and through soft degrees
Subdue them to the useful and the good.
Most blameless is he, centred in the sphere
40 Of common duties, decent not to fail
In offices of tenderness, and pay
Meet adoration to my household gods,
When I am gone. He works his work, I mine.

There lies the port; the vessel puffs her sail;
45 There gloom the dark, broad seas. My mariners,
Souls that have toiled, and wrought, and thought with me—
That ever with a frolic welcome took
The thunder and the sunshine, and opposed
Free hearts, free foreheads—you and I are old;
50 Old age hath yet his honour and his toil.
Death closes all; but something ere the end,
Some work of noble note, may yet be done,
Not unbecoming men that strove with Gods.
The lights begin to twinkle from the rocks:
55 The long day wanes: the slow moon climbs: the deep
Moans round with many voices. Come, my friends,
'Tis not too late to seek a newer world.
Push off, and sitting well in order smite
The sounding furrows; for my purpose holds
60 To sail beyond the sunset, and the baths
Of all the western stars, until I die.
It may be that the gulfs will wash us down;
It may be we shall touch the Happy Isles,
And see the great Achilles, whom we knew.
65 Though much is taken, much abides; and though
We are not now that strength which in old days
Moved earth and heaven, that which we are, we are:
One equal temper of heroic hearts,
Made weak by time and fate, but strong in will
70 To strive, to seek, to find, and not to yield.

(1833)

From *In Memoriam A.H.H.*

L

Be near me when my light is low,
    When the blood creeps, and the nerves prick
    And tingle; and the heart is sick,
And all the wheels of Being slow.

5   Be near me when the sensuous frame
    Is racked with pangs that conquer trust;
    And Time, a maniac scattering dust,
And Life, a Fury slinging flame.

Be near me when my faith is dry,
10   And men the flies of latter spring,
    That lay their eggs, and sting and sing
And weave their petty cells and die.

Be near me when I fade away,
    To point the term of human strife,
15   And on the low dark verge of life
The twilight of eternal day.

LIV

Oh yet we trust that somehow good
    Will be the final goal of ill,
    To pangs of nature, sins of will,
Defects of doubt, and taints of blood;

5   That nothing walks with aimless feet;
    That not one life shall be destroyed,
    Or cast as rubbish to the void,
When God hath made the pile complete;

That not a worm is cloven in vain;
10   That not a moth with vain desire
    Is shrivelled in a fruitless fire,
Or but subserves another's gain.

Behold, we know not anything;
    I can but trust that good shall fall
15   At last—far off—at last, to all,
And every winter change to spring.

So runs my dream: but what am I?
    An infant crying in the night:
    An infant crying for the light:
20   And with no language but a cry.

LV

The wish, that of the living whole
    No life may fail beyond the grave,
    Derives it not from what we have
The likest God within the soul?

5 Are God and Nature then at strife,
    That Nature lends such evil dreams?
    So careful of the type she seems,
So careless of the single life;

That I, considering everywhere
10   Her secret meaning in her deeds,
    And finding that of fifty seeds
She often brings but one to bear,

I falter where I firmly trod,
    And falling with my weight of cares
15   Upon the great world's altar-stairs
That slope through darkness up to God,

I stretch lame hands of faith, and grope,
    And gather dust and chaff, and call
    To what I feel is Lord of all,
20 And faintly trust the larger hope.

Ring out, wild bells, to the wild sky,
    The flying cloud, the frosty light:
    The year is dying in the night;
Ring out, wild bells, and let him die.

5 Ring out the old, ring in the new,
    Ring, happy bells, across the snow:
    The year is going, let him go;
Ring out the false, ring in the true.

Ring out the grief that saps the mind,
10   For those that here we see no more;
    Ring out the feud of rich and poor,
Ring in redress to all mankind.

Ring out a slowly dying cause,
    And ancient forms of party strife;
15   Ring in the nobler modes of life,
With sweeter manners, purer laws.

Ring out the want, the care, the sin,
    The faithless coldness of the times;
    Ring out, ring out my mournful rhymes,
20 But ring the fuller minstrel in.

Ring out false pride in place and blood,
    The civic slander and the spite;
    Ring in the love of truth and right,
Ring in the common love of good.

25 Ring out old shapes of foul disease;
        Ring out the narrowing lust of gold;
        Ring out the thousand wars of old,
    Ring in the thousand years of peace.

    Ring in the valiant man and free,
30   The larger heart, the kindlier hand;
        Ring out the darkness of the land,
    Ring in the Christ that is to be.
                                    (1833–50)

Crossing the Bar

Sunset and evening star,
    And one clear call for me!
And may there be no moaning of the bar,
    When I put out to sea,

5   But such a tide as moving seems asleep,
        Too full for sound and foam,
    When that which drew from out the boundless deep
        Turns again home.

    Twilight and evening bell,
10   And after that the dark!
    And may there be no sadness of farewell,
        When I embark;

    For tho' from out our bourne of Time and Place
        The flood may bear me far,
15 I hope to see my Pilot face to face
        When I have crost the bar.
                                    (1889)

Robert Browning

(1812–1889)

My Last Duchess

Ferrara

    That's my last Duchess painted on the wall,
    Looking as if she were alive. I call
    That piece a wonder, now: Frà Pandolf's hands
    Worked busily a day, and there she stands.
5   Will't please you sit and look at her? I said
    "Frà Pandolf" by design, for never read
    Strangers like you that pictured countenance,
    The depth and passion of its earnest glance,
    But to myself they turned (since none puts by
10 The curtain I have drawn for you, but I)
    And seemed as they would ask me, if they durst,
    How such a glance came there; so, not the first
    Are you to turn and ask thus. Sir, 'twas not
    Her husband's presence only, called that spot
15 Of joy into the Duchess' cheek: perhaps
    Frà Pandolf chanced to say, "Her mantle laps
    Over my lady's wrist too much," or "Paint
    Must never hope to reproduce the faint
    Half-flush that dies along her throat": such stuff
20 Was courtesy, she thought, and cause enough
    For calling up that spot of joy. She had
    A heart—how shall I say?—too soon made glad,
    Too easily impressed; she liked whate'er
    She looked on, and her looks went everywhere.
25 Sir, 'twas all one! My favour at her breast,
    The dropping of the daylight in the West,
    The bough of cherries some officious fool
    Broke in the orchard for her, the white mule
    She rode with round the terrace—all and each
30 Would draw from her alike the approving speech,
    Or blush, at least. She thanked men,—good! but thanked
    Somehow—I know not how—as if she ranked
    My gift of a nine-hundred-years-old name
    With anybody's gift. Who'd stoop to blame
35 This sort of trifling? Even had you skill
    In speech—(which I have not)—to make your will
    Quite clear to such an one, and say, "Just this
    Or that in you disgusts me; here you miss,
    Or there exceed the mark"—and if she let
40 Herself be lessoned so, nor plainly set

Her wits to yours, forsooth, and made excuse,
—E'en then would be some stooping; and I choose
Never to stoop. Oh sir, she smiled, no doubt,
Whene'er I passed her; but who passed without
45 Much the same smile? This grew; I gave commands;
Then all smiles stopped together. There she stands
As if alive. Will't please you rise? We'll meet
The company below, then. I repeat,
The Count your master's known munificence
50 Is ample warrant that no just pretence
Of mine for dowry will be disallowed;
Though his fair daughter's self, as I avowed
At starting, is my object. Nay, we'll go
Together down, sir. Notice Neptune, though,
55 Taming a sea-horse, thought a rarity,
Which Claus of Innsbruck cast in bronze for me!

(1842)

The Bishop Orders His Tomb at Saint Praxed's Church

Rome, 15—

Vanity, saith the preacher, vanity!
Draw round my bed: is Anselm keeping back?
Nephews—sons mine . . . ah God, I know not! Well—
She, men would have to be your mother once,
5 Old Gandolf envied me, so fair she was!
What's done is done, and she is dead beside,
Dead long ago, and I am Bishop since,
And as she died so must we die ourselves,
And thence ye may perceive the world's a dream.
10 Life, how and what is it? As here I lie
In this state-chamber, dying by degrees,
Hours and long hours in the dead night, I ask
"Do I live, am I dead?" Peace, peace seems all.
Saint Praxed's ever was the church for peace;
15 And so, about this tomb of mine. I fought
With tooth and nail to save my niche, ye know:
—Old Gandolf cozened me, despite my care;
Shrewd was that snatch from out the corner South
He graced his carrion with, God curse the same!
20 Yet still my niche is not so cramped but thence
One sees the pulpit o' the epistle-side,
And somewhat of the choir, those silent seats,
And up into the aery dome where live
The angels, and a sunbeam's sure to lurk:
25 And I shall fill my slab of basalt there,
And 'neath my tabernacle take my rest,
With those nine columns round me, two and two,
The odd one at my feet where Anselm stands:

Peach-blossom marble all, the rare, the ripe
30   As fresh-poured red wine of a mighty pulse.
—Old Gandolf with his paltry onion-stone,
Put me where I may look at him! True peach,
Rosy and flawless: how I earned the prize!
Draw close: that conflagration of my church
35   —What then? So much was saved if aught were missed!
My sons, ye would not be my death? Go dig
The white-grape vineyard where the oil-press stood,
Drop water gently till the surface sink,
And if ye find . . . Ah God, I know not, I! . . .
40   Bedded in store of rotten fig-leaves soft,
And corded up in a tight olive-frail,
Some lump, ah God, of *lapis lazuli*,
Big as a Jew's head cut off at the nape,
Blue as a vein o'er the Madonna's breast . . .
45   Sons, all have I bequeathed you, villas, all,
That brave Frascati villa with its bath,
So, let the blue lump poise between my knees,
Like God the Father's globe on both his hands
Ye worship in the Jesu Church so gay,
50   For Gandolf shall not choose but see and burst!
Swift as a weaver's shuttle fleet our years:
Man goeth to the grave, and where is he?
Did I say basalt for my slab, sons? Black—
'Twas ever antique-black I meant! How else
55   Shall ye contrast my frieze to come beneath?
The bas-relief in bronze ye promised me,
Those Pans and Nymphs ye wot of, and perchance
Some tripod, thyrsus, with a vase or so,
The Saviour at his sermon on the mount,
60   Saint Praxed in a glory, and one Pan
Ready to twitch the Nymph's last garment off,
And Moses with the tables . . . but I know
Ye mark me not! What do they whisper thee,
Child of my bowels, Anselm? Ah, ye hope
65   To revel down my villas while I gasp
Bricked o'er with beggar's mouldy travertine
Which Gandolf from his tomb-top chuckles at!
Nay, boys, ye love me—all of jasper, then!
'Tis jasper ye stand pledged to, lest I grieve
70   My bath must needs be left behind, alas!
One block, pure green as a pistachio-nut,
There's plenty jasper somewhere in the world—
And have I not Saint Praxed's ear to pray
Horses for ye, and brown Greek manuscripts,
75   And mistresses with great smooth marbly limbs?
—That's if ye carve my epitaph aright,
Choice Latin, picked phrase, Tully's every word,

No gaudy ware like Gandolf's second line—
Tully, my masters? Ulpian serves his need!
80   And then how I shall lie through centuries,
And hear the blessed mutter of the mass,
And see God made and eaten all day long,
And feel the steady candle-flame, and taste
Good strong thick stupefying incense-smoke!
85   For as I lie here, hours of the dead night,
Dying in state and by such slow degrees,
I fold my arms as if they clasped a crook,
And stretch my feet forth straight as stone can point,
And let the bedclothes, for a mortcloth, drop
90   Into great laps and folds of sculptor's-work:
And as yon tapers dwindle, and strange thoughts
Grow, with a certain humming in my ears,
About the life before I lived this life,
And this life too, popes, cardinals and priests,
95   Saint Praxed at his sermon on the mount,
Your tall pale mother with her talking eyes,
And new-found agate urns as fresh as day,
And marble's language, Latin pure, discreet,
—Aha, ELUCESCEBAT quoth our friend?
100   No Tully, said I, Ulpian at the best!
Evil and brief hath been my pilgrimage.
All *lapis*, all, sons! Else I give the Pope
My villas! Will ye ever eat my heart?
Ever your eyes were as a lizard's quick,
105   They glitter like your mother's for my soul,
Or ye would heighten my impoverished frieze,
Piece out its starved design, and fill my vase
With grapes, and add a visor and a Term,
And to the tripod ye would tie a lynx
110   That in his struggle throws the thyrsus down,
To comfort me on my entablature
Whereon I am to lie till I must ask
"Do I live, am I dead?" There, leave me, there!
For ye have stabbed me with ingratitude
115   To death—ye wish it—God, ye wish it! Stone—
Gritstone, a-crumble! Clammy squares which sweat
As if the corpse they keep were oozing through—
And no more *lapis* to delight the world!
Well, go! I bless ye. Fewer tapers there,
120   But in a row: and, going, turn your backs
—Ay, like departing altar-ministrants,
And leave me in my church, the church for peace,
That I may watch at leisure if he leers—
Old Gandolf—at me, from his onion-stone,
125   As still he envied me, so fair she was!

                                              (1845)

Walt Whitman
(U.S.A., 1819–1892)

A Noiseless Patient Spider

A noiseless patient spider,
I mark'd where on a little promontory it stood isolated,
Mark'd how to explore the vacant vast surrounding,
It launch'd forth filament, filament, filament, out of itself,
5   Ever unreeling them, ever tirelessly speeding them.

And you O my soul where you stand,
Surrounded, detached, in measureless oceans of space,
Ceaselessly musing, venturing, throwing, seeking the spheres to connect them,
Till the bridge you will need be form'd, till the ductile anchor hold,
10   Till the gossamer thread you fling catch somewhere, O my soul.

(1868)

To a Locomotive in Winter

Thee for my recitative,
Thee in the driving storm even as now, the snow, the winter-day declining,
Thee in thy panoply, thy measur'd dual throbbing and thy beat convulsive,
Thy black cylindric body, golden brass and silvery steel,
5   Thy ponderous side-bars, parallel and connecting rods, gyrating, shuttling at thy sides,
Thy metrical, now swelling pant and roar, now tapering in the distance,
Thy great protruding head-light fix'd in front,
Thy long, pale, floating vapor-pennants, tinged with delicate purple,
The dense and murky clouds out-belching from thy smoke-stack,
10   Thy knitted frame, thy springs and valves, the tremulous twinkle of thy wheels,
Thy train of cars behind, obedient, merrily following,
Through gale or calm, now swift, now slack, yet steadily careering;
Type of the modern—emblem of motion and power—pulse of the continent,
For once come serve the Muse and merge in verse, even as here I see thee,
15   With storm and buffeting gusts of wind and falling snow,
By day thy warning ringing bell to sound its notes,
By night thy silent signal lamps to swing.

Fierce-throated beauty!
Roll through my chant with all thy lawless music, thy swinging lamps at night,
20   Thy madly-whistled laughter, echoing, rumbling like an earthquake, rousing all,
Law of thyself complete, thine own track firmly holding,
(No sweetness debonair of tearful harp or glib piano thine,)
Thy trills of shrieks by rocks and hills return'd,
Launch'd o'er the prairies wide, across the lakes,
25   To the free skies unpent and glad and strong.

(1876)

Matthew Arnold

(1822–1888)

To Marguerite

Yes: in the sea of life enisled,
    With echoing straits between us thrown,
Dotting the shoreless watery wild,
    We mortal millions live *alone*.
5   The islands feel the enclasping flow,
And then their endless bounds they know.

But when the moon their hollows lights,
    And they are swept by balms of spring,
And in their glens, on starry nights,
10   The nightingales divinely sing;
And lovely notes, from shore to shore,
Across the sounds and channels pour;

O then a longing like despair
    Is to their farthest caverns sent!
15 For surely once, they feel, we were
    Parts of a single continent.
Now round us spreads the watery plain—
O might our marges meet again!

Who ordered that their longing's fire
20   Should be, as soon as kindled, cooled?
Who renders vain their deep desire?—
    A god, a god their severance ruled;
And bade betwixt their shores to be
The unplumbed, salt, estranging sea.

(1854)

Dover Beach

The sea is calm to-night.
The tide is full, the moon lies fair
Upon the straits;—on the French coast the light
Gleams and is gone; the cliffs of England stand,
5   Glimmering and vast, out in the tranquil bay.
Come to the window, sweet is the night-air!

Only, from the long line of spray
Where the sea meets the moon-blanch'd land,
Listen! you hear the grating roar
10   Of pebbles which the waves draw back, and fling,
At their return, up the high strand,
Begin, and cease, and then again begin,
With tremulous cadence slow, and bring
The eternal note of sadness in.

15   Sophocles long ago
Heard it on the Ægæan, and it brought
Into his mind the turbid ebb and flow
Of human misery; we
Find also in the sound a thought,
20   Hearing it by this distant northern sea.

The Sea of Faith
Was once, too, at the full, and round earth's shore
Lay like the folds of a bright girdle furl'd.
But now I only hear
25   Its melancholy, long, withdrawing roar,
Retreating, to the breath
Of the night-wind, down the vast edges drear
And naked shingles of the world.

Ah, love, let us be true
30   To one another! for the world, which seems
To lie before us like a land of dreams,
So various, so beautiful, so new,
Hath really neither joy, nor love, nor light,
Nor certitude, nor peace, nor help for pain;
35   And we are here as on a darkling plain
Swept with confused alarms of struggle and flight,
Where ignorant armies clash by night.

(1867)

Emily Dickinson

(U.S.A., 1830–1886)

I Like to See It Lap the Miles

I like to see it lap the Miles –
And lick the Valleys up –
And stop to feed itself at Tanks –
And then – prodigious step

5   Around a Pile of Mountains –
And supercilious peer
In Shanties – by the sides of Roads –
And then a Quarry pare

To fit its Ribs
10   And crawl between
Complaining all the while
In horrid – hooting stanza –
Then chase itself down Hill –

And neigh like Boanerges –
15   Then – punctual as a Star
Stop – docile and omnipotent
At its own stable door–

(c. 1862)

A Narrow Fellow in the Grass

A narrow Fellow in the Grass
Occasionally rides—
You may have met Him—did you not
His notice sudden is—

5   The Grass divides as with a Comb—
A spotted shaft is seen—
And then it closes at your feet
And opens further on—

He likes a Boggy Acre
10   A Floor too cool for Corn—
Yet when a Boy, and Barefoot—
I more than once at Noon

Have passed, I thought, a Whip lash
Unbraiding in the Sun
15   When stooping to secure it
It wrinkled, and was gone—

Several of Nature's People
I know, and they know me—
I feel for them a transport
20   Of cordiality—

But never met this Fellow
Attended, or alone
Without a tighter breathing
And Zero at the Bone—

        (1866)

A Route of Evanescence

A Route of Evanescence
With a revolving Wheel—
A Resonance of Emerald—
A Rush of Cochineal—
5   And every Blossom on the Bush
Adjusts its tumbled Head—
The mail from Tunis, probably,
An easy Morning's Ride—

        (1879)

To Make a Prairie It Takes a Clover and One Bee

To make a prairie it takes a clover and one bee,
One clover, and a bee,
And revery.
The revery alone will do,
5   If bees are few.

        (1896)

Lewis Carroll
(1832–1898)

Jabberwocky

'Twas brillig, and the slithy toves
   Did gyre and gimble in the wabe;
All mimsy were the borogoves,
   And the mome raths outgrabe.

5   "Beware the Jabberwock, my son!
   The jaws that bite, the claws that catch!
Beware the Jubjub bird, and shun
   The frumious Bandersnatch!"

He took his vorpal sword in hand

10   Long time the manxome foe he sought—

So rested he by the Tumtum tree,

    And stood awhile in thought.

And, as in uffish thought he stood,

    The Jabberwock, with eyes of flame,

15 Came whiffling through the tulgey wood,

    And burbled as it came!

One, two! One, two! And through and through

    The vorpal blade went snicker-snack!

He left it dead, and with its head

    He went galumphing back.

20 "And hast thou slain the Jabberwock?

    Come to my arms, my beamish boy!

O frabjous day! Callooh! Callay!"

    He chortled in his joy.

'Twas brillig, and the slithy toves

25   Did gyre and gimble in the wabe;

All mimsy were the borogoves,

    And the mome raths outgrabe.

(1872)

Gerard Manley Hopkins

(1844–1889)

Pied Beauty

Glory be to God for dappled things—

    For skies of couple-colour as a brinded cow;

        For rose-moles all in stipple upon trout that swim;

Fresh-firecoal chestnut-falls; finches' wings;

5   Landscape plotted and pieced—fold, fallow, and plough;

        And áll trádes, their gear and tackle and trim.

All things counter, original, spare, strange;

    Whatever is fickle, freckled (who knows how?)

        With swift, slow; sweet, sour; adazzle, dim;

10 He fathers-forth whose beauty is past change:

    Praise him.

(1877)

The Windhover:

To Christ our Lord

> I caught this morning morning's minion, king-
> dom of daylight's dauphin, dapple-dawn-drawn Falcon, in his riding
> Of the rolling level underneath him steady air, and striding
> High there, how he rung upon the rein of a wimpling wing
5> In his ecstasy! then off, off forth on swing,
> As a skate's heel sweeps smooth on a bow-bend: the hurl and gliding
> Rebuffed the big wind. My heart in hiding
> Stirred for a bird:—the achieve of, the mastery of the thing!
>
> Brute beauty and valour and act, oh, air, pride, plume, here
10> Buckle! AND the fire that breaks from thee then, a billion
> Times told lovelier, more dangerous, O my chevalier!
>
> No wonder of it: shéer plód makes plough down sillion
> Shine, and blue-bleak embers, ah my dear,
> Fall, gall themselves, and gash gold-vermillion.

(1877)

Spring and Fall: To a Young Child

> Márgarét, are you gríeving
> Over Goldengrove unleaving?
> Leáves, líke the things of man, you
> With your flesh thoughts care for, can you?
5> Ah! ás the heart grows older
> It will come to such sights colder
> By and by, nor spare a sigh
> Though worlds of wanwood leafmeal lie;
> And yet you wíll weep and know why.
10> Now no matter, child, the name:
> Sórrow's spríngs áre the same.
> Nor mouth had, no nor mind, expressed
> What heart heard of, ghost guessed:
> It ís the blight man was born for,
15> It is Margaret you mourn for.

(1880)

Kate Chopin
(U.S.A., 1851–1904)

Désirée's Baby

As the day was pleasant, Madame Valmondé drove over to L'Abri to see Désirée and the baby.

It made her laugh to think of Désirée with a baby. Why, it seemed but yesterday that Désirée was little more than a baby herself; when Monsieur in riding through the gateway of Valmondé had found her lying asleep in the shadow of the big stone pillar.

The little one awoke in his arms and began to cry for "Dada." That was as much as she could do or say. Some people thought she might have strayed there of her own accord, for she was of the toddling age. The prevailing belief was that she had been purposely left by a party of Texans, whose canvas-covered wagon, late in the day, had crossed the ferry that Coton Maïs kept, just below the plantation. In time Madame Valmondé abandoned every speculation but the one that Désirée had been sent to her by a beneficent Providence to be the child of her affection, seeing that she was without child of the flesh. For the girl grew to be beautiful and gentle, affectionate and sincere,—the idol of Valmondé.

It was no wonder, when she stood one day against the stone pillar in whose shadow she had lain asleep, eighteen years before, that Armand Aubigny riding by and seeing her there, had fallen in love with her. That was the way all the Aubignys fell in love, as if struck by a pistol shot. The wonder was that he had not loved her before; for he had known her since his father brought him home from Paris, a boy of eight, after his mother died there. The passion that awoke in him that day, when he saw her at the gate, swept along like an avalanche, or like a prairie fire, or like anything that drives headlong over all obstacles.

Monsieur Valmondé grew practical and wanted things well considered: that is, the girl's obscure origin. Armand looked into her eyes and did not care. He was reminded that she was nameless. What did it matter about a name when he could give her one of the oldest and proudest in Louisiana? He ordered the *corbeille* from Paris, and contained himself with what patience he could until it arrived; then they were married.

Madame Valmondé had not seen Désirée and the baby for four weeks. When she reached L'Abri she shuddered at the first sight of it, as she always did. It was a sad looking place, which for many years had not known the gentle presence of a mistress, old Monsieur Aubigny having married and buried his wife in France, and she having loved her own land too well ever to leave it. The roof came down steep and black like a cowl, reaching out beyond the wide galleries that encircled the yellow stuccoed house. Big solemn oaks grew close to it, and their thick-leaved, far-reaching branches shadowed it like a pall. Young Aubigny's rule was a strict one, too, and under it his negroes had forgotten how to be gay, as they had been during the old master's easy-going and indulgent lifetime.

The young mother was recovering slowly, and lay full length, in her soft white muslins and laces, upon a couch. The baby was beside her, upon her arm, where he had fallen asleep, at her breast. The yellow nurse woman sat beside a window fanning herself.

Madame Valmondé bent her portly figure over Désirée and kissed her, holding her an instant tenderly in her arms. Then she turned to the child.

"This is not the baby!" she exclaimed, in startled tones. French was the language spoken at Valmondé in those days.

"I knew you would be astonished," laughed Désirée, "at the way he has grown. The little *cochon de lait!* Look at his legs, mamma, and his hands and fingernails,—real finger-nails. Zandrine had to cut them this morning. Isn't it true, Zandrine?"

The woman bowed her turbaned head majestically, "Mais si, Madame."

"And the way he cries," went on Désirée, "is deafening. Armand heard him the other day as far away as La Blanche's cabin."

Madame Valmondé had never removed her eyes from the child. She lifted it and walked with it over to the window that was lightest. She scanned the baby narrowly, then looked as searchingly at Zandrine, whose face was turned to gaze across the fields.

"Yes, the child has grown, has changed," said Madame Valmondé, slowly, as she replaced it beside its mother. "What does Armand say?"

Désirée's face became suffused with a glow that was happiness itself.

"Oh, Armand is the proudest father in the parish, I believe, chiefly because it is a boy, to bear his name; though he says not,—that he would have loved a girl as well. But I know it isn't true. I know he says that to please me. And mamma," she added, drawing Madame Valmondé's head down to her, and speaking in a whisper, "he hasn't punished one of them—not one of them— since baby is born. Even Négrillon, who pretended to have burnt his leg that he might rest from work—he only laughed, and said Négrillon was a great scamp. Oh, mamma, I'm so happy; it frightens me."

What Désirée said was true. Marriage, and later the birth of his son had softened Armand Aubigny's imperious and exacting nature greatly. This was what made the gentle Désirée so happy, for she loved him desperately. When he frowned she trembled, but loved him. When he smiled, she asked no greater blessing of God. But Armand's dark, handsome face had not often been disfigured by frowns since the day he fell in love with her.

When the baby was about three months old, Désirée awoke one day to the conviction that there was something in the air menacing her peace. It was at first too subtle to grasp. It had only been a disquieting suggestion; an air of mystery among the blacks; unexpected visits from far-off neighbors who could hardly account for their coming. Then a strange, an awful change in her husband's manner, which she dared not ask him to explain. When he spoke to her, it was with averted eyes, from which the old love-light seemed to have gone out. He absented himself from home; and when there, avoided her presence and that of her child, without excuse. And the very spirit of Satan seemed suddenly to take hold of him in his dealings with the slaves. Désirée was miserable enough to die.

She sat in her room, one hot afternoon, in her *peignoir*, listlessly drawing through her fingers the strands of her long, silky brown hair that hung about her shoulders. The baby, half naked, lay asleep upon her own great mahogany bed, that was like a sumptuous throne, with its satin-lined half-canopy. One of La Blanche's little quadroon boys—half naked too—stood fanning the child slowly with a fan of peacock feathers. Désirée's eyes had been fixed absently and sadly upon the baby, while she was striving to penetrate the threatening mist that she felt closing about her. She looked from her child to the boy who stood beside him, and back again; over and over. "Ah!" It was a cry that she could not help; which she was not conscious of having uttered. The blood turned like ice in her veins, and a clammy moisture gathered upon her face.

She tried to speak to the little quadroon boy; but no sound would come, at first. When he heard his name uttered, he looked up, and his mistress was pointing to the door. He laid aside the great, soft fan, and obediently stole away, over the polished floor, on his bare tiptoes.

She stayed motionless, with gaze riveted upon her child, and her face the picture of fright.

Presently her husband entered the room, and without noticing her, went to a table and began to search among some papers which covered it.

"Armand," she called to him, in a voice which must have stabbed him, if he was human. But he did not notice. "Armand," she said again. Then she rose and tottered towards him. "Armand," she panted once more, clutching his arm, "look at our child. What does it mean? tell me."

He coldly but gently loosened her fingers from about his arm and thrust the hand away from him. "Tell me what it means!" she cried despairingly.

"It means," he answered lightly, "that the child is not white; it means that you are not white."

A quick conception of all that this accusation meant for her nerved her with unwonted courage to deny it. "It is a lie; it is not true, I am white! Look at my hair, it is brown; and my eyes are gray. Armand, you know they are gray. And my skin is fair," seizing his wrist. "Look at my hand; whiter than yours, Armand," she laughed hysterically.

"As white as La Blanche's," he returned cruelly; and went away leaving her alone with their child.

When she could hold a pen in her hand, she sent a despairing letter to Madame Valmondé.

"My mother, they tell me I am not white. Armand has told me I am not white. For God's sake tell them it is not true. You must know it is not true. I shall die. I must die. I cannot be so unhappy, and live."

The answer that came was as brief:

"My own Désirée: Come home to Valmondé; back to your mother who loves you. Come with your child."

When the letter reached Désirée she went with it to her husband's study, and laid it open upon the desk before which he sat. She was like a stone image: silent, white, motionless after she placed it there.

In silence he ran his cold eyes over the written words. He said nothing. "Shall I go, Armand?" she asked in tones sharp with agonized suspense.

"Yes, go."

"Do you want me to go?"

"Yes, I want you to go."

He thought Almighty God had dealt cruelly and unjustly with him; and felt, somehow, that he was paying Him back in kind when he stabbed thus into his wife's soul. Moreover he no longer loved her, because of the unconscious injury she had brought upon his home and his name.

She turned away like one stunned by a blow, and walked slowly toward the door, hoping he would call her back.

"Good-by, Armand," she moaned.

He did not answer her. That was his last blow at fate.

Désirée went in search of her child. Zandrine was pacing the sombre gallery with it. She took the little one from the nurse's arms with no word of explanation, and descending the steps, walked away, under the live-oak branches.

It was an October afternoon; the sun was just sinking. Out in the still fields the negroes were picking cotton.

Désirée had not changed the thin white garment nor the slippers which she wore. Her hair was uncovered and the sun's rays brought a golden gleam from its brown meshes. She did not take the broad, beaten road which led to the far-off plantation of Valmondé. She walked across a deserted field, where the stubble bruised her tender feet, so delicately shod, and tore her thin gown to shreds.

She disappeared among the reeds and willows that grew thick along the banks of the deep, sluggish bayou; and she did not come back again.

Some weeks later there was a curious scene enacted at L'Abri. In the center of the smoothly swept back yard was a great bonfire. Armand Aubigny sat in the wide hallway that commanded a view of the spectacle; and it was he who dealt out to a half dozen negroes the material which kept this fire ablaze.

A graceful cradle of willow, with all its dainty furbishings, was laid upon the pyre, which had already been fed with the richness of a priceless *layette*. Then there were silk gowns, and velvet and satin ones added to these; laces, too, and embroideries; bonnets and gloves; for the *corbeille* had been of rare quality.

The last thing to go was a tiny bundle of letters; innocent little scribblings that Désirée had sent to him during the days of their espousal. There was the remnant of one back in the drawer from which he took them. But it was not Désirée's; it was part of an old letter from his mother to his father. He read it. She was thanking God for the blessing of her husband's love:—

"But, above all," she wrote, "night and day, I thank the good God for having so arranged our lives that our dear Armand will never know that his mother, who adores him, belongs to the race that is cursed with the brand of slavery."

(1894)

A.E. Housman

(1859–1936)

To an Athlete Dying Young

The time you won your town the race
We chaired you through the market-place;
Man and boy stood cheering by,
And home we brought you shoulder-high.

5   To-day, the road all runners come,
Shoulder-high we bring you home,
And set you at your threshold down,
Townsman of a stiller town.

Smart lad, to slip betimes away
10 From fields where glory does not stay
And early though the laurel grows
It withers quicker than the rose.

Eyes the shady night has shut
Cannot see the record cut,
15 And silence sounds no worse than cheers
After earth has stopped the ears:

Now you will not swell the rout
Of lads that wore their honours out,
Runners whom renown outran
20 And the name died before the man.

So set, before its echoes fade,
The fleet foot on the sill of shade,
And hold to the low lintel up
The still-defended challenge-cup.

25 And round that early-laureled head
Will flock to gaze the strengthless dead,
And find unwithered on its curls
The garland briefer than a girl's.

(1896)

Duncan Campbell Scott

(CANADA, 1862–1947)

The Onondaga Madonna

She stands full-throated and with careless pose,
This woman of a weird and waning race,
The tragic savage lurking in her face,
Where all her pagan passion burns and glows;
5 Her blood is mingled with her ancient foes,
And thrills with war and wildness in her veins;
Her rebel lips are dabbled with the stains
Of feuds and forays and her father's woes.

And closer in the shawl about her breast,
10 The latest promise of her nation's doom,
Paler than she her baby clings and lies,
The primal warrior gleaming from his eyes;
He sulks, and burdened with his infant gloom,
He draws his heavy brows and will not rest.

(1898)

The Forsaken

I

Once in the winter
Out on a lake
In the heart of the north-land,
Far from the Fort
5 And far from the hunters,
A Chippewa woman
With her sick baby,
Crouched in the last hours
Of a great storm.

Frozen and hungry,
She fished through the ice
With a line of the twisted
Bark of the cedar,
And a rabbit-bone hook
15   Polished and barbed;
Fished with the bare hook
All through the wild day,
Fished and caught nothing;
While the young chieftain
20   Tugged at her breasts,
Or slept in the lacings
Of the warm *tikanagan*.
All the lake-surface
Streamed with the hissing
25   Of millions of iceflakes,
Hurled by the wind;
Behind her the round
Of a lonely island
Roared like a fire
30   With the voice of the storm
In the deeps of the cedars.
Valiant, unshaken,
She took of her own flesh,
Baited the fish-hook,
35   Drew in a grey-trout,
Drew in his fellows,
Heaped them beside her,
Dead in the snow.
Valiant, unshaken,
40   She faced the long distance,
Wolf-haunted and lonely,
Sure of her goal
And the life of her dear one;
Tramped for two days,
45   On the third in the morning,
Saw the strong bulk
Of the Fort by the river,
Saw the wood-smoke
Hang soft in the spruces,
50   Heard the keen yelp
Of the ravenous huskies
Fighting for whitefish:
Then she had rest.

Years and years after,

55 When she was old and withered,

When her son was an old man

And his children filled with vigour,

They came in their northern tour on the verge of winter,

To an island on a lonely lake.

60 There one night they camped, and on the morrow

Gathered their kettles and birch-bark

Their rabbit-skin robes and their mink-traps,

Launched their canoes and slunk away through the islands,

Left her alone forever,

65 Without a word of farewell,

Because she was old and useless,

Like a paddle broken and warped,

Or a pole that was splintered.

Then, without a sigh,

70 Valiant, unshaken,

She smoothed her dark locks under her kerchief,

Composed her shawl in state,

Then folded her hands ridged with sinews and corded with veins,

Folded them across her breasts spent with the nourishing of children,

75 Gazed at the sky past the tops of the cedars,

Saw two spangled nights arise out of the twilight,

Saw two days go by filled with the tranquil sunshine,

Saw, without pain, or dread, or even a moment of longing:

Then on the third great night there came thronging and thronging

80 Millions of snowflakes out of a windless cloud;

They covered her close with a beautiful crystal shroud,

Covered her deep and silent.

But in the frost of the dawn,

Up from the life below,

85 Rose a column of breath

Through a tiny cleft in the snow,

Fragile, delicately drawn,

Wavering with its own weakness,

In the wilderness a sign of the spirit,

90 Persisting still in the sight of the sun

Till day was done.

Then all light was gathered up by the hand of God and hid in His breast,

Then there was born a silence deeper than silence,

Then she had rest.

(1905)

Topics and
Questions for Study,
Discussion,
and Writing

Topics and Questions for Study, Discussion, and Writing

These topics and questions are intended to help you in your individual study by suggesting ways to approach the literature in the anthology. But as the heading indicates, they can also serve as the basis for discussions, and you can use almost any of the topics and questions to set up a writing project, whether a report, a close analysis of a short work, or a broader critical essay on one or more works or writers.

We intend these questions and topics to be suggestive, not definitive. They should open ways for you to think about literature and the age, not shut the door on further speculation. Even where we imply or state an answer to a question, you should not assume that this answer is the only answer, or even necessarily the "right" answer. Indeed, some suggestions are meant to draw attention to weaknesses in seemingly obvious assumptions so that you will go on from there to seek better answers. And just because you find a poem or a story mentioned under one heading, don't oversimplify and assume that that settles the matter for that work. You will find some works referred to in connection with several different themes and techniques, sometimes even apparently contradictory ones. No such classifications can settle how literature works or why it appeals. And of course there are many ideas, themes, and techniques besides those we mention here. Numerous and varied delights await you in the literature. All we do is provide a few hints and suggestions to help you begin your exploration.

Backgrounds and Preliminaries: Reference Books

To aid you as you begin your exploration of the twentieth century, here is a highly selective list of books that provide various kinds of background information about the twentieth century or that can serve you as useful references to consult on particular matters. Some of these themselves include bibliographies and suggestions for further reading.

Abrams, M.H. *A Glossary of Literary Terms*. 4th ed. New York: Holt, 1981.

Bullock, Alan, and Oliver Stallybrass, eds. *The Harper Dictionary of Modern Thought*. New York: Harper & Row, 1977.

Cirlot, J.E. *A Dictionary of Symbols*. New York: Philosophical Library, 1962.

Cox, C.B., and A.E. Dyson, eds. *The Twentieth-Century Mind: History, Ideas, and Literature in Britain*. 3 vol. London: Oxford UP, 1972.

Eagleton, Terry. *Literary Theory: An Introduction*. 2nd ed. Minneapolis: U. of Minnesota P, 1997.

Ellmann, Richard, and Charles Feidelson, eds. *The Modern Tradition: Backgrounds of Modern Literature*. New York: Oxford UP, 1965.

Fussell, Paul. *Poetic Meter and Poetic Form*. Rev. ed. New York: Random House, 1979.

Heble, Ajay, Donna Palmateer Pennee, and J.R. (Tim) Struthers, eds. *New Contexts of Canadian Criticism*. Peterborough: Broadview, 1996.

Holman, Hugh C. *A Handbook to Literature*. 7th ed. Upper Saddle River, NJ: Prentice Hall, 1996.

Lentricchia, Frank, and Thomas McLaughlin, eds. *Critical Terms for Literary Study*. 2nd ed. Chicago: U of Chicago P, 1995.

Shapiro, Karl, and Robert Beum. *A Prosody Handbook*. New York: Harper & Row, 1965.

Williams, Raymond. *Keywords: A Vocabulary of Culture and Society*. London: Fontana, 1976.

You will of course need a good dictionary, one especially attuned to Canadian English. Here are three suggestions:

The Canadian Oxford Dictionary. Toronto: Oxford UP, 1998.

ITP Nelson Canadian Dictionary of the English Language: An Encyclopedic Reference. Toronto: ITP Nelson, 1997.

Penguin Canadian Dictionary. Markham, ON: Penguin, 1990.

Fee, Margery, and Janice McAlpine. *Guide to Canadian English Usage*. Toronto: Oxford UP, 1997.

And any student of literature should have at hand some reference book on mythology, such as one of the following:

Bulfinch, Thomas. *The Age of Fable*. New York: Mentor, 1962.

Grant, Michael. *Myths of the Greeks and Romans*. New York: Mentor, 1964.

Hamilton, Edith. *Mythology*. New York: Mentor, 1969.

Another useful reference tool is a good up-to-date almanac or book of facts, such as *The World Almanac and Book of Facts* (New York: Newspaper Enterprise Associates).

Elements of Literature

1. *Meaning*

(a) We raise the term *meaning* with some trepidation, for too many readers misapply it to literature. Therefore let us get several points clear first: (1) Literature is not a guessing game, the hidden "meanings" waiting to be found by clever readers. (2) There are no simple equations between literary works and "meanings" (for such a "meaning" would reduce a crafted work to a prosaic statement of fact). (3) It is often possible to read a work of literature in a variety of coherent and sensible ways (hence a good work of literature can last through time, reaching beyond one generation); this doesn't mean that all readings are equally valid, but it does mean that there may be no "final answer." Try, therefore, to think of "meaning" in another way: think of it as the overall result or *effect* that the writer achieves by combining all the constituent parts—the story, the setting, the imagery, the form, the style. Don't make the mistake of identifying a poem or story with its *theme*. The term *theme* is often used to mean "motif," as when critics refer to "the theme of the double" in "The Secret Sharer." But it most often refers to the main subject or idea in a work. For a complex work like "The Secret Sharer," then, we could say that the theme was self-realization, or the irrational, or responsibility, or the nature of institutional codes; and there are still others. But since we can suggest several possible themes, to identify any one of them as "*the* meaning" would be seriously to oversimplify and falsify the story and Conrad's accomplishment.

(b) Now consider Woolf's essay "Evening over Sussex." It is "about" an artist's felt need to share her sense of beauty with others. But any reader who came away from it with the idea that that was its single "theme" would have missed most of what the piece is doing. Its *meaning* is the totality of the effects of this and other themes and of its style. One can say that the "theme" of Pound's "In a Station of the Metro" is the surprising and pleasant discovery of beauty in an unlikely place; but any attempt to state the full *meaning* of even so short a poem would also have to take into account the force of the word *apparition*, the nature of the metaphor "petals on a wet black bough," the movement from a long to a relatively short line, the monosyllabic beat of "wet black bough," the alliteration of "black bough," and the general similarity of the whole poem to a Japanese haiku.

(c) The *meaning* of a literary work cannot be summed up in a one- or two-sentence encapsulation of its main idea, like a moral tacked on at the end of one of Aesop's fables. (Does the moral that Thurber puts at the end of "The Rabbits Who Caused All the Trouble" adequately state the meaning of that fable?) One often needs to go through the step of *paraphrasing* a poem's content in order to make sure one understands that element of it; but the paraphrase can never take the place of the poem. No single element of a literary work can ever be considered equivalent to its meaning. To claim that a poem's paraphrasable content is "what it says" or "what it means" would be as absurd as saying that its rhyme scheme was its meaning, or that its meaning would appear as soon as you counted the number of open vowel sounds or the number of syllables in each line. In literature as in other forms of expression and communication, the medium constitutes a good deal of the message.

2. *Tone*

(a) *Tone* is usually defined as the author's attitude toward audience and subject matter. No written work can be without tone, and often it is essential that a reader grasp that tone intellectually, not just react to it subjectively, in order to appreciate a poem or other piece of writing, in order to understand *how* it is producing its effects. Think of a literary work as analogous to something spoken aloud, and then think of what we commonly refer to as "tone of voice"; the tone of a work, or of an utterance, inevitably influences or even determines how we take what is said. The tone of a writer in a given work, like that of a speaker of a given utterance, can be serious, lighthearted, casual, sarcastic, morbid, angry, jovial, condescending, begging, resigned, wistful, peremptory, earnest, reticent, moral, ironic, playful, tragic, contentious, scoffing, bragging, obsequious, exhorting, pleading, skeptical, pessimistic, optimistic, conversational, formal, critical, noncommittal, sentimental, flat, exuberant, scolding, morose, sad, happy, tentative, flippant, secretive, regretful, forgiving, rambunctious, complacent, apologetic, maudlin, and so on and on and on—all to various degrees and in various mixtures and combinations. All of the elements of style, as well as sometimes the choice of subject matter itself, contribute to the creation of tone in a particular work.

(b) Characterize the tone of each of the following works, and point out how it influences or determines the overall effect: the stories by Mistry, Mansfield, and Shields; the essays by Atwood, Gordimer, Gould, Orwell, and Updike; poems by Chrystos, Eliot, Ghose, Housman, Lane, Lucie-Smith, Nemerov, Nortje, Owen, Scott, and Sexton.

(c) And remember that in any work whose speaker is clearly distinct from its author, the question of tone may be more complex. The tone of the *speaker* of Swift's "A Modest Proposal," for example, is far from the same as the tone of Swift the satirist. Or look at a short poem with a *persona* as speaker, like Frost's "Stopping by Woods on a Snowy Evening." What is the speaker's own tone, or attitude, and how is it different from the author's?

3. Humour, Irony, Satire

(a) Learning is a pleasure all by itself, as we've said, but there is a major pleasure at hand also in the frequent *humour* in literature. Indeed, some works are intended primarily to amuse, and some quite serious literature depends on humour as one of the best ways to make a point. James Thurber once said: "I write humor the way a surgeon operates, because it is a livelihood, because I have a great urge to do it, because many interesting challenges are set up, and because I have the hope it may do some good." So remember that the twentieth century is not all gloom and doom; wit and humour are seldom far to seek. Grim as some elements and episodes have been and are in our day, one of the results of grimness has always been to draw forth humour—if sometimes of a bleak kind; what is the function of such humour? Why do we laugh at humour that is self-defensive or that attacks some target, usually personal or political, through irony, sarcasm, and satire?

(b) Begin your exploration of humour further back. Why is the twelfth line of Chaucer's "Prologue" funny? (Try stressing its first word.) How important is the humorous element of Shakespeare's sonnet 130, or Finch's "Adam Pos'd"? The grimness of Swift's satirical irony in "A Modest Proposal" doesn't—or shouldn't—preclude its also being humorous. At what points in Browning's "My Last Duchess" might a reader be expected to utter a cynical laugh? Is Carroll's "Jabberwocky" nothing more than laughable nonsense? (Does Cummings play with words in anything like the way Carroll does?)

(c) Irony is not necessarily humorous: consider for example Hardy's "The Convergence of the Twain," Hine's "Bluebeard's Wife," and Housman's "To an Athlete Dying Young." Is satire—whether ironic or not—ever other than funny, however serious its critical purpose? Consider for example Auden's "The Unknown Citizen," Cummings's "next to of course god america i," and Shields's "Mrs. Turner Cutting the Grass." Is Sexton's "Cinderella" funny, or does her tone go beyond irony to biting sarcasm? (How do you distinguish irony from sarcasm?) What is the effect of humour and irony—and possibly satire—in King's "A Coyote

Columbus Story"? Does humour allow King to say something that might not be possible, or as effective, otherwise?

(d) What is the function of comic wit in Malouf's "A Charm against the Dumps" and Updike's "Beer Can?"

4. Diction

(a) As a reader of literature, you have to pay close attention to the words writers use, for good writers do not choose or arrange their words casually. When Conrad has the narrator of "The Secret Sharer" describe his taking the anchor-watch himself as "unconventional," he is not only reinforcing what we already understand from the context but also suggesting to us something further about the character: the captain is not just behaving strangely, but is willing to defy conventions, an important fact that bears on the subsequent action in the story. When the captain speaks of his ship in port as being "invaded" by shore people, he sets up a thematic opposition between the worlds of sea and land. The seemingly innocent and straightforward word "blind," used to describe the dead-end street at the beginning of Joyce's "Araby," takes on special force as the story progresses.

(b) The short story and the lyric poem are tighter, more economical forms than the novel, and therefore they depend even more on exact word choice and arrangement. Poems like Yeats's "The Second Coming" and "Sailing to Byzantium" are obviously dense, compact. But so is a seemingly much looser, conversational poem like Chrystos's "Soft" or Nemerov's "Learning by Doing." Relatively light or humorous works, like Scott's "Bonne Entente" or Kavanagh's "Spring Day" or Thurber's fable, achieve their effects partly because they do not squander words.

(c) You also need to be aware of the difference between *denotation* and *connotation*. Two different words can denote—refer to—the same thing but connote—suggest—quite different feelings about it. Connotation is one method writers use to convey information indirectly. Why does Ondaatje use the verb *splayed* in the first line of "Prometheus, with Wings" instead of the similar *spread* or *spread out*? What is the connotative force of the word *chronically* in Larkin's "Church Going"? Is Blake using a loaded word when he refers to "each *chartered* street" at the beginning of "London"?

(d) Poets also sometimes use words to mean more than one thing at the same time. In Dylan Thomas's "The Force That Through the Green Fuse Drives the Flower," the adjective *dumb* in the refrain means both *mute* and *ignorant*; the word *sheet* in the final line has at least three senses that are relevant to what this unusually rich poem is saying. Roethke in "The Waking" also employs deliberate ambiguity. Consider the verb *take*, for example; if necessary, look it up in a good dictionary and see how many of its meanings fit the poem. Explain the double sense of Gustafson's title "Partial Argument."

(e) Similar to such ambiguities are the puns and other wordplay writers sometimes use—and not just for the sake of humour. Note the "mourning" and "morning" at the end of Barker's "To My Mother." Is he also punning on the word *condescend*? What is the effect of Rukeyser's reference to "the fruitfall" season? Did you spot the pun in the fifth line of Frost's "Design"? How does it function in the poem? Is the title itself a pun? Is the title of Larkin's "Church Going" a pun, or simply an ambiguity? In Joyce's "Araby," when you read the word *idle* you are meant also to hear the word *idol*.

(f) The relative formality and informality of diction is also a feature of language that writers make use of. Note for example how in "The Second Coming" Yeats sets a fairly high level of diction, with the result that the word *slouches*, near the end, acquires a great deal of force by contrast. Look for other instances of such manipulation of diction—including some where a relatively formal word leaps out at us from colloquial surroundings. (The matter of formality and informality is discussed more broadly in #15.)

5. Sentences

(a) Don't take sentences and sentence structure for granted. You can be sure that the writers don't. Even in poems using unconventional style, syntax and structure are still important. Cummings, for example, depends on the reader to sense how conventional syntax clashes with his distortions of it to produce new kinds of meaning. Note how Eliot uses parallel structure to enforce his effects in "The Hollow Men." What is the effect of the thirteen-line sentence— without any internal punctuation—that opens Dylan Thomas's "A Refusal to Mourn . . ."? Look at Wilbur's "Piazza di Spagna, Early Morning": one long sentence, punctuated and divided into lines in such a way that its movement echoes the movement being described. Look for other examples of poets using sentence length and sentence structure to enhance the effects of their poems.

(b) The creative ambiguities in Roethke's "The Waking" are partly a matter of diction, but they are also partly a matter of syntax. What does "I wake to sleep" mean? Can the line "I learn by going where I have to go" be read two different ways? Another poem that generates extra meaning from syntactical ambiguity is Merwin's "When the War is Over": try punctuating it, and reading it aloud, and you'll discover that the absence of punctuation and the arrangement of words permit dual readings at some points.

(c) Perhaps the effects of sentence structure are more often apparent in prose. What is the effect of the way Hemingway begins "In Another Country"? Note the relentless flow of simple sentences and compound sentences (which are simple sentences strung together with coordinating conjunctions): not until the end of the second paragraph do we come upon any subordinate clauses. Does the style of Munro's "Boys and Girls" (the uncomplicated sentences and relatively simple diction) actively contribute to the characterization of the narrator as (at the time of the action) an unsophisticated girl just beginning to be aware of herself? Analyze the opening paragraph of "The Secret Sharer" to see how Conrad uses balanced sentences to reinforce our sense of the way the narrator's mind is working at that point in the story.

(d) Look again at Lewis Thomas's essay on punctuation; then examine random samples of both the prose and the poetry in this anthology to see if other writers use punctuation marks the way Thomas recommends. Do poets generally use dashes and semicolons sparingly? Has anyone risked ruining a poem with an exclamation point?

6. Imagery

(a) *Image, images, imagery*: these are among the most commonly used words in discussions of literature, of what it comprises and what makes it work. Simply, an *image*, in literature, is anything that appeals to a reader's imagination through one or more of the senses. Most images are *visual*, calling on the sense of sight; but many are *auditory* (the sense of hearing), *olfactory* (the sense of smell), *gustatory* (the sense of taste), *tactile* (the sense of touch, and also the sense of hot and cold), and *kinesthetic* (the sense of motion). Occasionally poets will use *synesthesia*, a mixing of two or more senses in one image, referring to something that belongs to one sense in terms of another sense, as when Emily Dickinson in her poem about the humming-bird refers to "A Resonance of Emeralds," resonance being a quality of sound—though the transfer to colour is not unusual. More striking crossovers occur in "Ode to a Nightingale," when Keats calls for "a draft of vintage," "a beaker full of the warm South," one "Tasting of Flora and the country green, Dance, and Provençal song, and sunburnt mirth!" He hooks the sense of taste to each of the other senses. Find some instances of synesthesia in other poems: look for example at Rukeyser's "The Children's Orchard" and Thomas's "Fern Hill."

(b) Imagery may be either *literal* or *figurative*. Williams's "The Red Wheelbarrow," for example, consists of one image made up of three parts: the red wheelbarrow itself, its wetness in the rain, and the white chickens. The image is overwhelmingly visual, though some readers may also get a tactile sense of smoothness from "glistening," and perhaps even of the softness of the birds' feathers; and some may also hear drops of rain striking the wheelbarrow, or even chickens clucking. The image is entirely literal; we are meant to visualize the objects as real objects. But the image may, in our minds, begin to function figuratively, as symbol or metaphor, as we react to the words "so much depends upon" by formulating such questions as "so much what?" and "why?"

(c) In Frost's "Design," the spider and the flower constitute a literal image, but the poem is full of figurative images meant to work on our imaginations through our senses: "rigid satin cloth," "witches' broth," "snow-drop," "froth," "paper kite," "darkness," and so on. What senses besides sight do the images appeal to? Analyze and classify the imagery in Gustafson's "Of Green Steps and Laundry," Levertov's "The Rainwalkers," and Nemerov's "Learning by Doing."

7. Figurative Language

(a) Probably the simplest form of figurative language is the *simile*, a statement of a similarity between two dissimilar things. If you ask yourself what something reminds you of, or what it is like, you will probably answer in the form of a simile. Similes state comparisons explicitly, usually using *like* or *as*. In Ross's story "One's a Heifer," for example, the narrator says that the man's lantern is "like a hard hypnotic eye," which adds a great deal to our sense of its effect on him. When the man gives "an unexpected laugh like a breaking dish," the simile vividly evokes the sound in the reader's imagination. A later simile achieves comparable effects: "I worked blindly, helplessly, as if I were confined and smothering." What image does the simile create? As you read and reread the works in the anthology, you might want to list some of the similes you notice and comment on their effectiveness.

(b) A *metaphor* is usually a stronger figure of speech than a simile. Some metaphors are clearly condensed similes, omitting the *like* or *as* in order to make the comparison implicit, in fact to identify the two things with each other. In Ross's story, for example, the narrator says of the man, "He made a little silo of checkers." Stated as a simile, this would have been much less compact ("He made a pile of checkers on the table, like a little silo"). There is nothing wrong or inherently weak about a simile; but often the metaphor has the stronger impact. (Try rewriting the metaphor "my imagination at low ebb," from the same story, in the form of a simile.) The question "What is it like?" or "What does it remind me of?" is not likely to produce a striking metaphor like "the brief bivouac of Sunday," in Page's poem "The Stenographers," or "an alp of unforgiveness," in Plomer's "The Boer War." Such metaphors don't simply shortcut the process of comparison; they make the reader understand something (the sense of a thing, a perception, an idea) not by *likening* it to something else but by seeing it *through* that something else, like a glass filter. The simile works laterally, in other words, on the same plane; the metaphor works vertically, by adding another dimension to the understanding. Often it would take several literal statements to even begin to explain the impact of a metaphor; try for example to explain, in discursive literal prose, the metaphorical phrase "The mankind of her going" in Thomas's "A Refusal to Mourn the Death, by Fire, of a Child in London": you could write a whole essay on it. The *metaphor* speaks directly to our understanding and our emotions, without intermediary explanation and definition. Study the metaphors in the poems by Bogan, Hope, and Plath; in the essays by MacLennan, Orwell, Updike, and Woolf; and in any of the stories.

(c) In order fully to appreciate and enjoy the way a metaphor functions in a poem or story, you will have to study the whole work in detail. But during at least your first two or three readings, just let a stunning metaphor wash over you, as it was meant to do, both emotionally and intellectually. Here are a few examples to suggest the sort we mean:

"pierced by a bewilderment of birds" (Nemerov, "Learning by Doing")

"he sang his didnt he danced his did" (Cummings, "anyone lived in a pretty how town")

"lyric you in lilacs" (Giovanni, "Kidnap Poem")

"an eddy of semantic scruples" (Mahon, "Rage for Order")

"The hands drain from his jacket" (Ondaatje, "King Kong Meets Wallace Stevens")

"How time has ticked a heaven round the stars" (Thomas, "The Force That Through the Green Fuse Drives the Flower")

"The blood-dimmed tide is loosed, and everywhere/The ceremony of innocence is drowned" (Yeats, "The Second Coming")

"Slowly forming, with steel syntax,/The long sentence of its exploitation" (Scott, "Laurentian Shield")

There are hundreds of striking metaphors in these pages. Analyzing how they work will not spoil their effect; restored to their places in their poems, they will be even more striking than before. Look for them.

(d) One particular use of metaphor is worth special attention. Sometimes a central metaphor runs all through a poem. You can see such a "controlling" or "frame" metaphor at work as the "Colossus" in Plath's poem about her father. In "Laurentian Shield" Scott uses a continuing metaphor relating landscape to language. Sustaining a metaphor this way can be a strong unifying device. What is the dominant metaphor in MacEwen's "The Discovery"? How does it work in the poem? Find some other poems, or parts of poems, with controlling metaphors, and analyze how they work.

(e) An interesting kind of metaphor common in Old English poetry is the *kenning*, whereby something common is referred to in an unusual, often roundabout way in a compound; a *lord* for instance, might be called instead a *ring-giver*. In "Anglosaxon Street," Birney appropriately uses several modern versions of such images, for example *learninghall* and *hatedeeds*.

(f) There are many other kinds of specialized figures of speech and thought you may want to familiarize yourself with; among the more common and interesting ones are *synecdoche*, *metonymy*, and *transferred epithet*. And one particularly effective rhetorical device you should know about—a form of repetition—is *anaphora*. Look up definitions of each of these terms.

(g) By using another figurative device, *personification*, we can speak of an abstract idea or something nonhuman as if it were a human being. The narrator of Cummings's "Buffalo Bill's," for example, addresses "Mister Death," and Nemerov personifies an aged tree as "An Old Colonial Imperialist." Frye, writing about Frazer, combines personification and regular metaphor when he says that "his text walks over a thick pile carpet of footnotes." And Hodgins personifies a part of a human being as a whole one: "His mind pulled down the shades and hid." Consider the ways some of the works mentioned earlier use personification. In Ross's story, for example, at one point "The fields stared, and the sky stared." Look also at its use in Livesay's "Bartok and the Geranium."

(h) Another figurative technique, *allegory*, sustains a system of metaphors through a whole narrative. For example, a journey or quest often stands for human life or endeavour. An allegory systematically works or "means" on more than one level—a literal, physical, narrative level and at least one non-literal, usually abstract level. These levels of meaning correspond exactly to each other (Bunyan's Christian = mankind; his journey = human life; his goal, the Celestial City = Heaven). How do twentieth-century writers make use of this technique? Consider for example Forster's story "The Other Side of the Hedge," in which nearly all the surface details—including the journey itself—clearly stand for something on the second level. Look also at Frost's poem "After Apple-Picking." Fables (such as Thurber's) and parables (such as that of the Good Samaritan) are similar to allegory. But modern writers seldom use straight allegory; often what they do instead is set up a pattern of allegorical imagery, such as the life-voyage equation in Conrad's "The Secret Sharer." Are there any other allegorical elements in that story?

(i) Still another figurative technique, *symbolism*, is one of the strongest ways writers have of communicating meaning. Most symbols are simply physical objects—in literature, *images*—which stand for, mean, or suggest something else, usually an abstract quality or idea. In Housman's "To an Athlete Dying Young," for example, the rose is a traditional symbol of female beauty, and the laurel is a similarly conventional symbol of victory. In Joyce's "Araby" the narrator at one point compares himself, in a simile, to a harp, which is a traditional symbol of Ireland. In Forster's story, the hedge, in everyday life a boundary marker or barrier, becomes within the allegorical structure of the story a symbol of the border between one mental "country" and another, between two vastly different ways of thinking about life. In Frost's "Acquainted with the Night," the night seems to symbolize the darkness, danger, and uncertainty that plague human life and baffle our attempts at communication. But many symbolic meanings are created within a given work, not imported from outside. Early in Conrad's story, the cigar that falls from the narrator's mouth when Leggatt appears is, because of the way it was introduced, symbolizing the narrator's complacency. What other symbols of this sort do you find in "The Secret Sharer"? The "sleeping suit" (pyjamas) the captain often wears? Leggatt's white hat at the end? In Mansfield's story, is the fly a kind of symbol—for the boss and, through him, for us? (When you write about literature, be careful not to confuse the meanings of the words *symbolize* and *represent*.)

Form and Structure

One of the most important ways of coming to understand a piece of writing is to consider its *form* or *structure*. These terms can refer both to the physical shape of a work and to the arrangement of its parts and the relations between them. Essays have structure, as you know. The plot of a conventional story partly defines its structure. The form of less conventional works is also important: what for example is the effect of the impressionistic style of Woolf's pieces? You should have little difficulty analyzing the structures of the prose works in this anthology; in the process you will find out just how each one works and therefore come to a clearer understanding and appreciation of it.

8. Elements of Poetry

(a) Form and structure are just as important in poetry. As Louis MacNeice once said, "In any poet's poem the shape is half the meaning." The principles of form and structure offer one of the best ways to approach a poem. Look for example at a conventional poetic structure: the sonnet, a form with fairly rigid rules to challenge a poet's ability. We have included a variety of sonnets in this anthology so that you can trace the growth of the form. Strictly, a sonnet has fourteen lines of iambic pentameter. Most sonnets use one or the other of two basic structures: the English (or Shakespearean) and the Italian (or Petrarchan). Shakespeare's sonnets follow the rhyme scheme *ababcdcdefefgg*, which means that his sonnets consist of three quatrains and a closing couplet. You could draw the shape of the English sonnet like this:

Note how Shakespeare takes advantage of this structure in sonnet 73. In the first quatrain he compares his age, his time of life, to a certain season of the year; in the second he compares it to a certain time of day; in the third he compares it to a certain moment in the duration of a fire: three parallel metaphors, but referring to successively narrower time spans and therefore becoming increasingly intense. Then the couplet closes the sonnet by drawing from the metaphors a lesson for the person addressed. In a Shakespearean sonnet the couplet often works as a kind of punch-line, with a touch of epigrammatic wit; does this one?

(b) The Italian sonnet usually rhymes *abbaabbacdcdcd*, though variations in the last six lines are common (what it must not do is end with a couplet). This produces a poem with a different structure:

Such a structure sets up a different kind of thought, a two-part one. Instead of building up through three stages to a summarizing conclusion, this form of the sonnet invites a contrast between, for example, a problem and its solution. Or the first eight lines (the *octave*) can present an idea or a scene; then, following a "turn" of some kind, often a transitional word, the closing six lines (the *sestet*) can comment on it. Look at Milton's sonnet on his blindness.

(c) Examine the other sonnets in the "Traditions" section (by Spenser, Sidney, Shakespeare, Donne, Milton, Wordsworth, Shelley, Poe, and Scott) both to see how the poets make use of these forms and to see what variations they introduce, and to what effect. How for example does Sidney's choice of unconventional hexameter lines fit in with what this opening sonnet is saying? Then examine some modern sonnets (by Avison, Barker, Cummings, and Frost) for the same purposes. Is Frost in "Design" somehow combining or conflating the two basic forms of traditional sonnets? How do Avison and Cummings use the sonnet form ironically? Is Hopkins's "The Windhover" a sonnet? Consider its rhyme scheme. Recognizing that modern poets sometimes take greater liberties with conventional forms, try to decide whether the following poems basically function like sonnets: Heaney's "The Forge," MacEwen's "The Discovery," Ondaatje's "Bearhug," and Stead's "Poem to Suppose the Bird."

(d) The importance of form should be obvious. Consider the following statement: "So much depends upon a red wheelbarrow, glazed with rainwater, beside the white chickens." Written and punctuated as a sentence, it's a straightforward prosaic statement. But Williams didn't write it that way. By putting the statement into four similar stanzas, with spaces and line-divisions enforcing a particular rhythm, he forces us to read it differently:

> so much depends
> upon
>
> a red wheel
> barrow
>
> glazed with rain
> water
>
> beside the white
> chickens

The prosaic linearity is gone. The statement now evokes not only a different reaction in the reader, but even a different *kind* of reaction. By giving it this form, Williams has made it into a poem. The form makes all the difference. Find some other modern poems whose existence as poems depends partly if not entirely on the form they take.

(e) Much modern poetry is often thought to be formless. But it isn't. Poems with regular stanzas or verse paragraphs at least look as though they have structure, and if the line lengths are patterned and if there is a regular metre and rhyme, the obviousness of the structure is increased. The critical reader must still pay attention to the structure of such poems, but at least their physical shape invites such attention. It's when such features are minimal or entirely absent, as in some "free verse," that inexperienced readers often have trouble perceiving structure. What structure organizes Whitman's two poems? Each does at least have a break, signalled by a space: do those breaks mark a turn similar to that between the octave and sestet or a Petrarchan sonnet?

(f) Even poems that consist of only one stanza, poems that have no breaks, nevertheless have structures—sonnets for example. Consider Nemerov's "To David, about His Education." The line lengths are fairly uniform, but there is no rhyme. But note the slight rhetorical shift, the slight change of tone, when the third (and last) sentence begins with "Though": the humour continues, but the touch of resigned wistfulness with which the poem proceeds from the turn of "Though" to the end reveals the poem's shape, its clearly discernible movement. Auden's "The Unknown Citizen" has no breaks either, and its lines are irregular; it has rhyme, but that too is irregular. But when you read it you feel the punch of the closing couplet, not unlike that of some Shakespearean sonnets. The only place in the poem where rhyme *is* regular signals its essential structure.

(g) The point is that there are many kinds of form, shape, or structure in poems, sometimes marked by physical features such as stanzas and patterns of rhyme, and sometimes not. There are structures of thought, as in sonnets; perhaps the "meditation" is such a form, as in Donne's (admittedly prose) meditation or Wright's "The Beanstalk, Meditated Later," or Webb's "The Days of the Unicorns." A variation is the structure based on logic, such as Shakespeare's sonnet 116, or Owen's "Arms and the Boy," where the opening words of the three stanzas signal the reasoning process: "Let," "Lend," and "For"—two imperatives followed by a "because." Sometimes a good way to grasp the structure of a short poem is simply to analyze its syntax. There are associative structures, where one thing leads to another, such as in the three successive metaphors of Shakespeare's sonnet 73, or the kind that in Webb's "Marvell's Garden" invites a contextual reading because of the controlling allusions. Similarly, there are parodic structures, as in Shakespeare's sonnet 130. And of course a central or controlling metaphor is a strong structural device. Some poems make use of the structure of descriptions, for example Ashbery's "The Instruction Manual." There are rhetorical structures, such as the colloquial question and response form of Larkin's "Toads." Look for other poems that fit these descriptions.

(h) There are also dramatic structures, for some poems have plots—for example the ballads, or narratives like Cummings's "anyone lived in a pretty how town," Ezekiel's "Night of the Scorpion," Hardy's "The Convergence of the Twain," Nowlan's "The Bull Moose," Hine's "Bluebeard's Wife," and Owen's "Strange Meeting." What other structural methods are operating in these poems?

(i) One particular kind of dramatic poem is called the "dramatic monologue." Nearly all poems—meditations, narratives, satires, sonnets and other lyrics, and so on—are monologues: we hear one voice, sometimes the poet's, sometimes that of a *persona*, "speaking" the poem. But in a *dramatic* monologue, the speaker is definitely not the poet but rather a character speaking lines, just as a character in a play speaks lines on stage. As Browning masterfully handled the form in the nineteenth century, a dramatic monologue has one speaker talking to one or more specific listeners and in the process unintentionally revealing elements of his character, usually unfavourable ones. Note, in "My Last Duchess," the Duke's damning self-revelation as he speaks to the emissary about getting a new wife. Not all the speakers of dramatic monologues reveal their characters, however, and those that do don't always turn out to be unsavoury, like the monstrous Duke. But most such poems do have a special dramatic immediacy, sometimes even intensity, especially if they are set at some dramatic or even crucial moment. Look at other dramatic monologues to see how they either fulfill or depart from these characteristics and qualities: in the "Traditions" section, study Tennyson's "Ulysses," Browning's "The Bishop Orders His Tomb," and Arnold's "Dover Beach"; among modern poems, examine Frost's "Stopping by Woods on a Snowy Evening," Eliot's "The Love Song of J. Alfred Prufrock" and "Journey of the Magi," Hardy's "Channel Firing," Heaney's "Wife's Tale," Atwood's "Hesitations Outside the Door," Nemerov's "An Old Colonial Imperialist," and Wright's "The Beanstalk, Meditated Later." Is Housman's "To an Athlete Dying Young" in any sense a dramatic monologue? Try to make a case for Roethke's "The Waking" as a dramatic monologue. Look for still other poems that work partly or wholly as dramatic monologues.

(j) With any of these poems, and any others that are dramatic, it is essential that you perceive the "dramatic context," the setting, the circumstances amid which the action takes place. Larkin's "Church Going" obviously has a dramatic context. Does Lane's "The Children of Bogota," or is it just reported speech? You have to visualize the scene of Reed's "Naming of Parts" in order to appreciate the counterpoint of the instructor's flat, everyday tone and the recruit's poetic elaborations on them as he sits listening, perhaps gazing out the window. Or do you think the two voices belong to the same man—an inner and an outer monologue, so to speak?

(**k**) Most poems of course depend to some degree on sound for their effect (see the next section), but some use sound in a particularly pointed way. The structure of Reed's poem, for example, is in part *aural* in that it depends on our *hearing* the two sharply contrasted speech cadences. Listen also to Birney's "Wind-Chimes in a Temple Ruin." Some poems even combine an aural structure with a *visual* structure. Livesay's "Bartok and the Geranium," for example, works partly through a contrast between the visual and the aural imagery. (Listen to some Bartok recordings.) And the structure of Ross's "Spring Song" (from a collection titled *Shapes and Sounds*) comes across not only visually, with the two columns inviting separate as well as combined readings, but also aurally: read the two columns simultaneously and you should hear the frog chorus. A villanelle like Roethke's "The Waking" also depends partly on our both seeing the pattern and hearing the repeated refrain—formal features which Roethke takes advantage of and integrates with the poem's content. The structural force of repetition also contributes to such poems as Thomas's "The Force That Through the Green Fuse Drives the Flower," Yeats's "Long-Legged Fly," and even, at its end, Frost's "Stopping by Woods on a Snowy Evening."

(**l**) Some poems depend heavily on visual features for their impact—Herbert's "The Altar," for example. And some contemporary poets work with what is called "concrete poetry," in which visual form almost overwhelms the verbal medium. The nearest to this sort that we have included in this anthology is Morgan's "Opening the Cage"; but you may wish to do some research into this and related phenomena, starting perhaps with the work of the Scots poet Ian Hamilton Findlay and the Canadian poet bp Nichol.

9. *Sound and Rhythm*

(**a**) Because the effect of poetry depends so much on sound and rhythm, you should always read it aloud. Listen to other people read it aloud, listen to records, and practise reading it aloud, both to others and to yourself. Reading aloud will increase both your pleasure and your understanding. Poetry is meant to be heard.

(**b**) Study Coleridge's mnemonic "Metrical Feet" (written for his sons, Hartley and Derwent), the "sound and sense" passage from Pope's *An Essay on Criticism,* and read carefully Roethke's essay "Some Remarks on Rhythm." Then begin analyzing poems according to their patterns of sound and rhythm. "Blank verse" is anything but loose, even though it lacks rhyme— as the dignified formality of the passages from Milton's *Paradise Lost* amply testify. Even most so-called "free verse" moves rhythmically. What elements of sound and rhythm do you find at work, for example, in Whitman's poems? Prose, too, uses sound and rhythm, though often in different ways (rhyme and regular metre, for example, would be intrusive). Which prose pieces in this anthology do you think most suitable for reading aloud?

(**c**) Sound and rhythm are among the *formal* elements of a poem, working with the substantive content to produce the overall effect. (Sometimes, of course, they are themselves partly or even wholly the subject of a poem.) Like other formal elements, they need to be analyzed separately in order to be fully understood, but only so that you can reintegrate them with the other elements of the poem to restore its essential unity. Note for example how Spenser varied the form of the English sonnet by using a rhyme scheme that links the quatrains together. Frost uses a similar technique to affect the movement of "Stopping by Woods on a Snowy Evening" and "Acquainted with the Night," whose first four stanzas are in *terza rima*. (That latter poem has fourteen lines; is it a sonnet?)

(d) Exploiting the sounds and textures of words, Seamus Heaney's "The Forge" does more than simply describe a blacksmith's shop, with an iron anvil at the dark centre of its work-space: the poem evokes the sensations of being there. Try scanning a few lines of this poem—marking the stressed (ˊ) and unstressed (ˇ) syllables—according to Coleridge's scheme for the different kinds of poetic feet. Is there a predominant kind of metrical "foot" in the poem? What variations has the poet introduced, and why? Does the cluster of stresses in the phrase "short-pitched ring" or "beat real iron out" suggest the beating of a smith's hammer? Look for other techniques by which the poet controls sound and rhythm in this short poem:

> *alliteration*—two or more nearby words beginning with the same sound (<u>d</u>oor . . . <u>d</u>ark, <u>g</u>runts . . . <u>g</u>oes);
>
> *assonance*—nearby words with the same or similar internal vowel sounds (cl<u>a</u>tter . . . tr<u>a</u>ffic . . . fl<u>a</u>shing);
>
> *consonance*—clusters of similar consonant sounds (leathe<u>r</u>-ap<u>r</u>oned, hai<u>rs</u>);
>
> *internal rhyme*—or call it assonance and consonance combined (H<u>orn</u>ed as a unic<u>orn</u>, n<u>ew</u> sh<u>oe</u>);
>
> *onomatopoeia*—words that imitate the sound of what the words designate (hiss, slam, flick).

Note the *caesura*, or mid-line pause, indicated by the colon (:) in the eighth line. What does it do to the pace, rhythm, movement of that line? Does it create particular emphasis? Finally, go back over the entire poem in order to see how each instance of the devices of sound and rhythm contributes to the effect of the poem. Examine the sound patterns in other poems. Note how strong they are, for example, in MacBeth's "Owl." Note also in Plomer's "The Boer War" how the <u>d</u> sound enhances the metaphor of "deft abracadabra drums."

(e) Notice how in "Anglosaxon Street" Birney uses the rhythmic two-part line and heavy alliteration of Old English poetry. How do they add to the effect of the poem? Try to find and listen to a record of someone reading in Old English in such poems as *Beowulf* or "The Seafarer." Can you follow the lines? Does some meaning come through by way of the sound, in spite of how unfamiliar the words look on the page? Try reading Birney's poem aloud.

(f) Why does Cummings jam together the words "onetwothreefourfive" and "pigeonsjustlikethat" in the poem "Buffalo Bill's"? How does Owen use alliteration in "Arms and the Boy"? Analyze the sounds and rhythms of Thomas's poetry to see how they help create that poet's customary rich musicality. Listen to some recordings of Thomas reading his own poetry. How does Klein make the rhythms of "The Rocking Chair" appropriate to the subject? What is the effect of *enjambment* (running a syntactical unit from one line on to the next) in this and other poems? Why do you think modern poets choose to avoid the end-stopped line so much more often than earlier poets did? When reading aloud, do you pause, however slightly, when you come to the end of a line that isn't stopped? Should you?

(g) Owen favoured a kind of rhyme called *slant rhyme* (sometimes called near rhyme or half rhyme)—lines ending with sounds that are similar but not identical. Look at his "Arms and the Boy" and "Strange Meeting": what effect does this kind of rhyme have on the way the poem comes across to you? Do the slant-rhymed words relate to each other differently than do words that rhyme fully? Speculate on why he chose not to use slant rhyme in "Dulce et Decorum Est." Examine also the effect of slant rhyme in Birney's "Wind-Chimes in a Temple Ruin," Heaney's "The Forge," Kavanagh's "Spring Day," and Thomas's "The Force That Through the

Green Fuse Drives the Flower": can you make a case for its appropriateness in each, or is it sometimes apparently an arbitrary scheme?

(h) In the eighteenth century, a dominant form of poetry was *heroic couplets*—iambic pentameter lines that rhymed in pairs—with an occasional alexandrine (six-foot line) or triplet (three rhyming lines) for variety or emphasis. Look for example at the passage by Pope and the poems by Dryden and Finch. (Swift's poem, in tetrameter couplets, is unusual—which itself makes a kind of point.) Why should this neat and tidy form be so popular then, and why should it have been so little used in the twentieth century?

10. Elements of the Short Story

(a) Begin with something Alice Munro wrote about her craft: "I don't take up a story and follow it as if it were a road. . . . I go into it, and move back and forth and settle here and there, and stay in it for a while. It's more like a house." As a reader, you need to find ways to enter the house of fiction. You can get into a short story in several different ways. You can of course just "stay in it for a while": read it, and re-read it, until it soaks into you, until you *feel* what it is doing. That should always be the first way you approach a story. But then you should back off a bit and *think* about the story in order to discover why it worked on you in the way it did; "move back and forth and settle here and there." Begin to analyze the story; approach it via the avenues of each of its elements: character, plot, setting, and style.

(b) Character: Who are the characters? What kind of people are they? Who is the protagonist, or main character? Which characters change during the story? How are the characters made known to us—that is, what methods of characterization are used? Straightforward description and statement? Self-revelation, through either statements or actions? Do we get to know the characters through what others think of them? What are the relations between the characters, especially the main ones?

(c) Try such questions on some of the stories in this anthology: Who is the main character in Mansfield's "The Fly"? What kind of person is he, and how do we find out? What is his relation to the other characters? In Munro's "Boys and Girls," do we find out about the main character partly through what she herself tells us and partly, since she doesn't fully understand herself yet, by interpreting her actions? What is the nature of her relations with each of the other characters? Is the hired man important, or is he just part of the background, so to speak?

(d) Imaginative literature is interesting to people because it is about people. Stories about animals, robots, fantastic creatures, or other nonhuman beings are usually interesting—when they are—only because those beings behave like people. Human character is all-important. Study the ways in which writers have handled *character* over several centuries, beginning with Chaucer's presentation of the knight and his son, through Johnson's "Ned Drugget," to the self-revelation of Poe's Montresor and Browning's duke and bishop, to the methods of characterization in the stories by Brand, Conrad, Mansfield, Munro, Ross, Shields, Williams, and the rest. Consider, too, the development and presentation of the element of character in such poems as those by Dove, Frost, Heaney, and Mahon—to mention only a few to get you started.

(e) Plot: What happens? What is the action in the story? Why does it happen—that is, what is the cause-and-effect relation between the events? Is there a conflict between the protagonist and one or more antagonists, or between the protagonist and something else, such as "society" or "the way things are" or some particular set of beliefs or attitudes? Does some single major change occur, for example in the protagonist's knowledge or attitudes? What is the shape of the plot? Is there a climax—a moment of crisis or discovery?

(f) For example: What happens, and why—what is the chain of events—in Mistry's "Swimming Lessons"? What are the major conflicts among the characters? In Joyce's "Araby," is the protagonist partly in conflict with himself? Is he also in conflict with something about his environment or his society? Is the major climax of Conrad's "The Secret Sharer" the moment near the end when the captain brings the ship around? Are there other climaxes in the story as well? What about the plot of Mansfield's "The Fly"? Is there much of a plot at all? Is what the boss does to the fly the major action, or are the important events those that take place within the boss's mind? What major change or discovery occurs in Ross's "One's a Heifer"?

(g) Setting: What is the physical setting of the story? Where and when does the action take place? How important is the setting to the story's effect or meaning? Are there any significant social, economic, or psychological circumstances surrounding the action?

(h) What is the setting of Brand's "At the Lisbon Plate"? What about the time? How does your sense of the setting affect the way the story works, its meaning? Ireland, the setting of Hodgins's "The Lepers' Squint," is clearly essential to the story. How important is the motif of islands that runs through it? How important is the setting—a sailing ship at sea—to the meaning of Conrad's "The Secret Sharer"? What is the narrator's psychological state at the outset? How do Munro and Ross create the strong sense of their rural Canadian settings? Where and when does Poe's "The Cask of Amontillado" take place? How much does its effect depend on the mood or atmosphere that pervades it? How important is setting in Frame's "The Reservoir"?

(i) Character, plot, and setting—those are the givens, the literal and basic facts about any story; you have to know them before you can go on to appreciate, critically, the story as a whole. But much of a story's full effect depends on its style. Most of the elements of style (diction, sentence structure, figurative language, symbolism, and so on) are discussed in other sections, since they apply to other works besides short stories. But the understanding of fiction requires you to be aware of one other element of style as well, namely *point of view*.

(j) Point of view: What is the angle of narration? Who is telling the story? Is it being told by an "I," a *first-person* narrator? If so, is that narrator the protagonist, or a secondary character, or perhaps only a detached observer? The first-person narrator of Munro's "Boys and Girls" is clearly the protagonist, as is the captain in Conrad's "The Secret Sharer." But is the narrator of Williams's "The Use of Force" clearly the protagonist? And what of Hemingway's "In Another Country"?

(k) Or a story can be told from a *third-person* point of view: Mansfield's "The Fly" and Shields's "Mrs. Turner Cutting the Grass," for example. Third-person narratives are told by someone offstage, as it were. Such narrators can be *omniscient* ("all-knowing") or *limited* to some degree. The narrator of Lawrence's "The Horse-Dealer's Daughter" is omniscient, and lets the reader know pretty much everything that's needed to follow the story's intentions. But an omniscient narrator, though *knowing* all, need not tell all: for example, you'd have to class the narrator of Gallant's "From the Fifteenth District" as omniscient; he or she knows a lot, but certainly doesn't tell the reader everything. Omniscient narrators can be very selective about what they reveal. What effect does this have on the reader's job?

(l) Third-person point of view may be limited by there being what is called a "point-of-view character." In Hodgins's "Lepers' Squint," for example, the narrative is in the third person but much is seen through the eyes of the protagonist; we learn Desmond's thoughts, but not those of others, except as he imagines them. (What is the effect of the few instances where the narrator briefly shifts to an omniscient point of view, or into the thoughts of other characters?) What other stories in the anthology use a point-of-view character?

(m) Another point: If a story is told in the first person, can we assume that the narrator is trustworthy? Is the narrator telling us the truth, the whole truth, and nothing but the truth about what is going on? Conrad's narrator in "The Secret Sharer" is obviously a bit disturbed (after Leggatt appears, for example, he seems to be obsessed with the idea that Leggatt is his double), but he is nevertheless trustworthy: he isn't lying to us about himself, or about Leggatt, or about anything else, nor is he concealing anything from us unnecessarily. But what about Poe's Montresor? And what can you say about the narrator of Wilding's "The Words She Types"? Does such a narrator disappear into and in some ways become a part of the fiction being narrated? Is this story at least partly about the nature of fiction itself? The question of point of view can even be important in what is actually an essay rather than a story; the narrator of "A Modest Proposal" is not Jonathan Swift but a character created by Swift for the occasion—a *persona* or "mask." Does Klein's modern "A Modest Proposal" use a similar technique?

11. Beginnings and Endings

(a) Another way to get into a story is to examine its beginning. Read rapidly through Clark Blaise's essay "To Begin, To Begin." Then read it again, carefully, slowly, while at the same time examining the beginnings of each of the stories in this anthology. Test the opening of each story against Blaise's criteria for good beginnings. Then read around in the poetry in this anthology: how often do you find a beginning that "implies the opposite"? Are poems that begin that way always better poems? Do you find any exceptions, among either the poems or the stories? If so, try to account for them.

(b) What else do beginnings of short stories do? Analyze closely the beginning of Shields's "Mrs. Turner Cutting the Grass." How does the opening paragraph set the tone of the story to come? How does the first paragraph of Mistry's "Swimming Lessons" prepare us for the story to come? What symbols or metaphors does it announce, symbols and metaphors that will be carried through the rest of the story? How is the opening paragraph of Hodgins's "The Lepers' Squint" appropriate for what the rest of the story does? What is the purpose of the first paragraph of Brand's "At the Lisbon Plate"?

(c) Write a short story. Begin it well.

(d) How do short stories end? Investigate the ways writers begin and end their works, of whatever kind.

12. Elements of Drama

(a) Imitated action: In the *Poetics*, a book which defines many of the fundamental principles of European theatre, Aristotle asserts that drama consists of "imitated human action," a critical formula which sounds deceptively simple. In drama, the nature of this imitation and the quality of this action are inevitably at issue. Consider the various meanings of words like "dramatic" or "dramatize": they can refer to theatrical productions, of course, but they also suggest intensity, deception, posturing, fiction, exemplifying. How exactly does drama "imitate"? Does it, for example, precisely re-produce the rhythms and forms of human experience? If so, we would have very long, complex plays with loose rambling plots and too many characters to count: consider how many people you meet in a day, how many activities that involve you, and how much time and what shape those events take. Clearly the writing of drama, like other literary genres, involves selection, intensification, and stylization; drama doesn't "imitate" life or action in a direct manner, but alters its raw materials to suit particular purposes or meanings. The key question for readers and audience members to address critically is how those stylizations take place, and to what end. What kind of "imitation" does a particular playwright practise?

(b) Dramatic form: There are aspects of form particular to drama which distinguish it from other genres. When reading and interpreting a play, it's important to keep in mind its dramatic or theatrical qualities. Since drama is principally a textual form, and plays (such as the two reprinted in this anthology) consist mainly of words on the page, many of the techniques and approaches you use for poetry or prose can be applied with good results. Playwrights, like other writers, are very conscious of the ways in which language can be manipulated and shaped to particular effect. Consider, for example, the ways in which *Catastrophe* and *Jewel* use particular kinds of sentences, sound-patterns, imagery, diction, and rhythm. It is equally important, however, to bear in mind that these plays do not consist merely of words on a page, but are meant to be staged: recited out loud in particular voices, postures, and contexts. The formal characteristics of their language often depends upon how they are staged or produced. For example, think about the kinds of stage directions that Beckett and MacLeod include in their plays. They want their words to be understood as coming from the mouths of particular characters in specific situations. How would you stage each of these plays? How would your own staging reflect the language or style of the text of the play?

(c) Three unities: Aristotle also asserts in the *Poetics* that there are three "unities" in a good play: unity of time, unity of place, and unity of action. For Aristotle, the events of a drama must take place within a very specific time-frame; the unfolding of the action, for him, cannot be interrupted or compressed, but must match the time that it takes the play to be performed. In other words, if your play is two hours long, then the events it depicts must also take two hours. This is one way in which he understood drama to "imitate" action directly. Consider Beckett's *Catastrophe*. The event it depicts, the rehearsal of the last scene of a fictional play, takes exactly the same time as *Catastrophe* does; there are no cuts, no scene changes, no speeding up or slowing down. Similarly, the place remains unchanged, as does the action: there is one event, and there is one location here. Now consider *Jewel*, which also occurs in a particular place and time. How does MacLeod manipulate the sense of time and memory through Marjorie's monologue? What is the "action" in this play? Do all plays have to possess these three kinds of unity to work as drama? Clearly Aristotle's "unities" are arbitrary limits on staging that works of theatre challenge as often as they accept. What effect does the sense of fragmentation or disunity have on how we understand MacLeod's play? Isn't the breaking of convention in fact appropriate to a character who inhabits a broken or dissolute world?

(d) Voice: Who speaks in a play? Instead of an authorial narrator or a lyric first-person, for example, most of the voices in drama devolve upon characters. The author or dramatist doesn't usually speak directly to his or her audience, but instead presents ideas and events through fictional characters. Who in *Catastrophe* might be said to "speak for" Beckett? The director? The protagonist? How could you be sure? What about MacLeod: does Marjorie articulate the author's point of view? How does Marjorie's voice change over the course of the play? Do her attitudes or responses to life and death also alter? The playwright, in many ways, is represented by the web or community of voices that his or her play stages. Reading drama, we need to assess how the different perspectives in a play operate through, across, and against each other. How is a key concern, such as oppression or identity, addressed from many points of view? Does the play settle on a particular approach to an idea? Or is it concerned with the ways in which human beings work out their conflicts, if they can indeed be worked out?

(e) Character: How are characters created in the theatre? Certainly they have voices, which we can see on the printed page. But it is important to remember that actors bring many resources to a theatrical production. The body and voice of the actor are physically present in a production, and affect how we understand a character. Notice that both playwrights in this anthology specify certain physical traits for particular characters. Take one of the plays and try reading it in different voices: high, low, with accents, fast, slow, mumbling, shouting. Are certain deliveries more appropriate than others? How do you know? What in the text of the play itself suggests certain styles of delivery or acting? Try reading a part again, incorporating various gestures and postures: move your hands rapidly, keep your arms fixed at your sides, lie on the floor, lean against a wall, stand alone in the middle of an empty room. How and where you position yourself also affects how lines can be delivered, and what they come to mean. The playwrights often specify certain stage directions, but just as often parts are left quite open to the interpretations of actors and directors. Much like the critical interpretations of a literary work that you might present in an essay, a particular production of a play involves interpreting a given text, presenting a specific argument about how that play should be read or understood. In many ways, the staging of a play is also a critical reading of that play, and emphasizes themes or forms which are significant for those involved. Imagine yourself as a director or actor, working on *Jewel* or *Catastrophe*. What ideas would you want to bring out in your version? How would you stage the play? Why would you make certain choices about acting style, for example? What in each of the texts would you want to emphasize?

(f) Production: Staging a play involves more than voices and acting styles. Such elements as set design, lighting, blocking (the plotting of actors' stage movements), pace, costume, make-up, and even the venue where the play will be staged affect how we can interpret those texts. Again, playwrights often specify how they want their play staged, and we can use their stage directions and their suggestions about make-up, costume, and lighting (for example) to contribute to our critical interpretation of the play. Why, for example, is the protagonist of Beckett's play dressed in ash-grey pyjamas? If we were deliberately to alter the costume— against the expressed wishes of the playwright and contrary to what the characters themselves say—how would our reading of the play be affected or changed? Would such a change even work in the context of the play itself? What meaning would such a change have? In the first production of *Catastrophe* in France, the protagonist was wrapped from his armpits to his knees in rope (a change which Beckett himself believed ruined his play). What point was this production trying to make? Why do you think Beckett didn't approve? Does his disapproval mean that a particular staging is incorrect or wrong? Why does *Jewel* have to take place in Marjorie's mobile home? How would you depict that space on a stage? Think carefully about how the practical demands of the theatre affect how a play is written or staged. In your own imaginary production, how far could you go with your own vision of set, costume, and lighting?

(g) Perspective: Drama can also express perspective by changing the way in which the audience views a play. For example, most large theatres have a proscenium, a large arch indicating the boundary between stage and audience; often, heavy curtains are hung from the proscenium, and can be raised and lowered to indicate scene changes or breaks in the action. The proscenium also creates what dramatists call a "fourth wall," an imaginary barrier through which the audience appears to be looking. (It's called a *fourth* wall because the other three walls are erected on stage, by the set; it's as if you removed one wall of a room in order to see what's going on.) Not all theatrical spaces, however, are structured in this manner. A thrust stage juts out into the audience, a little like a pier, and the actors are surrounded by spectators. In theatre-in-the-round, the audience encircles the whole stage; there are no wings into which the actors can retire, and entrances and exits must be made either through the audience or from trap doors in the stage. Depending on how a stage is structured, our relationship to the actors and to the dramatic action varies. Is the audience, for example, made to feel separated from the events depicted in a play, or are audience members somehow included in the dramatic space? What effects might spatial arrangements have on our perspectives?

(h) Theatre on theatre: Many plays are about the making of plays. Of our selections, for example, *Catastrophe* actually dramatizes a rehearsal. What do you think about Beckett's attitude toward the theatre? Is he critical of how plays are shaped by authoritarian directors? Even if a play isn't literally about the theatre, forms of role-playing and staging are often at issue in a play. Most theatrical works comment, at least indirectly, on how drama functions. Consider *Jewel* in this regard: how are ideas of communication, for example, given dramatic form? Does Marjorie's narrative, in a sense, re-enact her life? Is she actually composing a story or play about her relationship with Harry? Does she re-examine the roles they played throughout their marriage, or the little dramas they staged in their lives? In *Jewel* we witness Marjorie making sense of her life. Theatre is often about giving form or shape to the raw material of life-experience; it examines not only the ways in which human beings think and act, but also the structures and strategies through which this examination can take place. Drama is about how we stage or dramatize ourselves, and a formal analysis of a play will often lead us to consider the ways in which we give meaning to our lives by adopting roles, by acquiring voices, and by acting out our ideas.

13. Elements of the Essay

(a) It has been noted that nonfiction, unlike poetry for example, uses direct statements to convey meaning. Unfortunately, that does not mean that essays are a more transparent form of writing and that their purposes and effects will be immediately obvious. In many instances, you may need to do some background work—looking up unfamiliar words or concepts, or researching the essay's context. Does part of a reader's response to Gordimer's "A Writer's Freedom" depend on her or his knowledge of apartheid? If you don't understand some element of an essay (a word, a concept, an historical reference) first see if you can make sense of it in context; then look it up.

(b) Other essays require a different kind of work, a kind of surrender to an indirect, metaphoric style. Marlatt's "musing with mothertongue" is perhaps the most obvious example included here, but Selzer's "The Knife" and the essays by Forster and Woolf achieve their aims using indirect means as well. In these instances, you may have to look at the essay's literariness, analyzing its images and other figures, its sentence structures and word choices, and even its sounds and rhythms. Consider Selzer's essay: What do you expect from the essay after reading the title? The first paragraph? Does the fact that Selzer is in fact a surgeon set up your expectations? The simile comparing the surgeon's knife to the bow of a cello or a tulip should alert you to the play of metaphor that gives Selzer's description of abdominal surgery a mesmerizing, sometimes lyric quality, just as his handling of punctuation in the first paragraph suggests the rhythm that paces the reader's movement through the essay.

(c) Essays are frequently categorized by their aims: they may be expressive, expository, or persuasive, to use one system of classification. Generally speaking, expressive essays attempt to convey the writer's impressions or experience to the reader; Woolf's "Evening over Sussex" and Marlatt's "musing with mothertongue" invite us into the writer's way of seeing, Marlatt's choice of the word "musing" in the title suggesting the loose and associative process at work in the essay. Expository essays attempt to explain something to the reader, using a variety of structures. The essay by Ngugi, for example, *narrates* the author's childhood experiences of language, from the Gĩkũyũ spoken at home to the English required in colonial schools, and *divides* language as a means of communication and a carrier of culture into three elements each to *illustrate* the "disastrous" effects of education in the colonizer's language on colonized children. Persuasive essays attempt to persuade the reader of something—for example, that creationism does not offer a sound scientific challenge to evolution and should not replace it in school science classes, in Gould's "Evolution as Fact and Theory," or that language does not merely express but also shapes and creates thought in Orwell's "Politics and the English Language." Of course, these categories are only generalizations; many essays have more than one aim and employ more than one mode. Gould defines "fact" and "theory," then uses these definitions as the basis for comparing creationism and evolution; Ngugi divides and classifies language as communication and culture; Orwell uses example and illustration, as well as classification and division, to support his argument. As you read, be aware of an essay's main and subordinate aims: Selzer uses process analysis, an expository technique, but does his essay explain how to perform surgery? How would you classify Thomas's "Notes on Punctuation"?

(d) Read Atwood's "Great Unexpectations," Updike's "Beer Can," MacLennan's "On Living in a Cold Country," and Frye's "Symbolism of the Unconscious." What are the main and subordinate aims of each essay? What structures help the writer to achieve those aims?

14. Formalist Criticism and Close Reading

(a) Most of the elements of literature that we have discussed so far are figures of language itself. Literary style involves the shaping, selection, and arrangement of words through careful, deliberate writing and editing. All of the texts in this anthology—stories, poems, essays, and plays—have been thoughtfully crafted, often through a great deal of time-consuming revision; we assume when reading critically that the forms, textures, and patterns that these works embody are intentional, that they are literally meant to be there. Such an assertion may seem obvious, but it is important to emphasize because it is an assumption that underlies what we call *formalism*, a mode of interpretation that has had a significant impact on contemporary literary criticism. Formalist critics tend to disregard anything but the text itself as relevant to reading and interpretation. In other words, an author's stated values or beliefs—or anything we know about the writer's life—have no necessary bearing on how we understand his or her writing. (Presuming that they do is what some formalist critics call an "intentional fallacy.") Nor do the various ways in which readers might respond to a text matter to formalists. (Presuming that readers' responses affect meaning is called an "affective fallacy.") Nor do particular cultural or social forces have any real interest for the rigorous formalist. Rather, formalist readings concentrate only on how the words on the page produce meanings; everything in a poem, essay, play, or story, all of its language, has meaning for the formalist.

(b) Focusing closely on how the language of a particular text operates is called "close reading." A key to understanding this critical method is offered in a couplet from *An Essay on Criticism*, an eighteenth-century primer on how to read and write well by Alexander Pope:

> 'Tis not enough no Harshness gives Offence;
> The *Sound* must seem an *Eccho* to the *Sense*.

Writing in a pleasing fashion isn't good enough, Pope asserts. In literary works, the form of the text, its "sound," is directly related to its meaning, its "sense." Pope claims that sound and sense actually echo one another: this correspondence is the basis on which formalist criticism operates. If we look closely at the language of a work of literature, the sounds and textures of the words themselves will always reflect the ideas that they communicate.

Consider, for example, T.S. Eliot's poem "The Love Song of J. Alfred Prufrock." Notice how feelings of habit and boredom are reinforced by the repetition of words and by the flat, even rhythms in Eliot's lines. The speaker of the poem is alienated and uncertain, and the poem's structure, to "echo" this feeling, is often fragmented, unstable, and oblique. There are obvious, sing-song rhymes in the text, which may be reminiscent of the "song" in the title, but which also suggest a very conventional, arbitrary pattern—a bit like doggerel or greeting-card verse. At times, Eliot deliberately composes jangling, clunky lines that, by failing to be great poetry, suggest the failures that the speaker of the poem is describing. At other points in the text, the verse is lyrical and smooth; does the speaker come to some sort of balance or find relief from his anxieties? A formalist reading would address such questions by concentrating closely on how the language of the text itself contributes to the meaning.

(c) This approach can be applied to essays, stories, and plays as well as to poems: How does an essayist's style reflect the argument, or the content, of his or her essay? How does the choice of certain words, or certain kinds of sentences, create a particular voice? How does the language of a play affect its meaning? What about the narrative structure of a short story? Does the form of a tale shape how it articulates an idea?

(d) Not all critical strategies are formalist, and different readers will often emphasize different meanings in a given text. Some readings will concentrate on particular political, social, or cultural values, while others will relate the author's background to his or her writing. Some will concentrate on the variety of readers' responses, while still others will address psychological or religious or philosophical aspects of a text. But no matter what your own interpretations of a work of literature might entail, it is very important to realize that the central principle of formalist criticism, the connection between form and meaning, is the cornerstone of all literary criticism. Whether you concentrate on the text in and of itself or you choose to explore other possibilities for interpreting literature (some of which we discuss in the following pages), your reading of a text, in order to be convincing to others as a valid interpretation, must be built on a foundation of direct analysis of the language and form of the text.

The Twentieth Century: Cultural Concerns and Critical Patterns

15. The Changing Language

(a) In the twentieth century literary language increasingly became less formal, more colloquial, more vernacular. As education has become more universally available, more people have become literate, but such a broadly educated population has also become one increasingly impatient with high style, formality, and "poetic diction" that strains to be different from everyday speech. Similarly, with the invention and spread of new media—film, radio, and television—many patterns of written style have given way to oral patterns: simpler sentences or even sentence fragments, everyday vocabulary, the cadences of speech. (Think also of how new computer media are changing language: in 1994 few people knew what "emoticon" meant; e-mail and Web pages, as new forms of communication, have brought about considerable language change.) A related change is that brought about by the shifting populations of the twentieth century: refugee movements, massive immigration, and the mobility made possible by easier transportation affected some of the cadences of the language and altered vocabulary. And as former colonies developed and new authors emerged there and in Black America and Britain, English dialect speech acquired a new legitimacy and political force.

(b) These comments describe a general trend only. There was a strong tradition of dialect in earlier centuries, as Chaucer's "Edward" and Burns's "To a Mouse" illustrate. And in the twentieth century, formal writing continued to be used when the subject, occasion, and intent required it, as for example in the essay by Frye. Some twentieth-century poems also exhibit formality and density—much of the work of Yeats and Dylan Thomas, for example. Nor is vernacular style peculiar to the twentieth century. Chaucer in *The Canterbury Tales* is often intentionally quite colloquial; and look at the deliberately down-to-earth language Shakespeare uses in sonnet 130 to contrast with the conventional images.

(c) Sometimes a writer uses different styles in one work in order to help make a point. Nortje's "Letter from Pretoria Central Prison" is in part a poem of contrasts. Note the mix of informal, conversational style with a little poetic heightening. Look for other examples of stylistic shifts within one work, as in Walcott's poems.

16. Experiments

(a) Paradoxically, as literary style has generally become simpler, writers have increasingly turned to experiments with language and to freer, experimental forms. In other arts, painters and musicians and sculptors and architects reacted to the twentieth century (and against the nineteenth) by experimenting with form, colour, shape, anti-melodics, disharmony—in short, in any ways they could. But writers, however much they might sympathize with the need to do something different in order to meet the challenges of the modern age, still have to use words. For many writers, the challenge is therefore to use words—and their sounds, and the space they occupy—in a new way.

(b) In experimenting with language, writers not only risk being misunderstood but also risk alienating their potential readers, which would prevent any communication taking place at all. E.E. Cummings is famous—to some, notorious—for his idiosyncratic style. He uses almost no punctuation or capitalization, distorts conventional syntax and sometimes spelling, and often breaks words and lines oddly. Some of these linguistic shenanigans were no doubt an assertion of individuality, a breaking free from old conventions. Nevertheless, in his poems every detail is calculated for its effect. If you are at first put off, exercise patience: the rewards can be great. And be sure to read his work aloud.

(c) John Cage, himself the perpetrator of bizarre musical (and rhetorical) experiments, is picked up nicely by Morgan in "Opening the Cage" (note the punning title). What do you think is Morgan's purpose? Do his lines make sense? What kind of sense? (Try reading them aloud, supplying your own oral punctuation.) What does the whole poem say, or imply, about Cage's remark? About poetry itself? (Could this poem, with its fourteen lines, be called a sonnet?)

17. Structuralism

(a) Structuralism is a critical approach to language, and to culture generally, that has emerged primarily from the work of Swiss linguist Ferdinand de Saussure. Saussure's theory is based on an understanding of languages as systems of signs; graphical forms, such as words or letters, which he called "signifiers," stand in for objects or ideas, which he called "the signified," to which they are only arbitrarily related. For example, the word "tree" as it is printed on this page has no direct connection to the object which it represents, the idea or image of a real tree in the world of experience. Saussure proposed that all languages formulate sets of rules that emerge from this fundamental sense of difference. Instead of claiming that the colour green is essentially connected to its signifier in English, the word "green," Saussure argued that we know what the word "green" can stand for because it is not "blue" or "red" or "brown." There is a system of arbitrary social conventions which enable us as speakers to differentiate among signs. A structuralist's task is to study the operation of the rules and conventions that constitute such a system of differences. Saussure himself distinguished what he called *parole*, the everyday speech of living people, from *langue*, the complex system of rules through and against which that speech occurs: the structural linguist examines everyday speech in order to work back to the underlying system of forms and values that give meaning to that language.

(b) Saussure's work had a powerful effect on the science of linguistics, influencing famous theorists of language including Roman Jakobson and Louis Hjelmslev. His work has also had considerable impact on the disciplines of cultural anthropology, especially that of Claude Lévi-Strauss, and literary criticism, including the work of Roland Barthes. Instead of dealing strictly with language, Lévi-Strauss has sought what he calls the "myths," the complex structures of social convention, underlying cultural practices. Barthes worked to establish systems of meaning both in extended literary texts and in popular culture. These broader applications of Saussure's ideas to processes of signification in human culture pursue what Saussure projected would be the science of "semiology"—the study of signs—a term which he coined, but which has since opened up into the field of *semiotics*, an extensive critical interrogation of the processes and conventions of representation in our world. Semiotics, which is often closely tied to structuralism, also draws on the work of American philosopher Charles Sanders Pierce, who studied the many forms which signs and representations can take.

(c) A structuralist literary critic reads works of literature and asks what formal characteristics those works share. Literature, structuralists assert, is actually a "language," with its own particular "syntax" or "grammar." Or, more exactly, structuralists would assert that literature is "structured like a language," and they would try to isolate the rules or conventions of that "language" in order to understand how it works. The Russian critic Vladimir Propp, for example, studied what he called "the morphology of the folktale." In his work, he attempted to describe the basic, underlying shape of a folktale: a morphology is a systematized structure. Are there specific patterns that make a folktale recognizable? Certain conventions of narrative or style distinguish this type of writing from others. Furthermore, Propp employs a concept of linguistic form—a "morphology" is both a scientific and a linguistic category—to explain what these distinguishing structures are. You could perform a similar kind of reading on the short stories or poems or essays in this anthology. If you were to work through as many of the poems in this text as you can, and then try to determine exactly what formal or structural elements they all share, you would be setting the stage for a structuralist reading. Can all poems be said to share certain features? What would they be? What might the "language" of poetry consist of? What are the underlying rules or conventions that determine what a poem is? These are difficult questions to answer conclusively: consider all the possible exceptions to whatever rules you might derive. Not all poems are written in verse, or are of a particular length, or have a specific tone or point of view. What exactly *do* they have in common? Or perhaps more precisely, what set of rules do writers work with—or against—when they compose poetry?

(d) It would be very difficult to do a structuralist reading of a single poem; structuralism is concerned with general paradigms and patterns. (Two structuralists, Claude Lévi-Strauss and Roman Jakobson, have produced a structuralist reading of a single lyric poem by the French writer Charles Baudelaire, in which they attempt to describe the underlying structure, the poetic "language" that shapes his text, but their essay remains quite close to a formalist close reading. The French critic Roland Barthes has also written *S/Z*, an extended study of the layers of language and sign-systems in a single work by the novelist Honoré de Balzac.) Often, structuralists are interested in expansive genres, like the novel or the epic, as dense sources for their linguistic patterns. Still, because of its focus on language and its investigation of the complex systems of rules and relationships that constitute contemporary culture (including literary work), structuralism has had a lasting influence on literary criticism. In particular, the discipline of semiotics, the study of how systems of signs and representations operate in culture, has emerged from structuralism to constitute an important branch of literary study.

18. Allusions and Influences, Traditions and Responses

(a) An *allusion* is a reference, either implicit or explicit, to something outside the poem or story or essay that can increase its significance. Usually allusions are to myths, to historical figures or events, or the characters or passages in other literary works. They are not automatic associations—they require conscious thought—though some allusions are more obvious than others. When Owen titles a poem "Dulce et Decorum Est," the allusion is none the less obvious, except that if you aren't familiar with the quotation, you will be urged, both by its unfamiliarity and its being in Latin, to look it up; and when you find the full line from Horace: "*Dulce et decorum est pro patria mori*" ("It is sweet and fitting to die for one's country"), your reading of Owen's poem becomes strongly coloured by the ironic and tragic light cast over it by those words, especially as he quotes them pointedly again at the end. Similarly, when Owen titles another of his poems "Arms and the Boy," you are meant to recall the opening words of Virgil's *Aenid*: "*Arma virumque cano*"—or, in John Dryden's English translation, "Arms and the man I sing." Again, by the allusion to the past, the poet achieves a powerful ironic comment on his present subject.

(b) Such literary allusions are common. When Yeats in "Long-Legged Fly" refers to the "topless towers" that were "burnt," and mentions "that face," you are meant to recall Christopher Marlowe's great lines about Helen of Troy and the Trojan War: "Was this the face that launch'd a thousand ships, / And burnt the topless towers of Ilium?" If you don't know them, you have to look them up. A good dictionary of quotations is sometimes necessary when you are reading literature.

(c) Similarly, you should have access to a Bible and at least a reference book or two about the Bible and about Greek and Roman mythology. A knowledge of Biblical and Classical stories is essential for understanding and appreciating much later literature. If necessary look up the stories of Lazarus, Orpheus, Daedalus, Icarus, Helen, and Prometheus in order to explain the allusions to them in works by Jennings, Poe, Conrad, Auden, and Ondaatje. How does Macpherson in her two poems make use of the story of Noah's Ark? How does the story of the Garden of Eden figure in Dobson's "The Bystanders" and Frost's "Nothing Gold Can Stay"? Is there a "Garden of Eden" reference in any other poems? What does Adam's "naming day in Eden" have to do with Page's "Cook's Mountains," Reed's "Naming of Parts," or Anne Finch's "Adam Pos'd"? Do any other poems deal with the importance of names, or naming?

(d) Morgan's witty allusion to John Cage is obvious. Ondaatje's allusions to Wallace Stevens and the remake of *King Kong* are also obvious, since the two become the subject of the poem. Eliot's allusion in the epigraph to "The Hollow Men" is recognizable to anyone who has read Joseph Conrad's long story "Heart of Darkness," which is about "hollow men"; but the rest of the epigraph will puzzle anyone who doesn't know about the rituals of Guy Fawkes Day in England.

(e) Some allusions may remain relatively obscure to you until you acquire more experience in reading literature. For example, in Dylan Thomas's "The Force That Through the Green Fuse Drives the Flower," "the crooked rose" is probably an echo of Blake's "The Sick Rose"; and "the hanging man" may well be intended to call up, in part, an image of Christ on the cross. (Could the reference to "the Tree" in Roethke's "The Waking" also be an allusion to the cross of the crucifixion?) Joyce's story "Araby" is chock-a-block with symbols and allusions—though one can understand the story on a literal or narrative level without recognizing them. And there are times when one can't be sure: for example, in the first paragraph of Conrad's "The Secret Sharer" is the simile of "a few scattered pieces of silver" intended to allude to the "thirty pieces of silver" paid to Judas? One can only keep the possibility in mind as one reads and try to decide if it is relevant, if it makes sense as an allusion; think perhaps of the theme of betrayal, or potential betrayal, that runs through the story. Are there any other religious or Biblical allusions in the story?

(f) Some allusions may be playful or ornamental; others are clearly serious, namely those that occur when poets turn to literature, or to the other arts, painting and music, whether for relief from the pressures of the age, for something stable amid chaos, for sustenance amid the aesthetic vacuum of mass culture, for trust and abiding values amid distrust, or simply for stimulus. How does Webb in "Marvell's Garden" make use of Marvell's "The Garden" and "Bermudas"? What does Bishop, in "The Unbeliever," do with her allusion to Bunyan? How effective is Birney's use of the Old English verse form in "Anglosaxon Street"? For form, too, can be a kind of allusion. Even parody is a kind of allusion: note how Cummings catches the sound and rhythm of vacuous political oratory in " 'next to of course god america i," and how the poem is largely made up of clichés and tags from popular songs. Is Kavanagh's "Spring Song" at all parodic? Would you call Yeats's implicit comment on Keats an allusion?

(g) How have Livesay and Morgan used music as a metaphor to explore the workings of the imagination? Consider also the allusions to musicians in Audre Lorde's "The Day They Eulogized Mahalia" and Lola Lemire Tostevin's poem. What do Mahalia Jackson and Billie Holiday represent in these poems?

(h) In "Musée des Beaux Arts," Auden refers specifically to Breughel's *Fall of Icarus*, but is he drawing upon some other painting as well? What paintings is Rosemary Dobson referring to in "The Bystander"? Is one of them also Breughel's *Fall of Icarus*? Is she trying to one-up Auden? Could the closing lines of Gustafson's "Partial Argument" be alluding to one of the same paintings, or do you think it alludes to Auden's poem itself?

(i) Remember that allusions derive not only from the past but from contemporary experience as well. And they can emerge from shared experiences of all kinds. For example, where does each of the following twentieth-century allusions come from: "the beginning of the long dash," kryptonite, "Frankly, Scarlett . . . ," the Starship *Enterprise*, "he shoots, he scores!," the problem that has no name? Compile a list of twenty more, from your own experience.

(j) Much modern poetry is thought to have stemmed from the work of Whitman, Dickinson, and Hopkins. Of course it's not so simple as that, but you can see for yourself some similarities and influences. For example, read Whitman's poems and then read the poems by Ashbery and Ginsberg. Such "free verse" (having no regular metre or rhyme) became quite common in the twentieth century.

(k) What Rich calls "Dickinson's metrics and verbal compactness" turn up often in twentieth-century poetry. Assemble some examples of them. For example, compare "A Route of Evanescence" with Plath's "You're." How do such compact lines and images differ from those of Donne, Wordsworth, or even Shakespeare?

(l) And Hopkins, who died in 1889 but most of whose poems weren't published until well into the twentieth century, bequeathed his "sprung rhythm" to modern poets—metre that defies traditional regularity but that enables unusual emphases and, in its way, echoes the cadences of speech. (Hopkins even marked his unusual stresses so that people would read his poems as he intended.) Do you find many twentieth-century poems using such rhythms?

19. Poststructuralism

(a) Poststructuralism is a broad term for a set of responses to structuralism. By allusion and reference, many works of literature implicate themselves in a vast historical and cultural network of texts. Critics often refer to this complex welter of relations among writings as *intertextuality*. Since structuralists seek to determine the underlying language, the rules that structure a given body of work, they need to be able to draw a clear boundary around that body of work, to ascertain what fits and what doesn't, in order to be able to arrive at a definite structural basis. The density and multiplicity of intertextual relationships, however, tend to make this task very difficult. If a literary work (such as MacLeod's *Jewel*) refers to a newspaper story (such as the sinking of the *Ocean Ranger*), does that mean that the newspaper is also literary? On what basis do we include or exclude newspaper stories from literature? Tom Raworth's poem refers to a fairy tale—"Snow White"—and to a song by Bob Dylan. Are these literary works? Or is the way in which they're used literary? What about a newspaper article by George Orwell: is *that* literary? What about Sylvia Plath's diaries? William Carlos Williams's grocery lists?

(b) Determining the paradigms and syntaxes of "literature" requires that you know clearly ahead of time what is or isn't literary. Otherwise, your conventions and rules are bound to be inadequate: something will be left out, or the wrong work will be included. Our sense of what literature is seems to come from our reading of literary texts. But in order to know what those "literary" texts are, you need to know already the rules and conventions you're supposedly looking for. Setting yourself this kind of task tends to set you spinning in a rather vicious circle (not unlike the cliché that asks which comes first, the chicken or the egg), an uncertainty that poststructuralists refer to as *indeterminacy*. Structuralists seek to produced centred, ordered systems of rules which explain how particular cultural and literary forms operate; poststructuralists argue that these centres are always impossible to determine, and that the systems of rules and paradigms that they anchor are merely fictions, arbitrary arrangements of conventions which have no absolute truth-value. Where many readers will try to isolate what is lasting or permanent or beautiful or true in a text, a post structuralist—while acknowledging the ways in which texts produce a sense of the true or the ethical or the beautiful—will emphasize the points at which writing comes unravelled, or tends to undermine itself: the *aporias* or "whirlpools" of doubt in a work where an assertion appears to work against itself.

(c) Consider Yeats's short lyric, "On Being Asked for a War Poem," which on first glance appears to be a rather simple assertion that poets should be "silent" about war. Yet, clearly the poet is not silent: he has spoken through these six lines about his view of war and war poetry, and so his poem is essentially paradoxical, since it speaks about not speaking. This is both a poem about not writing and a written response to the request in the title; it is a war poem, in other words, that denies being a war poem. The poet's "silence," then, consists in not being silent, which doesn't seem to make any sense. We could resolve this difficulty by claiming that Yeats is being ironic, and that he says in the last lines of the poem that he wants to write for young girls and old men rather than for soldiers, but such a reading really amounts only to dodging the issue here; Yeats claims he has "no gift to set a statesman right," that poetry isn't political, but his supposed withdrawal from the political realm is in fact a very political statement, offered in the public context of being asked to make a statement, through poetry, about war. The poet is a "statesman," one who states or asserts his positions aloud, but those assertions are made through a peculiar kind of verbal silence. This short poem involves a rather vexed examination of how the "silence" of poetry operates, and the text circles around a complex set of contradictions about speech and meaning, all in a few lines. This contradiction is an *aporia* or a linguistic moment when the truth that seems to be asserted at the heart of the poem (a truth which often depends upon certain ideas of language and communication) seems to undermine or undo itself.

(d) Working through such contradictions in close critical readings is sometimes called *deconstruction* by poststructuralists. The term *deconstruction* emerges from the work of the French philosopher Jacques Derrida, whose elaborate and detailed interrogations of philosophical and literary texts had a profound impact on late twentieth-century critical thought. While not all poststructuralists use deconstructive tactics in their reading, most are concerned—like Derrida—with questioning and even disrupting the fundamental structures of meaning and truth in literary work. Many recent writers are well aware of these developments in criticism, and incorporate into their poems, plays, and prose various strategies of disruption and decentring; consider the ways in which Lola Lemire Tostevin's poem displaces centres of meaning, or the slippery ironies of Tony Harrison's allusive language. If, as Yeats predicts in "The Second Coming," "Things fall apart; the centre cannot hold," poststructuralism offers us a means of examining the ways in which those centred truths are let go.

20. Myth and Archetype

(a) What is *myth*? What is a myth? Investigate this word and its complex of meanings. Raymond Williams, in *Keywords*, remarks that the word *myth* didn't appear until well into the nineteenth century; since then it has become very important in our culture—in art, literature, anthropology, and even psychology. How is Rich using the word in her essay when she writes of "the influence that the myths and images of women have on all of us who are products of culture"? Is a myth in some way the opposite of reality? What is the difference between myth and history?

(b) Can myth or myths work as ways to represent human experiences, emotions, aspirations? Read Frye on how literature and myth are related. Since he mentions Jung only briefly, do some research to find out something about Jung's ideas and his influence on modern thinking and literature. Are Jung's "archetypes" similar to myths? Are the old classical myths perhaps versions of these archetypes? Does modern literature continue to record versions of these archetypes?

(c) In a book on mythology, such as Bulfinch's *The Age of Fable* or Edith Hamilton's *Mythology*, read the story of Odysseus (or perhaps read Homer's *Odyssey* itself). Then read Tennyson's "Ulysses" for a version of the wandering hero's thoughts later in life. Then consider how Ghose builds his poem "Come, Sailor" around this story. In Ginsberg's "A Supermarket in California," how important is the word *odyssey* in this connection?

(d) How do fairy tales and fantasy also work, like myths, to articulate people's fears and hopes and beliefs and values? Are all good fairy tales violent? Consider the use Wright makes of fairy tale in "The Beanstalk, Meditated Later," and the use of fantasy or fairy tale in Sexton's "Cinderella," Simpson's "My father in the night commanding No," Webb's "The Days of the Unicorns," and Gallant's story. How important are myths and fairy tales and fantasies for people who want to live full lives? Can a person be fully "human" without them, or without dreams and mysteries of some sort?

(e) Read the tale "The Blue Beard" (in the "Traditions" section) and then examine how poets use it—for example, Atwood in "Hesitations Outside the Door" and Hine in "Bluebeard's Wife." Does Ross's story "One's a Heifer" contain any elements of the Bluebeard tale?

21. Freud and Jung

(a) Psychoanalysis and psychological criticism affected powerfully twentieth-century thinking and the ways in which we read. From the theories of Sigmund Freud about the human psyche—the underlying structure of the mind—have emerged a number of compelling approaches to texts and interpretation. Many Freudians assert that psychoanalysis is essentially a theory of language or discourse; the "talking cure" advocated by Freud involved patients' verbalizing hidden or unrecognized truths about themselves. This is also essentially a critical strategy.

(b) It might be said that critics read works of literature carefully in order to bring hidden meanings to the surface. Freud's book *The Interpretation of Dreams* suggests that there is a "latent" content in our dreams hidden within their "manifest" content—the actual images and events that appear when we sleep—which the analyst interprets in a meaningful fashion; if I repeatedly dream of snowshoes, for example, my analyst might try to suggest that there is a latent meaning in that image (perhaps I feel overwhelmed, as if I'm sinking into the "snowdrift" of my life). Jokes and so-called Freudian slips (saying one thing and meaning another) are also, for Freud, occasions when latent meanings momentarily break through the surface of normal, everyday language. Literary analysis and psychoanalysis can be seen as operating in parallel, and many literary critics adopt strategies from Freudian thought that enable us to decode certain ways of speaking or writing. Our own reading of a poem such as "Snake" by D.H. Lawrence, for example, might emphasize certain notions of masculinity or power that are not immediately apparent in the text itself.

(c) Freud also offers a detailed theory of human sexuality, and Freudian critics often use Freud's writings on masculinity and femininity, or on the Oedipus complex (Freud's elaborate paradigm for how young boys enter into manhood), to read and interpret texts. Lawrence's "Snake," for example, can be understood as a displaced "phallic" image, a "veiled" depiction of the male genitalia. Conversely, it is also possible to read a poem such as Medbh McGuckian's "The Hollywood Bed" as depicting certain notions of femininity and womanhood, as well as displaced images of female physiology, although Freud's analysis of female psychology has come under considerable attack as biased, reductive, and inadequate.

(d) Freudian critics often pursue certain notions of the "unconscious" in a literary text. Do certain characters, for example, reveal aspects of themselves of which they are unaware? Does a story such as "Araby" by James Joyce or "Boys and Girls" by Alice Munro explore how personalities and identities are formed for young men or young women? How? Psychoanalytic criticism also examines the ways in which the unconscious or the psyche of a particular author is written into that author's texts. What, for example, does Ernest Hemingway's writing reveal about who he was? What about Carol Shields's story? Or Rohinton Mistry's work? Do these writers reveal their particular interests or obsessions through their styles?

(e) Carl Gustav Jung was a student of Freud who later broke away from psychoanalysis to found his own version of psychology. Jungian psychology concerns itself with deeply rooted patterns of thinking and behaviour that Jung called *archetypes*. Paradigms such as the quest, the underworld or underwater journey, the cycle, the scapegoat or martyr, the masculine and the feminine can be said to inform not only the human psyche but also the literature that human beings produce. Jungian critics often search for the ways in which the archetypes structure writing. Louis Simpson's poem, for example, can be said to present an encounter with the masculine side of the writer's own personality, represented by images of his father. The images of the sea in Jack Hodgins's story might, for a Jungian critic, suggest unconscious turmoil in the characters or perhaps the generative, chaotic, primal "mud," as the story itself says, from which creative work emerges.

(f) Northrop Frye's theory of literary archetypes derives directly from Jungian psychology; his essay on James Frazer, as he makes plain, draws on Jung and Freud to explain how certain kinds of ritual and magic in the "remote" human past have been carried forward into contemporary literary practices, bringing along with them a set of deeply rooted structures of meaning and behaviour that make connections between literary symbolism and human nature.

22. *The Nature of Reality*

(a) What is "real"? What is "reality"? Clearly that is too complex an issue to come to a conclusion about here, but you might want to investigate the different ways people have attempted to confront these questions.

(b) Platonists, for example, identified the Ideal as the only true reality. In the Middle Ages there was an implicit faith in the divine order of things. Christian humanism gave way somewhat during the Renaissance to a revival of Greek humanism. By the eighteenth century, the Enlightenment, Alexander Pope could write:

> Nature, and Nature's Laws lay hid in Night.
> God said, *Let Newton be!* and All was *Light.*

But not long after, people began to question whether the power of Reason was sufficient. By 1802 the visionary William Blake could write:

> May God us keep
> From single vision and Newton's sleep.

In earlier ages writers by and large accepted the world they saw around them, and in what they wrote they expressed their sense of its stability. But by the nineteenth century some deep questioning was going on. Though we sometimes think of the Victorian period as one of complacency—one in which Robert Browning could have a character in an early play sing that

> God's in his Heaven—
> All's right with the world!

—the doubts and questionings multiplied. So-called "nature poets" continued to describe nature in order to reveal the manifestations of divinity, and they and others tried to comfort their readers as uncertainty and anxiety grew. But even William Wordsworth (far more than a "nature poet") at the beginning of the century wrote in his long autobiographical poem *The Prelude* how at one point in his intellectual growth, looking for "*proof*" about nature and right and truth, for something solid on which he could confidently base rules of behaviour, he

> lost
> All feeling of conviction, and, in fine,
> Sick, wearied out with contrarieties,
> Yielded up moral questions in despair.

(c) Inheritors of all this and more—of the massive changes in scientific, economic, social, and psychological thinking of the later part of the nineteenth century—writers in the twentieth century tended to reject or at least to question any supposedly absolute answers to the questions What is Reality? and What is Truth? Much literature, of course, including twentieth-century literature, characteristically tries to identify the realities of its time. But now the nature of reality is itself in doubt, as modern scientific discoveries continue to inform us. The more we find out, it seems, the less we know. The "uncertainty principle" associated with quantum theory extends into philosophy and art. Is any absolute answer therefore automatically suspect? Are all things relative? What does Forster mean when in his essay he says of Sargent's "great war picture" that "it was modern because it managed to tell a new sort of lie"? Consider the status of rationalism in Ezekiel's "Night of the Scorpion" (only time can cure) and Williams's "The Use of Force." In Conrad's "The Secret Sharer," does the rational or the irrational triumph?

(d) Explore the ways writers confront the question of reality, or realities. Is some degree of acceptance of reality necessary if we are to get along at all? Consider the narrators in Joyce's and Conrad's stories: each is snapped out of an illusion about life and made to face reality. Expectation and experience aren't always the same. What is the nature and cause of each of their illusions? Is the process of disillusionment necessarily the same as the move from innocence to experience?

(e) Gould uses the tools of science and logic in a quest for truth. Is he employing the scientific method? What is the "scientific method," and how does it work? Does it lead to proof, to certainty? What are the rules of evidence—for detection? for argument?

(f) Can a myth—or an illusion—sometimes be tantamount to reality? When Birney in "The Bear on the Delhi Road" says, "It is not easy to free myth from reality," is he suggesting that myth is somehow superior to reality?

(g) Consider what is said or implied about the power of the imagination in such works as Ashbery's "The Instruction Manual," Webb's "The Days of the Unicorns," Yeats's "Long-Legged Fly," and Woolf's "Monday or Tuesday."

(h) An important distinction to keep in mind is the one between the nature of reality itself and the way we know about reality. Another distinction would separate these issues from the *values* we attach to knowing or to reality. Poets and prose writers also make these distinctions, often shaping their work to probe one of these ideas more directly than another. Which works in this anthology seem to you to be asking us "What is real?" Which works are asking "How do you know what is real?" Which works emphasize the question of value, either of knowing, or of reality? What is Gould's attitude toward supposed scientific "truth"? What are "facts"? What is the status of truth in Gustafson's "Partial Agreement," Ross's "One's a Heifer," and Wilding's "The Words She Types"?

(i) "There are no ideas but in *things*," said American poet William Carlos Williams. Find works in this anthology that are partly or wholly about epistemology, about how we acquire knowledge. Consider for example Roethke's "The Waking" and MacEwen's "The Discovery." Do they distinguish between objectivity and subjectivity? Is it possible to be perfectly objective? Is there a danger that in trying to be objective, people so far deny subjectivity that they distance themselves from things and other people? Does the assertion of objectivity, of separateness, remove people from connection, deny their essential connectedness? Is this what Rich is talking about in her comments on her own poem, "Aunt Jennifer's Tigers"? Are there any poems or stories in the anthology about people being treated as things? Do ideas exist in things, or do ideas come from people?

23. *Modernism and Existentialism*

(a) In addition to the themes that have occupied and preoccupied writers—themes like war and violence, death, love and hate, the battle between good and evil, the contrast between appearance and reality—much thinking and writing in the twentieth century dwelt on new themes, or on new branches and more intense versions of older themes. The words *commando* and *guerrilla*, for example, appeared in the nineteenth century, but their widespread use accompanied changes in the methods of modern warfare. And though the terms *terrorist* and *terrorism* were first applied to certain kinds of acts in the eighteenth century, and similar acts no doubt occurred centuries before, they became very much twentieth-century phenomena in the degree to which they began to occur and the accompanying frequency of the terms.

(b) The twentieth century has so often been characterized as an age of violence, bureaucracy, and other depersonalizing forces that one might wonder how an individual, in the proper sense of the word, could hope to survive. Where can an individual, as opposed to a member of a collective or other group, hope to find any values to depend on, or even—so to speak—any place to stand, to assert his or her own identity? If being free means being able and allowed to choose, to exercise one's responsibility as an individual, what room do the modern forms of society provide? Questions like these converge in *existentialism*, a mid-twentieth-century philosophy associated with the French writers Jean-Paul Sartre and Albert Camus. Camus examined the absurdity of the human situation; his novel *L'Étranger (The Stranger)* depicts the alienation of a European in Algeria who murders an Arab. (In "At the Lisbon Plate," Dionne Brand criticizes Camus's crisis as a product not of existential anguish, but of colonialism.) Consider some of the works that suggest the necessity or desirability of independence, of making individual choices: Avison's "The Swimmer's Moment," Beckett's *Catastrophe*, Bhatt's "What Does One Write When the World Starts to Disappear?", Cummings's "anyone lived in a pretty how town," Forster's "Me, Them and You," Hacker's "Fourteen," and Langston Hughes's "Theme for English B." Would you include Updike's "Beer Can" in this category?

(c) Consider a modern version of the debate over free will and determinism. Does twentieth-century literature suggest that people are individually free to make choices? Or are they compelled by society to "obey orders," to follow routine? Some works seem to emphasize the compulsions of modern life—or of life in general. Note the idea of compelled behaviour in Birney's "The Bear on the Delhi Road." How strong is the sense of fate in Hardy's "The Convergence of the Twain" and "Channel Firing"? What is Frost's attitude toward fate in "Design"? Note how certain behaviour is forced on the narrator of Williams's story "The Use of Force." What do such works imply about human nature? And still other works seem to suggest that there is no freedom from convention and conformity—or do they? Consider the satiric tone of Auden's "The Unknown Citizen." Is the speaker of Larkin's poem exercising his freedom to rebel against the "Toads" of his life?

(d) Perhaps paradoxically, the pressures of mass-culture—toward conformity, togetherness, collectivism, repression of individuality, and the like—have at the same time increased for many the sense of alienation, isolation, loneliness. Consider modern expressions of these feelings, for example in Hodgins's story and Frost's "Acquainted with the Night." Is it there too in Guy Vanderhaeghe's "Cages" and Rohinton Mistry's "Swimming Lessons"? How do modern versions and causes of loneliness compare with those of old? Consider also Donne's assertion that "no man is an island" (in his "Meditation 17") and Arnold's direct contradiction of it in "To Marguerite."

(e) The causes of such modern dilemmas—the feelings of alienation, rootlessness, helplessness, and loss of individuality—lie in the massive changes that occurred in the twentieth century. Conscious of the loss of certainty, literary modernism responded to these dilemmas (particularly after the First World War of 1914–1918) by converting these themes into forms that emphasized fragmentation, dissolution, and ambiguity. Yeats, Eliot, Joyce, Woolf, and H.D. are representative modernists who are often also nostalgic for a lost sense of order. Although literary modernism flourished in the first half of the twentieth century, it provides a master narrative for much of what follows.

(f) Other societies have also lost their myths. The disappearance of a stable order—a disappearance all too neatly and cataclysmically emblematized by the First World War—led to chaos and confusion. Cherished institutions, traditional ideas, standards, and beliefs—values that had been accepted and depended on for generations—were suddenly gone forever, blown away by the winds of change and war. The loss of shared values led to moral disorder, to uncertainty, even to loss of meaning. In Mansfield's "The Fly," the boss, after the war and the loss of his son, feels that "life itself" has lost its "meaning." The individual was set adrift, not knowing where to turn for sense and significance and security, for something and someone to depend on, to put faith in. New myths were needed, new kinds of order, new places in which to locate values, to find meaning.

(g) Modern society is often said to be suffering from moral apathy. Those who think so attack people's materialism, their desire for instant gratification, their refusal to invest over the long run in the quality of a community's life or the persistence of its culture, and their apparent inability to act in accordance with or to insist upon public and private honesty. In some sense they see society's problems stemming not from a lack of values but from people's unwillingness to accept the fact that common values apply to them. They attribute whatever degree of moral apathy there is to the loss of a collective public faith. Interestingly, however, the twentieth-century experience revealed a basic division of attitude toward this new condition. For some, the disappearance of old beliefs represented a devastating loss of order and stability; it meant being cast adrift on an anarchic sea of doubt, uncertainty, and despair, a world like that of Eliot's "The Hollow Men." For others, the change was liberating, enfranchising; it meant the casting off of the bonds of old illusions, the possibility of change and progress, and the stimulating demand to make individual choices; it brought a world of promise and excitement. Which works do you think take this perspective? Look again at the way Arnold frames the problem at the end of the nineteenth century, and at Larkin's "Church Going" for a more recent exploration of the way in which the poet is torn in these two directions and tries to resolve his dilemma. Indeed, that poem asks the central moral question of the age: How is it possible to reclaim old values—or, if new values must be found, where are they to come from?

(h) Consider some of the answers that writers in this anthology remark on: looking for a source of values, some people turn to love (see for example Arnold's "Dover Beach," Wilbur's "Love Calls Us to the Things of this World," Chrystos's "Soft"); many turn to science; others find their values in political allegiances, in power, in the law, or in the state (see Mansfield and Conrad); still others turn to culture, art, even the very fact of creativity itself.

(i) One special source of solace in a sea of doubt is the world of things, of nature, of animals. Note that many writers focus on small things and creatures that surround us in our everyday lives, or find delight and significance in simple objects, such as Williams's "The Red Wheelbarrow" and "This Is Just to Say," and Klein's "The Rocking Chair." Are those who write about nature (compare those who write about childhood) naive about modern society? Or are they trying to say something highly sophisticated about the survival of values within it?

(j) For many people, however, including some modern writers, values lie in the past—in history and tradition. Some find such values codified in conventional systems of religion—which survived into the twentieth century despite contrary assertions about the death of God or the primacy of the state. Examine the religious statements—or the explicit or implicit statements about religion—in works by Eliot, Hardy, Larkin, Macpherson, Mahon, and others you may find; compare them with those in Donne, Herbert, Milton, Bunyan, and Hopkins. Clearly, doubt is not the prerogative of the twentieth century (see for example Arnold and Tennyson), but do the writers of present and past come to different conclusions about faith?

What implications about religious values are present in the poems by Robert Bringhurst and Daniel David Moses, in the essay by Frye, and the stories by Conrad, Hodgins, and Joyce? Consider also the force of Biblical allusions in many modern works: do they declare or imply belief? or a need for belief? or only the force of traditional systems of thought?

(k) Others believe that true value lies only in the individual—the free individual in a free society. But given the nature of the modern world, this is not an easy condition to attain, or maintain. How much distance, for example, must an individual keep from the state or from powerful businesses in order to remain an individual? (Remember Auden's "The Unknown Citizen.") There is also the danger that the individual can be swallowed up by mass-culture and a consumption-oriented or technocratic society—a danger present at least as long ago as Wordsworth's "The World Is Too Much With Us"; Ginsberg's poem is only one of many modern works that touch on this issue. Do Page's "The Stenographers" and Wilding's "The Words She Types" suggest that women are especially vulnerable?

(l) A related problem is that of responsibility. Is the state responsible for the individual? Are individuals responsible for each other, or only for themselves? If an individual—or group, or a government—turns entirely in on itself, is it guilty of ignoring or abandoning others? Is individuality a virtue or merely a form of egotism—a failure to share a sense of community? Such questions occur again and again in modern literature, most often implicitly but sometimes explicitly, as when Klein in his 1939 editorial "A Modest Proposal" asks ironically about the responsibility for the fate of the Jews trying to escape the Holocaust. What values does the parable of the Good Samaritan teach? On the subjects of guilt, responsibility, involvement, and noninvolvement, read Atwood's "It is Dangerous to Read Newspapers," Auden's "Musée des Beaux Arts," Dobson's "The Bystander," Frost's "Acquainted with the Night," and Harwood's "Father and Child." How important are these themes in the stories by Gallant, Mansfield, Munro, and Vanderhaeghe? Did it become more characteristic in the twentieth century to seek freedom from responsibility than to embrace it? Or is freedom only another twentieth-century myth?

24. Postmodernism

(a) Postmodernism is based on two major premises: that the "master narratives" of Western culture since the Enlightenment—progress, reason, equality, the self, for example—no longer have meaning, and that "reality" is no longer a given. The "*post*" of postmodernism establishes both a temporal and an oppositional relationship to modernism: as an aesthetic movement, postmodernism comes after modernism; but more importantly postmodernism may either disrupt or continue (or both disrupt and continue) modernism's assumptions. In response to the decentring of the self, the loss of meaning and fixed reference points, postmodernism offers playfulness and plurality. The modernist poet Ezra Pound once asserted that it was the artist's task to "make it new"; for postmodernists, by contrast, there is a sense of exhaustion and ennui, as if everything has already been done. Postmodernists aren't concerned with originality so much as with irony; accordingly, their strategies include parody, collage, pastiche, rewriting.

(b) Read, for example, King's "A Coyote Columbus Story" and Brand's "At the Lisbon Plate." In what ways do they rewrite past stories, and to what effect? Consider the function of replication and the forms of subversion in Marlatt's "musing with mothertongue," Mistry's "Swimming Lessons," Raworth's "Mirror Mirror on the Wheel," and Wilding's "The Words She Types."

(c) Postmodernism is also extremely self-conscious and self-reflexive. The stories by Mistry and Wilding, for example, are writing about writing. At what point in "Swimming Lessons" do we realize that the story we're reading is the same one that the narrator's parents are reading in the story? (This effect is heightened in *Tales from Firozsha Baag*, the collection of stories which concludes with "Swimming Lessons.") Think about what happens when you stand between two mirrors: images imbedded within images, an endless series of reflections. The American writer John Barth likens this postmodern condition to being "lost in the funhouse."

25. Politics, Race, and Language

(a) Racial and political issues repeatedly marked twentieth-century life. You will have met these ideas already if you have investigated topics like war or myth—or even childhood, for often it is the external world of race or politics that serves in an initiation story as the force that disrupts naiveté or innocence. (Look at Joyce's "Araby." How much of the sense of desolation and futility at the end of the story is created by the reference to the "English accents" of the two young men flirting with the young lady?) And while investigating the theme of war, you may have realized how often conflict has resulted from an urge to exert power over another people and how often the urge for power has been based upon notions of racial or cultural or sexual superiority. As the century developed, wars were fought not only to defend empires (both political and economic) but also to end them—sometimes to establish new ones. The British and French empires transformed themselves into different varieties of Commonwealth; the Portuguese colonies were made independent and the German colonies dispersed. Some colonies joined older nations (as Newfoundland joined Canada in 1949); some parts of older societies either seceded or threatened to or tried to (Corsica, Quebec, the Basque Provinces, Czechoslovakia—which itself was divided, decades later); some nations were divided (India, Korea, Germany—later reunited); others expanded into territory they claimed (U.S.S.R. into the Baltic republics; China into Tibet; Italy into "Italia Irredenta"); and many new nations came into existence, from Australia in 1901 to Tuvalu and Kiribati in 1978 and 1979. The 1990s saw tremendous political changes that transformed the map: the Berlin Wall came down, the U.S.S.R. dissolved, and Europe became an economic union. Because the British Empire had been so widespread, the English language became a literary language in many parts of the world, many of them represented in this anthology. One of the first things you might do is look to see which writers come from the Caribbean, Africa, Asia, Canada, the United States, the United Kingdom, Ireland, and the South Pacific, and ask yourself if the cultural assumptions and attitudes they hold will be the same. Why—and why not? Contrast Hope's vision of Australia with Mistry's vision of Canada. The South African novelist Nadine Gordimer says that "politics *is* character, in South Africa"; do you find any evidence for this equation in Nortje's "Letter from Pretoria Central Prison"?

(b) One of the dangers of living so close to the economic and political ironies of the present is that, in considering a subject like "empire," we may forget that empires were often established in a spirit of enquiry and of romantic, heroic adventure. Does this justify them or moderate our judgment of them? Contrast the attitudes in Marvell's "The Bermudas," written at the dawn of empire, with those in Lucie-Smith's "Imperialists in Retirement," Nemerov's "An Old Colonial Imperialist" or Brand's story. When Kipling, at the turn of the twentieth century, spoke of the "white man's burden," what was he talking about? Why had the notion become unacceptable by, say, 1970?

(c) Political and psychological theorists like Frantz Fanon and O. Mannoni have argued that behind every connection between European and non-European there has lain a presumed hierarchical relationship—a hangover of the master-slave relation, perhaps, or as Mannoni puts it, citing Shakespeare's *The Tempest*, a Prospero-Caliban connection. Is Blake in "The Little Black Boy" arguing partly in this context? Or Chopin in "Désirée's Baby"? When Brand analyzes the connection between European and colonial notions of culture, what conclusions does she draw, and what do these conclusions have to do with race? Is there a link to the violence depicted in "At the Lisbon Plate"? How do Langston Hughes's "Theme for English B" and Audre Lorde's "The Day They Eulogized Mahalia" reflect the Black experience in America? Are there connections to be made with the kinds of experience and responses to that experience suggested in "Shame On!" by Chrystos, a Native American writer, or "Pantoun for Chinese Women" by Shirley Geok-Lin Lim?

(d) There are many ways in which you can see connections between race or politics and literature—such as the way literature sometimes records recent events, or the way literature embodies or challenges the attitudes of a time. Walcott, for example, wrote "A Far Cry from Africa" in response both to British colonial policy and to the Mau Mau violence in Kenya— and in the knowledge of his own mixed racial heritage. Klein's "Political Meeting" is written in the context of the Quebec Conscription Crisis of the 1940s and with particular reference to the oratorical power of Montreal Mayor Camillien Houde. What kinds of contexts might apply to Sujata Bhatt's "What Does One Write When the World Starts to Disappear?" or Atwood's "It is Dangerous to Read Newspapers"? Literature has, of course, traditionally commented on political events and conditions (see Milton's "On the Late Massacre at Piemont" or Swift's "A Modest Proposal"). Try comparing a modern political poem with an earlier one. Or investigate the particular historical incident that underlies one of these works, and comment on the literary writer's effectiveness as a social critic.

(e) Often the political comment derives less from a particular event than from an attitude toward the general character of a society's life. Note how a poem like Auden's "The Unknown Citizen" exposes a general unease with bureaucratic procedures; note how the poems by Nemerov and Cummings—on the immediate pressures of the mercantile world—can be read as general critiques of economic systems. What political attitudes do Simpson's "The Island Mentality" or Gallant's "From the Fifteenth District" reveal? Do you believe these writers are wholly conscious of the assumptions in their works? Birney's "Anglosaxon Street" probes among other things the prejudices of a wartime community; how does he expose the ironies of such attitudes? How does Cummings use American slogans and popular and patriotic songs in "next to of course god america i" to attack wartime political profiteers? What political tensions lie behind Ghose's "The Remove"? Read Plomer's "The Devil-Dancers," Birney's "The Bear on the Delhi Road," Klein's "Indian Reservation: Caughnawaga," and Lane's "The Children of Bogota" as commentaries on race relations, as exposés of the dependent connections between rich and poor communities, and as analyses of the human condition; does your sense of each poem alter as you shift your focus? Is Gallant in her story talking about the relations between men and women and the relations between priest and people in the same political terms that other writers use to talk about race, poverty, power, and manipulation? What does Rich mean when she says she began "to feel that politics was not something 'out there' but something 'in here' and of the essence of my condition"?

(f) What connection is there between politics and language? Read the essays by Orwell and Ngugi. Is Orwell correct when he asserts (in "Politics and the English Language") that "All issues are political issues . . ."? What does Ngugi's essay suggest about "politics and the English language" when that language is an expression of imperial control? Is Scott's poem "Bonne Entente" about the political failure of language, or is it simply an entertainment? How can you judge its tone? Try listening to records of readings of poems from various English-language cultures (for example, recordings of Achebe, Birney, Frost, Roethke, and Dylan Thomas); how do the variations in speech sound and in dialect vocabulary contribute to the force of what the writers are saying? Is there power in being able to master a "standard" pattern of speech?

How would the deliberate use of variant patterns, often considered "substandard" (such as joual in Quebec, creole in the Caribbean, pidgin in Africa, Black English in the United States, or any provincial dialect in England), therefore become a political weapon? Does Goodison in "The Road of the Dread" or Burns in "To a Mouse" achieve any particular political force by using dialect? How does Dawe in "Life-Cycle" combine dialect speech with a metaphor based on Australian Rules football to epitomize the values of a whole culture? Now read Manhire's "An Outline"; how does he integrate three levels of reference to language: in order to talk about childhood and age, about the powers of the writer, and about a colony's inheritance of another world's tongue? What is the function of the word "amn't" in Boland's poem?

26. Postcolonialism

(a) Postcolonial literary criticism treats the literary culture of former colonies and examines the ideology and historical consequences of imperial expansion. Whether "post" is understood to mean "after" or "against," the term *postcolonial* insists on the historical realities of European appropriation of new-world territories and the oppression of their original inhabitants.

(b) However, the colonial experience has varied tremendously across time and space, even in the former British Empire. The English treated Africa, for example, as a source of resources and captive markets, so that the implantation of colonial societies resulted from administrative "trickle-down" rather than the large-scale settlement achieved forcibly in Australia by convict ships. In other places, both resource extraction and extensive settler societies are features of the colonial experience, as Canada and the West Indies demonstrate to different degrees. Somewhat confusingly, territories appropriated by these different methods are all lumped under the general heading "colonies."

(c) Several works in this anthology invite a postcolonial reading by virtue of depicting the effects of and resistance to colonialism: Ngugi's essay, the poem by Soyinka, and Chrystos's "Shame On!", for example. Brand's "At the Lisbon Plate" foregrounds the violence of colonialism through patterns of references, notably the slave trade, and throwaway references such as Rosa's maids, whom she calls "*as pretinhas*" (doesn't she know their names?) and her desire for a "little gun" to protect herself "when the trouble started." The end of empire, which means freedom for colonized Africans, spells trouble for the colonizers. By contrast, in "A Coyote Columbus Story" Thomas King transforms the master narrative of colonialism, what used to be called Columbus's "discovery" of the new world, using humour and a First Nations trickster figure to rewrite that story. What do these depictions do to your understanding of Christopher Columbus, about whom many of us know little more than that "in 1492 [he] sailed the ocean blue"? What, by extension, do these stories have to say about the centuries-long project of European imperialism and the possibilities of resistance?

(d) Other works which do not so obviously depend on postcolonialism's oppositional aesthetic can nevertheless benefit from a postcolonial reading. One example might be Katherine Mansfield's story "The Fly," in which old Woodifield's visit provokes the casual brutality of "the boss." Woodifield recounts his daughters' visit to "poor Reggie's grave" in Belgium, where the boss's son is also buried. The contrast between the neatness of the graveyards and the outrageous price of a little pot of jam, like the contrast between the infantilized old man and vigourous and successful boss, criticizes the often imperial or territorial aspects of war: " 'They think because we're over there having a look round we're ready to pay anything,' " that we haven't already paid enough. The boss who can claim to admire the struggles of the fly he drowns in ink is no different from the generals who send out troops, often colonial troops, and watch them die from a distance. So thoroughly is the boss disconnected from his feelings, in fact, that at the end of the story he cannot even remember the source of his "grinding feeling of wretchedness." What do you make of Mansfield's tone in the story? What does it suggest about changing attitudes toward war in this century?

(e) Read the poem describing Botany Bay and the account by Alexander Henry. What do they suggest about late eighteenth- and early nineteenth-century European attitudes to new-world territories? How does the contrast between the attitude expressed in the poem—its celebration of freedom from the constraints and hierarchies of English society—and the attitudes expressed in Henry's account strike you? How do such poets as Hope, Page, and MacEwen represent territory?

27. Sex and Gender

(a) The Bluebeard story has proved a useful device for modern writers who want to probe the relations between the sexes, especially the domination of women by men. Similarly, some feminist commentary suggests that the story of Odysseus's wanderings is a myth of male experience—of heroism, freedom, male wish-fulfillment—and that female experience is more cogently represented by the myth of Demeter and Persephone—of motherhood, creativity, purity, but also of susceptibility to male attack. In any event, maleness, femaleness, and the relations between men and women are among the most prominent themes in literature, with—especially from the last half of the twentieth century—the added emphasis brought to bear by the feminist movement. To begin your exploration of these important matters, you might look again at the Bluebeard story: do Duncan and Hine, as men, treat it differently from Atwood, a women poet?

(b) In choosing to call this section "Sex and Gender" rather than "Women and Men" (as appeared in the first edition of this anthology), we have made a conscious decision to highlight a distinction between biological sex and socially constructed gender. According to this understanding of human sexuality and society, old assumptions about sex differences—that "biology is destiny," for example—are viewed not as expressing inherent characteristics of the sexes, but as the creations of society, which has divided human characteristics between the sexes, according value only to some. While much feminist work has analyzed the implications of this system, typically called *patriarchy*, for women, it has also opened the door for examinations of how the idea of "male universality," once unassailable, is also a construction, and perhaps not so universal. Consider two short stories in this regard: Munro's "Boys and Girls" and "Cages" by Guy Vanderhaeghe. Are these stories about sex or gender? Does comparing them suggest the differences between the sexes, or a similarity in the social construction of gender? Might masculinity be a trap as much as femininity? Now look at the stories by Janet Frame, Margaret Laurence, and D.H. Lawrence. How do these writers present the move from childhood innocence to adult experience? Is this experience gendered? Are these stories different from, say, Joyce's "Araby?"

(c) One of the first places humans learn about the socially appropriate gender roles is of the course the family, the subject of many works in this anthology. Several are about mothers, for example, Barker's "To My Mother," Ezekiel's "Night of the Scorpion," Hacker's "Fourteen." Others portray fathers and fatherhood, directly or indirectly: Harwood's "Father and Child," Plath's "The Colossus," Roethke's "My Papa's Waltz," Simpson's "My father in the night commanding No," Ondaatje's "Bearhug." What do these portrayals say about motherhood and fatherhood as institutions? Are they different from the portrayal of, say, fatherhood in Jonson's poems from the "Traditions" section? Stories by Hodgins and Mistry, in addition to those of Munro and Vanderhaeghe, also depict family relations. Are mothers and fathers represented differently in fiction than in poetry?

28. Feminism

(a) For feminist literary criticisms and theories, the subject is women, as textual producers and productions. Feminist criticism might analyze the representation of women in a given text, research the work of early women writers excluded from what has been largely a male canon, explore language and the female body as a site for liberation, investigate women's access to the symbolic realm, and examine the connections between sexism, racism, classism, and heterosexism. In short, feminist critics choose from such a variety of approaches that it is more accurate to speak of *feminisms* than of feminism, many of them influenced by work in postcolonialism, Marxism, poststructuralism, and postmodernism.

(b) Read Browning's "My Last Duchess" alongside "Désirée's Baby" by Kate Chopin. One kind of feminist analysis might focus on the possessiveness set up in Browning's poem from the first word of the title (and echoed by the first line); what would this imply for the poem's chilling conclusion, in which the painting, and maybe the Duchess herself, are likened to other beautiful objects in the speaker's art collection? Is this possessiveness connected to the Duke's tone? How would you characterize it, and how do you respond to it? A comparison with Chopin's piece might suggest the degree to which women are objects in patriarchal culture; like the "last Duchess," Désirée is valued by her husband for her beauty—but only so long as he sees what he wants to see in her. Another kind of feminist approach might focus on the similarity between the way Armand Aubigny treats "his" wife and the way he treats "his" slaves, noting that Désireé is at his mercy no less than they. (Many feminists, beginning with Mary Wollstonecraft's *Vindication of the Rights of Woman* [1792], have used the analogy of slavery to explain the situation of women in patriarchy.) Still another reading might argue that Aubigny's rejection of his wife's presumed blackness is in fact a rejection of himself.

(c) Study carefully Rich's essay. Use it as a base from which to explore the other works in the anthology. She raises many issues to focus on: language, naming, traditions, myth-making, dreams, fantasy, imagination and reality, politics, self-realization, the dangers of objectivity and detachment, and of course the relations between—and the difference between—women and men. You might want to research "the earlier wave of feminism" that she refers to: who were its major figures? How much success did it have? How does today's movement differ from it? Read the essays by Atwood and Marlatt: do they develop similar kinds of positions, do they use similar means? How do they differ from Rich's, and what might that suggest about feminist criticism? Are Gordimer's remarks on "A Writer's Freedom" relevant here?

(d) Consider the many works in this anthology that focus on women, on women's experience, and on women in contrast to men. Here are a few to start you off: poems by Bogan, Page, Plath, Hacker, Atwood, Sexton, Lim, and Goodison; stories by Brand, D.H. Lawrence, Margaret Laurence, Munro, Shields, and Wilding. Would you label any of these or others "feminist"? According to what definition of feminism? What does Page's "The Stenographers" say about women's work? How does the double-edged satire of Anne Finch's eighteenth-century poem give it a feminist slant?

(e) Read Chrystos's poem "Soft" and the lyric by Lucy Ng in relation to Marlatt's "musing with mothertongue," which theorizes the female body as the site of women's writing. Does Marlatt's essay suggest a different way of reading women's writing? The French writer Hélène Cixous first offered the theory of l'*écriture féminine*, writing with the body, but the examples she gives of this kind of writing are—ironically—by men (one of whom was James Joyce). What does this suggest about the debate between nature and nurture, between biology as destiny as opposed to the social construction of gender?

29. Queer Theory

(a) Queer theory came into being out of a series of critical connections. One of these was the distinction noted above between biological sex and socially constructed gender. Such a distinction suggested to feminists that gender roles were the products of culture rather than nature; to members of the gay rights movement growing in North America since the 1970s, the distinction offered a means to see *sexuality* as culturally determined also. That is to say, children are socialized into "appropriate" gender roles—including the expectation that they grow up to get married to a member of the opposite sex. Then, too, critics influenced by Freud started to wonder: if children have to be indoctrinated into it from a very early age, maybe heterosexuality isn't so natural after all. Postmodern appreciation for the multiple, the trangressive, the unspoken suggested an approach to sexuality which disrupted the hegemony of heterosexuality. And then there was AIDS: in the face of government inaction and social apathy, groups such as ACT-UP in the United States developed deliberately confrontational strategies, notably "kiss-in" demonstrations and "outing" closeted gay people. Out of these interconnected theories and politics, "queer theory" was born.

(b) It is important to note that the body of work called "queer theory," although it came out of gay politics, is not the exclusive province of gay people. Instead, this work examines textual strategies of transgression, repression, and plurality; critical readings informed by queer theory look for areas of silence in a text and consider how they shape it. Look through the anthology for works which challenge conventional notions of masculinity, femininity, family, and sexuality and analyze the nature of the challenge. How are certain forms of expression—the love poems in the "Traditions" section, say—undone and remade in Chrystos's "Soft," a love poem by a woman for a woman?

30. Marxism

(a) Marxism is the general name for what has become a complex set of economic and political theories, many of which had a profound impact on literary criticism in the twentieth century. Although often diverse and various, these theories are based on the work of the nineteenth-century philosopher Karl Marx, and share a number of concerns and strategies. Marx himself was not particularly concerned with literature, and did not leave behind much in the way of critical commentary on texts. However, his thinking does offer many possible avenues to approach literature which were taken up by critics in the twentieth century.

(b) Marxism as literary method can be understood, first of all, as an investigation of labour, value, and production; how, we could ask, are specific texts produced? What kind of work goes into composing and publishing them? How do they acquire economic and cultural value? How is literary value ascribed to a work, and what does it consist of? Look, for instance, at Heaney's "The Forge," MacLeod's *Jewel*, Page's "The Stenographers," and Wilding's "The Words She Types." What do these works have to say about work?

(c) We can also understand Marxism as a call to revolutionary change. Do certain works in this anthology advocate a radical break with society or a violent transformation of the ways in which we organize ourselves socially? Do they present a critique of power imbalances or injustices in our world? What sort of change might literary texts present?

(d) Marxism also involves an investigation of the ways in which societies become stratified, the arrangement of our world into classes. How are certain echelons of society devalued or oppressed? What distinguishes a "working class" writer from writers of other social classes? How does the play of allusions in Tony Harrison's poem "On Not Being Milton" suggest the social values that are aligned with class hierarchies?

(e) Finally, Marxism is also concerned with the question of ideology. Marx himself defines ideology as "false consciousness," mistaking constructed human values for natural or universal truths. For example, I may think that they way I dress is the correct way, and that everyone who doesn't dress as I do is deviant or wrong; I assume that my way of doing things is natural, the only way, when in fact it is a product of my own ideas, biases, upbringing, or cultural inheritance; I have a "false consciousness" that what I do is universally true. This notion can provide a means of reading literary texts critically. What sorts of biases or prejudices does an author accept as true? Can we reveal the ways in which an author has a certain "false consciousness," mistaking a certain social or cultural construction as natural or true? Or, conversely, do certain literary texts themselves confront or debunk the false consciousness of others? Is literature itself a form of ideology-critique? How do literary texts examine the many assumptions that we make about what is true or right or good? How does false consciousness play out in relation to categories of race and gender in addition to class?

(f) Above all, Marxist critics argue that literature is a political activity, that it offers, in various forms, arguments both for and against certain political and social stances. Most Marxist thinkers assert the importance of considering carefully our position within the social and political networks of humanity. How are we implicated in debates over economic and social justice? Literature, in many ways, presents a powerful medium through which these issues can be confronted and debated.

31. The Role of the Artist, the Reader as Critic

(a) Is it any surprise that artists should believe that the imagination as it works in art is a special and important kind of reality or a necessary counterbalance to other kinds of reality? Consider in this context Auden's "Musée des Beaux Arts" and Yeats's "Lapis Lazuli." In Stevens's "Anecdote of the Jar," is the effect of the jar (a man-made object) on the wilderness (the natural world) good or bad? Read the poetic statements about the power and function of poetry in such works as Gustafson's "Partial Argument," Stead's "Poem to Suppose the Bird," Mahon's "Rage for Order," and the essays by Rich and Roethke. Is Kavanagh in "Spring Day" humorously puncturing what he sees as some of the over-serious pretensions of some poets? Is Yeats in "A Coat" contradicting others' assertions about the function of poetry? How then are we to interpret his "Lapis Lazuli" and "Sailing to Byzantium"?

(b) Some poetry is obviously about itself, about poetry, about art. (Some people say that *all* of it is. Would you agree? How could this be rationally—or irrationally—argued?) Look again at some of the works mentioned in the preceding sections—works which are themselves about writing—and also at the story by Hodgins. What images of The Poet or The Writer or The Artist do you infer from these works? What is the force of Forster's parenthetical remark that "artists are useful sometimes"?

(c) From time to time writers have seen themselves, and been seen by others, as creators in their own right, as wielders of great power, even as the heroes of their times—as social saviours, teachers, the conscience of their age, purveyors of sense and sensibility, custodians of the language and of the spirit of humanity for the masses. In his 1873 preface to *Literature and Dogma*, Matthew Arnold said that the meaning of *culture* is "to know the best that has been thought and said in the world." He was writing about the Bible and about the revolutionary decline in religious faith that he saw taking place; he was intent upon rescuing the Bible from theological dogmatists, whom he saw losing the battle against science, and restoring it to the masses as an important part of their literature. Culture, he said, "is indispensably necessary, and culture is *reading*. . . ." Where in this anthology do you find writers stressing the importance of literature, of reading? Why, for example, does Nikki Giovanni want to kidnap the reader? Does the role of the artist differ from culture to culture? What do you think is the role of the artist in our time and place? What is the role of the *reader*?

(d) All of this commentary we've been making is a way of inviting you into an active relation with these texts. You can analyze a text's form, you can debate its arguments, you can experience the worlds it creates. You can be moved, inspired, angered, comforted, challenged, but however you react, as a reader, you have a critical role to play.

INDEX
of Authors and Titles